14

BB

Modern Perspectives In Child Development

In Honor of Milton J. E. Senn

Milton J. E. Senn

MODERN PERSPECTIVES IN CHILD DEVELOPMENT

IN HONOR OF MILTON J. E. SENN

EDITED BY

Albert J. Solnit and Sally A. Provence
YALE UNIVERSITY

NEW YORK
International Universities Press, Inc.

Manufactured in the United States of America
by Hallmark Press, New York

Contents

Part I

Introductory Section

Part II

Biological Aspects of Child Development

Part III

Theoretical and Clinical Considerations in Child Development

Part IV

Pediatric Practice Today

Part V

Child Guidance Today

Part VI

Medical Education Today

Part VII

Education for Children, Parents, and Teachers

Contributors

Frederic M. Blodgett, M.D.
Associate Professor of Pediatrics, Yale University School of Medicine; Physician-in-Charge, Pediatric Outpatient Department, Grace-New Haven Community Hospital.

Ira K. Brandt, M.D.
Associate Professor of Pediatrics, Yale University School of Medicine.

Bettye M. Caldwell, Ph.D.
Research Associate, Department of Pediatrics, College of Medicine, State University of New York, Syracuse.

Laura V. Codling, A.B.
Assistant Professor (Psychiatric Social Work), Chief Psychiatric Social Worker, Child Psychiatry Unit, Yale University Child Study Center.

Norman J. Cohen, M.D.
Formerly, Yale University School of Medicine, Department of Pediatrics and Child Study Center; at present, Pediatrician, Children's Department, Rothchild Municipal Hospital, and Mental Hygiene Clinic of Kupat Cholim, Haifa, Israel.

ix

RICHARD T. CUSHING, M.D.

Pediatrician, St. Louis Park Medical Center, Minneapolis.

RICHARD L. DAY, M.D.

Professor and Chairman, Department of Pediatrics, University of Pittsburgh School of Medicine, and Children's Hospital of Pittsburgh.

MORRIS S. DIXON, JR., M.D.

The Wooster Clinic, Wooster, Ohio; Senior Clinical Instructor, Western Reserve University School of Medicine.

JOHN DORIS, PH.D.

Assistant Professor of Psychology and Chief Psychologist, Yale University Child Study Center. As of September 1, 1963, Associate Professor, Department of Child Development and Family Relations, Cornell University.

LAWRENCE K. FRANK, A.B., LL.D.

Formerly, foundation executive concerned with child growth and development. Author of *Projective Methods* (1948), *Society or the Patient* (1948), *Nature and Human Nature* (1951), *The Conduct of Sex* (1961); co-author with Mary H. Frank, *How to Help Your Child in School* (1950) and *Your Adolescent at Home and at School* (1956); co-author with others, *Understanding Children's Play* (1952) and *Personality Development in Adolescent Girls* (1953).

ALAN W. FRASER, M.D.

In the private practice of child psychiatry and psychoanalysis in New York City.

ANNA FREUD, LL.D.

Director, Hampstead Child-Therapy Clinic, London. Author of *The Psycho-Analytical Treatment of Children* (1927), *Introduction to Psycho-Analysis for Teachers* (1930), *The Ego and the Mechanisms of Defence* (1936); co-author with Dorothy Burlingham, *War and Children* (1942), *Infants Without Families* (1943).

J. ROSWELL GALLAGHER, M.D.

Chief, The Adolescent Unit, Children's Hospital Medical Center, Boston; Lecturer on Pediatrics, Harvard Medical School. Author of *Understanding Your Son's Adolescence* (1951), *Medical Care of the Adolescent* (1960); co-author with H. I. Harris, *Emotional Problems of*

Adolescents (1958); with I. H. Goldberger and G. T. Hallock, *Health for Life* (1961).

W. WALLACE GRANT, M.D.
Associate Professor of Pediatrics, University of Manitoba; The Children's Hospital, Winnipeg, Canada.

MORRIS GREEN, M.D.
Professor of Pediatrics, Indiana University School of Medicine; Director, Kiwanis Outpatient and Diagnostic Center, James Whitcomb Riley Hospital for Children. Co-author with Julius B. Richmond, *Pediatric Diagnosis* (1954).

GEORGE W. GREENMAN, M.D.
Department of Psychiatry, Yale University School of Medicine. Formerly, Instructor in Pediatrics, Yale University School of Medicine.

ALEXIS F. HARTMANN, SR., M.D.
Professor and Chairman, Department of Pediatrics, Washington University School of Medicine; Physician-in-Chief, St. Louis Children's Hospital.

BARBARA ILLINGWORTH, PH.D.
Research Assistant Professor of Biochemistry, Washington University School of Medicine.

REIMER JENSEN, PH.D.
Associate Professor, Advanced Teachers' College of Denmark, Copenhagen.

BARBARA KORSCH, M.D.
Pediatric Director, Observation Clinic for Children; Associate Clinical Professor of Pediatrics, University of Southern California; Consultant, General Pediatrics, Children's Hospital.

ROBERT B. KUGEL, M.D.
Associate Professor of Pediatrics and Director, Child Development Clinic, State University of Iowa and University Hospitals. As of September 1, 1963, Professor of Medical Science, Brown University, Providence, Rhode Island.

MARTHA F. LEONARD, M.D.
Assistant Professor of Pediatrics, Yale University School of Medicine and Child Study Center.

MELVIN LEWIS, M.B., B.S. (London), D.C.H.

Assistant Professor of Pediatrics and Psychiatry, Yale University School of Medicine and Child Study Center.

VERNON W. LIPPARD, M.D.

Dean and Professor of Pediatrics, Yale University School of Medicine.

SEYMOUR L. LUSTMAN, M.D., PH.D.

Associate Professor of Psychiatry, Yale University School of Medicine and Child Study Center; Faculty member, The Western New England Institute for Psychoanalysis.

AUDREY T. McCOLLUM, M.S.

Research Assistant, Psychiatric Social Work, Yale University, Child Study Center.

EVELINE B. OMWAKE, M.A.

Assistant Professor and Director of Nursery School, Yale University, Child Study Center.

GROVER F. POWERS, M.D.

Professor Emeritus, Pediatrics, Yale University School of Medicine; Honorary Chairman, Scientific Research Advisory Board, National Association for Retarded Children, Inc.

SALLY A. PROVENCE, M.D.

Associate Professor of Pediatrics, Yale University School of Medicine and Child Study Center. Co-author with Rose C. Lipton, *Infants in Institutions* (1962).

DANE G. PRUGH, M.D.

Professor of Psychiatry and Pediatrics, University of Colorado School of Medicine. Co-editor with H. C. Stuart, *The Healthy Child: His Physical, Psychological, and Social Development* (1960).

JULIUS B. RICHMOND, M.D.

Professor and Chairman, Department of Pediatrics, College of Medicine, State University of New York at Syracuse. Co-author with Morris Green, *Pediatric Diagnosis* (1954).

SAMUEL RITVO, M.D.

Associate Clinical Professor of Psychiatry, Yale University School of Medicine and Child Study Center. Faculty member, The Western New

England Institute for Psychoanalysis and The New York Psychoanalytic Institute.

SEYMOUR B. SARASON, PH.D.
Professor of Psychology, Yale University. Author of *Psychological Problems in Mental Deficiency* (1949), *The Clinical Interaction* (1954); co-author with Thomas Gladwin, *Truk: Man in Paradise* (1953), with Thomas Gladwin and Richard L. Masland, *Mental Subnormality* (1958), with Kenneth S. Davidson, Richard R. Waite, Frederick K. Lighthall, and Britton K. Ruebush, *Anxiety in Elementary School Children: A Report of Research* (1960), with Kenneth S. Davidson and Burton Blatt, *The Preparation of Teachers: An Unstudied Problem in Education* (1962).

ALBERT J. SOLNIT, M.D.
Associate Professor of Pediatrics and Psychiatry, Yale University School of Medicine and Child Study Center. Faculty member, The Western New England Institute for Psychoanalysis.

MARY H. STARK, M.S.S.
Assistant Professor (Social Work), Yale University School of Medicine, Department of Pediatrics and Child Study Center.

HENK VEENEKLAAS, M.D.
Professor and Chairman, Department of Pediatrics, University Hospital, Leiden, The Netherlands.

BETTY WESLEY, M.S.
Research Assistant in Pediatrics, Washington University School of Medicine.

MORRIS A. WESSEL, M.D.
Associate Clinical Professor of Pediatrics, Yale University School of Medicine.

HULDA J. WOHLTMANN, M.D.
Assistant Professor of Pediatrics, Washington University School of Medicine; Assistant Physician, St. Louis Children's Hospital.

ANNA W. M. WOLF
Formerly a staff member, Child Study Association of America, and Child Care Editor, *Woman's Home Companion*. Author of *The Parents' Manual: A Guide to the Emotional Development of Young Chil-*

dren (1941), *Our Children Face War* (1942); co-author with Suzanne Szasz, *Helping Your Child's Emotional Growth: A Pictorial Guide for Parents* (1954).

RICHARD E. WOLF, M.D.

Director, Pediatric Psychiatry Clinic, The Children's Hospital; Associate Professor of Pediatrics and Assistant Professor of Pediatric Psychiatry, College of Medicine, University of Cincinnati.

JOE D. WRAY, M.D.

Member of Staff in Medical and Natural Sciences of The Rockefeller Foundation; Visiting Professor, Department of Pediatrics, Universidad del Valle, Cali, Colombia, South America.

Foreword

● *VERNON W. LIPPARD, M.D.*

Yale University

Wilmarth Lewis, in his preface to *The Making of a Library*,[1] said, "Sixty is a horrible birthday, and anything that one's friends can do to make it bearable should be done."

Milton Senn's present and former colleagues and students have arranged to honor his sixtieth birthday—in fact, they have demonstrated their tribute to the man who is being honored for his interest in and work with children. What finer tribute could one conceive than a volume in which the scholarly works of one's friends and colleagues are expressed as freely as they would be if they were assembled in a huge seminar.

In arranging the Table of Contents, the editors have traced the growth of Dr. Senn's professional interests. The first section deals with the biological aspects of child development and is a reflection of his interests during his early days at Washington University and Cornell. Other sections dealing with theoretical and clinical con-

[1] *The Making of a Library.* Extracts from Letters 1934-1941 of Harvey Cushing, Arnold C. Klebs, and John F. Fulton. New Haven, privately printed at the Yale University Press, 1959, 69 pp.

siderations in pediatric practice and education, child psychiatry and child development reflect the expansion of his interests and the sphere of his influence during his years at Yale.

The past thirty years have seen a remarkable change in the field of pediatrics. It developed during the early part of the twentieth century as a specialty concerned with the care of physically sick children. It is now equally concerned with the prevention of illness and the physical, emotional, and social development of well children. The pediatrician alone cannot cover all this ground. In both research and clinical management, his skills must be combined with those of the biological and social scientists and educators as well as those of the other medical and surgical specialists. It is in this role of the child's physician and the coordinator of all those whose skills may be brought to bear in improving the health and well-being of the child that many of us see the future of the pediatrician.

This concept is gaining momentum and will influence the practices of child rearing throughout the world. Among those at the head of the movement is the man to whom this volume is dedicated. It should help point the way to others.

Introduction

• *ALBERT J. SOLNIT, M.D.*
• *SALLY A. PROVENCE, M.D.*

Yale University

On a warm June day in the 1940s, Milton Senn and another restless soul sat in the shade of a catalpa tree and talked together of their discontent with the then prevailing type of pediatric training as a preparation for the medical care of children. Something like it has occurred many times between Milton Senn and another person, and because it is both typical and personal it is felt to be an appropriate introduction to this volume.

As the story goes, the second person, three years out of residency training, had found the private practice of pediatrics disappointing and frustrating—a far cry from the satisfactions of ministering to the very ill and from the drama of the hospital wards. Only rarely in practice did one encounter an exotic or interesting disease; only rarely did one save a life. What came to the attention, day in and day out, were children with runny noses, infected ear drums, skin rashes or diarrhea—mundane and uninteresting conditions in themselves. If practice was disappointing it was also frustrating because children with feeding disturbances, sleep difficulties, or toileting problems often did not respond to the prescribed measures, and the young practitioner felt inept and ineffective in those areas of child care.

We would now know that what was missing from this pediatrician's training was an important point of view—that the child is a growing, dynamic individual in a family unit, a concept which implies an attitude as well as a knowledge of child development. The child development training that this "typical" pediatrician had experienced consisted of an understanding of physical growth, an exposure to Gesell which was interesting but not very useful in practice, and a few "recipes" for handling feeding, sleep, and toilet-training problems derived from Watsonian psychology which pediatrics had embraced so willingly. The discontented and searching practitioner did not know what was missing, but Milton Senn *did* know because he, in his own turn, had conducted a similar search and, having arrived at some ideas of how and what should be taught, had organized the Cornell-New York Hospital Child Development Institute. This training program also reflected his interest in other human beings, an interest which made it almost impossible for him to resist the appeal of one in search of more knowledge about children.

Senn's struggle toward a comprehensive and satisfying concept of the practice of pediatrics and of child care had begun at Washington University, St. Louis, in 1929, after he had completed medical school at the University of Wisconsin and served his internship. In those days in St. Louis, exciting advances were being made in the understanding of biochemical changes during illness and Senn was involved with Alexis Hartmann in studies of electrolyte balance, and of lactate metabolism. The pediatrician who did laboratory research had begun to occupy a prestige role and such research was an essential part of the academic position. Senn's early papers reflect this training and influence. Along with this rigorous and disciplined line of work—much of which was remote from contact with the child and his family—there was another strong current which arose from Senn's belief in the importance of the individual human being and his feelings.

Senn went to the Cornell Department of Pediatrics in 1933 as

director of the laboratories. He had a constantly growing conviction
that pediatrics must broaden its scope, and that the pediatrician had
a responsibility to the whole child. This concept, which we now
regard as a truism, was revolutionary and not at all popular in those
days. Senn left Cornell from 1937 to 1939 to take training in psychiatry, and on his return formulated and implemented his own
training program in child development. He believed that pediatricians had much to learn from psychiatry, education, and the social
sciences, and provided his trainees with a rich fare. For this he was
at times criticized for "confusing" them in their professional identity
and for promoting an eclecticism that might prove to be a disservice.
Since he was a pioneer and the program was constantly evolving,
such criticisms as well as his own perpetual questioning made him his
own severest critic. This resulted in a reshaping of this program and
in an increasing effort to integrate many aspects of it into the education of all pediatricians.

In 1948 he was asked by Yale University to organize and direct
a new center for children, in a program of teaching and research in
child development which would succeed Arnold Gesell's Clinic of
Child Development.

Fifteen years have passed since Senn came to New Haven to
establish the Child Study Center at Yale. He organized in the
Center a program of teaching and research which was firmly rooted
in clinical service. A Child Psychiatry Unit, a Nursery School, and
a Diagnostic Unit for developmental problems of infants and preschool children were the three areas of service around which a
variety of students including child psychiatrists, psychologists, nursery school teachers, social workers, and pediatricians received training. Research was encouraged in several areas of child development
with major emphasis placed upon research into personality development. It was typical of Senn that these various units were set up to
allow considerable autonomy of development and function which
his staff both valued and complained about since they feared that
he would be too little involved in their daily work. This was in part
influenced by Senn's appointment, in 1951, as Chairman of the
Department of Pediatrics at Yale to succeed the respected and be-

loved Grover Powers on his retirement. In accepting this appointment Senn saw an opportunity to stimulate the development of training in comprehensive pediatric practice both at the student and post-graduate levels. It was to be expected that Senn would have critics from two sides, as indeed he has—those with a classic pediatric orientation who reacted to the inclusion of psychological considerations in a training program as though these were diluting and endangering the science of medicine, and from critics in psychiatry who felt he was trying to make psychiatrists of all pediatricians.

In reality, Senn has supported and worked for broadening the concept of the pediatrician's role while insisting upon the need for careful and adequate training in each area of specialization. He remained convinced of the need to experiment and to seek. He has emphasized the need for the active cooperation of all people interested in children to contribute to their care and development without expecting that any one person can be all things to all people. It is probable that Senn has paid a high personal price in maintaining his eclectic attitude and in broadening his approach, for it has meant he has missed much of the direct professional satisfaction that comes from immersion in a single specialty or problem over a long period of time.

The contributions to this book follow Milton Senn's scientific development. Characteristically his development has remained rooted in biological thinking and humanistic values. This development has reflected his searching curiosity about areas of knowledge which are insufficiently illuminated and his dissatisfaction with the inadequate application of knowledge that is available. As a great teacher he has sponsored and supported the independent development of his colleagues and students. While his special attention has been focused on pediatric education and medical care of children, his perspectives about and work with children and their families have linked national with international factors, biochemical with psychological considerations, and molecular determinations with cultural and educational influences. One of Milton Senn's characteristics is well known: he is never satisfied with his own work or with the effective attention being given to children physically or psychologically. He has built his career on the conviction that children and families are our most important resources and on his scientific fascination with the intricacies of child development.

In the last analysis, Milton Senn is a highly complicated person, always accessible and available when he is giving to a fellow human being in need; and quite cautious, modest, and reserved when it is time for him to receive.

This volume will serve its purpose well if it offers examples of the scope of his interests, the scholarliness of his searchings, and his restless dissatisfaction with the plight of children in our world today.

We wish to acknowledge with appreciation the devoted cooperation received in organizing and editing this book from the authors of the individual papers. We also wish to express our warmest gratitude to Blanche Senn for wise counsel, to Elizabeth H. Sharp for competent and cheerful assistance, and to Lottie M. Newman for seasoned technical guidance. We are indebted to Jewell M. Eberlein and Ruth Parker for their steadfast cooperation.

Part I

Introductory Section

Grover Powers and Lawrence Frank have written essays that will help to convey the mood of this volume. Powers speaks humbly and philosophically to the clinical student, demonstrating how the continuing student is also the most effective scholar and teacher. Frank approaches child development as a scientific discipline that is of crucial and exciting importance to all scientific endeavors as well as to children and their families.

Remarks to Undergraduate Students of Clinical Medicine

● *GROVER F. POWERS, M.D.*

Yale University

For a few minutes during this first pediatric clinic hour of a new school year, I have planned at the suggestion of two staff members, but with hesitation and humility, to speak to you not about children either well or sick, but about ourselves as responsible members, *all*, of a medical institution of learning in this day of cynicism and rebellion, of bad manners and "what do I get out of it" questioning, of little faith and rare equanimity.

Medicine is one of the old recognized professions. That is, as Dean (Emeritus) Roscoe Pound (1949) says, "an organized calling in which men pursue a learned art and are united in the pursuit of it as a public service—no less a public service because they may make a livelihood thereby. Here, from the professional standpoint, there are three essential ideas—organization, learning, and a spirit of public service. The gaining of a livelihood is not a professional consideration. Indeed, the professional spirit, the spirit of a public service, constantly curbs the urge of that instinct."

Reprinted from *The Yale Journal of Biology and Medicine*, Vol. 22, No. 2, December, 1949.

As students in the clinical years you now join the hospital staff as physicians—without degrees and without licenses and without adequate experience, but physicians you are, nevertheless. As such you are members of a goodly company of persons directly responsible for the health of your fellow men and indirectly, but no less vitally, sharing responsibility for the health and the welfare of society. Leaders in our profession have viewed the far horizon and have envisioned us in the vanguard in the march of civilization. Writing many years ago, Virchow, father of cellular pathology, prophesied:

> Should medicine ever fulfil its great ends, it must enter into the larger political and social life of our time; it must indicate the barriers which obstruct the normal completion of the life-cycle and remove them. Should this ever come to pass, medicine, whatever it may then be, will become the common good of all. It will cease to be medicine and will be absorbed into that general simplified body of knowledge which is identifiable with power. . . . When we have exact knowledge of conditions of existence of individuals and of peoples, then only will it be possible for the laws of medicine and philosophy to gain the credence of general laws of humanity. Then only will the Baconian "Knowledge is Power" become accomplished fact.

And more recently, in our own day and generation and in our own school of medicine, Dr. Winternitz had the vision to fashion an Institute of Human Relations where medicine would take its vital and rightful place in a grouping together of biological and social sciences seeking, with law and religion, through physical, mental, and spiritual liaison to discover the bases upon which a better society might be built and human welfare promoted. Medicine of the past sought to make possible a healthy body—Curative Medicine; in a confused way it now seeks a healthy mind in a healthy body— Mental Hygiene; but, now and in the future, it must seek integration with life—a healthy person in a healthy society (Halliday, 1948).

The physician has his roots deep in the soil of the past, for tradition to him "is not a barren pride in departed glories"—as a statesman once said in reference to British political tradition, "it is something from which he derives a profound assurance, a sense of destiny, and a determination never to abandon what has been purchased" with such labor, skill, devotion, and sacrifice "by those who have gone before him." Medical "tradition is not a recollection of the dead; it is real and living and growing. It rests upon an unspoken, and perhaps in many cases, unrealized faith in the undefeated continuity of the (profession). A man with a deep sense of continuity sees himself not as an accidental unit doomed to vanish in a few years but as one of a great human procession, influenced and helped by those who have gone before him, responsible in his turn for giving help and encouragement to those who will come after" (Menzies, 1949).

You are the inheritors of this tradition and the beneficiaries of many generous philanthropies and appropriations; the future of medicine will be as you plan and work. As already stated, you are physicians in fact if not in name and you have assumed responsibility for health and happiness (in part) of human individuals based on the scientific training and knowledge you have received here and elsewhere and guided by such wisdom as you possess and develop. You are members now of a noble profession—one enriched by the careful observations and correlations and patient investigations of thousands of your devoted and indefatigable professional ancestors whose contributions and example are your priceless heritage.

And thus, attention having been directed to some of our indebtednesses, I come to the central theme of my remarks; I shall put it in the form of a quotation from an address by the great psychologist and philosopher, William James (1907):

> Does not the acceptance of a happy life involve a point of honor? Are we not bound to take some suffering upon ourselves, to do some self-denying service with our lives in return for all those lives upon which ours are built? To hear the question is to answer it in but one possible way, if one have a normally constituted heart.

It is a cliché to say that great universities are built not with bricks and mortar but with great teachers. For are we not all teachers, practitioners, and students—in varying degrees, of course, but nonetheless each of us here functions in all of these categories. Do not think for a moment because academic protocol designates you as "students" or "clinical clerks" and some of us as "faculty" that the sick, distraught human beings whom you will see as patients are going to make or should make any such distinction. And do not think or thoughtlessly assume that the reputation and the achievements and the prestige of the Yale University School of Medicine rest alone upon faculty, laboratories, or hospital; upon your qualities of character, mind, and heart also rest challenging responsibilities and great privileges, upon your sense of oneness in great endeavor, upon your loyalties and devotion to duties, opportunities, and teamwork, upon conduct, humanitarian and moral, as well as interests, intellectual and scientific—upon these equally rests the fair name of our School. Greatness in a school of medicine, I say, with all the strength of firm conviction and all the earnestness of worthy ambition for this institution, derives from all of the constituent members just as truly as it derives from human beings rather than from buildings and equipment.

To be a physician—that is a great responsibility, yes, but is it not a great privilege also? Think of your kinship with the great men and women who have wrought brilliantly and effectively in the advances of medicine science; think of those patient scholars equally gifted and equally worthy but unacclaimed because their results, as we say, were "negative"; think of the thousands of devoted, industrious, competent practitioners of the science and art of medicine; think of the teachers, public health workers, administrators; think of the rich opportunities to deal with people and families in all the vagaries and vicissitudes, in the successes and failures of life; think of the sickness of society and of the opportunities to do something to bring understanding, healing, and correction; and just think very seriously of the fact that you are here where many others long to be—others, perhaps, more, or at least equally, deserving of the privilege and who will never gain admission to any school of medicine! Think of these things, I beg you, and realize and act upon the fact that you are privileged far beyond the vast number of your fellow men.

In these so-called "clinical years," what are the senior students, i.e., the faculty, endeavoring to do for you the junior students? In pediatrics, are we going to try to "cover the ground," as some would suggest, or give a "comprehensive course"? Are we going to discuss the natural history and treatment and family and community repercussions of every important disease which may afflict the child? Are we going to point out each milestone on the pathway of growth and development of the growing organism and the maturing personality? No, what you acquire in the way of facts is largely incidental and can be gotten perhaps more easily from books and scientific journals without the aid of expensive hospitals, laboratories, and preceptors. What we in pediatrics seek to do by example, word, and deed is to demonstrate a way of life, a way of medical life, more narrowly—a way of pediatric life. How we obtain vital data in the child's history and appraise his environment, learn about family life, mother and father, sisters and brothers; what has taken place in his maturation; what illnesses he has had, what preventive measures have been taken, what indicated; what behavior reactions does he have; what signs and symptoms of illness does he exhibit; what diagnostic procedures are indicated; what treatment is necessary for the patient in the bed (and the sick parents in the waiting room); what report is to be made to the physician who referred the patient (not the "L.M.D.," please) or the visiting nurse who brought him in; what can be done in the home to create a happy and healthful environment; how can the nurse and medical social worker be helpful; what public health contacts are indicated? These are but sample questions and problems which are to be dealt with in a pediatric way of life and require an integration not to be secured from books and lectures and not easily measured by examination marks.

You have had opportunities and facilities for acquiring knowledge and methodologies in the basic medical sciences. By using this intellectual equipment, by observing and emulating the professional procedures of your more experienced fellow students (the clinical faculty), by examining and by careful, kindly questioning of patients or parents, by studying the literature, by discussing data with student and faculty colleagues—thus will you acquire skills in the practice of medicine and learn how to think about clinical problems, how to approach various situations and deal effectively and wisely with them. The internship is the crown and glory of this experience and that is the reason it matters so little, relatively speaking, whether your hospital service be "straight" or "rotating," surgical or pediatric; what greatly matters is fine quality and high standards and fair critiques of performance and conduct, professional and personal.

I might add, by way of footnote, that although we make no systematic effort to give a comprehensive "quiz course" in pediatrics, you will become familiar with the important aspects of the subject if you attend faithfully all the "required" courses in pediatrics given during the two clinical years; courses which vary in form and substance and which you well know you are not required, except by honor and self-interest, to attend.

By emulation, by repetition, by steady application, by experience and by practice, will you become what you all, I hope, seek to become—great physicians? Something more, I think, is required—something at the heart of all great achievement. What you call that "something more" matters not—character, wisdom, inner security—not the kind furnished by government subsidies or by private annuities but by your faith, faith in something, faith which is your own and gives meaning to life, a something of incorruptible good which in our sickworld society is badly needed. The poets know of what I am speaking:

> Wisdom was never learned at any knees,
> Not even a father's, and that father a king.
> .... I am not one
> Who must have everything, yet I must have
> My dreams if I must live, for they are mine.
> Wisdom is not one word and then another,
> Till words are like dry leaves under a tree;
> Wisdom is like a dawn that comes up slowly
> Out of an unknown ocean [Robinson, 1946].

And thus with training and wisdom may you attain to that group envisioned by Thomas Hardy (1921):

> We would establish those of kindlier build,
> In fair compassions skilled,
> Men of deep art in life development.

BIBLIOGRAPHY

Halliday, J. L. (1948), *Psychosocial Medicine: A Study of the Sick Society*. New York: Norton, p. 209.

Hardy, T. (1921), Chorus of the Pities. *The Dynasts: An Epic Drama*. London: Macmillan, p. 3.

James, W. (1907), Is Life Worth Living. *The Will to Believe*. New York: Longmans Green, p. 50.

Menzies, R. G. (1949), It Is a Good Tradition—It Cannot Die. *N.Y. Times Mag.*, July 10.

Pound, R. (1949), The Professions in the Society of Today. *New Eng. J. Med.*, 241:351.

Robinson, E. A. (1946), Tristram. *Collected Poems*. New York: Macmillan, p. 726.

Human Development: An Emerging Scientific Discipline

• *LAWRENCE K. FRANK, A.B., LL.D.*

Belmont, Mass.

It is often said that science does not study problems that may be interesting or even urgent, but only those problems for which it has methods and techniques. Hence, until the methods have been developed and perfected, according to this view, the study of human development, however urgent, must be deferred. But if we recall what happened in physics in the early years of this century, we will see that physics was suddenly confronted with a host of new events; becoming aware of radiation, of discontinuity, and the discovery that the atom is not a hard indivisible entity but a complex organization with a variety of energy transformations which offered unlimited possibilities for further study and exploration, as the development of modern physics has shown.

If physics had accepted the usual convention of refusing to study these new problems for which there were then no tested methods, it could not have explored the newly revealed physical world since the methods of classical physics were not relevant or applicable to these newly revealed atomic organizations. But recognition of these events evoked creative thinking, the formulation of new concepts, and the invention of new methods and techniques that were appropriate to these new problems and immensely fruitful. As Einstein remarked some years ago, "We now realize how much in error were those theorists who believed that theory could be inductively derived from facts." This correction by Einstein indicates that until we have a conceptual formulation, a theory, or a model, we are not able to advance our science, nor are we able to recognize and conceive events which we need to study.

Today there is a growing recognition of the need for studying multidimensional, dynamic events requiring conceptual models for their study, as distinguished from specific hypotheses concerned with the relation of two variables, abstracted from their organic context. Moreover, these new conceptual models will enable us to think about processes that produce different products and by such an approach we escape from the rigidities of linear, cause-and-effect thinking, and the search for mechanisms derived primarily from physical theory.

We may say, then, that accepting the challenge of the problem of human development with a willingness to explore for new concepts and models, to utilize new ways of thinking, involving new criteria of credibility, as pioneered by physics, may provide the new orientation we await and give rise to a new discipline of human development. Not only are there sound scientific reasons for such exploration and ample sanctions for such a courageous, imaginative approach, but there are compelling human needs to justify any attempts to create a new discipline of human development.

If we are to have anything that will warrant the terms primary prevention, health care, preventive medicine, and mental health, we must have a more comprehensive understanding of the development of the human individual from conception on, with a recognition of the many hazards and vicissitudes to which he is exposed, but also the potentialities which the human organism may exhibit at each stage of his life career. This requires a recognition of the "organism as a whole" and the dynamic functioning of the organism-personality.

The study of human development from conception through old age will probably become the central core of medical education in the future, and thereby provide a larger conceptual framework for utilizing the growing contributions from the basic medical, life, and human sciences.

Medicine, public health, education, psychology, nursing, social work, dentistry, the care and treatment of the so-called exceptional child, and the various other professions and organizations concerned with human beings are all handicapped by lack of knowledge and understanding of human development. Moreover, each of these separate disciplines, professions, and agencies operates with a different conception of the human organism-personality and (by so much) is blocked in communicating with others and likely to frustrate the work of others concerned with the same human subjects (Frank, 1962). The growing practice of urban and regional planning may prove to be a self-defeating enterprise unless informed by recognition of human development and what is necessary for the conservation of human life and personality from birth through old age.

The tasks of a science of human development are exceedingly complex and at present almost baffling. The need for such an enterprise cannot be exaggerated; yet it is difficult to see how and where such a new scientific discipline can arise because the university departments and the various research institutes are dedicated to the study of specialized problems of individual disciplines which promise great professional awards and prestige for their investigation.

But the opportunity is open for a scientific "break-through," to use a popular term, that will put the study of human development at the forefront of the life sciences, recognizing the recently formulated conception of cybernetics, of self-organizing systems, of non-linear relations (Wiener, 1961; Elsasser, 1958).

LIMITATIONS OF TRADITIONAL METHODS OF STUDY

Our traditional ways of thinking have fostered a strong inclination to reify events, making data into supposed entities, and giving a name to whatever we select for observation. By so doing we convert what should be a verb into a noun and punctuate a series of ongoing events like a snapshot. We also have been schooled for a long time in fractionating wholes, such as organisms, into a number of seemingly discrete parts, more or less arbitrarily cutting up the whole, according to our preconceptions and assumptions about the relation of variables. This is essential to the experimental method of investigation.

As Whorf (1940; see also Carroll, 1957) has emphasized, our language almost compels us to think and speak in terms of a temporal lineal sequence: an actor or subject, some action or verb, focused on a predicate or object, that which is acted upon. And our methods of study have been concerned with the discovery of "mechanisms" and linear relations between two variables as measured in a sample of subjects. These analytic methods have been immensely productive and given us a body of knowledge of how these isolated events operate, through what we call "mechanisms," but these are essentially scientific artifacts.

We have been aware of and have always been confronted by "organized complexities" (Weaver, 1948),[1] such as organisms, personalities, cultures, societies, and human institutions, schools, hospitals, and factories. However, only within recent years has there been any systematic effort to study these as ongoing, operating, functioning wholes which cannot be understood by any aggregation of discrete findings of parts as revealed by experiments on isolated preparations in a laboratory setting where the preparation has been cut off from its full functioning and normal inputs and outputs *in situ*.

THE HUMAN ORGANISM AS AN OPEN SYSTEM

We are gradually realizing that much of our scientific study and our ability to predict are concerned with closed systems, that is,

---

1 "These problems—and a wide range of similar problems in the biological, medical, psychological, economic, and political sciences—are just too complicated to yield to the old nineteenth-century techniques which were so dramatically successful on two-, three-, or four-variable problems of simplicity. These new problems, moreover, cannot be handled with the statistical techniques so effective in describing average behavior in problems of disorganized complexity.

"These new problems—and the future of the world depends on many of them— require science to make a third great advance, an advance that must be even greater than the nineteenth-century conquest of problems of simplicity or the twentieth-century victory over problems of disorganized complexity. Science must, over the next fifty years, learn to deal with these problems of organized complexity."

systems or organizations, isolated, or arbitrarily limited or deprived, of all inputs, except definitely controlled inputs, as in a nerve-muscle preparation, for a rigidly controlled experiment; or a study of children who are, so far as possible, isolated from any events that might interfere with the testing of an experimental hypothesis. To gain control over events and isolate the "mechanisms" or to discover the linear relations between variables, we create these artificially closed systems. Our findings are therefore essentially artifacts, valuable and significant artifacts, by which we build up our various disciplines and improve our techniques for manipulating events.

But a living, growing, developing, maturing, aging organism is an open system, as von Bertalanffy (1950) has pointed out, with continual inputs and outputs. It is compelled as an organism to maintain continuous intercourse with the environment and, if human, to learn as a personality, to live in a symbolic cultural world, exhibiting purposive, goal-seeking conduct. Moreover, each individual is a unique organism, with his unique heredity, his own body size, shape, rates of growth and development and aging, and his own individualized experience that has shaped his idiomatic relations to the world of events and to other persons and to himself.

It is frequently asserted that only by a number of separate, independent approaches to human development studies can we hope to achieve a somewhat clumsy and inadequate correlation of these many scientific findings. This is because the variety and multiplicity of functional processes and activities of the human organism-personality, with its many differentiated and specialized organ systems, its highly specialized functions, its idiosyncratic behavior and patterned conduct, present a seemingly impossible task for scientific investigation, except by the long-accepted procedures of fractionating and analyzing the individual, in attempting to reveal the relationships that can be handled by recognized anlytic techniques and statistical methods.

This way of thinking and of investigating rests upon a number of assumptions that are now taken for granted as unquestionable, indeed as the only basis for scientific study of human development. Thus it is assumed that we can study human development only by measuring the observable *products* of growth and development, the changing dimensions of an organism-personality, while neglecting or ignoring the pressing question: what are the *processes* of development which give rise to and produce such observable products. As Woodger (1929) remarked many years ago, we tend to study organisms in "timeless space" as in the cadaver where structure-functional-behavior processes have been arrested so that we can deal with the inert human body and measure its static configuration, its organs, and its other components at rest. The living organism is, however, continually fluctuating in size, in shape, and in its varied outputs and inputs.

Also by convention, we study human behavior and relations in "spaceless time" as if the organism-personality were living in time with no spatial, environmental context; therefore only the temporal aspects of his activities are significant, as in the usual stimulus-response sequences. This assumption of spaceless time fosters the further assumption that the organism-personality is exposed only to those stimuli-situations that have been selected for observation and that all other events, internal as well as external, are irrelevant or have been excluded. The ecology of human development, however, is becoming increasingly significant as we recognize that all human behavior and development occur in a geographical, cultural, and social context to which the individual is continually related and which therefore participates in his development, his functioning, and his conduct.

Today we are realizing that in approaching dynamic events we cannot confine our study to fixed, static entities related only by classic conceptions of spatial displacement, speed of movement, and quantities of energies transmitted or expended. We need to ask: what are the processes operating whereby a given transaction produces different products according to when and where and how much and upon what that process is operating?

At this point we might say that in studies of human development, the focus should be on revealing the process as the invariant, on the assumption that the same process may be operating in a variety of contexts or organisms to produce different products (what I call "multiproductivity"). One can see such related reactions in mammalian reproduction where the same process of ovulation, fertilization, gestation, and parturition produces such different mammalian organisms and in man produces such uniquely different individuals. Conversely, as von Bertalanffy (1950) has pointed out, different processes may produce similar, or equivalent products, which he has called "equifinality." Moreover, as Heinrich Klüver (1936) emphasized some thirty years ago, in biology and psychology we must employ the method of equivalent and nonequivalent stimuli, recognizing that different stimuli or inputs may be equivalent for initiating specific actions or developments.

The long-accepted assumption of a passive organism waiting to be stimulated to behave or to function has become invalid, as we have discovered that living organisms are continually functioning at greater or lesser intensity. But in so many of our studies of human development we tacitly assume that what we do to and for a subject is the "cause" of what we observe in his functioning and behavior or we impute some specific motivations as a "cause" of his behavior.

THE CONCEPT OF PROCESSES

If we are to pursue the study of processes of development, we must escape from the familiar assumption of linear relations and recognize that in organism-personalities, we are dealing with circular, reciprocal feedbacks, with nonlinear relationships, in which the antecedent may initiate a response of much greater magnitude, not limited as in cause and effect or stimulus and response.

So long as we are guided by the classic formulation of physical events as occurring through the transfer of energy in necessary and sufficient quantities to cause the observed effect, we are limited in our ability to conceptualize a process. This process operates not according to power engineering but according to communication engineering in which a message, such as a signal, sign, or symbol evokes in the recipient a response with only a minimum of energy being transmitted. His response is a function of his present state or condition, patterned by his previous life experience, thus resembling a Markoff process.

If we conceptualize the process in this way, we may escape some of the rigidities and limitations of cause-and-effect and stimulus-and-response thinking for the study of human development. We can approach the study of human development as a series of concomitant processes for which we need conceptual models; this is the most promising way we can formulate the multidimensional events in "organized complexities." Models, we should note, are not theories or explanations but attempts to construct, actually or conceptually, analogues of what we are seeking to understand, for which simple hypotheses are not adequate (Society for Experimental Biology, 1960). This approach is similar to general systems theory, at least in so far as it is being developed by various students of organizations who are attempting to find a new approach to the study of such organizations.

As one such model we might usefully consider the problems and methods of medicine which are concerned with the intact, functioning organism-personality with its individual vulnerabilities, its strengths and potentialities for self-repair, living in an environment with its peculiar hazards and its opportunities and resources. The physician of today has at his command a wide array of diagnostic procedures so that from a complete "work-up," he can usually obtain a variety of findings on a patient, including the many laboratory tests, X-rays and other diagnostic procedures, most of which can now be quantified. To utilize these many reports, the physician must employ what may be called the method of "biological relativity," that is, he must enlarge or attenuate the significance of each quantified report, of each test, according to the age, sex, body build, and present complaint or illness, previous illness and treatment. He must recognize the relative significance of each of these separate findings to all the other findings, including what he elicits in the history from the patient or discovers elsewhere about the patient's family life and other interpersonal relations, his ethnic, cultural background, his religion, and his persistent affective reactions of anxiety or guilt, shame, and hostility. Only as the physician can and does attempt to "relativize" the many findings on a patient can he make these often elaborate and quantified reports meaningful for that identified patient in an attempt to make an accurate diagnosis and prognosis of that individual patient.

Medicine recognizes the changes that take place in the human organism at different age periods and under varying life conditions; therefore its model is a flexible or plastic conception, not a rigid organization. With this model of an intact functioning organism, the physician examines a patient and relies upon a variety of tests to discover in what ways and to what extent that individual patient deviates from his conceptual model, and he infers from such deviations what is the health or ill health of that patient, viewed in terms of "biological relativity." As Dr. Holmes has been reported to have remarked years ago, "The relation of a heart to the pair of lungs of an individual patient is more significant to medicine than the relation of that heart to ninety-nine other hearts."

This medical procedure may be cited as an example of approaching an individual in terms of ongoing processes, since the physician recognizes that the same basic physiological processes are operating in each individual patient, but in unique combinations and configurations and with different degrees of efficiency and organic congruence, subject to a wide variety of disturbances and deficiencies in any individual person. Thus a medical examination might be viewed as a pattern for study of human development which might be extended over a period of years, ideally from birth or conception through old age to death, so that the sequential and cumulative processes of development can be observed in all their complexity and in their almost unlimited variety of products. Looking at a patient's history the physician tries to reconstruct his previous experience from the patient's account of his previous illness and activities, etc.

If we take the medical pattern as a possible guide for further thinking and possible adaptation to the study of human development, we may see a number of promising leads for exploration, utilizing the conception of processes. We may say that development implies persistence with change, continuing existence of an identified organism-personality which is to be observed for a long span of years without being lost in a sample or becoming an anonymous unit in a frequency distribution.

An organism persists by changing (1) through *incremental growth* and *replacement growth,* the renewal of those cells and tissues and fluids and also of their chemical constituents that are continually being discarded and replaced; (2) by development and integration of differentiated cells and tissues, with their specialized functional capacities for its ever-changing internal and overt activities; (3) by maturation in which an organism changes in the sense of relinquishing and rejecting what he has previously attained, learned or achieved, in order to replace it with, or to incorporate it within, a new function or process more appropriate to his growing size, shape, functioning, and other developing capacities. We can observe maturation in the shift from sucking at the breast or bottle to self-feeding, in changing from creeping and crawling to erect posture and walking. Maturation is here viewed as more than the emergence of unlearned patterns to indicate how the whole sequence of earlier patterned functions and behavior is reorganized and recombined, making possible the emergence of new patterns essential to human development (especially in embryological growth and development); and (4) by the aging process which, as George Minot pointed out many years ago, is most rapid in the embryo-fetus and continues to operate all through the life career, becoming more rapid and pervasive in the later years of life, especially in some organ systems, but at different rates for each individual.

Despite these truly amazing changes beginning with the fertilized egg, the individual organism-personality persists as an identifiable unit who copes with all these life tasks and becomes successively a child, an adolescent, and then an adult. While he must struggle to achieve a personal identity, he never loses his biological identity which encompasses these varied and pervasive changes in the process of development.

This means that an adequate conception of human development should embrace the full range of these many concomitant processes and transformations as they occur within the more or less elastic configuration of a given identifiable individual. This individual at every moment must carry on all his vital functioning, yet cumulatively alter almost all his dimensions and, as at puberty and in pregnancy, undergo profound changes in his or her organic functioning.

Years ago I suggested that we try to imagine purchasing a Model-T Ford and driving it continuously for twenty years, during which period it has been gradually transformed into a Rolls-Royce, despite daily use, a variety of accidents, untold incidents, and the many vicissitudes of travel. However fantastic this may seem, it is scarcely adequate as an analogy for the truly extraordinary sequence of human development, from conception through to old age, and it neglects the capacity for reproduction exhibited by human organisms.

While human development begins with the fertilized egg, it becomes observable only in the infant who undergoes a series of abrupt transitions, shifting from a liquid to an air environment and becoming functionally independent of the mother. Later the child is expected to learn to cope with the many and varied demands, restrictions, and opportunities for living, first, as an organism in the geographical world, then as a personality in a symbolic cultural world, while participating in a social order.

THE TASK OF FORMULATING DEVELOPMENTAL EVENTS

When we approach the study of human development by formulating a series of models, we may be able to develop some analogues of the dynamic operational activities exhibited by the developing organism. Such models enable us to conceive of a number of concurrent ongoing processes and events by which organized complexities grow, develop, and age, while continually functioning as organisms (Singer, 1961).[2]

The task is to formulate these developmental sequences so that the great array of empirical observations can be articulated into an

2 Cf. the following statement about another field of human studies: "The point which needs to be stressed here is that political science in general, and international relations in particular, suffer from a serious paucity of concepts and models by which we might seek to describe, explain, or predict with fullness and clarity. Our conceptual poverty strikes this writer as perhaps the greatest single handicap in the development of everything from low-level empirical generalizations to a full-blown theoretical scheme. Some judicious and selective borrowing and adaptation might definitely be in order."

integrated, coordinated conception of human development which will at once draw upon these many findings but will give them an over-all comprehensive interpretation that enables us to gain understanding of human development. But we must recognize that no one process or any single model will be adequate since we are dealing with the multidimensional organism-personality, moving through space-time, undergoing a number of transformations, while carrying on a number of simultaneous functions and exhibiting a variety of behavior and relationships.

While the basic physical, chemical, and biological processes operating in the human organism are similar to other organisms, they operate as patterns in human organisms within boundaries, constraints, temporal sequences, and ever-changing spatial dimensions and relations which are articulated and synchronized by positive and negative feedbacks. These patterns make possible the living functioning organism with its highly individualized specificity.

We can assert today that these processes seem to be orderly in their operation, while producing different products. They exhibit sequential patterns, often with a variety of feedbacks, although not always effectively synchronized with each other or fully articulated in their varied interrelations. Thus we can see a high degree of regularity, but not uniformity, in human development. We can assert that human development seems to occur as an orderly, regular process which every individual experiences, like traveling along the same highway. But each individual, with his or her own unique heredity and highly individualized nurture and experience, will travel along that highway at his or her own rate of progress, and attain the dimensions of size, shape, weight, functional and other capacities that are uniquely individualized. With such a concept of development we may then ask: what processes seem to be necessary to permit or make possible orderly, regular, developmental sequences while producing such different individuals as products?

THE GROWTH PROCESS

Obviously we must assume a growth process since the initial stage in human development occurs in the multiplication of cells which we call incremental growth that continues until differentiation and specialization become necessary for survival of these rapidly multiplying cells. Then we see the growth process continuing in and through differentiated cells that give rise to tissues and organ systems, as the embryo begins to evolve into a fetus with many alterations and replacements, but continues to function through the same functional organic patterns and with much the same internal constraints, integration, synchrony, and articulation that persist throughout its life career. This is to say, before birth the organism has become large and complex enough, through incremental growth and differentiation, to become an organism capable of functioning in the extrauterine existence into which it suddenly will be expelled.

A model for the processes we call differentiation may soon become available as we learn from contemporary studies of the interactions of DNA and RNA within the cell. These interactions are apparently subject to impulses from nerves which may alter the proteins being produced. Apparently the genetic code operates in conjunction with ongoing cytoplasmic organs and cellular processes. The genetic control of cellular replacement and of new growth may become weakened and ineffectual under changing conditions as in aging. We might speak of "tired genes" as no longer capable of directing differentiation, apparently permitting the emergence of cancer cells which by their undifferentiated growth threaten the integrity of the organism and the operation of the organ systems.

For an adequate conception of this growth process we must also recognize replacement growth that continues to operate as some cells in the organism are discarded and replaced by new cells. Of great significance is the process whereby many of the basic chemical constituents of the organism are continually being replaced, as shown by studies using isotopes and tagged atoms so that there is an almost continuous input and output, a taking in, a retention and a release, and also an output or elimination of various chemical constituents of an organism (Frank, 1946). Indeed we are compelled to think of an organism as a persistent but ever-changing configuration in which, and through which, the environment is continually flowing and ebbing, as we recognize in the observable functions of breathing, of eating and eliminating through urine, feces, sweating, etc. This is also true in the environmental relationships of intake and response to impacts of barometric pressures, ultraviolet radiation, warmth and cold, etc.

Incremental growth may be viewed as a balance of retention over loss in the continuous and everchanging intercourse of the organism with its environment. Indeed, it may be desirable to recognize that an organism can be likened to a semipermeable membrane between the external environment and the internal environment. Each component of this internal environment must maintain communication with the external environment, if not directly, at least through various media of communication and transport, such as nerves, blood stream and lymphatic system, and the varied sensory apparatus with its complicated filters, buffers, amplifiers, transducers, etc.

We should note here that the more or less structured inputs of food such as proteins, carbohydrates, and fats are broken down into their various chemical constituents by digestion so that they can be utilized by each component of the organism for growth and replacement within the unique configuration of that organism.

Thus each organism builds its own idiosyncratic proteins by using the common elements taken in by food to synthesize its own proteins according to its genetic code. This truly amazing capacity becomes credible when we view the organism as a dynamic system in which the constituents are being replaced at different rates, as they are constellated into the patterns of that individual organism and become functional within the unique organic context.

Human development exhibits not only the regularities and often predictable sequences of these processes, but it also displays patterning and configural relations characteristic of "individuality" (Williams, 1956). These specific patterns and their uniqueness are often neglected because of our preoccupation with the search for regularities and central tendencies and the emphasis upon the variations among individuals in frequency distributions.

Models of the *growth* process are now being formulated (Kavanau, 1961; Weiss, 1955), and there is a wealth of findings waiting to be further conceptualized in terms of a dynamic process operating in a variety of organic components, each of which exhibits what we call aging.

INTRAINDIVIDUAL VARIABILITY

The focus of most studies on human development has been upon the *inter*individual variation, to the neglect of the *intra*individual variability—the cyclical fluctuation in the individual organism's process and also in its various dimensions, internal and external. Almost all organ systems such as the heart, lungs, stomach, intestines, etc., are continually enlarging and contracting, as do the striped muscles when the organism is active. Moreover, the quantity, intensity, and concentration of secretions, including the production of enzymes, also vary almost continuously along with these various functional operations. A recognition of this dynamic constellation of ever-changing processes may be contrasted with the classical emphasis upon structures, fixed entities, and normative dimensions.

THE CONCEPT OF THE ORGANIZING PROCESS

A conceptual formulation of the growth process must be supplemented by a model of the organizing process, by which the differentiated and specialized components of an organism become coupled, integrated, articulated, synchronized, and so on, whereby the various identifiable parts, cells, tissues, fluids, and organ systems operate as an organized whole, not as a series of discrete independent components, each with its unrelated functioning activities.

Our thinking about organization has long been frustrated by the familiar assumption of a "whole" made up of "parts" to which some mysterious entity or power called organization is added. We have long been perplexed by the old dichotomy of structure versus function that now becomes increasingly irrelevant as we learn to think in terms of space-time (Frank, 1935). We may escape from these perplexities if we can conceive of an organizing process as a circular, reciprocal operation whereby the so-called parts, which we have artificially isolated, are coupled in such a way that what any one part or component does is always coupled with and communicated to all the other parts, which in turn exhibit reciprocal responses and communications to that part. Thus, we may say that the parts or components create or give rise to the organized whole which reciprocally governs what they individually do, in truly circular, nonlinear relations.

A simple-minded example of this may convey the meaning of the foregoing. We are familiar with a football team and recognize how a number of identified individuals are assigned, each to a specific position and a role in the team. They learn to perform that role and to communicate with other members of the team, according to whatever they have practiced as ways of playing the game. In all the different line-ups and however the individual players are deployed on the field, each member of the team continually communicates and relates his activities to the other ten players and they likewise communicate and relate to him. Thereby these individualized, but patterned, purposeful activities and continually changing relations of each of the eleven players give rise to what we call the team organization. This is not an entity but a dynamic process arising from the articulated, concerted, synchronized performance by the individual components of the team who create the team, which then controls what each member of the team does. This may sound complicated because it is a circular operation. It sounds complicated only because we have no adequate terminology for these nonlinear, circular feedback types of relations that give rise to what we call an "organization." In "organization" we find the many components (or parts) creating a whole which then controls the activity of those components or parts which constitute that which is organized.

Obviously an ensemble or aggregation of discrete undifferentiated parts, inert and unrelated except that they may be spatially contiguous and temporally present at one time, cannot give rise to organization because there is nothing happening that can be organized and the components are not reciprocally coupled. Our vain attempt to understand organisms and human organizations becomes explicable in terms of our inadequate language and our reliance upon static concepts and analysis of wholes which make it difficult, if not impossible, to describe adequately these circular, reciprocal processes and the interrelationships they maintain. But a dynamic approach in terms of processes and the interrelationships they maintain may give us an insight into organisms and organizations and indicates how we might reformulate our problems with some hope of finding more illuminating and fruitful approaches (Wiener, 1961[3]).

The activity of interrelated activities by all members of a group gives rise to what we call social order as we see in the organization of a team or other human organizations or institutions.

A COMMUNICATION PROCESS

As I have indicated, all components of an organized whole must be coupled with each other and capable of communicating through some network that permits messages to be conveyed to and from each component using a number of different communication channels. Accordingly we may propose a communication process as essential to our quest, recognizing that by communication we mean more than the transmission of words or the sending or receipt of conventionally coded messages. Communication in an organism takes place, not only by transmission of a variety of messages through different channels, but also by transportation of physical and chemical components through the blood stream and lymphatic system, with the many hormones, enzymes and catalysts, the feedbacks and the direct physical contacts of cells and tissues. We must recognize that every molecule by its spatial configuration is a coded message, just as the sequence of letters give each word its specific meaning.

The whole organism is engaged in this continual communication, within the organism and also with the environment, through an incessant flow of messages that initiate, accompany, and reveal the ever-changing states or conditions, needs or requirements, readiness or unreadiness to function. These messages may be called physical, chemical, and biological, according to whatever criteria we may use, so that at one moment we are dealing with an electrical message, and by using another criterion we find that it is also a chemical message. These messages arise from the energy transformations by

[3] See Chapter on Self-organizing Systems.

which each process originates and emits one or more kinds of signals that can usually be measured but which may evoke highly variable responses from the parts or components receiving such messages.

In all these communications the organism is exhibiting organization as I have defined it before, regulating its internal functioning operations so that each input is transmitted as an appropriate message to the specialized recipient of that message within the organic complex. Thus incremental and replacement growth occurs as the inputs from the environment are routed as messages through communication-transportation channels to their several destinations (metabolic pathways) where they add to, or replace, and provoke the components receiving such messages.

Through internal communications, the large number and variety of ongoing functional activities and processes in an organism are synchronized and regulated, thus making possible the articulation and sequential patterning of all the identified physiological "mechanisms" that participate in the basic processes. Central in these internal communications are the variety of internal feedbacks, both positive and negative, and the various hormones by which the living organism develops its self-regulation, self-repair, and self-direction, and also involving feedbacks evoked from the environment.

A model of the communication process becomes necessary to deal with the problem of human development, recognizing that, as an organism grows and becomes progressively organized internally and related to the external world, the number and complexity of its communications enlarge.

Within the organism, as we have seen, the nervous system and its several divisions provide one of the major communication channels, along with the blood stream and the lymphatic system through which messages are continually being sent and received. There seems to be a high degree of reciprocal, internal communication since one component of the organism may send a message to another requiring a response either immediately or with some delay. Then that receiving component sends the needed message as we see, for example, in the interchange of hormones, the speedy release of glycogen when required for meeting stress situations, and similar events in which the organism's resources are quickly mobilized for emergencies, defense, or self-repair.

The relation of the organism to the environment is carried on not only by these physical inputs but by sensory inputs for which each species has a built-in capacity selectively to receive and to evoke from the environment and to transmit to other organisms. Thus through what we call vision, hearing, smelling, tasting, and tactile contacts, the organism communicates with the environment. Its varying responsiveness is largely governed by the internal functional processes that maintain or arouse its alertness and focus its scanning of the environment for the messages it requires or seeks. But more important for the human, the child learns to regulate his functioning as in eating, eliminating, sleeping, motor behavior, and emotional reactions by responding to symbols, such as words, spoken or written, and his own inner speech.

Recent studies on sensory processes indicate that our previous assumptions may be in need of revision and enlargement as we recognize more clearly the processes of filtering, integrating, mingling, and amplifying messages, especially in the reticular activating system, through which proprioceptive messages mingle with exteroceptive inputs from sensory receptors. In these operations we might find some clues to a resolution of the ancient mind-body problem and some insights into the development of psychosomatic disorders (Rosenblith, 1961). Also significant for this discussion is the recent work on sensory deprivation, indicating how the organism-personality is dependent upon a continual input of messages from the environment, especially culturally patterned messages, for maintaining its stability and direction. Also important is the recognition of sensory overloads that occur when the organism-personality is exposed to more messages than it can handle and therefore may find its integrity seriously threatened.

The development of an organism from conception, and especially from birth, may be viewed as the cumulative development of the capacity for communication, especially for calibrating incoming messages and for scanning and exploring the environment, to evoke the messages required for organic functioning and survival and for purposive behavior. As the organism matures it develops new and greater sensitivities and a readiness to respond selectively to messages (Frank, 1961).

THE STABILIZING PROCESS

Communication processes are essential to the organizing process and vice versa, and both serve and are served by the stabilizing process, which, as the organism develops, becomes increasingly capable of maintaining its organic integrity despite continual internal fluctuations and the sometimes severe impact and deprivations from the environment. This stabilizing process is not to be understood as the maintenance of a static equilibrium to which after each oscillation the organism returns, but rather as a dynamic process whereby the organism, while growing and developing, changing in size, shape and exhibiting new functions, maintains its organic integrity and stability and continues to exhibit a dynamic state in the midst of all the varied inputs to which it is exposed.

In order to live in a cultural, social world of human meanings and values, the child also must learn to stabilize the environment by perceiving and transforming the world of events into the symbolic cultural world that can be dealt with by socially approved adaptations and practices. A child learns to impute meanings to situations, events, and persons as defined for him by more experienced persons and then to act in response to the meanings which he himself has attributed to them. This is a transactional process, a circular reciprocal feedback operation, capable of utilization in a great many different ways as shown by the variety of cultures all over the world and by the great variety of individual personalities within those cultures that display such differences. As Kurt Goldstein (1939) has emphasized, for human living the individual must learn to equalize and stabilize his threshold or sensory inputs so that the many variations of size, shape, and intensity, etc., in the world, do not distract, mislead, or confuse the individual. In the process of equalizing this threshold the child develops a highly selective awareness, plus inattention to whatever is considered unimportant, and he learns to

pattern his perception of the world according to group requirements, but always idiomatically biased and often distorted.

A LEARNING PROCESS

We may assume, or we may conceive, a learning process (possibly
another phase of the creative process) operating with the communicating and stabilizing processes. Faced with new capacities, new
demands, new opportunity, the organism begins to alter its established patterns of functioning and communicating and behaving, so
that it can maintain its integrity and more effectively engage in
purposive striving. Here we must recognize the unique capacity of
the human organism for speech and his capacity for symbol recognition and use, whereby the human child can learn to live in a symbolic cultural world, communicating symbolically with others and
also with himself through inner speech.

An adequate model for human communication and for stabilization requires recognition of the many subtle patterns used in human
conduct and human relations. These patterns include sexual relations
as a mode of communication and stabilization, as well as for purposive striving.

The recognition of what is called *paralanguage* has enlarged our
conception of human communication and provided clues to many
puzzling aspects of human relations. We now are becoming aware
of the many modes of nonverbal communication, through changing
postures, stances, and distance-maintaining activities, gestures, facial
expressions, and varying tones of voice. Tactile communication which
includes a wide variety of interpersonal contacts has been largely
overlooked or neglected by students of personality development and
expression who have not recognized how tactile communications,
beginning in infancy and continuing throughout the life cycle,
become especially important in all sexual relations and activities
(Frank, 1957).

We can emphasize justifiably that human development occurs as
the organism continues its organic functioning and its continual
intercourse with environment, while undergoing a succession of

minor and sometimes major changes, not only in its size, shape, and functioning, but in all its relations with the environment and other organisms. Only a conception of processes may embrace such a series of dynamic events.

We can see this progressive capacity for dynamic stabilization occurring in the development of the child. As an infant he has an inadequate capacity for homeostasis (Wolsterholm and O'Connor, 1961), but as he grows older he learns to sustain internal perturbations and larger and larger fluctuations in organic functioning, as exhibited by his acceptance of prolonged intervals for eating, eliminating, and sleeping. He also demonstrates his increased capacity for stabilization through his ability to curb and regulate emotional disturbances and quickly to recover complacency after such disturbances or extreme and prolonged exertion.

Again in adolescents we see how the juvenile organism undergoes a significant loss or relinquishment of earlier established processes of stabilizing. As he grows in size and must learn new patterns of homeostatic control for his enlarging organism, he is subject to greater fluctuations and homeostatic disturbances that are gradually brought into the so-called "steady state" of maturity. In the light of this we might hazard the generalization that growth, both incremental growth and replacement growth, and development of new functional capacities are not compatible with stability of functioning; hence during or immediately after any rapid growth episodes, the organism must develop new and more effective processes of dynamic stabilization.

The so-called "steady state" of maturity seems to be a condition of dynamic stability that is highly idiosyncratic, with more or less idiomatic deviations from so-called normal regulation. In order to maintain a dynamic stability in a continuously changing environment, the individual must develop a highly selective awareness and a patterned perception created by continual filtering, reducing, amplifying, and transforming his sensory and other inputs, and by utilizing buffers and other compensating functions.

But as Pittendrigh (1958) has emphasized, the concept of organism is meaningless without a recognition that its organization is *purposive,* that is, is oriented to goal seeking; he speaks of teleonomy, neither teleology nor a strict causal relation which, as Mayr (1961) has shown, is not biologically valid. Thus we need a concept of a *purposive* process which need not imply any mysterious entelechy, but rather can be formulated rigorously, as Rosenblueth, Wiener, and Bigelow (1943) proposed some years ago, as a process of continual feedbacks, a model which today can be elaborated and refined.

The developing organism exhibits a cumulative capacity for scanning the world and evoking the feedbacks that guide, correct, or orient it to the goals it must seek in order to survive and to function as an organism—more specifically to gain food and safety and to mate so that the species will continue. Only man has developed the capacity to create a symbolic world and to use signs and symbolic language as feedbacks for guiding his goal-seeking activities. Thereby he transforms the world of nature into a cultural world for purposive striving, transforming his naïve behavior into patterned conduct for group living, oriented to his cultural world. For this human living he relies upon his learned recognition of specific signs and symbols and also upon his inner speech and other internal feedbacks.

But as indicated earlier, man is and continues to function as an organism throughout his life; therefore he continues to be exposed to all the biological and physiological messages that clamor for organic recognition and response. These messages may compete with the symbolic messages and the inner speech upon which a personality relies for guidance. Sometimes these external, biological, and internal physiological messages may provoke an organic response which conflicts with the culturally patterned conduct which the individual is expected to exhibit and which he may be striving to attain.

Thus we are faced with the necessity of recognizing that a *purposive* process which is learned never becomes as effective or reliable as the other organic processes I have described. Nevertheless this formulation of a purposive process is necessary for a comprehensive conception of development since the purposes sought by the individual alter as the organism-personality grows, develops, and ages. Purposive striving requires a capacity to ignore distracting events or messages that might divert the individual from seeking goals, with reliance upon selected feedbacks for self-direction.

THE CREATIVE PROCESS

We have accepted the concept of organic evolution as controlled by a genetic process, conceived today as a mode of communication in which the genes are considered to be code scripts that guide growth, development, and maturation by the kind of information which they provide. We have emphasized the persistence of the genotype, the stability of the patterns that are replicated in each generation, but we have forgotten that the evolutionary process was essentially a creative process in so far as it gave rise to many different species that have existed in the ages past, some of which still survive today. Every species, apparently, may be thought of as a new configuration, a variation upon, a recombination and development of, the basic biological processes or organisms.

For a comprehensive conception of development, especially of human development, we will need to recognize the creative process whereby out of a given past there emerges something new and different, often completely novel. Thus each human infant arises as an individual, a totally different organic configuration into which maternal and paternal genes have been combined in unique combinations and various novel permutations. Here we see the creative process operating in human development to produce the unique human infant who will later become a unique human personality.

While it may seem farfetched, nevertheless, we may speak of human development as essentially creative, in so far as each individual, with his unique heredity, grows and develops as a unique organism and becomes an idiosyncratic personality, selectively accepting and learning from the world what is relevant and required for his individual capacities and functioning. Thus the same basic organ systems and functional activities are constellated in new and complicated configurations, with combinations and permutations that are different in each individual. As indicated, the protein molecules of individuals are unique since that basic protein molecule permits an almost infinite array of combinations, each a new and unprecedented production. Moreover, as Roger Williams (1956) has shown, each individual is a unique constellation of chemical constituents.

Likewise each individual organism, especially human organisms, with their highly varied hereditary patterns and individualized nurture, may be considered as a product of a creative process that produces the idiosyncratic organism-personality whose life career becomes the focus for studies of human development. We cannot assume that we have a homogeneous sample because all the subjects in that sample are of the same age, sex, or belong to one of the familiar categories we usually employ. Chronological age is not a dependable criterion because individuals grow, develop, mature, and age at different rates. Moreover, each individual subject in a sample has his *intra*individual variability so that measurements taken at a given time may find the individual at different points in his or her particular cyclical fluctuations. Hence those measurements may mask the functional processes being observed.

It is clear that each organism-personality creates his own private world, his "life space," his "idioverse," by his individualized perception and communication with the world, whereby he is able to participate in the public world but lives in his own idiosyncratic way, ignoring and rejecting or attempting to escape whatever is not relevant, congruous, or consonant with his idiomatic patterns of perceiving, functioning, and communicating. Thus we see in the development of the human organism-personality how the processes of growing, organizing, communicating, stabilizing, purposive striving, and the creative process operate to produce the idiomatic personality who in turn creates his life space while participating in maintaining the symbolic cultural world and the social order in which he relates to other persons.

SUMMARY

If we are prepared to study human development, approaching living, growing organism-personalities in terms of a dynamic conception of development, occurring through a number of concurrent processes, we may be able to gain more understanding of what takes place, beginning at conception and continuing through the successive stages of the life career.

Such an enterprise would give rise to a new discipline which would embrace much of the various life sciences, or draw upon them, but approach the organism as a dynamic configuration that cannot be fractionated without losing or destroying our understanding of the basic processes of development. As indicated, this does not imply a rejection of the various disciplines; but it would mean, as in medicine, an attempt to go beyond the specific quantified findings of the life sciences, their concern with "mechanisms," "factors," and the relation between selected variables, to a multidimensional approach to the intact living, growing, developing, aging organism-personality.

When we look at the recurrent regularities exhibited by a group of persons, we can speak of culture and social order as statistical concepts, but as soon as we focus on any individual member of a social order and observe his unique ways of developing, behaving, thinking, and feeling, we are dealing with a personality, as a clinical concept. These are complementary ways of approaching human behavior, and to a large extent our emphasis has been upon the statistical or nomothetic to the neglect of the clinical or idiographic approaches through which we can begin to understand the processes of human development as they occur in an intact living person.

Aging especially calls for a model of a process congruous with and illustrative of growth processes; aging may be viewed as a failure of the growth process when the renewal and replacement of cells and of components of the organism is inadequate for maintaining healthy full functioning (Frank, 1946).

The emergence of human development as a scientific discipline may be viewed as the fruition of the past forty to fifty years of studies and investigation by the various life sciences, medical sciences, and social sciences. It is the beginning of a new approach to the many problems and needs that have until recently been considered inaccessible or too complex for scientific study.

BIBLIOGRAPHY

Carroll, J. B., ed. (1957), *Language, Thought, and Reality: Selected Writings.* Cambridge: M.I.T. Press.
Elsasser, W. (1958), *The Physical Basis of Biology.* New York: Pergamon Press.
Frank, L. K. (1935), Structure, Function and Growth, *Phil. Sci.,* 2:210-235.
———— (1946), Gerontology. *J. Gerontol.,* 1:1-12.
———— (1957), Tactile Communication. *Genet. Psychol. Monogr.,* 56:209-255.
———— (1961), *The Conduct of Sex.* New York: Morrow.
———— (1962), Interprofessional Communication. *Amer. J. Pub. Health,* 51:1798-1804.
Goldstein, K. (1939), *The Organism.* Yonkers, N.Y.: World Book Co.
Kavanau, J. L. (1961), Predictions of the Growth Model for Normal Chicken Growth. *Science,* 134:1627-1628.
Klüver, H. (1936), The Study of Personality and the Method of Equivalent and Non-Equivalent Stimuli. *J. Personal.,* 5:91-112.
Mayr, E. (1961), Cause and Effect in Biology. *Science,* 134:1501-1506.
Pittendrigh, C. S. (1958), Adaptation, Natural Selection and Behavior. In: *Behavior and Evolution,* eds. A. Roe & G. G. Simpson. New Haven: Yale Univ. Press.
Rosenblith, W., ed. (1961), *Sensory Communication.* Cambridge, Mass.: M.I.T. Press.
Rosenblueth, A., Wiener, N., & Bigelow, J. (1943), Behavior, Purpose and Teleology. *Phil. Sci.,* 10:18-24.
Singer, J. D. (1961), The Relevance of the Behavioral Sciences to the Study of International Relations. *Behav. Sci.,* 6:333.
Society for Experimental Biology (1960), *Analogues and Models* [Symposium, No. 14]. New York: Academic Press.
von Bertalanffy, L. (1950), The Theory of Open Systems in Physics and Biology. *Science,* 111:23-29.
Weaver, W. (1948), Science and Complexity. *Amer. Scientist,* 36:536-544.
Weiss, P. (1955), Specificity in Growth Control. In: *Biological Specificity and Growth,* ed. E. G. Butler. Princeton: Princeton Univ. Press.
Whorf, B. L. (1940), Science and Linguistics. *Technol. Rev.,* 42.
Wiener, N. (1961), *Cybernetics,* 2nd ed. New York: Wiley.
Williams, R. (1956), *Biochemical Individuality.* New York: Wiley.
Wolsterholm, G. E. & O'Connor, M., eds. (1961), *Somatic Stability in the Newly Born.* Boston: Little, Brown.
Woodger, J. H. (1929), *Biological Principles: A Critical Study.* New York: Harcourt, Brace.

Part II

Biological Aspects of Child Development

The first article in this section is of historical as well as scientific value since it was with Alexis F. Hartmann, Sr., that Milton Senn did some of his earliest research in pediatrics, which was biochemical. Milton Senn was in the Department of Pediatrics, Washington University School of Medicine for four years, 1929-1933, serving as resident, research fellow, and instructor in the wards and laboratories of the St. Louis Children's Hospital. Much of his research time was spent in early studies of the metabolism of Na-lactate with particular reference to its clinical use in the treatment and prevention of metabolic acidosis.

The rapid advancement of biochemistry as a major tool in assessing and investigating human development is also reflected in the work of Ira K. Brandt which links the break-throughs in genetics to child development via the chemical understanding of crucial enzyme systems and their maturational deviations. At the same time as biochemical studies are pushing forward, the ability to observe and record in the naturalist's tradition is well represented by George Greenman's study of visual behavior in the newborn infant, and some of the implications suggested by these observations. Richard L. Day has written a short essay to demonstrate the importance of maturational correlations in establishing the relationship of the endocrine system to skeletal development, especially in the female. Frederic M. Blodgett has demonstrated a synthesis of clinical and theoretical thinking as he raises questions from clinical observations that illuminate the relationship between maternal deprivation and growth retardation in the child via endocrinological and biochemical dynamisms.

Congenital Multiple Enzyme Deficiency: Glycogen Storage Disease with Deficient Muscle Phosphorylase and Liver Glucose-6-Phosphatase

- *HULDA J. WOHLTMANN, M.D.*
- *ALEXIS F. HARTMANN, SR., M.D.*
- *BARBARA ILLINGWORTH, Ph.D.*
- *BETTY WESLEY, M.S.*

With the technical assistance of

- *MARIE MORTON*
- *HELEN K. STUCKSTEDE*
Washington University

Single congenital enzyme absence or deficiency giving rise to serious disturbances of metabolism has been frequently encountered and described, but as yet multiple absence or deficiency, except as an expression of immaturity, has been rarely seen (Eberlein et al., 1962; Perkoff et al., 1962). This subject has recently been reviewed by one of the authors (Illingworth, 1961). In the child described in this paper, a most bizarre and serious picture developed as a result of marked deficiency in two important enzymes—muscle phosphorylase and liver glucose-6-phosphatase.

D. M., a boy ten months old, was referred to the St. Louis Children's Hospital on 8-20-60 by Dr. R. L. Britt of Evansville, Indiana, to whom we are indebted for the early history and findings. A diagnosis of glycogen storage disease had been made by him on the basis of a liver biopsy and glycogen staining of sections. The boy had first been seen at six and a half months of age because of irritability, anorexia, respiratory distress, and an enlarged abdomen. A blood chemical analysis at that time revealed a CO_2 content of 5.7 and a Cl concentration of 106 mEq. per liter, NPN of 40 and blood sugar of 12 mg./100 ml. Intravenous pyelograms demonstrated delayed emptying of both kidneys with evidence of bilateral obstructive uropathy, the sites of obstruction not being apparent. Clinical improvement followed administration of cortisone at dosage levels first of 100 and later of 50 mg. per day. One sixth molar sodium lactate was added to his formula of skimmed milk with subsequent maintenance of his serum CO_2 content at normal levels. Because of a twenty-four-hour period of anuria and an apparent worsening of his general condition, he was transferred to the St. Louis Children's Hospital for special study.

Physical examination revealed a poorly nourished ten-month-old infant, weighing only 6 Kg. despite an enlarged abdomen. All muscles were weak with a flabby, almost gelatinous feel. He could not sit alone, support his head, or hold on to his toys. The liver was enlarged to the iliac crest and extended well across the midline. The left kidney could be easily palpated and was thought enlarged. Routine examination of urine, except for a small amount of protein which persisted, and of the blood, except for a Hb. concentration of 7.4 gm. per 100 ml., was unremarkable. Chemical analysis, however, of the blood serum revealed the following (Table 1):

TABLE 1

Blood Serum—8-20-60					
		mEq./liter			
Cations			Anions	mg./100 ml.	
Na	135.0	Cl	94.0	NPN	160
K	5.5	HCO$_3$	17.8	Sugar	110
Ca	5.7	Prot.	13.0		
Mg	(2.0)	Inorg. P.	7.4		
	148.2		132.2		
		Diff.	16.0		

As seen from the electrolyte balance, a considerable amount of anion was unaccounted for, and as indicated by later studies (Table 3) was almost certainly lactate.

Intravenous pyelograms revealed ureteropelvic junction obstruction bilaterally. X-rays of the chest and an EKG indicated normal heart and lungs. The admittance NPN of 160 mg./100 ml. fell to 33 two days later, following spontaneous urination beginning shortly after admission. The chemical analysis of the blood then was as shown in Table 2.

TABLE 2

Blood Serum—8-22-60					
Cations	mEq./liter		Anions		mg./100 ml.
Na	136.0	Cl	91.0	NPN	33
K	4.7	HCO$_3$	23.8	Sugar	37
Ca	(5.0)	Prot.	13.0	Choles.	325
Mg	(2.0)	Inorg. P.	2.1		
	147.7		129.9		
		Diff.	17.8		

Again considerable undetermined anion must have been present. On this occasion hypoglycemia and hypercholesterolemia were also noted.

Cortisone therapy, 50 mg. daily, was continued. For prevention of recurrence of acidosis, an equivalent amount of sodium bicarbonate was substituted for sodium lactate so as to allow study of his endogenous lactate metabolism. The total daily dosage amounted to 6 mM./Kg. divided in 8 equal, 3 hourly portions (5 ml. of a 7.5% solution in each of 8 feedings). A work-up directed toward glycogen storage disease was then begun.

On 8-25-60, while on cortisone, he was given 1.75 gm./Kg. galactose. Results are shown in Table 3.

When the one-hour blood sample was obtained, marked hyperpnea, suggestive of acidosis, was noted. A serum CO$_2$ content was found to be 9.6 mEq./liter. Additional oral sodium bicarbonate was

TABLE 3

Response to Oral Administration of Galactose—1.75 gm./Kg.
8-25-60

| | WHOLE BLOOD | | | | | SERUM |
| | mg./100 ml. | | mEq./L | | μmoles/L | mEq./L |
	Glucose	Galactose	Lactate	Pyruvate	Citrate	CO$_2$ Content
Fasting	21.0	0	11.1	0.44	91.5	—
½ Hour	70.0	0	13.6	0.66	99.7	—
1 Hour	48.0	0	12.4	0.93	96.8	9.6
2 Hours	48.0	0	12.4	0.66	66.8	—
3 Hours	34.0	0	11.7	0.44	68.8	6.3
7½ Hours	—	—	—	—	—	24.0

administered and the test continued for two more hours. The ingested galactose was apparently so rapidly metabolized that none was
ever detected in the blood. The negligible rise in glucose indicated
that there was a complete absence of liver glucose-6-phosphatase activity, and the rise in pyruvic and lactic acids suggested increase in the
anerobic type of glycolysis as a result of galactose administration. At
the beginning and the end of the test, hypoglycemic values were
again evident, also in keeping with reduced liver glucose-6-phos-
phatase activity.

On 8-27-60 and again on 8-31-60, while still on cortisone, he was
given glucagon, 20 mcg./Kg. intravenously, with the results shown in
Table 4.

TABLE 4

| | Whole Blood Sugar mg./100 ml. | |
	8-27-60	8-31-60
Fasting	75.4	67.4
20 Min.	lost	54.6
40 Min.	49.4	26.5
60 Min.	49.4	32.6
90 Min.	33.2	8.5
120 Min.	21.0	—

The responses to glucagon were most bizarre, the blood sugar
failing to rise in keeping with the previously suggested deficiency in

liver glucose-6-phosphatase, but, instead, quite unexpectedly falling to very low hypoglycemic levels.

He was next given I.M. 0.2 ml. aqueous adrenalin hydrochloride 1:1000, on 8-29-60 and again on 9-12-60 with the results shown in Table 5.

TABLE 5

	Whole Blood Sugar mg./100 ml.		Lactic Acid mg./100 ml.
	8-29-60	9-12-60	9-12-60
Fasting	45.4	63.6	26.5
20 Min.	21.0	30 Min. 37.6	44.5
40 Min.	33.2	2 Hrs. 8.5	75.0
60 Min.	24.4	Deficit 55.1	Gain 48.5
90 Min.	24.4		
120 Min.	21.0		

As with glucagon, the failure of blood glucose to rise was anticipated on the basis of probable liver glucose-6-phosphatase deficiency, but again an unexpected rapid fall to very low hypoglycemic concentrations occurred. The extent and rapidity of fall following both glucagon and adrenalin compare with those sometimes seen in hypoglycemia-prone children after administration of insulin and/or leucine (Hartmann et al., 1961). In the second adrenalin test, the gain in lactate noted (48.5 mg. per 100 ml.) was only a little less than the total fall in glucose (55.1).

On 8-30-60, when his serum showed a CO_2 content of 23.6, Cl. of 81.0, lactate of 10.5, and pyruvate of 0.33 mEq. per liter, with NPN of 33.0 and cholesterol of 225 mg. per 100 ml., a standard oral glucose tolerance test was performed (Table 6).

The response was a mildly diabetic one and in keeping with postulated glycogenosis due to deficiency in glucose-6-phosphatase. At the end of four hours, the blood sugar was again exactly at the fasting level—54.6 mg. per 100 ml. Neither lactate nor bicarbonate was followed during this test. No clinical signs of acidosis developed.

TABLE 6

Time	Capillary Whole Blood True Sugar mg. per 100 ml.
Fasting	55
30 Min.	153
60 Min.	145
90 Min.	158
120 Min.	145
180 Min.	75
240 Min.	55

On 9-1-60, under local anesthesia, Dr. James M. Stokes secured rectus muscle and liver samples for study. As determined by one of us (B. I.), a biopsy sample of the liver contained 6.4 per cent glycogen and the muscle 0.3 per cent glycogen. In autopsy samples the glycogen content was 5.6 per cent for the liver, 0.7 per cent for the psoas, 1.5 per cent for the heart and 4.8 per cent for the kidney. Glycogen isolated from the liver biopsy had a normal structure and was digested to the extent of 37 per cent by phosphorylase free of amylo-1, 6-glucosidase.

Glucose-6-phosphatase activity was measured in homogenates prepared from the biopsy liver (53 micrograms phosphate split from glucose-6-phosphate/100 mg. liver/hour), the autopsy liver (27 micrograms/100 mg./hr.), and the autopsy kidney (46 micrograms/100 mg./hr.). The values obtained were 5 to 10 per cent of those found in normal tissues, indicating marked deficiency in glucose-6-phosphatase.

The biopsy muscle was shown to have significant activity when tested for UDPG (uridine diphosphate glucose)—glycogen transglucosylase (16 units/gram) (Hauk et al., 1959). Amylo-1, 6-glucosidase activity was measured in the muscle by a modification (Illingworth, 1961) of the method of Hers (1959) which depends on the limited reversibility of the enzyme as expressed by the incorporation of C^{14}-glucose into added glycogen. A value of 60 counts/min./mg. of reisolated glycogen was obtained; this is in the normal range. Amylo-1, 6-glucosidase was also found to be present in the liver by the use of a specific, low molecular weight substrate (Illingworth et al., 1962).

An unexpected finding (as shown in Table 7) was the extremely low level of phosphorylase activity in the muscle. Two separate homogenates were made of the biopsy muscle and the procedure repeated with the psoas removed at autopsy. The heart and liver had phosphorylase activities which could be considered to be in the low normal range (Illingworth, 1961; Hauk et al., 1959; Hers, 1959) but the muscle phosphorylase was significantly diminished. It should be noted that phosphorylase was not completely missing, as has been reported in one type of glycogen storage disease (Schmid and Mahler, 1959; Mommaerts et al., 1959).

TABLE 7

Phosphorylase Activity in Muscle

	Without 5′-Adenylic Acid (units/gram)	With 5′-Adenylic Acid (units/gram)	With 5′-Adenylic Acid μmoles G-1-P Split min./gram
Rectus	0	267	7.6
	0	117	4.0
Psoas	0	212	5.1
Heart	504	596	16.8

Electron microscopic study of the liver was carried out by Dr. Grisham. He found an abnormal relationship of the hepatic cells to sinusoids in that no microvilli were noted on the sinusoidal borders of the hepatic cells. Material with the typical structure of glycogen filled the cyloplasm of all parenchymal cells and was also present in some nuclei. Mitochondria appeared swollen and were enmeshed in the glycogen. Typical endoplasmic reticulum was almost nonexistent. Portal structures did not appear to be altered.

After these studies the infant was gradually taken off cortisone and received none for fourteen days. Again, several very low blood sugars (8.5-12.2 mg./100 ml.) were obtained. Cortisone was restarted and blood sugars once again ranged between 50-150 mg./100 ml. Despite repeated severe episodes of hypoglycemia, this infant did not appear grossly brain damaged.

Because there was some doubt about the quality of the galactose used in the first test,[1] and because no galactose was noted in any of the blood samples, galactose was again fed on 9-26-60 after discontinuation of cortisone on 9-15-60. Fasting (6-hour) glucose was already very low—12.2 mg./100 ml.—rising only to 24.9 at 30 minutes and falling again to 12 mg. and remaining there throughout the test. All galactose levels were 0 except the 30-minute sample which was 9.5 mg. per 100 ml.

During this test he became very weak and again developed Kussmaul respirations, suggesting rapid development again of acidosis. CO_2 content and lactic acid concentrations were not determined during this test, but extra sodium bicarbonate was again administered with lessening of hyperpnea.

Galactose was given a third time on 10-6-60 after resumption of cortisone therapy. As with the previous two galactose tests, he developed marked Kussmaul respirations with one lactic acid level reaching 23.1 mEq./liter, the pH of the blood dropping to 7.10 and the CO_2 content to 9.7 mEq./liter. The following were the blood sugar levels (Table 8):

TABLE 8

	mg./100 ml.	
	Glucose	Galactose
Fasting	67	0
½ Hour	50	9
1 Hour	46	9
1½ Hours	50	9
2 Hours	46	0
3 Hours	59	0
4 Hours	35	0

Again blood glucose failed to rise and actually fell appreciably—from 67.0 to 35.0 mg. per 100 ml.—despite a galactose level which never exceeded 9 mg. per 100 ml.

A fourth galactose tolerance test was made on 11-12-60, with results as shown in Table 9.

[1] It gave a positive reaction for glucose with Testape. However, no detectible amount of copper-reducing substance could be removed by yeast fermentation.

TABLE 9

| Time | Capillary Whole Blood True Sugar mg./100 ml. | |
	Glucose	Galactose
Fasting	44	0
60 Min.	47	12
105 Min.	42	15
180 Min.	49	0

For the fourth time clinical acidosis developed, improving after extra sodium bicarbonate administration. On this occasion no hypoglucosemia developed. However, blood glucose, somewhat low, failed to rise in response to galactose feeding.

Another peculiarity of this boy was that he seemed to be always hungry and would consume large quantities of milk and solid infant food both during the day and night. The nursing personnel had noted that his thirst and appetite were good but perhaps not unusual when his temperature was normal, but that it was enormous when his temperature was elevated. Over a two-week period, total caloric, protein, fat, and carbohydrate intake were calculated (Table 10). Caloric intake ranged from 98 to 239 calories per kg. Protein intake varied from 4.8 to 9.4 gm./kg. The fever noted throughout this period was not associated with any other finding of infection. At times it seemed controlled by skin exposure and increase in water administration. A protein bound iodine was 4.9 micrograms per 100 ml. at this time.

On 2-11-61 he was found unresponsive and dyspneic. Respiration was labored with prolongation of the expiratory phase and wheezing. A serum CO_2 content was 10.9 mEq./liter. He was given additional sodium bicarbonate and seemed to improve. Within a short time, he again developed severe respiratory distress and expired. This terminal episode occurred during an epidemic of bronchiolitis, affecting a number of patients on the metabolic division. His marked muscle weakness which included the respiratory muscles may have played an important role in his unexpected death.

Table 10

Food Intake and Body Temperature

DATE Oct. 1960	BODY WT. Kg.	CALORIES per Kg.	CARBOHY- DRATE gm.	FAT gm.	PROTEIN gm./Kg.	RECTAL TEMP. Range °C.	PARENTERAL FLUID ml.
5	6.7	173	108	53	9.4	37.7-39.0	
6	6.0	98	64	24	4.8	37.4-39.2	400
8	7.2	159	126	51	6.2	37.4-38.9	400
9	7.3	167	154	43	7.4	37.4-38.4	400
10	7.1	178	141	56	6.9	37.5-38.6	
11	7.3	200	173	60	7.7	37.2-39.0	
12	7.4	173	161	42	8.8	37.5-38.4	
13	7.4	208	206	54	7.8	37.0-38.4	400
14	7.2	212	191	56	8.9	37.4-38.4	
15	7.5	155	121	51	7.2	37.6-38.5	
17	7.4	178	160	51	7.7	37.0-38.1	
18	7.8	184	179	51	8.3	37.0-37.8	
19	7.6	183	183	52	6.5	37.6-39.6	
20	7.6	239	243	66	8.3	36.3-39.3	
21	7.9	160	141	55	6.3	37.4-39.1	

Post-Mortem Findings. Gross autopsy findings for the most part confirmed previous clinical observations. For a sixteen-month-old child, weighing only 8.4 kg., the liver was very large and slightly congested, weighing 1290 gm. The heart was slightly enlarged weighing 53 gm., with some hypertrophy and dilatation of the left ventricle. The lungs were moderately atelectatic and slightly congested and edematous. There was bilateral hydronephrosis (right 63 gm., left 59 gm.), with multiple 1-3 mm. yellow, friable stones within the calyces and pelves. There was bilateral stenosis of the uteropelvic junctions, and atrophy of the adrenal cortex, consistent with prolonged adrenal corticosteroid therapy.

Microscopically, nothing beyond what was seen in the biopsy samples was noted.

COMMENT

The usual clinical findings of the von Gierke type of glycogenosis were present in this child. The renal enlargement, however, was due chiefly to bilateral uretero-pelvic stenosis and hydronephrosis, and not to glycogen deposit. The tendency toward hypoglycemia was unusually marked but could be controlled satisfactorily by adrenal steroid therapy. Even more striking was the tendency for lactate accumulation under ordinary conditions, but especially when carbohydrate metabolism was influenced by galactose administration. As a consequence, the child's acid-base balance tended to be one of persistent metabolic acidosis, requiring rather large amounts of sodium-bicarbonate administration for compensation. Amounts effective for ordinary circumstances were insufficient to protect against the acidifying effects of ingested galactose, during standard galactose tolerance tests. In this respect, the metabolic deviation was somewhat like one seen recently (Hartmann et al., 1962) in a child without glycogenosis or proven enzyme deficiency.

The tendency toward development of hypoglycemia, which was regarded as basically due to deficiency of liver glucose-6-phosphatase, was strikingly accentuated by administration of epinephrine and glucagon. In both of the glucagon experiments as well as after each of the two administrations of adrenalin, the blood glucose fell immediately, the falls persisting until quite low levels were reached. This bizarre response occurred without initial rise, and seemed independent of the initial level of blood glucose, which was normal in the glucagon experiments and one of the epinephrine tests, and moderately hypoglycemic in the other. After galactose feeding, on the first occasion an initial hypoglycemic level first became normal, with then a return to hypoglycemia. Similar behavior was seen after the second administration of galactose, with, however, only slight initial rise in glucose. In the third test, no initial rise in glucose preceded the later fall. In the fourth test, there was no definite effect on the levels of blood glucose, which remained moderately hypoglycemic. Such responses suggested that the hypoglycemia developing after epinephrine, glucagon and galactose was not the result of insulin stimulation from either hyperglucosemia or hypergalactosemia. The response to glucose feeding, with a very good early rise of blood glucose and later fall only to the initial level, also suggested no unusual insulin stimulation. It was unfortunate that direct measurements of insulinlike activity of the blood under different circumstances were not made. The one such measurement was on 9-26-60, after a five-hour fast, when the blood sugar was very low —8.5 mg. per 100 ml. On this occasion, by the epididymal fat pad method, insulinlike activity was 843 micro units per ml. (the lambda value being 0.170), which has to be regarded as high, the range of normal in our hands by the same method being 200 to 500, with an average of 350 micro units per ml. It therefore must be conceded that hyperinsulinism as well as inability to form free glucose from glucose-6-phosphate might have contributed to the hypoglycemic tendency. So would have the very high rate of metabolism. From the data in Table 10, it can be calculated that this child expended, on the average, 180 cal./Kg./24 hr. With the assumption that carbohydrate supplied 50 per cent of such energy expenditure, it would follow that the rate of glucose utilization would be .94 gm./Kg./hr. If there could be no replenishment of glucose from endogenous sources because of the deficiency of liver glucose-6-phosphatase, and if there were no exogenous supply of glucose (as during the fasting state, including the periods of study in the epinephrine, glucagon and galactose studies), the fall of blood glucose, assuming equilibrium with total body water equal to two thirds the body weight, would be at the rate of 2.35 mg. per 100 ml. per minute. The highest observed rates of fall during the initial periods of the tests were sometimes of the same order of magnitude, approximating one fourth to one half the calculated maximal rate of fall. It would be reasonable to expect that, as the blood glucose reached hypoglycemic levels, glucose metabolism would decrease in rate, and blood glucose would fall, therefore, less rapidly. Such might then be a simple explanation for the hypoglycemia seen in this child.

There remains for speculation the explanation for the high rate of metabolism which probably was the cause for the unusual appetite, the fever, the poor weight gain, and the frequent development of hypoglycemia. The normal protein-bound iodine value should exclude hyperthyroidism as a cause. Might the following be a simple explanation? Because of the frequent hypoglycemia (the result of the deficiency of liver glucose-6-phosphatase and possibly also hyperinsulinism), the usual metabolic mixture was low in carbohydrate and high in fat and particularly protein (the intake of the latter averaging 7.5 gm./Kg./24 hr.), with the result that total metabolism was stimulated by the specific dynamic action of the latter.

SUMMARY AND CONCLUSIONS

A child born both with marked deficiency of liver glucose-6-phosphatase and muscle phosphorylase showed the following features:

1. Clinically he was extremely weak, with slow growth despite an enormous appetite.

2. Fever was prominent, and apparently on a metabolic basis.

3. Chemically, there was a disorder of metabolism which allowed lactic acid to accumulate to the point of persistent acidosis, which could be controlled by addition of sodium bicarbonate to all feedings.

4. There was also a marked tendency for the development of severe hypoglucosemia, which could be controlled by adrenal corticosteroid.

5. Adrenalin, glucagon, and especially galactose accentuated the metabolic defects in a most striking way.

6. The marked muscle weakness was probably instrumental in his death when bronchiolitis with respiratory obstruction developed.

BIBLIOGRAPHY

Eberlein, W. R., Illingworth, B. A., & Sidbury, J. B. (1962), Heterogeneous Glycogen Storage Disease in Siblings and Favorable Response to Synthetic Androgen Administration. *Amer. J. Med.*, 33:20-26.
Hartmann, A. F., Sr., Wohltmann, H. J., & Holowach, J. (1961), Medical Progress: Recognition and Investigation of Hypoglycemia. *J. Pediat.*, 58:864-875.
———— ———— Purkerson, M. L., & Wesley, M. E. (1962), Lactate Metabolism: Studies of a Child with a Serious Congenital Deviation. *J. Pediat.*, 61:165-180.
Hauk, R., Illingworth, B. A., Brown, D. H., & Cori, C. F. (1959), Enzymes of Glycogen Synthesis in Glycogen-Deposition Disease. *Biochimica et Biophysica Acta*, 33:554-556.
Hers, H. G. (1959), Études enzymatiques sur fragments hépatiques application a la classification des glycogénoses. *Rev. Int. Hepat.*, 9:35-55.
Illingworth, B. A. (1961), Glycogen Storage Disease. *Amer. J. Clin. Nut.*, 9:683-690.
———— & Brown, D. H. (1962), The Properies of an Oligo-1,4→1,4 Glucantransferase from Animal Tissues. *Proc. Nat. Acad. Sci.*, 48:1783-1787.
Mommaerts, W. F. H. M., Illingworth, B. A., Pearson, C. M., Guillory, R. J., & Seraydarian, K. (1959), A Functional Disorder of Muscle Associated with the Absence of Phosphorylase. *Proc. Nat. Acad. Sci.*, 45:791-797.
Perkoff, G. T., Parker, V. J., & Hahn, R. F. (1962), The Effects of Glucagon in Three Forms of Glycogen Storage Disease. *J. Clin. Invest.*, 41:1099-1105.
Schmid, R. & Mahler, R. (1959), Chronic Progressive Myopathy with Myoglobinuria: Demonstration of a Glycogenolytic Defect in the Muscle. *J. Clin. Invest.*, 38:2044-2058.

Mammalian Developmental Enzymology

• *IRA K. BRANDT, M.D.*

Yale University

Perhaps the pediatrician's most important contribution is his recognition of the significance of the developmental status of an individual in the evaluation and management of medical problems. The principle, however, is applicable to all age groups, since the ontogenetic process begins at the moment of conception and ends at the death of the organism. In addition, the developmental appraisal must be comprehensive in scope if it is to be of optimum value. This necessitates a multidisciplinary approach and therefore brings together many workers using different techniques.

One of the ways in which the developmental status can be defined is through the study of the variations in the activity of a number of enzyme systems as the organism goes through its ontogenetic sequence. These variations may be age specific not only as to the physiological function concerned but also as to the particular species, organ, subcellular fraction, and isozyme studied. Specific instances of

The studies of the writer which are cited in this review were supported by the Southern Connecticut Chapter of the National Kidney Disease Foundation, the Association for the Aid of Crippled Children, and the Public Health Service (RG-6992).

each will be described along with some of the experimental work carried out in order to provide some insight into the fundamental mechanisms involved.

AGE SPECIFICITY

It has been recognized for some time that the newborn infant may have an appreciably higher serum bilirubin concentration than is found in older individuals. This is particularly true with reference to the premature baby, who may develop hyperbilirubinemia to a degree severe enough to bring about kernicterus even in the absence of hemolytic disease.

When subjected to the van den Bergh test the excessively accumulated bilirubin has been found to be primarily "indirect-reacting" material. The other fraction, the "direct-reacting" portion, is but slightly increased in concentration. It has therefore been inferred that the toxic effects of bilirubin on the newborn infant are due to the accumulation of the "indirect-reacting" fraction.

The identification of the two types of bilirubin was thus a matter of some clinical importance. This was completed in 1957 by the work of Schmid, who demonstrated that the "direct-reacting" material is actually a diglucuroniside of bilirubin, whereas the "indirect-reacting" type is the unconjugated form of the substance.

This suggested a mechanism for the hyperbilirubinemia found in the newborn. Since the bilirubin diglucuroniside concentration ordinarily does not become appreciably elevated, it was assumed that this material can be excreted by the infant quite effectively. The accumulation of the unconjugated form, however, indicates that the mechanism for its excretion is not well developed in the newborn, and that the rate-limiting step of this mechanism may well be that of conjugation with glucuronic acid. The fact that the total bilirubin concentration continues to rise until the fourth day of life, and that this is followed by a fall to a normal level over a period of days to weeks, suggests that the particular enzyme system which catalyzes the conjugation process is relatively inactive in, or even absent from, the liver of an infant before the age of four days.

Grodsky et al. (1958) and Brown and Zuelzer (1958) have demonstrated in animals the appearance during the developmental process of an enzyme activity which conjugates glucuronic acid to bilirubin. This enzyme, referred to as "glucuronyl transferase," catalyzes the transfer of the glucuronisyl moiety of uridine diphosphoglucuronic acid to a bilirubin molecule. The latter investigators, working with microsomes isolated from homogenates of guinea-pig liver, were unable to detect any activity in material from late fetal animals. Activity appeared shortly after birth, however, and increased to adult values over a period of several weeks.

Here we have then an example of an age-specific reduction in a given physiological function which may be explained by a reduced activity of the particular enzyme which is responsible for this function. There are other examples of such a relationship. In addition, many enzyme activities have been studied purely for the purpose of determining whether a developmental pattern is present. In a number of instances this has been found to be the case. This material has been reviewed by Knox et al. (1956), Kretchmer (1958, 1959), and Driscoll and Hsia (1958).

It is worth noting that not all of the developmental changes are in the direction of increase with age. Schachter et al. (1959) found that liver slices from newborn rats can couple a glucuronisyl moiety to the acyl group of salicylic acid whereas material from adults cannot. The essential point for the present discussion, however, is that there is a developmental pattern.

SPECIES SPECIFICITY

As one might well expect, the pattern of development of a given enzyme need not be the same even in fairly closely related species. While a number of interesting examples may be cited, there is one study that indicates in a somewhat teleological fashion a possible mechanism of control of the variation in enzyme activity with age.

Nemeth (1959) worked out the development of tryptophan pyrrolase activity in liver taken from several species. Assaying homogenates of rat tissue he found little activity present before fifteen days of age, but within the next five days there was a rapid increase to adult values. On the other hand, while material from the liver of the rabbit also did not demonstrate activity at the time of birth, one day later this was present and was equivalent to that of an adult. Furthermore, guinea-pig liver already possessed a small amount of tryptophan pyrrolase activity during the last phases of gestation as well as at the time of birth. This, too, rose to adult values at one day of age.

It is of interest that the rat is born in a state that is quite immature when compared to that of the guinea pig, while the rabbit falls in between the two. After a gestation period of twenty-one days the newborn rat is hairless, his eyes and ears have not opened, his temperature regulation is poor, and his attempts at locomotion are largely unsuccessful. The gestation of the rabbit is longer, thirty-one days, and results in a slightly more mature animal. After a sixty-eight-day gestation period the newborn guinea pig is a comparatively well-developed beast, with hair, open eyes and ears, and the ability to move about fairly well.

Thus we see a direct relationship between the length of gestation, the degree of maturity, and the developmental schedule of the tryptophan pyrrolase activity of the liver. This sort of approach would tend to give the rather vague word "mature" less of a relative and more of an absolute meaning, since one could imagine a common ontogenetic schedule for all three species with the incident of birth taking place at different times, as determined by selective forces during the evolutionary process. It is obvious that such a view is, to say the least, highly speculative.

ORGAN SPECIFICITY

It is known that certain organs will demonstrate a given enzyme activity while others will not. Usually there is a correlation between the presence of the enzyme and the related function which it is assumed to perform in the particular organ. The enzymic developmental patterns for each organ may differ, however, and in at least one instance may not correspond to the functional development.

Creatine phosphokinase, an enzyme associated with muscular

contractility, is present in both skeletal and cardiac muscle, and has a specific developmental pattern for each of these tissues. Read and Johnson (1959) found that this enzyme activity is first detectable in the heart muscle of the fetal rabbit at sixteen days gestation, whereas none is present in the gastrocnemius muscle until twenty-three days gestation.

While the appearance of creatine phosphokinase activity coincides with the development of contractility in the gastrocnemius, it is of interest that it is not detectable in the beating heart muscle of the fourteen-day-old fetus. The latter was the earliest stage that they studied, but it is known that beating begins even earlier, suggesting that the metabolism of the early fetal myocardium may differ from that of the older organism.

SUBCELLULAR FRACTION SPECIFICITY

With the development of techniques for rupturing cells and isolating the nuclear, mitochondrial, microsomal, and soluble fractions, many enzyme activities have been found to be located exclusively in one or another of these components.

While a transfer of enzyme activity from one cell fraction to another as development progresses has not been demonstrated in mammalian tissues, there is some evidence that this takes place in the liver of the chick embryo. Solomon (1959) has shown that, as the glutamic dehydrogenase activity of the supernatant fraction falls during the last week of embryonic development, that of the mitochondrial fraction rises. This may merely indicate, however, that the wall of the mitochondrion of the younger embryo is less capable of retaining its contents during the isolation procedure than that of an older animal. The paucity of data in the literature in this regard precludes any definite conclusion.

ISOZYME SPECIFICITY

Methods have recently become available which have permitted rather fine separation of mixtures of proteins while allowing them to remain in a relatively native state. Thus investigators have been able not only to detect many more fractions but also to assay these fractions for various enzyme activities. It has been noted that certain enzyme activities may be detected in a number of fractions of material prepared from the same tissue, rather than in single fractions as one might have expected. It may be concluded from this that in some instances a given enzyme activity in a given organ may be a property of several different types of protein molecules. Markert and Moller (1959) have called these *isozymes*.

Employing the technique of starch gel electrophoresis they have been able to demonstrate a predictable pattern of distribution of enzyme activities specific not only for individual tissues but also for different age groups. For example, each of the four isozymes with lactic dehydrogenase activity in the mouse heart has been shown by Markert (1960) to disappear, to reappear, or to change in concentration from the late embryonic to the adult stage.

Kaplan's group (Kaplan and Ciotti, 1961; Cohen et al., 1962) has been able to differentiate several "molecular species" of enzyme protein by other methods. They have shown that specific minor changes in the structure of the coenzymes will alter the *in vitro* kinetics of the lactic dehydrogenase activity of tissues taken from a newborn animal in a different manner than that taken from an adult animal. Furthermore, they have been able to demonstrate immunochemical differences in the enzyme protein.

It is to be expected that further studies of these fractions will significantly increase our understanding of the process of ontogenesis.

ALTERING THE DEVELOPMENTAL PATTERN

While the material cited above has added an exciting new dimension to the study of development, it is primarily of a descriptive nature. As such it provides us with a biochemical definition of the ontogenetic process as well as an explanation for certain clinical phenomena, e.g., the hyperbilirubinemia of prematurity. Some of the work done in attempting to elucidate the mechanisms controlling these changes will now be considered.

Nemeth (1959) has carried out an extremely interesting experiment in which he has demonstrated an alteration in the developmental pattern by means of varying the length of gestation. As cited above, tryptophan pyrrolase activity is not detectable in the liver of the newborn rabbit, but at one day after birth it is present and in an amount equal to that of adult tissue. A fetus delivered by hysterotomy four days before term shows a similar increase to adult values at one day of age, thus implicating the birth process as having a major role in the development of this particular enzyme activity. As further evidence for this conclusion Nemeth found that maintaining the fetuses *in utero* for an additional four days by means of injection of chorionic gonadotropin prevented them from developing the amount of enzyme activity which they would have acquired had they been born at term. In contrast to the other two groups of animals, however, their livers did demonstrate some tryptophan pyrrolase at birth, but only to a slight degree.

Sereni et al. (1959) were able to affect the developmental sequence in another manner. They noted that the liver of the newborn rat had very little tyrosine transaminase activity, but that at twelve hours of age this had increased to such an extent that it exceeded that of adult tissue. This predictable rise did not take place, however, if the rats were adrenalectomized immediately after birth. The effect of adrenalectomy could be reversed by the administration of cortisol, indicating that secretion of the latter by the adrenal gland was an integral factor in the determination of the developmental pattern of this enzyme. Interestingly, in some instances in which adrenalectomy was delayed until forty-five or more minutes after birth, there was no interference with the normal increase.

Thus we have two examples of situations in which the developmental schedule is altered. It may be noted that both are dependent upon the phenomenon of birth which is accompanied by some process, in the one case unknown, in the other the release of adrenal steroids, which must occur within moments after birth in order to effect its objective. This suggests involvement of a "trigger mechanism," a reaction which is required at a specific time in order to start up a given process, yet is not required for the maintenance of the latter. This may well be a fundamental characteristic of the developmental process in general.

UNMASKING OF EXISTING PROTEIN

Basically the most important consideration is whether the appearance of an enzyme activity during the ontogenetic sequence represents the synthesis of a "new" type of protein molecules, or whether the latter have existed previously, but in an enzymically inactive state. The following studies tend to favor the latter hypothesis. Kretchmer (1959) found that large amounts of ascorbic acid activate para-hydroxyphenylpyruvic oxidase obtained from the liver of premature infants. This explained the clinical observation of Levine (1947) wherein premature infants excreted unusually large quantities of the substrate (parahydroxyphenylpyruvic acid) and its immediate precursor (tyrosine) if they did not receive liberal amounts of ascorbic acid orally.

The possibility that the enzyme protein may exist before the appearance of its activity in at least some instances suggests certain therapeutic possibilities. In a situation where an immature individual is in difficulty because of the incomplete nature of his complement of enzyme activities, such as the premature infant with hyperbilirubinemia, it is conceivable that some technique may be developed to bring about the rapid unmasking of a given activity to a degree adequate to provide assistance. Another equally interesting and important possibility concerns the genetically determined disorders of metabolism. A number of these are due to deficiency or absence of specific enzyme activities, some of which (such as phenylalanine hydroxylase, the enzyme which is deficient in phenylketonurics) are normally absent from the tissues of the fetus but fail to appear at the scheduled time in the ontogenetic sequence. It is again conceivable that at least some of these defects represent the failure of an existing enzyme protein to become active and that a therapeutic procedure for such a situation might be developed.

It is pertinent to point out that in considering therapeutic possibilities, the use of activators (unmaskers of existing protein) and inducers (*vide infra*) appears to be more promising than the administration of the particular protein to the deficient individual. The problems of supply, preparation, membrane transport, and a relatively short half-life—to mention a very few—would seem to render such a prospect rather unlikely.

ACTIVATION AND INHIBITION

Another of the methods employed in determining whether or not an enzyme protein exists in an inactive form in the young is to test it for simple, *in vitro* activation or inhibition. This is done by adding the inactive tissue to that from an adult and comparing the total activity of the mixture with that of a quantity of adult material equal to that present in the mixture. If there is greater total activity in the reaction vessel containing the mixture, this is presumptive evidence that "activators" in the adult tissue were able to unmask the activity of existing enzyme protein in the tissue of the young animal. Should the mixture exhibit less total activity, this would indicate that some material present in the newborn's tissue not only has continued to inhibit the latter's enzyme but has also inhibited that of the adult tissue. Failure to find a difference in the activity of the mixture would suggest either that the adult tissue does not contain activators peculiar to the mature state, that the young animal's tissue does not contain inhibitors, or that inhibitors may be present but are so tightly bound to the newborn's tissue that they cannot dissociate from it and are therefore not detectable by this method. The above discussion is rather oversimplified, but this does not affect the basic thesis.

In almost all cases in which this experiment has been tried the total activity has remained unchanged, so that the possibility of isolation of activating or inhibiting factors is rather remote.

An exception to the general rule has been reported by Fouts and Adamson (1959). They have shown that homogenates of liver from newborn rabbits inhibit the l-amphetamine deaminase activity of material from adult animals to a marked degree. Thus in this particular instance the appearance of the enzyme activity during development might be more precisely defined as the disappearance of an inhibitor. Other factors may be involved, however.

SYNTHESIS OF NEW PROTEIN

The hypothesis that the appearance of an enzyme activity during the developmental sequence represents the synthesis of an entirely new type of protein molecule is an attractive one. This could be explained in terms of a currently popular concept whereby the genetic information, stored in the nuclear deoxyribonucleic acid (DNA), is imparted to ribonucleic acid (RNA), which in turn is responsible for the synthesis of the specific protein molecules. The site responsible for the developmental sequence could therefore be either the nuclear DNA, implying that the sequence is itself contained in the genome, or the subsequent mechanisms for the tangible expression of this information. The latter possibility will be discussed first.

INDUCTION AND REPRESSION

The processes whereby the rate of synthesis of a particular protein is increased or decreased are referred to as "induction" and "repression," respectively. This is in contrast to the "activation" and "inhibition" referred to previously in which only the *activity* of a fixed quantity of enzyme protein is affected. A number of enzymes are known to be inducible or repressible. It should be stated parenthetically that the substances which induce, repress, activate, or inhibit an enzyme frequently are neither substrates nor products of the reaction which it catalyzes.

Tryptophan pyrrolase has been shown to be inducible (Knox, 1951) in that five hours after injection of its substrate, tryptophan, into an adult animal there is a significant increase in the activity of the liver when compared with controls. Nemeth (1959) attempted to induce the appearance of tryptophan pyrrolase by injecting substrate into fetal and newborn animals five hours before sacrifice. Tissues from animals younger than the age at which the enzyme usually appears were unaffected by the procedure. Those from animals whose age was such that activity of some degree would normally be present demonstrated appreciable induction. A number of investigators have reported similar results when working with enzymes known to be inducible in the adult animal.

Alteration of the developmental pattern of an enzyme activity which is not inducible by the Knox technique is being attempted by the writer. The multi-enzyme system responsible for the conjugation of benzoic acid to glycine becomes detectable in rat liver within the first week after birth and rises slowly until the age at which the animals are weaned. At this time there is an acceleration of the rate of increase, and adult values are attained at about one month of age (Brandt, 1960). The usual technique employed in the demonstration of induction did not result in an appreciable change in activity in adult and in newborn animals. A longer-term experiment was indicated, however, since the more rapid rate of increase in enzyme activity after weaning might well have been a reflection of an appreciable quantity of substrate in the diet. It was found that the administration to female rats of either a synthetic diet which contains little if any benzoic or para-aminobenzoic acid (PAB) or one to which has been added 1 per cent PAB does not appreciably affect the developmental pattern of hippuric-acid-synthesizing activity in their offspring—this despite the fact that PAB crosses the placenta.

The inability to induce the premature appearance of an enzyme which has a predictable developmental schedule suggests that such a process is not involved in the usual ontogenetic sequence. It may well be, however, that certain substances which are as yet undefined may indeed be responsible, and that further study will reveal their presence and nature. This is to be expected since there is reasonable evidence that most of the changes in enzyme activity as the organism develops actually represent changes in the amount of enzyme protein; by definition, then, induction rather than activation.

The converse mechanism, that of repression, has never been adequately tested. This would imply a decreased rate of synthesis of the given enzyme in the young animal because of the presence in its tissues of a specific agent which would not be present to any appreciable extent in the adult. In a pilot experiment, the author injected two groups of immature rats with homogenates of livers of newborn and adult animals, respectively, for a period of two weeks. No significant difference in *in vitro* liver hippuric-acid-synthesizing activity was noted, but the inadequacy of such an experiment to test the hypothesis is rather obvious.

The therapeutic implications concerning inducers and repressers are similar to those mentioned for activators and inhibitors in the section "Unmasking of Existing Protein."

DIRECT GENE ACTION

A more likely basis for the developmental sequence is that the genome, and therefore most likely the nuclear DNA, contains not only the information necessary to direct the synthesis of an enzyme but also that which dictates at which stage the synthetic process is to begin. The evidence for such a statement is to a great extent intuitive. Some work with lower forms of life, however, lends support to the hypothesis.

Gall (1958) has reviewed the chromosomal aspects of the process of differentiation. Certain tissues of larval Drosophila and other Diptera are unique in that their cell nuclei contain chromosomes which, during the so-called "resting phase" between cell divisions, not only are large enough to be visualized by light microscopy but also have a characteristic pattern of banding. There is good evidence that the unusual size of these chromosomes results from each being made up of a thousand or more chromatids rather than the one or two in the usual "resting phase" chromosome. In this specific instance the cores of the chromatids, which are DNA chains, are straightened and elongated because some degree of uncoiling has taken place in at least the lighter segments between bands. Corresponding segments of each chromatid are contiguous, and the cumulative effect is to render the chromosome thick enough to be visualized by light microscopy. The bands are thought to be structural evidence of specifically localized condensations of DNA and have been associated with specific genetic loci.

It has been noted that certain segments of these chromosomes may become altered in appearance. These alterations seem to be localized enlargements ("puffs") which may in certain instances progress to the point where it appears as though a doughnut encircles the chromosome at the particular locus ("Balbiani rings"). Studies indicate that in these expanded areas there is a reduced concentration of DNA and an accumulation of RNA and protein. Gall hypothesizes that the decrease in density of the DNA results from a localized unwinding of the chain which thus occupies a greater volume than that which it had previously occupied. He further theorizes that this unwinding of the DNA exposes certain active sites of its molecular structure to the surrounding medium and that these sites proceed to bring about the synthesis of RNA and protein in a process tantamount to instructing a bearer with a specific message from a particular gene. The ribonucleoprotein then conveys the information to other parts of the cell. Thus, he has a histological representation of the process cited under "Synthesis of New Protein" above. The fact of particular importance to the present essay is that there is a developmental pattern to the occurrence of the puffs and Balbiani rings. Certain of these are seen only at specific stages of development of the larva and only in specific tissues.

Thus in Gall's hypothesis we have a genetic mechanism for bringing about the appearance of certain enzyme activities. Various segments of the chromosomal DNA unwind at specific stages of development, transfer their particular bits of genetic information to RNA, which then carries the latter to the other parts of the cell where it is effected.

It is well to point out, however, that one cannot test this hypothesis in mammalian organisms very readily. Since the chromosomes of this group are not visible to light microscopy unless the cell is involved in a mitotic process (except for one of the X chromosomes of the human female), it is assumed that they are in a completely unwound state. Presumably the DNA is also present in an unwound state and therefore all of the genetic information is exposed at all times, rather than during specific phases of ontogenesis. This still remains as another extremely interesting area for investigation.

INTERACTION OF GENOME AND ENVIRONMENT

Even if one assumes that the genome contains the necessary information for controlling the developmental process, one must recognize that the expression of that information is subject to modification by influences outside of the cell. Not only may certain experimental situations such as those discussed in the section "Altering the Developmental Pattern" be cited, but also the literally infinite number of ways in which less specific environmental influences are known to affect gene action. Indeed, if after mitotic division in early embryonic life "daughter" cells share equally in the DNA of their "mother" cell and thus receive identical information, then it is logical to assume that cell differentiation is necessarily dependent upon a non-DNA system within the cell. In turn, this must be affected by events occurring outside the cell. Ontogenesis may therefore consist of a series of periods of activity of specific portions of the DNA of specific cells, all in response to specific environmental conditions peculiar to the individual cells.

RIBONUCLEIC ACID AND INDUCTION

Several investigators have carried out experiments which, while not concerned specifically with enzymes, are nonetheless pertinent to our discussion. In these studies RNA has been employed as a tissue induction agent. Although the primary genetic information is most likely stored in the DNA, similar work using this material has been extremely limited.

Niu (1958a, b) conducted a series of experiments on hanging-drop cultures of ectoderm from the gastrula stage of salamanders. In a considerable percentage of those cultures into which he placed RNA isolated from various organs of calves, there resulted a growth of tissue which had a pattern specific for that of the organ from which the RNA was obtained. The organ specificity, despite the extreme species difference, is of great interest.

Hrubesova et al. (1959) employed ribonucleoprotein isolated from the spleens of adult rabbits which had received injections of salmonella organisms two days before sacrifice. Under these conditions no antibody was present in the animals at the time of sacrifice. The material was then injected into five-day-old rabbits. Even though rabbits are ordinarily unable to produce antibody until twenty days of age, the injected baby animals developed antibody to salmonella three to five days later.

DeCarvalho and Rand (1961) also found RNA to be an effective agent. They prepared the material from various organs of normal rats and from Novikoff hepatoma cells. Pretreating tumor cells with RNA from spleen and kidney did not affect the ability of these cells to form tumors when injected into the peritoneal cavity of test animals. However, pretreatment with RNA from hepatoma cells increased the incidence of tumors, and pretreatment with RNA from normal liver markedly reduced the incidence of tumor formation. In other experiments normal liver cells were given intraperitoneally to one group of animals after pretreatment with RNA from normal liver cells and to another group after pretreatment with RNA from hepatoma cells. No tumors resulted in the former, while a significant number developed in the latter group. A third series of experiments was performed in which hepatoma RNA was injected intraperitoneally into adult rats, intravenously into pregnant rats, and subcutaneously into newborn rats. Appreciable percentages of the adults, the offspring of the pregnant animals, and the newborn rats developed tumors, while a control group injected with RNA from normal liver developed none.

Hess et al. (1961) worked with RNA prepared from several organs. They noted that only RNA isolated from pituitary glands was able to bring about an increase in ACTH content of the pituitaries of rats when injected into the peritoneum. RNA from liver and pancreas was not effective.

It must be pointed out that these experiments cannot be interpreted as providing conclusive evidence for the specific inductive capacity of the RNA preparations employed. Other substances are well known to bring about similar effects. Indeed, Yamada (1958) has reviewed studies which suggest that protein may be more important as an experimental embryonic induction agent than RNA.

On the other hand, the work does point out some very exciting possibilities for further investigation. It is conceivable that such techniques may some day be employed to bring about a premature maturation for therapeutic purposes or to cause the synthesis of a vitally necessary enzyme which would otherwise not have appeared in a particular individual because of a lack of the corresponding gene.

SUMMARY

It is possible to define the developmental process in terms of age-specific variation in the activity of a number of enzymes. This variation may also be specific for the species, organ, subcellular fraction, and isozyme studied, and in most cases cannot be altered experimentally. In several instances, however, certain processes occurring at about the time of birth seem to affect the developmental schedule.

In general the relatively reduced enzyme activity in young animals has not been found to be associated with the presence of inhibitors or the absence of activator substances. Nevertheless, there is some evidence which indicates that the appearance of an enzyme activity in the developmental sequence may represent the unmasking of a previously existing protein rather than the synthesis of a new type of protein molecue. The latter process makes for a more attractive hypothesis, however, in that it conceives of the ontogenetic process as being more directly controlled by gene action.

Recent experimental work has involved the modification of the expression of gene action in higher forms of life by the administration of exogenous RNA preparations. While still in the preliminary stage, it does suggest some exciting therapeutic possibilities. It is conceivable that in time to come one may be able to bring about the appearance of an enzyme activity in an individual who lacks it, either because of immaturity or because of absence of the necessary genetic information.

BIBLIOGRAPHY

Brandt, I. K. (1960), Hippurate Synthesis in the Newborn Rat. *Amer. J. Dis. Child.*, 100:538.
Brown, A. K. & Zuelzer, W. W. (1958), Studies on the Neonatal Development of the Glucuronide Conjugating System. *J. Clin. Invest.*, 37:322-340.

Cohn, R. O., Kaplan, N. O., Levine, L., & Zwilling, E. (1962). Nature and Development of Lactic Dehydrogenases. *Science*, 136:962-969.

DeCarvalho, S. & Rand, H. J. (1961), Comparative Effects of Liver and Tumor Ribonucleic Acids on the Normal Liver and the Novikoff Hepatoma Cells of the Rat. *Nature*, 189:815-817.

Driscoll, S. G. & Hsia, D. Y. (1958), The Development of Enzyme Systems During Early Infancy. *Pediatrics*, 22:785-845.

Fouts, J. R. & Adamson, R. H. (1959), Drug Metabolism in the Newborn Rabbit. *Science*, 129:897-898.

Gall, J. G. (1958), Chromosomal Differentiation. In: *Chemical Basis of Development*, ed. W. D. McElroy & B. Glass. Baltimore: Johns Hopkins Press, pp. 103-135.

Grodsky, G. M., Carbone, J. V., & Fanska, R. (1958), Enzymatic Defect in Metabolism of Bilirubin in Fetal and Newborn Rat. *Proc. Soc. Exp. Biol. & Med.*, 97:291-294.

Hess, M., Corrigan, J. J. Jr., & Hodak, J. A. (1961), The Effects of Nucleic Acids on Pituitary ACTH Content. *Endocrinology*, 68:548-552.

Hrubesova, M., Askonas, B. A., & Humphrey, J. H. (1959), Serum Antibody and Gamma Globulin in Baby Rabbits after Transfer of Ribonucleoprotein from Adult Rabbits. *Nature*, 183:97-99.

Kaplan, N. O. & Ciotti, M. M. (1961), Heterogeneity of the Lactic Dehydrogenases of New-born and Adult Rat Heart As Determined with Coenzyme Analogs. *Biochimica Biophysica Acta*, 49:425-426.

Knox, W. E. (1951), Two Mechanisms Which Increase in vivo the Liver Tryptophan Peroxidase Activity: Specific Enzyme Adaptation and Stimulation of the Pituitary-Adrenal System. *Brit. J. Exp. Path.*, 32:462-469.

——— Auerbach, V. H., & Lin, E. C. C. (1956), Enzymatic and Metabolic Adaptations in Animals. *Physiol. Rev.*, 36:164-254.

Kretchmer, N. (1958), Metabolic and Enzymic Changes During Development. In: *Physiology of Prematurity*, ed. J. T. Lanman. New York: Josiah Macy Jr. Foundation, pp. 11-58.

——— (1959), Enzymatic Patterns During Development. An Approach to a Biochemical Definition of Immaturity. *Pediatrics*, 23:606-617.

Levine, S. Z. (1947), Tyrosine and Phenylalanine Metabolism in Infants and the Role of Vitamin C. *Harvey Lectures*, 42:303-331.

Markert, C. L. (1960), Biochemical Embryology and Genetics. In *Proceedings: Symposium on Some Problems of Normal and Abnormal Differentiation and Development*. Bethesda: National Cancer Institute, pp. 3-18.

——— & Moller, F. (1959), Multiple Forms of Enzymes: Tissue, Ontogenetic, and Species Specific Patterns. *Proc. Nat. Acad. Sci.*, 45:753-763.

Nemeth, A. M. (1959), Mechanisms Controlling Changes in Tryptophan Peroxidase Activity in Developing Mammalian Liver. *J. Biol. Chem.*, 234:2921-2924.

Niu, M. C. (1958a), The Role of Ribonucleic Acid in Embryonic Differentiation. *Anatomical Record*, 131:585.

——— (1958b), Thymus Ribonucleic Acid and Embryonic Differentiation. *Proc. Nat. Acad. Sci.*, 44:1264-1274.

Read, W. O. & Johnson, D. C. (1959), Creatine Phosphokinase Activity in Heart and Skeletal Muscle of Fetal Rabbits. *Proc. Soc. Exp. Biol. & Med.*, 102:740-741.

Schachter, D., Kass, D. J., & Lannon, T. J. (1959), The Biosynthesis of Salicyl Glucuronides by Tissue Slices of Various Organs. *J. Biol. Chem.*, 234:201-205.

Schmid, R. (1957), The Identification of "Direct-Reacting" Bilirubin As Bilirubin Glucuronide. *J. Biol. Chem.*, 229:881-888.

Sereni, F., Kenney, F. T., & Kretchmer, N. (1959), Factors Influencing the Development of Tyrosine Transaminase Activity in Rat Liver. *J. Biol. Chem.*, 234:609-612.

Solomon, J. B. (1959), Changes in the Distribution of Glutamic, Lactic, and Malic Dehydrogenases in Liver Cell Fractions During Development of the Chick Embryo. *Develpm. Biol.*, 1:182-198.

Yamada, T. (1958), Embryonic Induction. In: *Chemical Basis of Development*, ed. W. D. McElroy & B. Glass. Baltimore: Johns Hopkins Press, pp. 217-238.

Visual Behavior of Newborn Infants

• *GEORGE W. GREENMAN, M.D.*

Yale University

Vision is one of the most important of the special senses available to human beings. Its importance exceeds the essential role it plays in perception of the outside world and in differentiating the self from the nonself. One of the primary ways in which humans communicate on a nonverbal level is by looking at one another. When visual communication does not exist between humans, something deviant or pathological often exists in the relationship.

Observations of the visual behavior of newborns were included in a longitudinal study of child development initiated in 1958.[1] Data will be presented in this paper to show that the newborn infant has the capacity to follow a visual stimulus with his eyes. This is discussed in terms of its somatic and psychological significance.

[1] This study was a cooperative research project which included the Departments of Neurology, Obstetrics and Pediatrics of the Yale University School of Medicine and the Child Study Center of Yale. The obstetrical study, directed by Lee Buxton, M.D. and Clarence D. Davis, M.D., was an evaluation of the training for childbirth program. The child development study, directed by Gilbert Glaser, M.D. and Sally Provence, M.D., included pediatric and neurological examination, developmental tests, and a variety of observations of mother and child. The study was aided by Grant B2355 from the National Institute of Neurological Diseases and Blindness, U.S. Public Health Service.

Uniform data concerning the capacity of a newborn infant to follow a visual stimulus with his eyes are not to be found. The prevalent medical opinion is that vision is greatly underdeveloped at birth. Thus, Shaffer (1960) states there is no focusing and no indication of following light throughout the first month. According to Nelson's *Textbook of Pediatrics* (1959), sight in the first few weeks is limited to the ability to distinguish light from darkness, and by one month the eyes will follow bright objects. Ford (1960) says that the neonate will fix a light with his eyes but does not follow it smoothly. Weerekoon (1957) reports the newborn follows a brightly colored toy only after the first month. Langworthy (1933), however, states that infants fix objects with the eyes at birth and many will follow a slowly moving object with the eyes a few hours after birth. Gough (1962), in a recent study, found that newborns fixed their eyes on their mother's faces while being fed by the middle of the second week. Before this, their eyes were usually closed.

The psychological literature contains many reports indicating more advanced visual behavior. Ling (1942) studied the development of visual fixation in twenty-five newborns over a ten-week period. Four infants, between the ages of seven minutes and seventy-five minutes, the only ones so tested, followed her fingers as she fluttered them across their field of vision. McGinnis (1930) found in a study of six newborns that the ability to make pursuit eye movements is present within a few minutes of birth. It is of interest that Ling and McGinnis minimized their observations by remarking that the phenomenon was rudimentary and that newborns do not follow in the adult fashion. Gesell et al. (1949) wrote that the newborn follows the movement of the dangling ring with his eyes through a short arc when it is brought into the periphery of his vision. In a detailed study of four newborn infants, Wolff (1959) described visual pursuit movements. Graham et al. (1956) found visual fixation and following to be of sufficient value to include it in a battery of tests designed to show behavioral differences between normal and abnormal infants.

Other aspects of the visual behavior of neonates have been studied in recent years. Gorman et al. (1957) studied the visual acuity of infants from one and a half hours to five days of age by eliciting opticokinetic nystagmus with a large screen, testing extramacular vision. Ninety-three of 100 infants tested gave a positive response, and the authors felt that the test would be valuable in determining the presence or absence of vision.

METHODS AND SUBJECTS

One hundred twenty-seven babies were studied. They were born to upper-middle-class parents, and all the mothers were primiparas. The infants were born at term and their condition at birth was good. Minimal anesthesia was used for delivery, so none of the babies was narcotized.

Ninety-seven infants were examined within fifteen minutes after birth and the remaining 30 were seen for the first time within the initial twenty-four hours. Each baby was examined two or more times during the lying-in period of five days. One (or both) of two visual stimulus objects was used, the standard 4-inch red ring from the Gesell infant test and a bright red mass of interlocking plastic rings. The stimulus was first presented in the line of vision approximately 10 inches from the face of the infant lying supine. If no response was obtained, the infant was picked up, cradled in the examiner's arms in the feeding position, and the stimulus was presented again. The cradling seemed to have an organizing effect, and when it was done, many infants followed who had not previously done so.

When it appeared that the infant fixed his eyes on the object, it was moved in an arc horizontally from one side to the other and then vertically. A positive response was recorded only when the infant followed the stimulus with his eyes two or more times.

Few babies were examined while being fed, but it was customary to try to sooth a fussy baby by letting him suck on a pacifier, which was usually the examiner's finger. In the early part of the study, the stimulus was presented while the baby was sucking. This was soon abandoned since the yield of following was so low. Instead, the examination was done after the pacifier was removed while the baby was lying quietly with his eyes open.

If the baby seemed to be awake but had his eyes closed, several things were done to try to get him to open them. One of the most successful was to subdue the light in the room. Another was to gently open the lids for a moment; once this was done the infant frequently kept them open. The sharp ring of a bell near his ear also would cause an infant to open his eyes and occasionally keep them open. Graham's technique of holding an infant vertically, upright or upside down, was not tried (Graham et al., 1956).

Escalona (1962) has discussed the problem of the crucial importance of the state of the organism on its behavior and has emphasized the necessity of taking this into account in any investigation of infant behavior.

A moderate degree of photophobia during the first few days of life was noted during this study and had been noted by others. In most instances, light had to be subdued before the infant would open his eyes at all or widely enough so that they could be observed. In addition, the practice of instilling silver nitrate into the eyes immediately after birth is still widespread. This acts as an irritant increasing the photophobia and, if not rinsed out well, can cause a chemical conjunctivitis. If precautions are not taken to decrease the light intensity, the infants' eyes may be partially or entirely closed during much of the neonatal period creating an obvious obstacle for observing their function.

RESULTS

One hundred twenty, or 95 per cent, of the total group of 127 infants showed visual following one or more times within the first ninety-six hours after birth. The relationship between a positive response and age is illustrated in Table 1. There was a steady increase in the

TABLE 1

Relationship of Babies Showing Visual Following to Age in Hours

	Del. Rm.	½-12 hrs.	12-48 hrs.	48-96 hrs.
Number examined	97	32	113	104
Number following	25	18	86	78
Percentage following	26%	56%	76%	75%

percentage of infants following the stimulus from the first few moments of life to the age range of twelve to forty-eight hours. No further increase in a positive response occurred after forty-eight hours. An infant who followed on one of the early examinations did not necessarily give a positive response at a later time.

The babies' eyes lagged behind the stimulus as it moved across the visual field. There appeared to be a series of fixations with the eyes repeatedly catching up with the ring. As a result, the movements appeared uneven and jerky. No attempt was made to note whether mono-ocular fixation was the rule as stated by Gesell et al. (1949) and Ling (1942), but conjugate deviation of the eyes occurred in all instances. At no time did one eye appear to move independently of the other. Some of the more visually attentive infants turned their head to follow the stimulus as it moved out of their field of vision. More frequently, following stopped after the stimulus had moved through an arc of approximately 90 degrees. Horizontal following was slightly easier to elicit than vertical following. During the time that the baby's eyes followed the stimulus, his body movements ceased and all of his attention appeared to be devoted to the task at hand.

The relationship of visual following to the time elapsed since the last feeding was studied. No significant difference was found in the percentage of positive responses between those infants who had been fed within the previous thirty minutes and those who had not been fed for two hours and for four hours.

DISCUSSION

The newborn has a large repertoire of responses that are specific for the neonatal period and gradually disappear during the first three to five months of extrauterine life. Examples include the Moro reflex, reflex palmar and plantar grasping, and automatic walking. Most or all of these behavioral manifestations are exceedingly primitive, and there is general agreement that the cerebral cortex is not necessary for their production. Indeed, there is a correlation between their disappearance and evidence of increasing cortical activity (Ford,

1960). Since it is stated by some (Ford, 1960; Irwin, 1942; Kleitman, 1955) that the cerebral cortex does not function at the time of birth, the observations of the newborn's visual behavior raise two questions. Is visual following another neonatal reflex, and is it possible to have vision, including conjugate deviation of the eyes, without the cerebral cortex being present and functioning?

One of the characteristics of the various neonatal reflexes is that they diminish and disappear. Some are replaced by similar, voluntary behavior such as the volitional grasping and walking. No studies have been published reporting that visual following shows a similar dropping out or replacement by a more mature pattern. On the contrary, it appears only to improve. Ling (1942) found steady improvement in sustained visual fixation from a few hours after birth to a peak at four to five weeks. McGinnis (1930) and Gesell et al. (1949) report a steady increase in the ability of the newborn to use his eyes. In our experience with forty-one infants seen at four weeks of age in another study all showed more mature visual behavior than they had during the first five days. Large numbers of infants have been followed longitudinally at frequent intervals by us and numerous other investigators from the age of four weeks on. The findings consistently have been that vision progressively matures. Fewer infants have been seen between the ages of five days and twenty-eight days, but in no instance have those seen not shown visual pursuit. Thus it seems that visual pursuit is not the same type of response as most of the neonatal reflex phenomena. It appears to be the beginning of man's ability to use his visual perceptual apparatus, although no intentionality is implied in the neonatal period.

There is general agreement that the cerebral cortex must be at least partially intact to permit vision in the adult human. Bilateral destruction of the cerebral cortex results in blindness (Ford, 1960; Walsh, 1957). Opticokinetic nystagmus, a manifestation of a visual phenomenon essential for ocular fixation of moving objects (Ford, 1960), is obliterated by lesions of the optic pathways in the temporal and occipital cortex (Crosby, 1953; Ford, 1960). Gorman et al. (1957) have demonstrated that opticokinetic nystagmus can be readily demonstrated in the newborn. It would appear, unless one postulates a different mechanism for the newborn, that the parts of the cerebral cortex involved with vision are functioning at birth. It is probably inaccurate to refer to the newborn as decerebrate or as a brain-stem preparation (Irwin, 1942; Kleitman, 1955).

The study of visual behavior of infants with known congenital brain malformations or lesions should clarify further the role played by the cortex at birth. It was possible, recently, to study until death at five months the behavior of an infant who had an autopsy diagnosis of a severe central nervous system anomaly known as cebocephaly. In most respects, this baby's neonatal behavior was indistinguishable from that of an infant with an intact central nervous system. The Moro reflex, prone behavior, grasping, and automatic walking were all normal. The striking difference was the absence of visual following at any time. Similar findings were observed in an infant with severe hydranencephaly. In both infants, the higher brain structures were malformed or damaged, and the most obvious behavioral difference between them and normal infants was lack of visual pursuit.

Eliciting visual behavior as part of the clinical assessment of a newborn also needs further exploration. A moderate amount of practice and often a large amount of patience are required to elicit a response. A newborn who fails to show a response on repeated evaluations under favorable conditions for examination should be suspect. Graham and co-workers (1956) found that traumatized newborns had a lower score on a visual scale than did untraumatized newborns. This conforms with our observations that 95 per cent of normal infants showed a positive response.

Relatively advanced functioning of the visual apparatus, particularly its cortical connections, is predicted in the early ontogenesis of the human fetus. Until the fifth or sixth fetal month, the surface of the cerebral cortex is smooth and lacks the convolutions and fissures of the term fetus and the older individual. The calcarine fissure, along whose lips lie the visual receptive areas of the cortex, begins to appear at the twentieth fetal week and is among the earliest of the sulci to form (Patten, 1953; Polyak, 1955). This fissure is also one of the first to appear during phylogenesis (Polyak, 1955).

Neuroanatomical evidence that the optic system is ready to function at the time of birth is provided by Langworthy's studies (1933). He found that the optic nerves, tracts, and pathways in the brain had little myelin at the time of birth but rapidly become myelinated thereafter. He presents evidence that stimuli from the eye appear to accelerate myelinization in the optic system.

What appeared to be generalized attentiveness to the visual stimulus has been observed under other circumstances. If a baby is nursing, for example, he is physically quiet and is less responsive to outside stimuli. He does not respond as readily to sound or follow the visual stimulus as well. Gough (1962) made similar observations, noting that babies tend to immobilize their eyes while feeding. If an infant is actively moving his body and a bell is rung, he characteristically quiets and seems to be attentive to the sound. These behavioral observations suggest that the newly born infant reacts in a total fashion to a given stimulus and that, for a time, other stimuli are not responded to.

One of the earliest ways that an infant can communicate with his mother is to look at her. Often during the lying-in period, mothers happily and excitedly report that their babies are looking at them. Holding and cuddling the baby may be rewarded by increased visual attentiveness. The pleasurable feeling a mother receives from having her newborn infant look at her may be viewed by her as one of the satisfactions for her efforts in delivering and caring for him. It is a way of consolidating the relationship between mother and child. It serves the infant in a biological sense by enhancing his care. It serves him psychologically by giving more pleasure to the nurturing person and thus increases the quality and frequency of his stimulation.

SUMMARY

In this study 127 infants, ninety-six hours of age or less, were examined one or more times to determine their ability to follow a visual stimulus with their eyes. The results showed that 120, or 95 per cent, of them showed a positive response; 97 were examined within the first twenty minutes after birth, while they were still in the delivery room; 25, or 26 per cent, followed the stimulus. The percentage of babies showing a positive response increased with age up to seventy-two hours. The literature was briefly reviewed, and the embryological, anatomical, physiological, and psychological aspects of early vision were discussed.

BIBLIOGRAPHY

Crosby, E. C. (1953), Relations of Brain Centers to Normal and Abnormal Eye Movements in the Horizontal Plane. *J. Comp. Neurol.*, 99:437-480.

Escalona, S. K. (1962), The Study of Individual Differences and the Problem of State. *J. Amer. Acad. Child Psychiat.*, 1:11-37.

Ford, F. R. (1960), *Diseases of the Nervous System in Infancy, Childhood and Adolescence* (4th ed.). Springfield: Charles C Thomas.

Gesell, A., Ilg, F., & Bullis, G. (1949), *Vision, Its Development in Infant and Child*. New York: Paul B. Hoeber.

Gorman, J. J., Cogan, D. G., & Gellis, S. S. (1957), An Apparatus for Grading Visual Activity of Infants on the Basis of Opticokinetic Nystagmus. *Pediatrics*, 19:1088-1092.

Gough, D. (1962), The Visual Behavior of Infants in the First Few Weeks of Life. *Proc. Royal Soc. Med.*, 55:308-310.

Graham, F. K., Matarazzo, R. G., & Caldwell, B. M. (1956), Behavioral Dffierences Between Normal and Traumatized Newborns. *Psychol. Monogr.*, 70, No. 428.

Irwin, O. C. (1942), Can Infants Have IQ's. *Psychol. Rev.*, 49:69-79.

Kleitman, N. (1955), The Role of the Cerebral Cortex in the Development and Maintenance of Consciousness. In: *Problems of Consciousness*, ed. H. A. Abramson. New York: Josiah Macy, Jr. Foundation.

Langworthy, O. R. (1933), Development of Behavior Patterns and Myelinization of the Nervous System in the Human Fetus. *Contributions to Embryology*, 24, No. 139, Carnegie Institute of Washington.

Ling, Bing-Ching (1942), A Genetic Study of Sustained Visual Fixation and Associated Behavior in the Human Infant from Birth to Six Months. *J. Genet. Psychol.*, 61:227-277.

McGinnis, J. M. (1930), Eye Movements and Optic Nystagmus in Early Infancy. *Genet. Psychol. Monogr.*, 8:321-427.

Nelson, W. E., ed. (1959), *Textbook of Pediatrics* (7th ed.). Philadelphia: W. B. Saunders.

Patten, B. M. (1953), *Human Embryology* (2nd ed.). New York: Blakiston.

Polyak, S. (1955), *The Vertebrate Visual System*. Chicago: Univ. Chicago Press.

Shaffer, A. J. (1960), *Diseases of the Newborn*. Philadelphia: W. B. Saunders.

Walsh, F. B. (1957), *Clinical Neuro-Opthalmology*. Baltimore: Williams & Wilkens.

Weerekoon, L. M. (1957), The Development of Vision. *Ceylon Med. J.*, 4:33-35.

Wolff, P. H. (1959), Observations on Newborn Infants. *Psychosom. Med.*, 21:110-118.

An Editorial Note on Bone Age

• *RICHARD L. DAY, M.D.*
University of Pittsburgh

Bone age of children as measured by roentgenographic methods is a useful index of maturation. It is widely recognized that bone age is more closely correlated with the progress of a child toward sexual (reproductive) maturity than is height or weight. This communication is intended to explain why maturation of the skeleton is more closely related to maturation of endocrine function than is height. The explanation does not lie in any special sensitivity of the areas of calcification to the influence of circulating hormones. It is rather a feature of the arithmetic of the notation used in describing growth of bone which enhances the degree of the correlation. When height is expressed in a different way, that is, as per cent of mature height, its correlation with such a marker of maturity as onset of menstruation approaches in magnitude the correlation of bone age with menarche. One does not know in advance the ultimate height which a child is destined to attain as an adult. In the case of bone age, however, the value at maturity is known for everyone.

All of these points have been made previously by Simmons (1944). Her publication has not been noticed by pediatricians to the extent it deserves.

In Simmons's work, children were measured throughout the growing period so that the age at which the girls had their first menstrual period was accurately noted as was their final height when growth ceased. It was possible to re-express height at different ages as "per cent of mature height." This measure, "per cent of mature height," is analogous to "height age," except that it applies to the particular individual in question. It is a fraction of which the numerator is the height and the denominator the actual height attained by the child when growth has ceased. It is a value which is not, as is the notation for "height age," dependent upon a population average. A child's ultimate height cannot be foretold, so that "per cent of mature height" can be used only in retrospective studies. In the case of bone age, however, the adult value is known with certainty. It happens to be the same for all adults. If all adults had a similarly identical height, either height or height age might be expected to correlate well with other measures as, for example, the age of menarche. Simmons's study was retrospective. She prepared correlations of (1) height, (2) skeletal age, and (3) per cent of mature height with the date of menarche. Menstruation was selected as a marker of maturity because of its definiteness and the accuracy with which it is likely to be reported in the case of children being seen at regular intervals.

Simmons's results as abstracted from her paper appear in Table 1.

TABLE 1

Data from Simmons

Correlations (r) of age at menarche with bone age, height, and per cent of mature height calculated at different ages

| | Coefficient of correlation of age at menarche: | | |
Age	with height	with bone age	with height expressed as per cent of terminal height
10	—.425	—.611	—.655
11	—.546	—.670	—.764
12	—.529	—.800	—.811
13	—.377	—.867	—.779
14	—.082	—.850	—.624

From these figures it appears that the coefficients of correlation between bone age at ten, eleven, twelve, thirteen, and fourteen years with the age at onset of menses are seen to be quite high and certainly very much better than the corresponding correlations of height with age at menarche. When height is expressed as per cent of mature height actually attained by each child, the correlation is greatly improved, and approaches that when bone age is used. It seems reasonable to interpret these figures as showing that growth in height is actually well related to maturation. The advantage of bone age as an indicator of maturation is not so much a particular aspect of calcification of the skeleton as the fact that one always knows in advance what bone development will be at cessation of growth.

SUMMARY

Bone age is a more useful measure of maturation than is height or "height age" because one knows in advance what bone age will be at maturity. In retrospective studies by Simmons, height expressed as per cent of mature height actually attained was found to correlate almost as well as bone age with the ultimate date of menarche.

REFERENCE

Simmons, K. (1944), The Brush Foundation Study of Child Growth and Development. II. Physical Growth and Development. *Monographs of the Society for Research in Child Development*, 9, Serial No. 37. Washington, D.C.: National Research Council.

Growth Retardation Related to
Maternal Deprivation

• *FREDERIC M. BLODGETT, M.D.*

Yale University

Children suffering from maternal deprivation have frequently been shown to be small in physical size (Blodgett et al., 1956). The purpose of this report is to describe one such patient who has recovered from severe retardation of growth and discuss the possible pathogenesis of this growth suppression as a consequence of hyperactivity of the adrenal cortex—emotionally engendered.

Robert C., a five-year-old white boy, was brought to the Pediatric Clinic of the Grace-New Haven Hospital on September 9, 1957, by his aunt. She reported that he was being neglected by his parents and kept restrained in bed, except for meals. Little attention was given to his need for cleanliness and he was left to void and defecate in his bed. She stated that the father was nervous and an alcoholic and that the mother was becoming so emotionally deranged that she was unable to care for her children. The child's appearance confirmed many of the aunt's charges, and he was admitted to the hospital for study and treatment.

From a number of interviews and from Robert's clinic record, the following relevant, historical data are condensed.[1] He was born prematurely on August 31, 1952, weighing 4 pounds, 1 ounce (2040 grams). Persistent diarrhea had been the only medical complication of his mother's pregnancy. The delivery was normal and required no medication or anesthesia. The child had breathed within five seconds after birth. Because of his weight, he was kept in the premature unit for three weeks and then discharged as a healthy infant, weighing 5 pounds and 5 ounces (2550 gms.). At age twenty-one months, 7-30-54, he had been examined in the Emergency Room of the Hospital because he ate poorly and was difficult to feed. The details of his care since birth could not be adequately obtained, but the father recalled no major illnesses. The findings revealed delayed motor development and an iron deficiency anemia. In response to treatment with ferrous sulphate, his hemoglobin rose from 6.2 to 12.2 gms. in four weeks and he first began to sit alone during this time. Appointments given for further care were not kept.

When he was four years of age, his father brought him to the Clinic because he had not learned to walk. His father reported that he had not stood alone until three years of age, and could say only a few single words. Bladder and bowel training had not been accomplished. The child was stunted, measuring 36 inches (91.5 cms.) and was markedly underweight at 27½ pounds (12.75 kg.). He could take only a few steps with a broad-based gait before falling. His poor muscle tone, lack of coordination, and general retardation suggested the diagnostic impression of a variant of amyotonia congenita or hypotonic cerebral palsy. His hemoglobin was 11.2 gms. Further examination of his neurological and endocrine status were scheduled, but Clinic appointments were again broken; he received no further

[1] The work reported in this paper depended on the cooperative work of many people involved in Robert's problems. It demonstrated the contribution of social workers, nurses, and of the physicians in various areas of specialization, and how these could result in a plan for the child. This plan was realized through the cooperation of the community social work agencies with the Department of Pediatrics. In particular, the author would like to acknowledge the contributions of Kenneth McRae, M.D., Winnipeg Children's Hospital, Winnipeg, Manitoba, Canada; Mrs. Kathryn N. Grausz, Department of Social Service, Grace-New Haven Community Hospital; and Sally A. Provence, M.D., Associate Professor of Pediatrics, Yale University School of Medicine and Child Study Center.

medical care until he was brought to the Clinic by his aunt, one year later.

At the time of Robert's admission to the hospital it was learned that his three siblings, aged seven, five, and two years were well, and no concern was expressed about their development or behavior. There was no history of neuromuscular or growth defect in the family.

The marked extent of the social and emotional disturbance of the family gradually became clear as the social workers obtained further information from the father, mother, relatives, and community social agencies. Both parents had concluded their education after one year in high school. The father, age twenty-nine, was alcoholic, unable to hold employment consistently and frequently dependent on the City's welfare agency for prolonged periods. He had been hospitalized on one occasion in a state mental hospital and had left against the physician's advice. The mother was in the fifth month of her sixth pregnancy. She was described as a thin, worn-looking, young woman who was frightened, tense, and emotionally depressed. She had obtained no prenatal care, nor had she sought treatment for severe ulcerated varicosities of her legs. In several interviews with the social worker she described how the patient had been kept excessively isolated in bed at home. She had always considered him as "slow" and felt ashamed of him. The mother recalled that during his stay in the premature unit she had never visited him; that he was difficult to feed as an infant, and had become increasingly stubborn and unmanageable. She felt that the worries about family finances and food and the difficulties with her husband upset her so much that she lost control of herself and took out her feelings on the children, especially the patient. She was quick to blame herself for his trouble.

Physical examination showed Robert to be small and retarded in motor development. His weight was 27 pounds (12.5 kg.), height 36¼ inches (92 cm.), head circumference, 19 inches (48 cms.), BP 100/70, temp. 99.2 (37.1°C) per rectum. The boy had grown only ¼ inch and had lost ½ pound weight during the year (see Fig. 1). He remained thin and had a protuberant abdomen. He was still unable to walk more than a few steps before falling, using a plodding, broad-based gait. Speech was indistinct, though he was able to combine several words. His hair was matted and showed the nits of pediculosis capitis. Despite his wretched appearance he was responsive to the attention of others. Examination of the respiratory, cardiac, and genitourinary systems was normal. No pathology of the sensory organs, cranial nerves or central nervous system could be found.

Laboratory examinations revealed 6,850 white blood cells per cu. ml. The differential count was normal, but there was a mild degree of anisocytosis and hypochromia of the red blood cells. The hemoglobin was 10.2 gm./100 ml. Urinalyses showed a clear color, pH of 5.5, and specific gravity of 1.025. Acetone, albumin, cells and casts were not found, but a reducing substance was present transiently on the eleventh hospital day. Three subsequent analyses were normal. Stools did not reveal excessive fat on gross or microscopic examinations. The total protein of 7 gm./100 ml. was divided between 3.9 gm. albumin, and 3.1 gm. globulin. Blood calcium was 10.2 mg./100 ml., phosphorus 5.8 mg./100 ml. and the alkaline phosphorus was 11.4 B.U. Cultures of the nose and the throat yielded a normal flora. Serum tests for syphilis and intradermal tests for tuberculosis were negative. X rays of the wrist showed retardation of skeletal maturation, revealing a bone age of 2 years, 6 months when interpreted according to the standards of Greulich and Pyle (1950). X rays of the skull and chest revealed no intracranial, pulmonary, or cardiac pathology. No evidence of vitamin deficiency disease was seen, but definite demineralization of the bones was present. There were numerous lines of growth arrest present at the ends of the long bones.

Developmental examination revealed retardation in all aspects of development.[2] The motor system was the most severely impaired, its level of functioning being at the fourteen- to fifteen-month level. Speech and some types of problem solving were at the three-year level, while his imaginative play reflected knowledge and ca-

[2] The initial developmental examination as well as the follow-up assessment of Robert's psychological status were performed by Sally Provence, M.D., from whose records relevant material is summarized.

pacity for thought that were slightly above the three-year level. Those items that reflected his level of intellectual functioning were in the high-grade mentally defective range. His personality development was impoverished and deviant. Relationships with people were disturbed, being characterized by both an indiscriminate friendliness and a tendency to interact with the adult by fighting, especially in the feeding situation.

The impression from this examination was of a severe impairment of development due to inadequate nurturing.[3] This inadequacy took the form of (1) deprivation of the positive, stimulating, and protective aspects of maternal care; (2) a restriction of motor activity and an impoverishment of his environment caused by his confinement in bed in the back room; and (3) acts of aggression toward the child from his harassed and overburdened mother.

The history suggested that deprivation of both calories and emotional stimuli could have occurred; the developmental examination supported this view and the findings on physical and laboratory study revealed no other etiological factor to account for his growth retardation. The assumption was made that he could eat, absorb, and gain adequately, and the hospital care was adapted to provide the most favorable environment to test this postulation. In so far as possible, one nurse on each shift was assigned to him. She, with the cooperation of the dietician, selected his diet to suit his taste and to provide as large a quantity as he wished. The nurse also attended him as continuously as possible, permitting him the freedom to select his play, and providing him with the physical assistance and protection he needed as he moved about the ward. Laboratory and other studies which might require fasting or otherwise disturb his adjustment were kept to a minimum.

Robert adjusted to this regimen quickly. His dietary intake was unorthodox but abundant. He initially preferred desserts, crackers, and ice cream, but came to request bacon, sausages, and eggs for breakfast daily; meats and potato for lunch; and eggs with at least,

---

3 While Robert does not fall into the category of the "battered child" syndrome, it will be recognized that both maternal deprivation and the "battered child" syndrome have in common unfavorable and life-threatening parental care.

on one occasion, seven slices of toast for dinner. The nurse was interested in him and his eating, but did not force or fight with him. His caloric intake varied considerably, to some degree depending on who was feeding him, but it generally exceeded 120 cal/kg. In eleven days he gained 2½ pounds. During this period there was also a marked improvement in his mood, appearance, and activity. He became very friendly and outgoing, almost indiscriminately bestowing his affections on all. Gradually one nurse became especially attentive to him. He became very demanding and intolerant of her leaving him when she went off duty. His speech improved consistently, and he quickly became able to walk all around the ward, though his gait remained awkward and he occasionally fell. The degree of improvement associated with this change in his environment indicated the pertinence of the family disturbance to the child's illness. A program of foster home care was recommended in order to continue Robert's rehabilitation. With relief, the family accepted this plan.

In the ensuing four years the patient has made excellent progress. His linear growth accelerated at a rapid rate, averaging 6 inches per year for 25 months, by which time, at the age of seven years, he had reached the 50 percentile (Fig. 1). He maintained his growth along the 50 percentile to 50¾ in. (130 cm.) by the age of nine years. His weight increased equally rapidly, and at the age of nine years he weighed 70½ pounds (31 kg.), which was the 88th percentile. The rate of skeletal maturation as judged from bone age accelerated less rapidly and by nine years was interpreted as a bone age of 7½ years, approximately 18 months behind his chronological age.

He was seen for follow-up psychological evaluation by the same examiner on four subsequent occasions, the last time at the age of eight and a half years. There was dramatic improvement both in his intellectual functioning and in his personality development during the three-and-a-half year period. At the last examination he was functioning in the dull normal range of intelligence. There were some significant deficits in regard to his way of relating to others and impairment of thinking and learning that appear to be residual effects of the early traumatic experiences. These impairments are similar to those reported by Provence and Lipton (1962) in a group of children who had been institutionalized during the first two years of life. Since these findings are not the focus of this paper, they are mentioned only to add to the description of Robert.

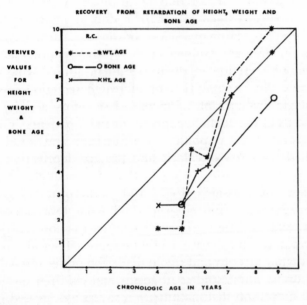

FIGURE 1

Chart showing recovery from retardation of growth in height, weight, and bone maturation. Height and weight ages are derived from the growth charts of H. C. Stuart.

DISCUSSION

The mechanism of the retardation of linear growth in some emotionally deprived children is not clearly established. Senn (1945) has reported that an aggressive attitude on the part of the mother might lead to a distaste for food and terminate in prolonged anorexia and malnutrition. Inadequate intake of calories and other nutriments is, of course, one factor. In addition to this, mechanisms through which growth suppression comes about have been considered from several points of view. One assumption has been that there is a growth hormone deficiency secondary to inadequate caloric intake. Talbot et al. (1947) ascribed growth retardation in some healthy dwarfs to a functional hypopituitarism, with depressed secretion of growth hormone, secondary to a prolonged inadequate caloric intake. Studies in laboratory animals by Mulinos and Pomerantz (1940) and Srebnik and Nelson (1962) indicate a reduction of pituitary growth hormone under circumstances of general malnutrition and diets specifically deficient in proteins. Human studies, however, have not confirmed the findings in animals. Golden et al. (1961) reported enhanced growth hormone secretion in thirteen human adults dying of neoplastic disease. The presumption of increased secretion was based on morphologic evidence of an increased secretory activity of the acidophilic cells of the adenohypophyses of these patients. This finding was interpreted as a response to malnutrition and could be correlated with the severity of caloric and protein deprivation during the last seven days of life. Using histopathologic differential cell counts, Tejada and Russfield (1957) studied the pituitary glands of nineteen Guatemalan children who died from kwashiorkor, prekwashiorkor, and marasmus. They concluded that no morphologic evidence for panhypopituitarism could be found. They also reported evidence of thymic atrophy and lipoid depletion of the adrenal cortex in these children. These studies in adults and children do not substantiate the suggestion that malnutrition causes a decreased production of pituitary growth hormone. They do suggest evidence of ACTH production and increased activity of the adrenal cortex. In view of these findings, other mechanisms interfering with growth need to be considered. Patton and Gardner (1962) have discussed the possibilities of disturbances in intestinal absorption and intermediary metabolism induced by emotional disorders, and mediated from the cortex of the brain through the hypothalamus, pituitary, and autonomic nervous system.

Our proposition is that in addition to other mechanisms, there are indications that the activity of the adrenal cortex may contribute to growth suppression. First suppression of growth is seen in the hyperadrenocorticism of Cushing's syndrome. Second, growth suppression is associated with prolonged treatment of children with cortisone (Blodgett et al., 1956). This second type resembles in several respects the growth problem seen in Robert. Suppression was temporary in each instance; growth resumed at a rapid rate when the situation presumed responsible was alleviated, i.e., when the patient in this report was put in a more favorable environment, and when cortisone was discontinued in the children on treatment. In both situations, there was demineralization of the bones, transient retardation of the rate of skeletal maturation, and it seems unlikely that inactivity alone could explain the osseous decalcification noted in this child. Thus skeletal demineralization may be another similarity between Robert and children treated with cortisone. A striking dissimilarity was presented by this undernourished child on comparing him to the plump or "cushingoid" child taking cortisone. However, it is known that not all children taking adrenal steroids eat enough to gain weight. Patients with anorexia nervosa appear to be one exception to the expected stimulation of appetite and larger caloric intake in most children treated with cortisone. The lack of obesity in this child does not necessarily exclude the possibility that his growth was suppressed by an excessive production of endogenous adrenal steroids. It is probable that he also was underfed and may have been anorexic as a result of the disturbed relationship with his mother.

That psychological factors are involved in linear growth has been demonstrated by Widdowson (1951). Her study of the growth of children in orphanages in postwar Germany demonstrates that superior gains in height and weight occurred in those children who were in charge of a house mother whose fondness for children created a favorable state of "mental contentment" in the children. Slower gains were made by children in other orphanages who, despite a large caloric intake, were psychologically upset due to the frequent harsh criticism of the house mother in charge. These observations suggest that an unfavorable psychological environment may operate independently of caloric intake to retard linear growth.

There are studies which demonstrate a relation between the psychologic state of the human and the activity of the adrenal cortex. Mason et al. (1961) have collected evidence from monkeys that shows an elevation of the 17-hydroxycorticosteroid plasma level during the conditioned emotional disturbances. Fox et al. (1961) have collected data from humans suggesting the hypothesis that the more a person reacts emotionally, the higher the urinary excretion rate of 17-hydroxycorticosteroids.

These observations could be combined with those previously cited to postulate that Robert's retardation of growth was related to a hyperactivity of his adrenal cortex induced by an emotional disturbance that stemmed from his relationship with his mother. This disturbed relationship was characterized by a deficiency in the mother's nurturing, protective care, and further compounded by her hostile feelings and punitive acts which she communicated in a direct and uncontrolled manner. The child's eating and apparently other aspects of his care contained too little gratification and were often associated with threatening painful experiences. The emotional disturbance thus resulted in malnutrition and in failure to establish strong and meaningful personal relationships. This would be an instance in which Spitz's (1951) term "psychotoxic" is useful as a description of the adverse influence in Robert's development in addition to the meagerness of positive nurturing experiences. It should be re-emphasized that Robert's mother had family and personal problems that overwhelmed her and rendered her unable to care adequately for this particular child.

SUMMARY

Recovery from growth retardation in a five-year-old boy suffering from a deprived and disturbed relationship to his mother has been presented. Evidence has been recorded and discussed suggesting that the suppression of linear growth may be the consequence of an emotionally engendered hyperadrenocorticism.

BIBLIOGRAPHY

Blodgett, F. M. Unpublished observations.
———— Burgin, L., Iezzoni, D., Grifetz, D., & Talbot, N. B. (1956), Effects of Prolonged Cortisone Therapy on the Statural Growth, Skeletal Maturation and Metabolic Status of Children. *New Eng. J. Med.*, 254:636.
Coleman, R. W. & Provence, S. (1957), Developmental Retardation (Hospitalism) in Infants Living in Families. *Pediatrics*, 19:285.
Fox, H. M., Narawski, B. J., Bartholomay, A. F. & Gifford, S. (1961), Adrenal Steroid Excretion Patterns in Eighteen Healthy Subjects: Tentative Correlations with Personality Structure. *Psychosom. Med.*, 23:33.

Golden, A., Bondy, P., Chambers, R. W., & Geiger, C. L. (1961), Adenohypophyseal Changes in Patients Dying of Neoplastic Disease. *Yale J. Biol. & Med.*, 33:299.

Greulich, W. W. & Pyle, S. I. (1950), *Radiographic Atlas of Skeletal Development of the Hand and Wrist*. Stanford, Calif.: Stanford Univ. Press.

Mason, J. W., Mangan, G., Jr., Brady, J. V., Conrad, D., & Rioch, D. McK. (1961), Concurrent Plasma Epinephrine, Norepinephrine and 17-Hydroxycorticosteroid Levels During Conditioned Emotional Disturbance in Monkeys. *Psychosom. Med.*, 23:344.

Mulinos, M. G. & Pomerantz, L. (1940), A Condition Resembling Pseudohypophysectomy Produced by Malnutrition. *J. Nutrition*, 19:493.

Patton, R. G. & Gardner, L. I. (1962), Influence of Family Environment on Growth: The Syndrome of "Maternal Deprivation." *Pediatrics*, 30:957.

Provence, S. & Lipton, R. (1962), *Infants in Institutions*. New York: International Universities Press.

Senn, M. J. E. (1945), Influence of Psychologic Factors on the Nutrition of Children. *Amer. J. Pub. Health*, 35:211.

Spitz, R. A. (1951), The Psychogenic Diseases in Infancy: An Attempt at Their Etiologic Classification. *The Psychoanalytic Study of the Child*, 6:255-275. New York: Int. Univ. Press.

Srebnik, H. H. & Nelson, M. M. (1962), Anterior Pituitary Function in Male Rats Deprived of Dietary Protein. *Endocrinology*, 70:723.

Talbot, N. B., Sobel, E. H., Burke, B. S., Lindeman, E., & Kaufman, S. B. (1947), Dwarfism in Healthy Children: Its Possible Relation to Emotional, Nutritional and Endocrine Disturbances. *New Eng. J. Med.*, 236:873.

Tejada, C. & Russfield, A. B. (1957), A Preliminary Report on the Pathology of the Pituitary Gland in Children with Malnutrition. *Arch Dis. Childh.*, 32:343.

Widdowson, E. (1951), Mental Contentment and Physical Growth. *Lancet*, 260:1316.

Part III

Theoretical and Clinical Considerations in Child Development

Milton Senn has identified himself as an eclectic in child development. However, he seems to have viewed himself in this way not to avoid commitments but in order to add to and integrate the perspectives and data of all sciences that concern themselves with early human development. It is characteristic of Senn that he has committed himself in a continuing way to a psychoanalytic view of children and their development in a family setting, reflecting his search for a clinical understanding of children in depth. Accordingly, the first three articles in this section represent psychoanalytic thinking in this area. The first of the three essays is Anna Freud's classical paper on regression, and the second is a report from the longitudinal study that Milton Senn initiated in collaboration with Ernst Kris at the Child Study Center. This paper concerns itself with an important principle of child development, i.e., the complicated and inevitable interrelationships between constitution and environment, as demonstrated in the report by Ritvo, McCollum, Omwake, Provence, and Solnit of one case from the longitudinal study. The third paper, that of Alan Fraser, illustrates the investigative importance of the psychoanalytic treatment of individual patients. In this report through psychoanalytic reconstructions the adult's psychopathology can be related to the characteristics of early love object relationships, thus adding to our knowledge of mental activity in early childhood.

The next four papers in this section deal with specific clinical problems in the developing child. John Doris provides a definitive survey of our knowledge of the evaluation of intellectual functioning, placing particular emphasis on the brain-damaged child. He discusses the crucial question of the limits of our knowledge in this area, especially in the use of standard intelligence tests. In the next paper Robert Kugel presents data from a study of familial mental retardation that questions the basis for such a diagnosis and pointedly suggests that neurophysiological and psychosocial correlates are essential considerations for research in mental retardation. The next two papers by Solnit and Green and by Lewis and Solnit represent collaborative studies in a pediatric setting by pediatricians and child psychiatrists. The first paper illuminates the child's reactions to the fear of dying and the second discusses the care of certain suicidal adolescents on a pediatric ward. At the end of this section Dane Prugh provides an extensive survey of the literature with the aim of considering the multiple factors that are involved in producing illness, especially psychosomatic disorders, in childhood. This can be compared to Lawrence K. Frank's introductory essay on human development, which attempts to gather together under the organizing influence of communication theory all that is known about child development biologically, psychologically, and socially. Prugh's and Frank's points of view are similar in regard to the processes of feedback and the modes of mutual interaction of cells, organs, systems, and persons in a particular ecological setting. However, Prugh's main focus stems more clearly from the physiological traditions of Walter B. Cannon, whereas Frank's perspectives intrinsically reflect his and Milton Senn's conviction that discussions of child development not be limited by any one approach.

The Role of Regression in Mental Development

• *ANNA FREUD, LL.D.*

Hampstead Child-Therapy Clinic

Psychoanalysis as a clinical and theoretical field offers its own workers possibilities which range from developmental to normal and abnormal psychology. But psychoanalysts have always had the reputation of straying in their work beyond their own confines and, with the aim of "applying" their theories, to make contact with other disciplines. Psychiatry, education, the social sciences, mythology, religion, literature, art, etc., are among the earlier realms of application. General medicine (under the term of psychosomatics) and pediatrics are among the later ones. On every one of these occasions, the gradual approach between the two fields depended on a few pioneering figures, rooted on either one side or the other. In pediatrics the name of Dr. Milton Senn will remain connected with the groundwork for such linkage with analysis.

The clinical data for this paper have been collected in the Hampstead Child-Therapy Clinic which is maintained by grants from the following Foundations: The Field Foundation, Inc., New York; The Ford Foundation, New York; The Foundations' Fund for Research in Psychiatry, New Haven, Connecticut; The Grant Foundation, Inc., New York; The Psychoanalytic Research and Development Fund, Inc., New York; The Taconic Foundation, New York.

It has been felt for a long time that the pediatrician and the child analyst share much common ground. Both have as the object of their observation the immature individual who is in a fluid state of incomplete development, characterized by rapid changes, where the interaction between inborn and environmental influences is more open to view than it will be in maturity. Both, therefore, have to reckon not only with the child himself but with his management. For both, the experiences gained from the sick lead automatically to application to the healthy and to methods of prevention.[1] In therapy, both suffer from the uncooperativeness of their patients, since young children seldom, if ever, seek help actively or are ready to describe their symptoms. Where symptomatology is concerned, in both instances, the similarity between child and adult is frequently a superficial one, the same pathological manifestation carrying different weight and outlook in the growing individual. Both pediatrician and psychoanalyst are in a situation where the maturational forces work simultaneously with their own therapeutic efforts, and where in the final result of recovery it is not easy to distinguish how far the patient has responded to treatment and how far his ills have been "outgrown." Above all, it can be said with justification that both, the pediatrician as well as the child analyst, assist the curative factors which are normally active in the young organism. Therapy is directed toward freeing the organism from "obstacles to his growth so that he can move with reasonable security through succeeding developmental stages."[2]

While these identities in themselves might have led to an earlier, and profitable, link-up between the two professions, there are other and theoretically more essential differences which were effective in keeping them apart. The pediatrician who has been trained in the conditions governing organic growth does not take readily to the different principles which are governing the mental side. Brought up in chemistry, biochemistry, biology, anatomy, physiology, genetics, etc., he has acquired a high valuation of laboratory methods and

[1] As in the Well-Baby Clinics.

[2] See for this and some earlier formulations, Report No. 38, The Diagnostic Process in Child Psychiatry, of the Group for the Advancement of Psychiatry, Aug., 1957.

experiments which are not valid in the other realm. Trained as an exact scientist, he feels a natural bias against a field in which—to his mind—assumptions, conclusions, hypotheses, and subjective interpretations reign supreme. In the long run, it was only the "illogical" behavior of the child patients themselves which impressed the pediatricians: their conversion symptoms such as headaches, pains, constipation, digestive upsets without visible organic cause; asthma and eczema with their fluctuations in intensity and their unknown origin; the sleeping and feeding troubles of the young; anorexia of the adolescent; enuresis and incontinence where they are purely functional, etc. In spite of his readiness to diagnose and treat, exactly and scientifically, these psychosomatic (as they are called now) troubles of the child left the pediatrician helpless, and gradually more prepared than before to contemplate an approach which, itself inexact and to all appearances erratic, proves capable of following the child patients into their psychological intricacies.

It is the object of the present paper to describe in detail the process of *regression,* this being one of the specific principles which are operative only on the mental side and, as such, are strange to the physician. To acknowledge and learn to diagnose the results of the regressive process may contribute toward familiarizing the pediatrician with mental manifestations in the child, both normal and abnormal, which otherwise remain inexplicable.

The physician is familiar with the processes of growth on the organic side. Bones, once formed and developed, do not reassume their former infantile appearance; physiological or neurological processes, once risen to a certain level, maintain it; glandular action matures, sheds infantile forms, and substitutes others. The more mature levels of development replace the earlier ones. In short, growth proceeds in a straight progressive line until maturity is reached, invalidated only by intervening severe illness or injuries, and at the end, by the destructive, involutionary processes of old age.

The pediatrician may assume automatically that the same is true of the child's mental and emotional equipment, i.e., that here, too, a developmental line is selected by the individual and pursued to its conclusion. But expectations of this kind are not borne out by facts, and therapeutic actions based on them will miscarry. That does not imply that orderly maturation fails to play its part in drive development, or in the gradual perfection of the rational part of the child's personality, the ego. It means to say merely that progression is not the only force in operation and that equal attention needs to be paid to the regressive moves which are its inevitable accompaniment and counterpart.

REGRESSION IN DRIVE AND LIBIDO DEVELOPMENT

Where sex development is concerned, for example, we observe in children the now well-known sequence of libidinal stages, each named after the body zone which for its duration plays the leading part in providing autoerotic, i.e., sexual, stimulation: oral, anal, phallic stage. On each libidinal level of development we find, also maturationally coordinated with it, the corresponding manifestations of the aggressive drive: biting during orality; sadism, destructiveness during anality; competitive masterfulness in the phallic stage. This line corresponds further with a distinct sequence of emotional attitudes toward mother, father, siblings, etc.: dependence, helplessness, demandingness, greed in the oral stage give way to clinging and possessiveness in the anal child; these again to the jealousies, rivalries, demonstrativeness on the phallic level, the latter being the bodily equivalent of the emotional experiences which belong to the oedipus and castration complex. So far, these are lines of progress, comparable in their forward direction to any similar developmental line on the organic side.

Now for the other aspect of the picture. We conceive of this development in the sense that the consecutive positions (and the persons which serve as satisfying objects at each stage) are invested with drive energy, and that this energy (libido, aggression) moves forward from one position to the next. But in spite of forward movement taking place, no station on the way is ever fully outgrown, as it is on the organic side. While one part of the drive energy is on its forward course, another part—of varying quantity—remains behind. For example, the thumb-sucking infant will not give up his interest in sucking automatically when the bulk of his drive energies centers already around anality; some of the former pleasure in oral erotism will remain intact and will survive. Similarly, some of the anal interests will survive the child's transition to the phallic stage. In short, no drive position once held, however obsolete it may appear, will really be abandoned.

It is not essential here whether the survivals of the former stages remain in consciousness or are relegated to the repressed unconscious. In either state they are capable of binding and retaining drive energy. Whenever difficulties, disappointments, frustrations occur, then, at a later date, these stations of the past, or "fixation points" as they are called, come into their own again by exerting a retrograde attraction on later energies. Libido will flow back to them, to the impoverishment of the later levels. This creates the puzzling pictures where older children, or adolescents, or adults, lose interest in the libidinal or aggressive outlets which are appropriate to their ages and hark back to childish wishes and concerns.

Such regression may be temporary, the drives—after a pathological interval—may pursue their forward course again. More often it is permanent, meaning lasting complications, repercussions, and damage to the individual's sexual normality or the age-adequate, constructive employment of his aggressive powers.

Surely, there is nothing on the organic side of human development which prepares the physician for the appreciation of the importance of such fixation points and nothing which matches the regressive pull exerted on the organism through this formation.[3]

REGRESSION IN EGO DEVELOPMENT

Regression appears different where it occurs on the side of the child's ego, although the same principles are active in the process: return to earlier mental structures and, with it, return to more primitive modes of functioning, representation, and expression.

[3] It may be useful for the pediatrician to know that, apart from the usual hazards which a child meets in his development, any deliberate interference with the legitimate quantity of gratification at any stage can set up fixation points. Examples are deprivation as well as overindulgence in the management of the child by the mother in general, or on the medical side: dieting as deprivation in the oral phase; enemas, suppositories as overstimulation in the anal phase, etc.

Temporary Regressions in Normal Development

There is, first, regression as a normal, never-failing accompaniment to all newly acquired achievements of the child which is well known to all mothers, nurses, or teachers of the young. It is taken for granted by them as a characteristic of childish behavior and, as such, rarely mentioned. In their mental growth, children do not take a straight-forward path but, as it is popularly expressed, take "two steps forward and one back." This refers to all their functioning, from control of motility, speech, bladder and bowel control, manners, to such ethical virtues as impulse control, ability to wait, social adaptation, honesty, fairness, etc. The capacity to function on a high level of achievement is in itself no guarantee that the performance will be stable; on the contrary, it is more normal for the child, and a better guarantee for later mental health if, during the state of growth, he reverts occasionally to more infantile modes of behavior before these are abandoned: from being toilet trained to messing, from sensible speech to nonsense talk, from play with toys to body play, from constructiveness to destructiveness, and from social adaptation to pure egoism. What mothers describe as surprising in diagnostic interviews are not these relapses but, on the contrary, those other instances where their children have taken a single step forward which, for once, was not reversed. This may have been a sudden transition from the breast to the bottle, or bottle to cup; in toilet training one single incident, after which there were "no more soiled nappies"; an incident at bedtime after which there was "no more calling out"; in habits a sudden weaning from the dummy, or the thumb, or from sleeping with a favorite toy, etc. These happenings are recognized as exceptions, and we know that they are in general not to be welcomed. To use the method of trial and error, progression, and temporary reversal is more appropriate to healthy mental growth.

Temporary Ego Regression Under Stress

It is another fact, well known to educators, that ego achievements are not maintained at their height when children are under the influence of fatigue, anxiety, pain, or any other strain. Every mother knows that the tired child at bedtime behaves like a much younger child; although well adapted in daytime, he may begin to fret, to whine, to babble nonsense, to be unreasonable, clinging, and demand the physical attentions of the toddler stage. Every nursery school teacher knows that her pupils at the end of the morning will be less concentrated than in the beginning, that construction toys will be thrown about, that tempers are shorter, manners lapse, and partnership with playmates ends more easily in quarrels. Mothers and nurses are aware that pain, fever, bodily discomfort, and fear of medical examination bring out the infant in the child. Not all child patients who are unruly in the pediatrician's waiting room, or who kick and scream under examination are really backward in upbringing or behavior. The examining pediatrician, although able to record an accurate account of the child's organic growth, will rarely be in a position to see his patients at their mental best. As regards their food and sleeping habits, their cleanliness, their occupations and behavior, ill children are in the majority regressed children, with many of their age-adequate functions in abeyance.

Regression has been studied also in young children who are separated from their parents, in wartime institutions or in hospitals. There the state of distress, caused in them by the experience, reveals itself in various forms of which the loss of functions such as speech, toilet training, etc., is an important one. That in such regressions they return step by step along the line taken before in forward development, is borne out by the fact that it is invariably the latest achievements which are lost first.

Such regressive lapses receive little attention if they are temporary. The healthy child at home or in nursery school next morning will be once more in full possession of his faculties. The ill child will resume his former status when recovered. The hospitalized children or those separated for other reasons may take longer to overcome infantilisms in behavior, especially their clinging and demanding, if separation has been of longer duration and has been traumatic.

But, taken as a whole, regression under stress is a normal mechanism and is based on the immature individual's flexibility. It is useful as an answer to the strain of the moment and an attempt to adapt to it; it is always available to the child as a response to frustration which otherwise might be too difficult to bear. As such a response, it is short-lived and reversible.

Perhaps a device comparable to it on the physical side is the ability of some children to lower all their reactions during illness and "sleep through it."

EGO REGRESSION RELATED TO DRIVE REGRESSIONS

Regressions in the ego lose their beneficial aspect and turn into a threat to development and mental health as soon as they become permanent, i.e., irreversible. In the immature individuals, this happens predominantly following on a regression in their drives.

When, as described above, drive energy flows backward after frustrations in the phallic phase to fixation points in anality or orality, the ego, i.e., the side of the child which represents adaptation, morals, and intelligence, has to choose between alternative reactions. He may acquiesce in the occurrence, accept once more the infantile, primitive desires and fantasies as they return from the unconscious, and, with it, lower all his demands on himself and his standards of performance. The result will be what both child analyst and pediatrician regard as an "infantilism." Children of this kind seem younger than their years and, although no "obvious" reason can be found for it, they lag behind their contemporaries in behavior, habits, play, school performance, or general adaptation to environment. They may soil or wet with indifference; or attack and hurt other children without experiencing compassion or regret; they may destroy inanimate objects; be egotistic and irresponsible; or appropriate what does not belong to them, etc.; worst of all, educational influence usually proves helpless with regard to them. Their regressed drives have come to terms with their regressed ego, and in the absence of conflict between the two there is no sufficient incentive for them to behave otherwise. They are incapacitated by a mental state which has to be understood as the result of "total regression" (or rather partial id plus partial ego regression). Not to be "age adequate" characterizes the essential nature of their disturbance.

The alternative reaction of a child whose drives have regressed is the following: his ego remains firm and refuses to give in to the demand for primitive satisfactions, however great the pressure toward them may be. He keeps up his former reasonable functioning, the height of his achievements, and the moral and ethical demands made on his behavior by his conscience (superego). But this attitude, although more ambitious and in the developmental sense more appropriate than the former one, leads as inevitably to pathology, though of a different kind. The child becomes a prey to severe anxieties and to internal conflicts in which his ego and superego engage in battle with the drives. The result is an infantile neurosis built on the pattern of adult neuroses, with symptom formation set up as a compromise between the conflicting inner agencies.[4]

From the foregoing it is obvious that it is the more highly developed child with the better organized personality who tends to produce not infantilisms but neurotic symptoms. To appreciate this last fact may serve to make pediatricians more tolerant and more understanding toward the neurotic psychopathology of their child patients with which, not without reason, they feel often out of sympathy.

SUMMARY

Mutual interests of pediatricians and child analysts are described and obstacles to mutual understanding are indicated. *Regression,* a mental process, is described with the aim of extending the applica-

---

[4] It may be confusing to the pediatrician that also with these neurotic cases apparently simple psychosomatic manifestations exist side by side with the complex psychological symptoms; also that some of this symptomatology hardly differs from the infantilisms mentioned above (for example, enuresis, incontinence). The child analyst's answer to this is that the difference lies not in the outward appearance of the pathological manifestations but in their inner structures. The infantilisms are returns to form of behavior which have been age adequate for an earlier stage of development; the neurotic symptoms are rooted in two sides of the personality and constitute an attempt to combine opposing tendencies: they express in one and the same action the primitive drive with its urge for satisfaction and the ego's fight against this satisfaction taking place.

tion of psychoanalytic concepts to pediatrics. Regression in drive and libido development, and in ego development are discussed in order to illuminate the psychic states of health and illness in child development. Although temporary regressions are characteristic of healthy development, permanent regressions are associated with deviant development.

Some Relations of Constitution, Environment, and Personality as Observed in a Longitudinal Study of Child Development: Case Report

- *SAMUEL RITVO, M.D.*
- *AUDREY T. McCOLLUM, M.S.*
- *EVELINE OMWAKE, M.A.*
- *SALLY A. PROVENCE, M.D.*
- *ALBERT J. SOLNIT, M.D.*

Yale University

In 1949 Ernst Kris and Milton J. E. Senn organized a longitudinal study at the Child Study Center of Yale University in which psychoanalytic hypotheses and methods were combined with pediatric and child development concepts in an effort to observe and study personality development. Kris and Senn had independently noted the pressing need for such a study in order to make available a method of investigation that could eventually lead to a refinement of old hypotheses and to the emergence of new and more useful formulations in psychoanalysis, child development, and pediatric care.

In the words of Ernst Kris (1953): "The purpose of the study derives from the fact that both clinicians and theoreticians expect longitudinal investigations in personality development to supply essential data for the understanding of personality and for the early diagnosis, and hopefully prevention, of personality disturbances."

This research was supported by a grant from The Commonwealth Fund, New York.

Psychoanalysis as a body of knowledge organized around certain hypotheses has increasingly become a general psychology concerned with normal as well as abnormal behavior. Having contributed an essential method for the retrospective study of human behavior, psychoanalysis in the last decade has suggested that direct observational studies could lead to a re-examination and refinement of psychoanalytic theories of the emerging and functioning personality. Accordingly, this study was intended to suggest new hypotheses, refine old ones, and formulate psychoanalytic hypotheses in child development in such a way as to make them testable. It was not intended or considered feasible to use a longitudinal study to verify psychoanalytic theory. At the same time certain workers in pediatrics and child development recognized that psychoanalysis as a theory and method offered the most promising explanation of personality development. Although American centers of child development had been interested for many years in the use of present assessments and measurements for the prediction of future developments in the child, their focus had been primarily on physical characteristics and on certain aspects of psychological development that could be quantified, e.g., psychometric examinations.

DESCRIPTION OF THE STUDY AND METHODOLOGY

In the Yale Longitudinal Study of Child Development the retrospective and prospective outlooks were combined when educators, pediatricians, psychoanalysts, psychologists, and social workers worked together as expert observers of child life in various settings and as specialists in their own field. In this way they were able to make direct observational data available as a basis for predictions which could be reviewed later.

In this report contributions to the methodology of longitudinal studies are not discussed, nor is a critique of method intended. This presentation will describe the operational method of the study and demonstrate certain aspects of it, focusing in particular on one of the children studied.

The study began when women in their first normal pregnancy

were interviewed in the obstetrical clinic of the university and community hospital. The criteria for selection were that the child be the first born, that the mothers give no evidence of manifest major psychiatric illness, and that the family might be expected to remain in the community for at least five years. The families were asked for their cooperation in return for complete pediatric care and for attendance in the Child Study Center Nursery School at the appropriate time.

An important feature of the study was the provision of pediatric, educational, and psychological services for the children. Kris and Senn had concluded independently that the act of rendering service was an essential variable of such research. They expected this would make possible continuity of observation and access to relevant data which otherwise might be missed or be difficult to assess. As Kris (1953) pointed out, action research requires people who have been trained to treat or prevent illness, and to offer help, support, or guidance. It is part of their training and daily experience, including their personal and professional contact with psychoanalysis, to be aware of the influence that their service and intervention exercises on the field of observation. The observational data will be distorted and incomplete whenever this is not taken into account. The investigator acts within the field of his observation and is part of the process which he studies. In such instances, certain precautionary measures are taken to protect the validity of the data. Among these are the independent recording of data by nonparticipant observers, participation in frequent, regular, formal, and impromptu conferences, and the inclusion of subjective reactions in the written reports.

In the first year of the study, when eighteen families were involved, the mother was interviewed regularly during prenatal visits by a social worker who had a continuing contact as the home visitor after the birth of the child. The pediatrician, who was introduced to the family toward the end of the pregnancy, served as the child's physician and as an observer of the child and family in well- and sick-baby care. The pediatrician also administered periodic developmental tests. On the basis of these observations the pediatrician made assessments of the child's maturation and development. The nonparticipant observers attempted to assess maturation and development of the child by observing in the delivery room, newborn nursery, and well-baby clinics.

Nonparticipant observers, that is, observers not engaged directly in the service functions to the child and family included psychologists specially trained in infant observations, pediatricians, psychoanalysts, and social workers. The well-baby clinics provided opportunities to observe infant and maternal behavior through a one-way vision screen and to observe and record interaction of mother and child with one another and with the pediatrician.

In addition to the action-research aspect of the investigation, there was another guiding principle, namely, that the investigation adapt itself to the growth of the child. This principle insured the acquisition of data that would be relevant to the formulation and description of a dynamic life history of each child. In addition, this flexibility in providing services and in observing and collecting data permitted the development of methods and procedures that might be useful to other investigators in longitudinal studies of children and families. Thus, when the children were in their third year, they entered nursery school. Observations were made there by psychoanalysts and nursery school teachers, while the children were involved in an appropriate educational experience. In providing an appropriate educational experience for a child, the nursery school teacher assesses the ways in which a child learns. The recognition of problems of learning and the ways in which they are overcome yield essential data about the child's adaptive capacities. Just as the pediatrician assesses the child while in the process of providing pediatric care, the educator assesses while teaching.

When the children were one year of age the study population was decreased out of the conviction that more intensive observations on a few families would be more productive and useful than less data per family from a larger number of families. Twelve families were studied in the second year of life, ten in the third year, six in the fourth, and when the children reached the age of five, there were five families being studied in which there were ten children. Thus, ten of the study children were observed in the first year of nursery school. During one session each week in the first year at nursery school each child had a special adult assigned to him. This was the psychoanalyst who observed and interacted with the child as a "play-mate," an observer, and at times as an assistant teacher.

In addition to the observations in the nursery school, the children, ages three to five, were seen by the analyst in the therapy room. Originally it had been assumed that this would be a modification of the usual therapeutic situation for purposes of observation and exploration. In some instances, the need of the child resulted in this becoming therapy as well. In three of the children, including the one who will be reported in this paper, the therapy became child analysis. Pediatric and social work contacts continued. From the age of three and a half years, psychometric and projective tests were administered periodically by a clinical psychologist, just as the pediatrician had administered the infant tests.

The retrospective outlook of clinical psychoanalysis suggested which experiences should be closely observed for the gathering of data relevant for understanding the child's development. For example, data about the feeding experiences of the child were collected and organized predictively. This made it possible to understand better the influence of such crucial experiences on later development. Equally important was the idea that the data about early feeding experiences would be understood better when they could be viewed retrospectively in the treatment, as well as being viewed in relation to what had been anticipated or predicted earlier. In other words, the relative importance of a current experience for the child may become clear only in the future, when prospective and retrospective data can be combined. Similarly, as seen in the family to be presented, the point at which certain data emerge is relevant, i.e., why the mother's disturbance and the history of family disturbance became evident at a particular time in the study. The child's life history was regularly approached in terms of the interaction between a child with particular equipmental characteristics and his environment, especially the parents. In this context, the normal developmental crises such as weaning, separation, and sphincter control were valued as observable situations in the life history in which modes of adaptation and defense and characteristics of regression could be more clearly understood. By developmental crises we mean normal regular occurrences that are crucial for later development. They are points of progression and regression. Such crises were viewed as expected concomitants of development that might be a stimulus or a barrier to development. Ernst Kris (1953) said, "A crisis in the child's life may constitute an important phase of his ego development in which certain aptitudes and abilities become available to the personality at the same time as certain susceptibilities are heightened."

In this longitudinal investigation it was envisaged that the combination of prospective and retrospective viewpoints could provide the data for an understanding of the interaction of genetic and dynamic factors in the development of the child. This combination would permit the systematic study of life histories necessary for understanding in what way certain personality characteristics arise and how they persist, i.e., how the sameness of personality manifests itself despite developmental changes. The nature of the data and the interdisciplinary composition of the group of observers enabled us to approach these problems, as Kris (1953) stated, "by demonstrating the interaction between the child's growth, his changing instinctual needs, the differentiation of various ego functions, and the vicissitudes of his object relations."

In the following report on Jerry R. we will bring longitudinal data that suggest the basis on which fruitful hypotheses emerge from such a study. The hypothesis that this presentation will help to define is that the predisposition to motor activity, where reinforced by sexualized stimulation from the environment, will interfere with the capacity to postpone and to sublimate, and will promote impulsivity to an abnormal degree. Other useful hypotheses will also be implied.

As the presentation consists of relevant excerpts from the observations made by social worker, pediatrician, nursery school teacher, and psychoanalyst, the form of the presentation itself will illustrate the methodology of the study described above while at the same time demonstrating the service-centered aspects of this action research.

Case Report

Family Background

The role of the home visitor and interviewer in the study was by its nature more mother-focused than the pediatric, nursery school, and psychoanalytic contacts. The mothers were made aware, from the initial contacts during pregnancy, of the interviewer's interest in her individuality, her earlier intrafamilial relationships, and her ongoing experiences as wife and mother. In periods of maternal stress or crisis, the interviewer made available her clinical skills as psychiatric social worker; it is noteworthy that the family data were in a number of cases greatly enriched by the unfolding of material during such periods. The interviewer's parallel function, after the child's birth, was that of observer of intrafamilial interaction, particularly of mother and child. This function was carried out both in the home and, on a nonparticipant basis, during the well-baby clinics. In the case of Jerry, a psychologist had functioned as interviewer-observer through the first year of Jerry's life, at which time the social worker assumed the dual role.

Jerry's parents were both from lower-class families of Mediterranean descent. The maternal grandmother had had a long sociopathic history, with several periods of protective institutionalization in adolescence. The maternal grandfather was a withdrawn, seclusive man who had repeated episodes of frank psychotic illness, the most recent diagnosed as involutional depression with paranoid tendencies. Mrs. R.'s childhood was marked by the violent marital conflict of her own parents, punctuated by threats of separation and accusations as well as evidence of mutual infidelity. The grandfather made several suicide attempts. During the entire time of the study, Jerry and his family lived in a tiny apartment separated by a thin partition from the apartment of the turbulent grandparents.

At the time of Jerry's birth, Mrs. R. was in her early twenties. She was a woman of low-average intelligence who had had a grade-school education. She was a physically active woman, whose actions were quick and restless. She was emotionally labile and volatile, a woman of shifting and tempestuous moods who frequently gave evidence of a poor capacity for impulse control. With the social worker, she readily discussed personal problems, including bodily preoccupations and both marital and premarital sexual experiences. At times she approached these topics with a candor which seemed exhibitionistic. Her bodily concerns focused on frightening sensations in the chest and pelvis, which she feared were signs of cancer. She also paid much attention to bowel functions, giving herself enemas readily to relieve a variety of discomforts, including headache. She was a neat and clean housekeeper who devoted much energy and interest to her home. She made a bright, cheerful, clean and much-adorned home out of a small apartment in a decrepit building.

Mr. R., ten years older than his wife, was a man of low-average intelligence with little schooling. He was the only son in a large family, and was reared by his father and sisters after the early death of his mother. His childhood was characterized by predelinquent behavior which he hoped to prevent in his own children. After a roaming, adventurous adolescence he returned home to his father and worked with him for several years until the father's death when Mr. R. was twenty. This death had a devastating effect on Mr. R. who went from a regular working life to a pattern of psychopathic behavior and indolence, finally interrupted by enlistment in the military service, where he continued his psychopathic behavior. A chronic recurrent infection was discovered on routine X-ray at the time of discharge from the service. After hospitalization for a year he resumed his dissolute life and had to return to the hospital because of a recrudescence of his illness. He was warned that he had to "slow down" if he wanted to live, and this he gave as one of his motivations for marriage. The infection continued to spread so that Mr. R. had to be hospitalized for another year after the marriage, and it was only then that he told his wife of his illness. He was treated for the infection and followed closely during his recovery until Jerry was two years of age.

The attendant financial insecurity and Mr. R.'s sexual demands and jealousy were principal sources of conflict in the marriage. Jerry was drawn into the repeated family crises both as an observer and on occasions as a participant. Mr. R.'s way of dealing with his own illness was inconsistent and contradictory. On the one hand he was docile in observing a regime which included rest and attention to nutrition; on the other hand he gambled with danger by keeping irregular hours and undertaking physically arduous jobs. This alternation between quietude and extreme activity, between docility and the courting of danger, became a marked behavior pattern repeatedly observed in Jerry in nursery school and in treatment.

Mrs. R.'s pregnancy with Jerry appeared uneventful, although she later revealed that she had been recurrently preoccupied with the idea that the fetus was dead, and that her father had suffered from an acute episode of psychiatric illness during her pregnancy. As labor began, Mrs. R. betrayed her need both for activity and for excitement by attempting to "walk off" the pains, wishing to postpone entering the hospital as long as possible. During the last hours of labor and the delivery, Mrs. R. was considered by the staff to have successfully utilized the techniques of what was then known as the "natural childbirth" program.

Mrs. R. attempted to nurse Jerry during the newborn period, but was distraught by her feeling that he was not satisfied. Her observed feeling of frustration, combined with disgust at the messiness of the dripping breasts, reduced her to exhaustion and tears. The situation was relieved when bottle was substituted for breast; the maternal responses around feeding were considered prompt, appropriate to Jerry's needs, and tender. Jerry's nutrition was not a concern again until the second year.

Mrs. R. was much preoccupied, however, with Jerry's bowel functioning. Discomfort and distress on the part of the infant were readily interpreted as being caused by constipation or gas; whenever Jerry was ill, the mother's first concern was with his bowels. Starting in the first months of life, the mother massaged the anus with suppositories, and manipulated a thermometer in the rectum in order to aid Jerry to defecate and expel gas. The extent and the method by which this was done was learned only three years later, when the mother was observed doing the same with the younger brother. Bowel training was started early and was easily achieved. In this the mother was firm, at times even severe, and consistent, and regularly showed her pleasure at Jerry's compliance with her training.

As Jerry's skill and range in motor activity increased, his mother responded to his getting into things as a provocation of her which she met with retaliation and punishment. His first words were "bad boy," and a wooden cooking spoon became the symbol for an imminent spanking. With the parents and the grandparents he experienced an excited, stimulating, rough-house type of physical handling. The mother was more consistently gentle, soothing, and comforting during Jerry's illnesses.

After the first year Mrs. R. complained increasingly of feeding as a problem. Both parents were anxious and concerned that poor nutrition would precipitate in Jerry the same chronic infectious illness from which the father had recovered. The father insisted that the boy eat three complete, balanced meals a day. By the fourth year the quarrel over eating was very intense. Jerry's refusal to eat a proper breakfast at one point precipitated such a sharp quarrel between the parents that the father left home for several days.

At fifteen months, Jerry appeared at home as a thin, wiry child who was almost constantly in motion; he was touching, manipulating, and getting into everything that he could reach. By not putting things out of his sight or reach, the mother seemed to invite Jerry to touch or break all the prohibited objects in the house. She usually made no attempt to remove him from the neighborhood of a forbidden object. Frequently, by warning him before his intent to handle or damage something was clear, she seemed to draw his attention to a prohibited object in which he himself appeared to have no spontaneous interest.

Furthermore, the mother was inconsistent in her prohibitions. She might punish Jerry for handling an object once and then ignore his repetition of the same previously forbidden action. On some occasions, the mother responded immediately with punishment; at other times, the punitive outburst was delayed while her tension built up. Furious outbursts by the mother were immediately followed by reconciliations in which she quietly and affectionately cuddled him. When Mrs. R. was not angry or furious with Jerry she displayed genuine warmth and affection toward him. These vicissitudes frequently took place with great rapidity. Similarly, alternation between violent activity and quiescence later became a feature of Jerry's behavior in nursery school and in his treatment.

It was striking that the mother was never observed to interact with Jerry in play. Although the objects forbidden to Jerry were in view in the home, his own toys were generally kept out of immediate view in a toy chest; they were offered to him when he was placed in his playpen out of doors, and then he was virtually engulfed by toys. Mrs. R. was never observed to make a toy attractive to Jerry by investing it with her own energy and interest; on the contrary, there were repeated observations of interference, both when Jerry engaged in play with the interviewer and when he attempted to engage in independent play with an object.

A brother was born when Jerry was three. With the birth of the baby the mother turned away from Jerry and he became the "bad" child while the baby was the "good" one. Mrs. R. spoke of how much more she was enjoying the baby than she had Jerry. According to her, the baby was cuddly and contented, whereas Jerry had been wiry and wiggly. Mrs. R. seemed to enjoy the second child's greater placidity. However, she was observed actively stimulating the baby's body, as though she had to make this placid infant into a wiggly baby like Jerry.

Jerry also was handled from the beginning by his father in an exciting, stimulating, seductive way. A scene was observed in the home when Jerry was three in which the father had worked Jerry into a high pitch of excitement by teasing, tickling, poking, slapping, and kissing Jerry and asking the child to make love to him. Thus, both parents were observed using the child to a marked and unusual degree as an object to arouse and stimulate their own impulses and upon whom they could discharge both their sexual and aggressive impulses to an abnormal and unusual extent.

THE USE OF INFANT TESTING IN THE LONGITUDINAL STUDY OF
JERRY'S DEVELOPMENT

This section of the report illustrates the use of infant testing in a
longitudinal study of personality development. In our study, standardized developmental tests have been utilized in infancy and throughout the preschool years. In this report we limit ourselves to a general
discussion of infant testing in the first year of life and to a presentation
of the first year test findings. The principles involved are not different at the older ages. We shall then discuss the significance of these
findings for an assessment of some of Jerry's endowment characteristics and some aspects of his development in the first year.

The infant tests employed in this study were the Hetzer-Wolf
baby test from the Viennese scale and the Gesell developmental
examination. The testing was done by the pediatrician at the time
of the regular visits to the well-baby clinic, and the testing session
preceded the pediatric examination and interview. The mother was
with the infant, and although the child was subjected to the usual
stress of the examination, the general aim was to make the conditions
of the testing as comfortable and pleasant as possible for the infant
and his mother.

The first step in the interpretation of the results was to establish
a general maturity level or developmental age, indicating the infant's
developmental level in weeks or months. The developmental quotient, namely, the ratio of the developmental age to the chronological
age, was then computed.

The child's developmental profile in any one test can be expressed graphically by plotting the developmental quotient in each
of the sectors into which the test items are grouped. In the Gesell
test these sectors are gross motor, fine motor, adaptive, language, and
personal-social. In the Hetzer-Wolf test they are designated as perception, body, social, learning, material, and intelligence. In examining normal infants, one may find a wide variety of developmental
profiles at any one age. One infant may show his most advanced
behavior in the motor sector, while another is highest in adaptive,
language, or social development as measured on these tests. Some

infants remain true to themselves for many months, with one sector consistently most advanced, while in other infants first one and then another sector leads.

The significance of a particular profile for understanding the individuality of an infant has been one of our interests from the beginning. This significance can be discerned by the analysis of the patterns of success and failure in the individual sectors (Provence and Lipton, 1962). This method would correspond in some respects to the "scatter analysis" utilized by Escalona and Leitch (1952). The hypothesis on which it is based has been stated in their report as follows:

> Marked discrepancies between maturity of behavior in different areas of development (as assessed by developmental tests) reflect developmental deviations and are associated with disturbances of the child's adaptation to the social, biological and physical environment. Irregular levels of maturity displayed within a single test may also reflect a disequilibrium in the child's adaptation to the demands of everyday existence.

We have found the tests useful in supplying several types of information about the developing infant. The infant tests can be used as a functional neurological examination. Certain constellations of findings on the test may be either suggestive or diagnostic of specific central nervous system disorders. These disorders may be of a structural, physiological, or functional nature.

Some items on the test yield information about the relationship between the maturation of the apparatus in a neurophysiological sense and the capacity of the infant to make use of the available functions. Ernst Kris recognized that this permits one to make some distinctions in the first year of life between the developing ego and the apparatus used by the ego. In the infant who is developing well, one may not be aware that these are two distinct components of development, but when discrepancies occur the tests provide important information.

Various authors have commented on disturbance in development as an indicator of the nature of the mother-infant relationship. Some workers (Spitz, 1945; Escalona and Leitch, 1952; Spitz and Wolf, 1946; Roudinesco and Appell, 1950) have used infant tests in their studies. In our experience the tests have been helpful in reflecting mother-child interaction. Repeatedly in this study a characteristic of development, as measured on the test, was the first clue to a disturbed mother-infant relationship. This leads to the formulation that the infant is best understood at a particular time if one pays careful attention to (1) his equipment for development; (2) his environment; and (3) the interaction between the two.

The focus of the longitudinal study developed our interest in viewing the test findings in the framework of psychoanalytic theory. In the early years of the study Dr. Katherine M. Wolf stimulated us with her interest in relating the findings on the Hetzer-Wolf baby test to psychoanalytic concepts. It soon became apparent that other tests and other types of infant observations also yield data that could be evaluated in terms of their relevance to psychoanalytic propositions.

Test material from the study of Jerry will be presented from the tests at eighteen weeks, forty-one weeks, and fifty-two weeks to illustrate the points that have been made. The major focus will be on one sector of development, the motor area, although other sectors will require comment. We shall refer to the intervening tests in order to provide as much continuity as possible.

Jerry was tested on seven occasions during the first year of life. All his developmental quotients on the fourteen separate tests were above 100, and all except one were between 107 and 147, indicating that he was not below average at any time. As a newborn infant he was characterized as strongly active and vigorous. He was rated at 4 plus active, that is, within the range of normal activity at the top of the scale. The tempo of his movements was rapid. Somewhat more than many neonates, Jerry reacted with massive discharge movements and some tremulous movements in response to external stimuli and in situations of discomfort such as hunger. The terms active, hypertonic, and jittery were also applied to him. He was not in constant motion, however, and he had no abnormal movements. In periods of quiescence he was well relaxed. Muscle tone was high but not pathological; tendon reflexes were brisk. No abnormal reflex behavior was present then or at any later time.

At his first two tests which are not reported in detail, he showed excellent development. He was highest in motor, language, and social development, but he also demonstrated well-organized and fully age-adequate responses in all other sectors of development. On his third test at eighteen weeks he had a developmental quotient of 116 on the Viennese scale and 122 on the Gesell scale. Motor, social, and language were his highest sectors of behavior. He was reaching out to touch his mother's face or hair and to grasp toys, which he manipulated with his free hand and mouthed or gazed at with apparent interest. Body control in prone, supine, and sitting positions was advanced for his age, and he could change position voluntarily. He was able to avoid an unpleasant stimulus by actively turning away. He demonstrated normative maturational patterns as well as good use of the emerging skills with evidence of pleasure in using them. He clearly discriminated between his mother and strangers but was not actively fearful of the stranger. He initiated a social contact by smiling spontaneously and showed displeasure when social contact was broken by the adult. Language development was high and was particularly impressive in the person-linked areas of language behavior. He had an alert interest in the inanimate object, and he showed displeasure at the loss of a toy, an advanced response. At this age such an interest in materials is believed to be linked to the human object relation and would be presumed to reflect a reasonably satisfactory mother-infant relationship (Provence and Ritvo, 1961). Also, the observation was made that both parents indulged in considerable tactile stimulation, body manipulation, and rough-house play, which often produced an excited gleeful state in him. In our observations the mother was at times gentle and tender, and at other times exciting and intense in her handling.

On the next examination at twenty-seven weeks he was successful on all items at the key age level and had minimal scatter in the various sectors. At this time he performed in a well-organized, well-integrated way in all sectors measured by the two tests.

At forty-one weeks (nine months and eight days) his developmental quotients remained average on both tests. However, for the first time he had failures on some test items at his age level. Motor development was advanced, and he seemed preoccupied with motor activity. He was pulling to stand, creeping, cruising, and walking with two hands held, all in a well-coordinated manner. He was able to use his motor equipment to change positions and to go to his mother or to any other desired object. Also he was able actively to get rid of something he did not want or to flee from it. Language development was age adequate, and social development remained excellent. He played pat-a-cake and waved bye-bye, initiated social contact, and clearly understood social gestures. Some aspects of his adaptive behavior and his reaction to the inanimate object were of some concern to the examiner. He definitely tended to hold or manipulate only one object at a time. He did not do well on test items requiring that he combine objects or handle multiple stimuli. We assumed that such adaptive items on the test shed light on the infant's integrative functioning, and for the first time we had questions about this aspect of Jerry's functioning. He had much less interest in the test materials than he had shown earlier. He accepted them and exploited them briefly but without the interest and energy shown before.

We noted the lack of good balance between his high motor and social behavior on one hand and his disturbed adaptive performance and reduced interest in inanimate objects on the other. We thought this might be a temporary finding related to his preoccupation with the mastery of a new skill, walking, and we expected that the balance might be restored when mastery of walking was achieved. However, between ten and twelve months, Jerry showed increasing signs of developmental difficulty. A great deal of unchanneled motor discharge activity became evident. He was described as extremely active in contrast to descriptions of the preceding few months, when he was considered active but not excessively so. His overactivity was combined with a lack of interest in the inanimate object and an easy distractability. During this period it was observed that Jerry used motor activity as the preferred route of tension discharge, and his well-developed motor skills were involved increasingly in the conflicts with his mother. Since Jerry's mobility and increased skill in throwing often evoked an excited response from his mother, such behavior also became available to him as a method of provocation and retaliation. Paradoxically in his mother's arms he was often observed to be quiet and relaxed. Mrs. R.'s report of his behavior at home paralleled the observations during the tests of this period. She said that since the age of ten months he had been throwing toys, trying to push over furniture, and hitting and pulling at her. The usual sequence was the mother's prohibition of an action, followed by Jerry's butting at her or pulling her hair. Then she would hit him and he would hit back. For the first time she expressed concern that he might become a bad, uncontrollable boy. In his contact with his mother and the examiner, Jerry was often charming and engaging. He approached the adult and initiated contact by smiling or with a word. He enjoyed active play such as a game of rolling the ball. He talked well and had both vocabulary and language comprehension at the one-year level. His mother was proud of his language, and it seemed to be an important area of contact between them.

His lack of interest in the test materials and toys and his failure to use them adaptively became more marked. There was minimal drive to obtain an object or to solve a problem when an obstacle was introduced. With frustration he would begin to bang or to throw. He cast objects in a provocative way, looking especially at his mother as though to observe the effect. Jerry's deficit in combining objects persisted and suggested a persisting disturbance in integrative functioning. A disturbance in learning was postulated at this time on the basis of disturbed object relations. Moreover, the rapid regression in his behavior which came at times with fatigue, but more often under the impact of the mother's stimulation, suggested an increasing conflict with the mother that was causing the disturbance in his functioning.

The fifty-two-week examination revealed a developmental quotient of 111 and 114 on the two tests. Jerry functioned better than he had for several months during the testing session, demonstrating more interest in and attention to the materials and giving a better organized and better integrated performance. He walked well without support. He manipulated objects without difficulty and had no problems of eye-hand coordination. He remained an active child, moving quickly with vigor and with good coordination. Although motor skills were used as a preferred mode of discharging tension, they also served as a source of gratification in the mastery of aim-directed activities that were not in conflict.

It is relevant that on this fifty-two-week test great care was taken to help Jerry get through the test. He was examined at the beginning of the session when there was no evidence of fatigue or irritability. The pace of the examination was rapid enough to keep him interested. Tasks or materials which were thought to be potentially exciting, disorganizing, or evocative of negative behavior were deferred until the end of the test. With maximum adaptation by the examiner, he functioned pretty well; and though he threw objects a great deal, he did not become disorganized.

This relatively good performance stands in sharp contrast to his behavior later in the session when the influence of his mother's scolding and punitiveness became evident: (1) he became less well coordinated in motor activity and threw himself about in a heedless manner; (2) there was a deterioration of the ability to explore objects and to use them for problem solving—he could only throw or mouth them; (3) he demonstrated a decrease in perceptiveness of his environment, especially dramatic in regard to the perception of potential dangers; (4) there were several retaliatory aggressive outbursts against his mother; and (5) when she became very annoyed and harsh he responded with complete quiescence and a forlorn, frightened look.

Summary

Throughout the first year Jerry could be characterized as an active child. It was only in the newborn period and after forty-six weeks that he was called markedly or extremely active. At all times the tempo of movements was relatively fast and movements were vigorously executed. During this year he increasingly used his motor equipment as an avenue of discharge for both loving and hostile feelings toward the mother. This use of his motor equipment often appeared to increase his state of disorganization. He appeared to derive pleasure from the motor activity itself as well as from using it to move toward or away from people and other objects in his environment.

There were contrasting states of motor activity and quiescence. Although he was often active and vigorous, he also had periods of quiescence and relaxation—sometimes when left alone, at other times when held close in the arms of the parents. There were many times when he did not use his motor skills in a defensive way, e.g., at the end of the first year he was afraid of the pediatrician's stethoscope and needle, but he never actively resisted being examined or tried to move away.

Although his vocabulary was adequate, the use of language seemed linked to the relationship to the mother in a way that was not entirely favorable. It tended to be more of a game than a tool for real communication; e.g., he repeatedly mimicked words she asked him to say so long as he was successful and could get approval from her. His apparent difficulty in inhibiting the immediate discharge of impulses, seen most dramatically in his motor activity, extended to other areas of functioning as well and may be linked to the problem of thinking and learning observed when he was older.

The degree of disorganization under stress after nine months of age was another indication of his ego disturbance. Moreover, his mother's handling, by precipitating and facilitating massive discharge in the child, resulted in a decreased ability to tolerate tension. From nine months on, his failure to use toys and test materials in an adaptive way was striking. A lost toy did not seem important enough to look for, and any obstacle made him turn away to some other objects or activity. The deficit in his use of the inanimate object foreshadowed the later disturbance in sublimation. This assumption is based upon the hypothesis that the way in which the normally developing infant reacts to test materials and makes use of toys in the latter half of the first year reflects, in part, the availability of neutralized energy for functioning.

This includes the developing capacity for sublimation. From

what we knew about the relationship between Jerry and his mother we postulated that the intensity and mode of discharge of her aggressive and libidinal drives in her contact with Jerry operated against Jerry's developing those modes of behavior which would facilitate the establishment of sublimated activities.

The relative part played by equipment factors and maternal handling in producing the disturbance in ego functioning in Jerry cannot be settled. His excellent development during the first eight to nine months suggests that his equipment was adequate. However, there can be genetically or constitutionally determined disturbances in development which appear only after months or years. It is clear that the way in which Jerry's mother interacted with him contained many elements believed to have a disorganizing and impeding influence on the child's development.

NURSERY SCHOOL

In keeping with the original plan of the project to adapt the investigation to the growth of the child, the nursery school was the next step in providing the setting for the study of the children and their families. To this end, the nursery school offered the benefits of nursery school education which supplements and extends certain functions of the home. In this way it was an important feature of the service-centered approach of the project. The educational setting of the nursery school presented a unique opportunity for making important observations on various aspects of the personality development of the children. One can observe how the children develop relationships with persons other than their parents; one can see how they manifest individual ways of tolerating tension and controlling discharge; one can observe a child's characteristic rate and mode of regression in the face of tension or conflict; one can observe how the child functions in an atmosphere which is stable yet tolerant and offers opportunity for the mastery of skills. Through his play and relationships in the nursery school, the child may manifest disturbances which are reactive to specific situations in the home. In this regard the relevance of the nursery school observations was particularly enhanced because they could be viewed in the framework provided by the observations of the other investigators.

Jerry entered nursery school at twenty months upon the recommendation of his pediatrician, who thought the early entry in nursery school before the other study children started was warranted and indicated, because his poor investment in toys and his inability to play with them, which was first observed at nine months, had persisted. The pediatrician also thought Jerry's general development might benefit by his being in a supportive but neutral educational atmosphere because the fighting and overstimulation with the mother seemed to be an important factor in perpetuating Jerry's inability to play with toys, an inability which had important implications for those capacities of his ego related to learning, integration, and sublimation.

It was evident that Jerry would need a teacher of his own to help him with his learning problems—a nursery school teacher who could be guided by our increasing knowledge of his equipment and development, including the difficulties in store for him as a result of growing up in his environment. One of us (E.O.) became Jerry's teacher at this time. This section will describe Jerry as he appeared in the nursery school, attempt to assess his gains, and discuss the teaching measures which were effective in helping him with his learning problems.

Within the first session of his nursery school experience Jerry displayed most of the characteristics by which he later became identified by all who observed him. He was hyperactive, impulsive, poorly controlled, reckless, negative, and aggressive toward other children. He was provocative and impish but generous with tender glances and gestures. He was often described as elfin by observers before they knew him well. This impression was supported by his thin face, ready grin, bright brown eyes, and straight dark hair trimmed by the barber and plastered down by his mother to subdue a cowlick. But to anyone who knew him well, Jerry's seriousness, self-concern, and wariness dissipated the initial impression of an elfin or clownish character. To those who were accustomed to the appropriate dependence of the toddler, Jerry, before he was two, was dramatically on his own. The total effect was of a disturbed but lovable child with a great deal of charm. Ernst Kris once said of him that "his id kept shining through."

A description of Jerry's initial school performance in certain sectors of development may suggest the range of problems for him and his teacher at that time. These also serve to forecast the gamut of future difficulties. His *gross motor* performance presented a confusing picture. He was wiry, agile, and constantly in motion. But he stumbled when running, bumped into furniture, flung himself instead of jumping, and charged wildly instead of running smoothly as his seeming agility suggested that he could. He showed no judgment, caution, or control. The danger for him and others in this respect was clearly apparent. An observation made by the pediatrician when he was fourteen months that he "extended himself beyond his ability" applied with striking accuracy. A unique pattern of activity and quiescence observed in other situations was demonstrated in a variety of ways in the nursery school where, for instance, in the midst of flinging dolls and covers from the doll bed, he would fall upon it and lie briefly but quietly in a babylike pose. In general his physical activity seemed to give him pleasure, and the teaching problem was more in regulating and limiting the use of his gross motor equipment rather than promoting such forms of play.

Where *fine motor skill* and *eye-hand coordination* were involved, the clumsiness which the pediatrician had begun to observe at eighteen months and the low investment in objects also noted by her earlier combined to present a major nursery school problem for him. His only interest in play materials was to snatch, throw, or brush them out of the way. It made no difference whether they lay on the table or whether another child was using them—for Jerry, toys were for throwing. He had none of the two-year-old's sense of the possibilities of a toy for manipulation or adaptation to dramatic play interests. He was so poorly organized both in play and behavior that it was difficult to say when ideas were at work or to study the nature of them. He did not ask the usual "what" and "why" questions of the young child. He did not listen to words, and he rarely stopped to watch anyone else do something.

His *language* seemed impressive when he started school. He parroted many phrases as if he understood them, and he knew the tag lines of various nursery rhymes his mother had taught him. However, he did not use speech for communication except to ask where his mother or his teacher were. He knew and used appropriately certain "emotional" words and phrases upon occasion, such as "love you" or "bad boy."

Jerry's *social behavior* revealed discrimination in his contacts with children and also with adults, even though most of his contacts with children turned out badly. He could be comradely, affectionate, and responsive, but he kicked, pushed, pinched, and bit indiscriminately. He was affectionate and responsive with his familiar teacher but maintained a friendly reserve with others. He checked on her whereabouts when she was out of sight but except for questioning showed no sign of anxiety. His mother remained with him in the beginning, but after she left he was easily reassured when reminded of her return.

Unlike other children, Jerry failed to display anger in the situations which ordinarily provoke protest. When removed bodily from a fracas, he adapted to the teacher who picked him up and remained quietly in her arms or on her lap. He sometimes continued to kick and thrash if this was what had been interrupted, but he did not fight to get away. He never had a temper tantrum and he rarely cried. Several years later he sulked when disappointed or whined if in a bad mood, but rage and outbursts of emotion were never part of his pattern. This was the way Jerry appeared between twenty and twenty-five months—disruptive, disturbed, but engaging.

As he continued in school he remained hyperactive, impulsive, and indicated disturbance in a variety of ways, but in the areas of organization and control he was capable of periods of improvement. This was true in the over-all picture, but he had intermittent periods of deterioration and disorganization when all signs of gain would be lost in typical wild, disruptive activity. When he returned to school for his second year he joined the group of nine study children with the same teacher. Although his effect on this group was less electrifying than on the initial group, he was still somewhat like lightning playing around the edges, about to strike any moment at any place. Even with this slight slowing down, the vigilance of his teacher was essential to any successful performance. Although there was improvement in the second year, Jerry continued to have difficulties. He made friends with children, began to show an interest in manipulative materials and quieter play, and his physical activity was less driven and reckless. Dramatic play of an active nature became a source of pleasure and an avenue for expression of ideas as well as for discharge of energy and tension.

However, during the following school year, which began when he was three years and five months old, he was so disruptive that the school would have referred him in any case for psychiatric evaluation because it would have been impossible to keep him in the group without help for him and consultation for the staff. Fortunately it was part of the longitudinal study plan to start the contact with the psychoanalyst during the fall of the year that the children would be three years and six months old. By this time Jerry was showing a moodiness and general ill-humor. Evidence was accumulating in the nursery school that he was having trouble over his younger brother. The degree of organization and control which he had displayed the year before were lost in diffuse, wild, disturbing behavior. His indiscriminate hitting had changed into swift, sure punches and slaps which even the most sturdy of his agemates could not cope with, however aggravated. Any altercation between two children invited his participation. He took over their battle and fought to the finish. It was becoming clear to us that fear played an important part in his unrest and that he was attacking head on any object or situation which frightened him. He always had to be prevented from throwing or biting the pet mice, hamsters, rabbits, etc., in the nursery school. He had once bitten the rabbit as if to keep it from biting him. His joining any conflict situation between two other people now suggested that it was his fear of such situations that threw him into them. After his therapy was under way his fighting diminished in frequency, but he was otherwise disorganized and difficult to handle much of the year. He continued to be the most accomplished fighter in the nursery school and never met his match there. Throughout this third year in school the content of Jerry's play was meager and his investment in materials low. He could rarely settle down to listen to stories or music and could not join any group situation that required quiescence or control. His major pleasure was in outdoor play where he was given free use of the equipment with help in observing safety measures.

In Jerry's final year when he was four years, five months to five years, two months old he functioned surprisingly well considering the bleak picture of the preceding year. However, there were obvious gaps to a solidly good performance. Although he developed skill in many areas it was clear that he had a learning problem. Despite his successes in individual situations, there was no stability, no productivity, nor any recognizable learning pattern that one could count on for prediction of later school achievement. The integration of mastered skills that one looks for in a child with several years of a good educational experience and maturation of equipment seemed to be absent. He lacked the capacity to manipulate symbols or to use symbolic representation; he had a low interest and productivity in the elaboration of self-initiated play and dramatic activity. However, he was working hard. He had become involved with puzzles, games, etc., and his frustration and impatience when he was unsuccessful did not distract him in his effort, although he leaned heavily on help and encouragement. He was proud of his control and his ability to complete a task but found little enjoyment in the process of learning a skill. This may have reflected his own awareness of his difficulty in learning. He was independent and responsible in physical habits and care of his possessions, an area in which his mother had trained him consistently and well. He was inclined to belligerence when in a bad mood but was by then established as a referee who issued the orders about when and how to fight. The fights he did engage in were still carried through without show of feeling—no tears, no breakdown, no need for a recovery period. His dramatic play, which in the early months in school could only be described as "gymnastics with sound effects" and which was merely suggestive of his fantasy, now came to include some identifiable fantasy around reality themes such as housekeeping play, repairmen, cowboys, bandits, etc. But even at five his impulsivity and hyperactivity were the predominant features rather than ideas, continuity, planning, or purpose. The other children, who considered Jerry a colorful addition to play, contributed the plan and purpose and counted on Jerry for exciting action and sound.

In the language area, Jerry's performance was irregular. He had a good vocabulary and could express himself effectively, but a disturbance was noted in his tendency to accompany play with a running commentary composed of a chain of loose word associations. This was in some way compatible with the bizarre note in all his independent dramatic play. It is only possible to describe this by giving an example:

Jerry was seated at a table composedly fitting together the pieces of his favorite puzzle, a horse picture. Hearing the bell of a toy fire engine being used by a playmate, Jerry flew from the table to a corner where some high boots were kept. Jerry wore these frequently and called them "fireman's boots." In his mad dash he stopped midway to go through the motions of sliding down the firehouse pole. He landed in a sitting position and pulled on the boots, tossing his own shoes into the air. The boots on, he jumped up shouting "Puss in Boots! Heigh ho me darry—o! On to the fire!" Instead of joining the fire play which had seemed to inspire this, he picked up a pole and rope which was within his range of vision and sat down on a box to go fishing. "Catch him!" he said as he juggled the rope. "Catch the bandit!"

Jerry had a fair fund of information about people, places, animals, machines, and what they all do, and held his own fairly well in conversation about the experiences and events which interest children. However, in his play he was more likely to identify with the machines he watched than the people who operated them. He became very serious about "learning" around his fifth birthday when his mother was beginning to tell him that in school you had to work hard and learn. At home she was trying to teach him to recognize letters and words and to spell, but his conversation about this in school indicated his confusion. However, her teaching had the effect of promoting his interest and effort in any nursery school activities or games which involved identifying objects, colors, etc., or matching items. His performance at such times indicated considerable development in perception and memory if not in reasoning, problem solving, or concept formation. He had, with months of "tutoring" with puzzles, caught the idea of looking for a clue, but he always had difficulty finding it. Although he learned to solve some complicated puzzles, a new puzzle, albeit simpler than one he had mastered, was again very difficult for him.

All this may suggest that Jerry was an extraordinarily difficult child to teach. It was clear that in order for him to have an educational experience it was necessary to furnish and supply a controlling structure because among other things, this was lacking in the rest of his life. However, offering a controlling structure to a child who recognized no limits, had no investment in materials, could not tolerate tension, and regularly put himself into physically dangerous situations required the continuous close presence of a teacher who could assume the role of regulator in his life. This meant starting him off to desirable forms of play, stopping him from the undesirable, and making adjustments in the environment to enable him to master problems. Translated into literal terms, it was necessary to restrain him physically from attacking and directly to manipulate his body into safe and acceptable positions, e.g., holding his hands around the swing ropes because otherwise he would let go in mid-air; bending his body to show him how to jump instead of fly through the air with no regard for distance; folding his hand around the handle of the mallet to hammer a peg through the standard nursery school hammer board. In water play at a sink, the single quiet activity in which he always had a high investment, it was possible to keep him from throwing water-filled containers only by guiding his hand to pour and empty instead of flinging them. It did not seem possible to teach him by telling him what to do or even demonstrating. It was only possible to help him begin a task by starting it for him. Once started it was possible to keep him at it if the teacher stayed with him, stringing her beads while he laboriously worked at his, hammering pegs while he did, etc. He showed no resentment if other children were incorporated in the activity and seemed to enjoy the social aspects of shared play. However, until he finished school, there were few times when he engaged in sustained quiet play if his teacher were not present.

It was clear in the beginning that it would be more to his advantage if the teacher tried to teach him how to jump and climb safely rather than prohibit this because of possible danger for him. However, where limiting was indicated the teacher, by physically restraining him, did help him to observe rules about where he could climb, throw, and jump. Active physical play involving parts of the body other than his hands and fingers came easily to him. Through the years that he was in nursery school his teacher had held his hand to push the string through the bead, place the peg in the hole, throw rather than heave a ball, hammer nails, saw through a piece of wood, complete a puzzle, build with blocks, make a sand pie, and paint a picture. In this way he built up a repertoire of nursery school activities acceptable to him and the demands of the situation and which seemed to foster inner control and organization. In conclusion, the process of teaching Jerry involved much more of what Ernst Kris characterized as "lending ego to the child" than is required for most children in a nursery school setting. Through the relationship and through participation in his activities some increase in ego strength seemed to have been achieved.

In summary, Jerry made some decided gains in nursery school, but there were areas in which the improvement was limited. These included his general learning problem, the previously described language disturbance, and his anxiety about himself. Regression under impact of stress was a very prominent feature of his behavior at five as it was at two. Those gains he did make were in the area of control and organization, concept formation, communication, and social behavior. An observer had said of Jerry shortly before he was two that she found him very charming but that she would hate to have to live with him. At five years he had not lost his charm, but he was easier to live with.

PSYCHOANALYTIC TREATMENT

In the section on infant testing we have discussed Jerry's characteristically high level of motor discharge rooted in the equipment of the child. We also have shown how the interaction of equipment with environment resulted in disturbances of integrative capacities and of the ability to tolerate tension and inhibit discharge, capacities so crucial for sublimation and learning. The high level of motor activity which was characteristic of the child at birth and in early infancy became an important mode of adaptation to the environment as seen in his preference for discharge of tension by motor activity.

The report from the nursery school described the appearance of these same elements later in the nursery school setting and substantiated the earlier prediction of difficulties of learning and sublimation. That section also described the manifestations of conflict and anxiety in the nursery school and Jerry's way of coping with them by attacking what he feared.

Throughout the period of the treatment he continued to react to the threat of separation, damage, and loss of love with a return to hyperactive, attacking, aggressive behavior. These threats arose principally from the repeated crises at home in which the parents threatened to separate, in connection with his own intercurrent mild illnesses, and in relation to the birth of his younger brother. On one occasion the father did leave the house for a few days following a fight between the parents which started over Jerry's refusal to eat the complete breakfast his father felt was necessary to ward off the danger of a disabling infection such as he had suffered.

In the psychoanalytic investigation and treatment of Jerry we find again the same pattern of interaction of equipment and environment. However, more specific information is added about the psychic content of the conflict, its relation to current developmental crises, and the nature and structure of the defensive and adaptive mechanisms the child employs. The longitudinal nature of the study then makes it possible to use this information together with the data from infant testing and from nursery school observations to formulate more sharply the hypotheses stated in the first part of this paper.

The analysis, which lasted for two years, started at the age of three and a half when it was evident to the investigators on the team that the child needed the combined efforts of nursery teacher and child analyst to help him with his impulse disorder. The mother, too, found Jerry difficult to cope with and was willing to cooperate with the treatment.

Outwardly, Jerry showed no qualm about leaving nursery school to come upstairs with the analyst to the treatment. The hyperactivity was again immediately in evidence. He burst into treatment like a tornado. He went quickly from one activity to another, throwing and breaking toys, spilling paints and water, and shouting in a loud, piercing voice. The tendency to be engaged immediately with the adult in an excited, sexualized, exhibitionistic exchange was demonstrated in the first hour. He urinated before the analyst in the toilet and took his pants off and sat on the toilet for a bowel movement. The wild, uncontrollable, destructive behavior was carried out in a provocative way, looking to see what the analyst's response would be but with no manifest fear of him. As in the nursery school, he attacked what he feared with bursts of motor activity. The anxiety could be inferred in his need to bolt suddenly from the room and run downstairs to the nursery school, both to get back to the safety of the teacher and to see which rival in the school was taking his place with her.

The most sustained play in the early part of the treatment was with cooking and feeding. He first fed a doll with the toy nursing bottle, then drank from it himself. This play repeatedly ended with his either smashing the bottle against the wall or throwing both the doll and the bottle out the window. Here again he preferred the discharge in action to fantasy play. The brother was at that time six months old and was for the mother more and more the "good" child, whereas Jerry was the "bad" child. The casting behavior which had been prominent in Jerry since the latter part of the first year now seemed to take on the specific meaning of getting rid of the brother. The partial and shifting identifications with the mother in feeding the baby and with the baby in being fed by the mother could also be seen in this play.

The rapid alternation between intense motor activity and quiescence, which had been observed in Jerry with his mother during the infant testing in the first year and which had also been characteristic of him in the nursery school, appeared quite prominently in the treatment as well. In the treatment the alternation was linked to a variety of ideational contents close to the current conflicts in Jerry's life.

When he bolted from the room at the peak of excited, destructive activity he raced down the hall, hurling himself on the floor and sliding to rest on his back. He then lay perfectly still with his legs in the air and often with his eyes closed, presenting the buttocks and genital region to the analyst. Jerry had been seen assuming this posture in the home while the baby was being diapered. Gradually it was possible to obtain some of the fantasy content associated with this behavior which became more frequent in the treatment hours. Jerry said there had been an explosion which had entered his back and killed him. In this way Jerry expressed his dangerous and exciting wish to be attacked by the analyst, an attack modeled after the mother's insertion of suppositories and thermometer, which she was repeating at that time with the younger brother. Another likely model for the position assumed by Jerry was the mother's position in intercourse in the bed alongside Jerry's crib. This bedroom scene was played out more directly on many occasions later in the treatment. The alternation between activity and quiescence with the fantasy content described above suggested strongly that at this time it represented Jerry's identification with the sexual role of both parents.

A short time later when the father was going back to work, Jerry began to undertake difficult physical "jobs" such as trucking blocks and furniture in imitation of his father. Repeatedly in the middle of a "job" he lay down to rest on the couch in the analyst's office, which he preferred to the treatment room across the hall for enacting family scenes, particularly bedroom scenes. The rests were necessary because hard work made him "sweat like hell" and if he did not rest he would "get sick in the chest and die." With this he issued a further warning that the analyst should stay away from him lest he catch a cold from Jerry. When he rested he wanted the analyst to lie down on the couch with him as his father did at home.

This literal and direct repetition in action of scenes and sequences from his home without much distortion or disguise with elaborated fantasy was characteristic for Jerry. The paucity of elab-

orated fantasy can be regarded as the result of the strong environmental influence in the direction of discharge by motor activity.
Later in the treatment when Jerry's anxiety was lessened and his
motor activity could be limited, there was an increase of fantasy
material in the treatment. In this fantasy the alternation between
activity and quiet was seen again in another context. Jerry enacted
frank bedroom scenes in which he and the analyst were sleeping
together and various animals came and made ferocious attacks on
one or the other of them. The attack, whether made by him or the
analyst, resulted not in a painful reaction but in a gleeful noisy
burst of activity with acrobatic jumping.

Jerry's increasing anxiety in connection with his wish and fear
to be attacked by the analyst led to the development of a phobic
symptom in the treatment. Jerry was afraid that there was a monster
in the room adjacent to the treatment room. The monster would
yell at him, scratch him, and bite him. Jerry's response to the monster was varied. At times he stated frankly he was afraid and wanted
to leave the room and go back to the nursery school, refusing to
come back to the treatment room without a companion or some
tool or piece of equipment from the teacher. At other times, however, when the monster was asleep he shouted loudly or blew on a
whistle to wake up the monster, and then he would run away shouting, "Hurry up! He's coming after us." On one occasion he picked
up a gun and went yelling into the hall to capture the monster.
In the corridor he lay down perfectly still, and when the analyst
asked what had happened he said the monster had shot him in the
abdomen. Until that time Jerry's fear of cap pistols and the noise
they made had prevented him from handling the gun any more than
to pick it up gingerly for a moment and put it down again. With
the appearance of the monster and the need to overcome the exter-
nalized danger the gun and holster became a standard part of the
preparation for the treatment hours.

. The characteristics of the monster were overdetermined. It had
some of Jerry's features and some features of the violent and dangerous parents. Also, the location of the monster in the next room on
the other side of the closet wall corresponded to the physical arrange-

ment at home with the psychotic grandfather on the other side of the bathroom wall. The grandfather had been discharged recently from the hospital where he had been recovering from an acute psychotic episode, and the mother was at the time very concerned that the grandfather might make another suicidal attempt.

With the appearance of the monster Jerry's attitude toward the analyst changed. He was more directly friendly, less attacking and destructive, and allowed the normal physical contacts without becoming very excited. Tying the monster (in the form of a doll), the bad cowboys, and the analyst seemed to make him more comfortable in the treatment hour. The fear of the monster was not only a displacement of Jerry's fears of the analyst but was also a projection of his own aggression which was dangerous because he feared it would bring an attack from the analyst as it did from the mother. To the interpretation that he liked to be noisy and act big and strong because then he did not have to be afraid of the monster, he acquiesced and shouted several times that he was superman. On returning to the nursery school that day he made "monsterlike" attacks on several children, trying to choke one and throwing a toy at another. For a brief period while the phobic reaction was pronounced there was some lessening of the hyperactivity, and it was possible to limit his activity and engage him in fantasy play to a somewhat greater degree.

In the treatment situation motor activity was again the predominant mode of discharge for Jerry. The observation of the child in the treatment, with the access it provided to the fantasies and ideational content, enabled us to see the changing meaning of the same behavior. In the first year, under the impact of the intense stimulation of the mother's handling, this initially very active child used his motor equipment increasingly in the service of massive discharge of both loving and hostile feelings toward the mother. However, he could be relaxed and quiet when he was held and cuddled by the mother. Later, in the fourth and fifth years, when the internal crisis of organization in the child is so largely concerned with conflicts typical of the phallic phase—intrusiveness versus being penetrated, body intactness versus being damaged, exhibiting with pride versus being exposed to shame or humiliation—Jerry was still in the family environment. This environment was characterized by an intense stimulation of a kind which bears directly on the normal conflicts of the phallic phase. These conflicts were intensified by the direct exposure to the sexual activity and fighting of the parents, the birth of a brother, and the family's anxiety over dangerous illness. In this setting the psychoanalytic observation permits us to see that the alternation between activity and quiet is repeatedly an alternation between active and passive aims toward the love object, between masculine and feminine, and between identification with the sexual roles of both parents. In Jerry's psychic life, activity to a significant degree had become equated with fantasies of penetration and intrusion, inactivity with fantasies of being passively entered and penetrated. When these fantasies were strongly stimulated in the treatment by the contact with the analyst, the resultant anxiety precipitated a phobic reaction. By this reaction both the danger from Jerry's own violence and excitement as well as the fantasied danger from the analyst could be more effectively warded off. This he accomplished by externalizing and projecting the wishes and impulses onto the monster where it could be played with, run away from, jailed, or bound and tied in the form of a toy or doll.

In the treatment we can see that the motor activity is again the preferred mode of discharge of tension. The observation of the child in the treatment, which gives greater access to the fantasies and ideational content, enables us to see the changing meaning of the same behavior. At this time the alternation between activity and quiet is very closely related to the patient's desires, expectations, and fears concerning his bodily intactness and is reflected in the leading anxieties of the phallic and oedipal phase.

From the treatment we learned that Jerry's preferred mechanism of defense was identification with the aggressor. This mechanism of defense as well as its precursor, the direct attack on the thing he feared, made extensive use of the predisposition to motor activity which had been characteristic of this child from the beginning and had played such an important part in the early adaptation to the mother. This would suggest, for study in a larger number of children, the hypothesis that there may be a more general and regular relationship between the proclivity to motor discharge and the preference for this defense, although, obviously, more than one factor is involved in the establishment of a defense.

SUMMARY

In these reports we have brought only a small part of a very large set of data on one child. We have focused primarily on one characteristic of the child which was prominent from birth, namely, his motor activity. We have tried to show how the longitudinal study of this child and his environment by methods adapted to the growth and service needs of the child (i.e., infant testing, nursery school, psychoanalytic treatment) has enabled us to follow this characteristic or trait of the child and to understand more fully its changing meaning in the behavior of the child. We have observed the reinforcement of this equipment factor in the direction of even greater activity and toward a pronounced polarization of extremes of hyperactivity and quiescence. An important factor in this reinforcement was the employment of the child by the parents to an unusual degree as an object upon whom they gratified their instinctual strivings in a direct and relatively unmodified way. This resulted in intense stimulation to high levels of excitement with rapid discharge in motor activity. Some of the consequences could be seen in Jerry's low ability to tolerate and maintain heightened levels of tension without resorting quickly to the preferred motor discharge.

A concomitant finding in the first year, described in the pediatric report, was the disturbance in developing functions of control, integration, and inhibition, essential functions of the ego. In the nursery school, from twenty months Jerry was an impulsive child, lacking in controls, reacting typically to frustration and anxiety with massive motor discharge. At the same time, learning difficulties and poor capacity for sublimation were in full evidence in nursery school. These functions were further hampered by Jerry's tendency to go rapidly from one discharge opportunity to another, behavior that is more characteristic for primary process. In the nursery school quiescence also was sought as a discharge opportunity for particular affects. In the treatment, as described above, the predisposition to activity played a prominent part in the form of expression of the instinctual strivings specific to the phallic phase and also in the mode of defense against anxiety.

One of the problems the study was interested in was to examine how the personality development of the young child may be related to certain innate characteristics of the infant's constitution or equipment. To do this one needs an assessment of the equipment at birth and its maturation, as well as an assessment of the interaction of the child with his environment, mainly the mother, the father, and others in the family. The influence of the environment on the predisposition or equipment must be considered an important factor for the development of the child. As Kris pointed out in emphasizing some of the extreme possibilities, the environmental influence may reinforce the predisposition or it may act in the opposite direction. The child will have different personality characteristics and adaptations if his predispositions are reinforced than if they are mitigated. A more specific hypothesis in this area would be that there is a relationship between the innate equipment characteristics of the child and the mechanisms of adaptation the child prefers to use. If we view adaptation from the standpoint of its relations to defense (Hartmann, 1939), we may hypothesize further that the preferred mechanisms of defense employed by the child to cope with conflicts with the external world as well as with his own developing organization will retain prominent features of the early adaptations.

BIBLIOGRAPHY

Escalona, S. & Leitch, M. (1952), Early Phases of Personality Development: A Non-normative Study of Infant Behavior. *Monographs of the Society for Research in Child Development,* 17, Serial No. 54. Evanston, Ill.: Child Development Publications, 1953.

Hartmann, H. (1939), *Ego Psychology and the Problem of Adaptation.* New York: International Universities Press, 1958.

Kris, E. (1953), Unpublished Report from the Longitudinal Study of Personality Development. New Haven: Yale University Child Study Center. (Presented at the XXth International Psycho-Analytical Congress, Paris, 1957.)

Provence, S. & Lipton, R. C. (1962), *Infants in Institutions.* New York: Int. Univ. Press.

———— & Ritvo, S. (1961), Effects of Deprivation on Institutionalized Infants: Disturbances in Development of Relationship to Inanimate Objects. *The Psychoanalytic Study of the Child*, 16:189-205. New York: Int. Univ. Press.

Roudinesco, I. & Appell, G. (1950), Les répercussions de la stabulation hospitalière sur le developpement psychomoteur de jeunes enfants. *La Semaine des Hopitaux* (Paris), 26:2271-2273.

Spitz, R. A. (1945), Hospitalism. An Inquiry Into the Genesis of Psychiatric Conditions in Early Childhood. *The Psychoanalytic Study of the Child*, 1:53-76. New York: Int. Univ. Press.

———— & Wolf, K. M. (1946), Anaclitic Depression. *The Psychoanalytic Study of the Child*, 2:313-342. New York: Int. Univ. Press.

A Relationship Between Transitional Objects and Preconscious Mental Processes

• *ALAN W. FRASER, M.D.*

New York, New York

This paper is a clinical essay exploring the concept of a particular kind of object choice described by Winnicott (1953). I propose to broaden the concept beyond the point to which it has been carried in the literature and to discuss some as yet unexplored theoretical territory where it might find special usefulness.

Winnicott reasoned that the material possession so often used by the young child as a comforting object constitutes an intermediate step in various "transitions" which the developing ego functions must make. Chief among these is the transition from a narrow, intense experiencing of the mother-self unit to a broader experiencing of the immediate environment. The interrelating of the "inner reality" and the "outer reality" is a lifelong task, but obviously of priority status in childhood when both "realities" are being experienced for the first time. Winnicott postulated that the establishment of illusions is essential in several different ways for the successful accomplishment of this interrelating. In one of these illusions the transitional object participates: it is capable of seeming to belong to and representing the mother or the self interchangeably. Consequently, when the child is pushed toward new objects in the course of development, he can conjure up the mother in the transitional object and obtain some of the relief from anxiety previously obtained from the mother herself. The transitional object is part of himself because he can manipulate it; it is part of the mother because he can so imagine it to be. Winnicott emphasizes that something other than a material object can fill the same function—a word, or a tune, for example. This would naturally be more difficult to observe, but this idea suggests at the outset that Winnicott is talking about a widespread and subtle phenomenon.

The ego evidently finds this flexibility of assigning attributes to the transitional object gratifying, for the child guards carefully his privilege of control over the object. The adults, if all goes well, do not seriously challenge the child's illusions about this object. In this way the transitional object becomes an "intermediate area," its attributes labeled neither as fully "real" nor as completely "not real" —neither all "me" nor all "not me." Such permitted illusions of shared realities persist in later life in different forms in certain pathological syndromes, in play, in art, and in religion.

Since Winnicott's original description, the transitional object has been mentioned in several contributions by others. Stevenson (1954) gave phenomenological descriptions of such objects in older children, and mentioned the regressive coloring of all use of transitional object, but she did not offer any new theoretical formulations. Kris (1955) suggested that the ego's use of the transitional object with its capacity for "proper illusion" constitutes one of the earliest stages of sublimation. Greenacre (1955, 1960) and Mittelmann (1955), writing on fetishism, saw disturbances in the developmental period of the transitional object as leading to fetishism. Weissman (1957) mentions the transitional object as related to an illusion of a maternal part object. His emphasis was to contrast transitional object with the fetish, which he finds to be a delusion of a maternal part object. Eissler (1959) made Winnicott's transitional object congruent with a fetish object utilized to achieve an isolation of an object carrying a high narcissistic cathexis. Here again, the role of the transitional object is confined to the sphere of object relations.

Greenacre (1959), discussing play, suggested that the rhythmic use of the transitional object (sucking, stroking) is related to much which later on is called play.

Rosen (1958) described a woman who retained a material comforting object into adult life. This patient was an intuitive thinker in whom problem solving preferentially utilized preconscious processes. Invoking Kris's ideas on the ego's regression to preconscious processes in the service of creativity (Kris, 1938, 1944), Rosen concluded that Winnicott's concept of transitional object has an important bearing on this aspect of the thought process. That is to say, regression to preconscious thinking in later life is analogous to regressing to an intermediate area of object cathexis in earlier life. The analogy is warranted because both mental operations depend upon a temporary utilization of a regressed kind of thinking. The situations are analogous, but not equivalent, because the childhood situation tends to center its thinking on a material object, where the later model is less dependent upon such a concrete object.

My own thoughts on these matters were stimulated by some analytically obtained observations of a young woman who reported her utilization of a transitional object between her tenth and twentieth years. Her well-preserved memories of the acquisition of this object may be described in her own words: "I was out shopping with my grandmother, a rarity, when I saw her, the doll, alone and unhappy on the shelf. I took her home. Grandmother showed tolerance and even enthusiasm. Mother said, 'This is the last doll you'll ever have,' and kept trying to throw her out when I wasn't looking. [There had been dolls in earlier years, but they had not been cherished; indeed no adequate comforting object existed at the appropriate age.] I told the doll right away that I was sorry I didn't feel very strongly about her right then, but that I would try hard to feel. Soon the feelings came. I pressed them into the doll by laying my head on her and thinking hard." This interaction occurred especially at bedtime, and was accompanied by sucking one thumb. The accompanying fantasy evolved from an earlier one: the bed had been imagined as mother, and for years the sensation of sinking into the bed had been pleasant. But it grew anxious: there was a feeling of sinking too far, so as to smother. The doll was interposed between "self" and "mother," and a sense of comfort came from the doll rather than from the bed representation of mother. In short, the doll was, among other things, a fantasy protection against excessive closeness with the mother.

Certain of Winnicott's specifications for the transitional object emerge even from this initial description: the doll was an illusion tolerated by one mother, though scorned by another; it was cherished and defended by the child for its value as a comforter. The patient unexpectedly informs us that the comforting process was connected in her mind with an interchange of emotion, and that, for her, emotion and thinking were closely related. Here we are already carried beyond the Winnicott position and are encouraged to think of this transitional object as implicated in more than libidinal cathexis and in the diminution of anxiety. Further, we learn that a transitional object can be the recipient of a projection: on first sight the child saw the doll as having *her* feelings. At first this was entirely projection, for the doll was realistically perceived as having no feelings of its own. An identification was effected gradually: the child herself felt "empty" and she discovered by exploration that the doll's interior was empty of anything valuable. Hence they were "alike." This is one of a list of permutations of meanings regarding the doll to which I shall add in the course of further observations.

There are other facts from the patient's life which have a bearing on our subject. She was the only child of a powerful and ambitious woman. During the pregnancy, the mother's only pregnancy, it was decided that the maternal health and well-being were threatened. More childbearing was prohibited, thus burdening the patient from birth with the whole responsibility for "ruining mother's health" and requiring her to contribute all the gratitude for "the risks mother took to have a child." A week-long labor consolidated the ambivalence in the mother and established the atmosphere for the early mother-child relationship. Rearing was from the beginning absolutely unvarying in style. It took the form of appearing to guarantee a solution for everything in exchange for total submissiveness. Food was provided without manifestations of hunger, and it was *provided*, not merely offered. Full compliance with detailed regulations about the time, rate, quantity, and technique of eating was demanded and obtained. Ideas about the evils of dirtiness were inculcated thoroughly, and the child was not given responsibility for cleanliness. The mother observed all toileting, and herself scrubbed the anal canal after every evacuation until well toward adolescence, i.e., until the first revolt of the child, which began after the transitional object was taken up. The vagina was similarly treated, and the eyes were washed daily with an antiseptic. For about the first three years, care of an umbilical hernia completed the list of direct body invasions by the mother. She reduced the hernia deeply with her finger after bathing, and could carry this out with pleasure rather than with anxiety.[1] In order to accommodate the mother's business schedule, these ministrations had to be confined to the beginning of each day. During most of the day the child was under the care of a nurse. This nurse was truly devoted, but lacked any independence. She was as subservient to the mother as was the child. Although still in the family in the patient's adult life, it was impressive to observe how little she seemed to mean to the patient. Apparently this was a "mammy" whose contribution to rearing was rather completely submerged by a mother who did not neglect the child in the quantitative sense but rather overpowered her with a kind of massive attack which left no room for an illusion that anyone else could be a mother.

The father produced almost no chink in this rather stony construction. Inferior in education to his wife, he passively accepted her rescuing and rebuilding a business he had inherited. When his daughter grew up brilliant, talented, and deeply troubled, his separation from her became more and more severe. He was baffled by her, and she was disillusioned by him. He, like the nurse, contributed little to changing the pervading conflict between mother and daughter. Adult life was reached with the *status quo* virtually unchanged:

---

[1] All data presented concerning the parents have been confirmed by them.

the daughter still ambivalently relied on the mother for direction in even the simplest matters of life.

Some readily accessible fantasies dating from before the tenth year were based upon the details of eating and toileting. The child felt that both ordinary food and the food of thought were essential for keeping up her "level of energy," a term preferred by her to terms like "good feelings," or "good spirits." But the level of energy had to be adjusted cautiously, for she thought that as her own energy rose, mother's fell. They were still "connected by a tube," and their fates were never their own, but were determined by the other. This fantasy was rooted in the guilt-producing legends about her birth and offered a solution of sorts. If she and mother are still connected by a tube, then she is still unborn, and therefore has not done the ultimate injury to mother nor experienced injury to herself. But the unborn condition, while it avoids the maximum injury and preserves mother, is not welcome because it smothers self. Her size must be nicely controlled so that if a second birth (growing up) is to occur, mother will not be injured. Since both food and learning increase size, sometimes both must be curtailed. The whole matter was complicated by the child's growing tall early and always being considered "big for her age." Moreover, intellectual precocity was obvious to all. In trying to keep the delicate balance of size and braininess, the child demanded extracurricular tutors, sometimes two for the same subject. Outwardly, the goal was to get perfect marks and please mother; inwardly, she dreaded too much achievement, and ingeniously used the mutually contradictory tutors to dampen her natural thinking and learning processes. These processes were, as in many gifted persons, markedly preconscious. However, unlike most such persons, she took no pleasure in preconscious thinking. She was made anxious, especially in adolescence, by her ability to think intuitively. This kind of thinking suggested personal powerfulness—braininess, "big headedness." The tutors were to explain every step, to forestall any appearance of personal mental power. She was actually frightened by the gaps in her thinking. In structural terms, her ego was defective in a way which made it difficult to tolerate a temporary regression to a facile, intuitive, primary-process kind of thinking.

These fantasies about energy level and food and learned (incorporated) materials were further elaborated by combining them with fantasies about body invasions by mother. Food and learned materials were dreaded because they wore away the body interior. They were abrasives like the invading washcloth and the cybalum. Neither food nor learning could be foregone, because the energy which they provided was clearly perceived as sustaining life. Moreover, to eat well and to learn well brought maternal approval. Caught between the need to sustain life and love on the one hand and the danger of self-destruction by abrasion on the other, the child naturally went to extremes in both eating and fasting and in learning and refusing to learn. An examination phobia was added at an early age to the learning anxiety: the extent of body damage by the introjection of learned materials would be revealed to the teacher in the academic examination as similar damage was revealed to the mother in the examination of the stool. The higher (bigger) the marks the more damage was disclosed. A painful struggle resulted between the facile tendency toward high marks (utilizing much talented preconscious thinking) and the need to keep marks low enough to escape the implications of self-destruction and destruction of mother.

In such a setting, then, the doll was acquired and utilized. The first two years or so of its use consisted, besides the game of interchange of emotion, already described, of quite ordinary doll play. The rubber body was washed, dressed, and intensely cherished. During these two preadolescent years, revolt against mother's regulations increased markedly, but not without much anxiety and compensatory phases of total submissiveness. A new utilization of the doll was added to the older ones. In connection with puberty and menarche a game was devised where one of the doll's legs was inserted into her vagina.[2] This became one of the most important methods, lasting well into late adolescence, for gradually mastering the traumata (and also repeating the pleasure) experienced in the

[2] Kestenberg (1956) discusses masturbation with a doll in connection with discovery of the vagina.

childhood cleaning. This game produced orgasm, but its chief conscious satisfaction was to observe that neither the doll nor her own body was injured. In this way she was attempting also to master the anxiety of the birth fantasies, based upon the legends, as well as of the cleaning experiences. Accompanying this play was a quite literal fantasy of impregnation by a penis and the subsequent birth of a treasured infant to be reared in a manner exactly opposite to mother's policies. Active and passive aims were thus satisfied by the same object. In this play the doll was used to represent simultaneously: (1) a part of mother (certainly the finger, and probably on a deeper level, the nipple as well); (2) her whole self being born from mother; (3) the anticipated penis which would magically remove all strife from her relationship with mother; (4) her own child. Menarche had exacerbated her fantasies of castration, condensed into the thought "I am empty." Emptiness had a certain charm, because it was equivalent to smallness and therefore to harmlessness; but it was frightening because it suggested the beginning of personal dissolution. In this conflict the original attribute of the doll—that it was empty—was emphasized during the play. By this means, while she was using the doll to produce a feeling of bodily fullness, by vaginal insertion, she could at the same moment be thinking, "It's only an empty doll." In her words, and these are particularly important for the generalization I wish to make later about transitional objects: "The thing was to feel neither full nor empty, but full-empty."

The first sexual object sought outside the family was a homosexual one: at sixteen there was a time of seeking out schoolmates for sexual play portraying an idealized mother-child relationship. Here again, the child assumed the mother and child roles alternately. The doll was not utilized in this play.

When heterosexual objects came to play a role at about seventeen, her behavior paralleled closely that with the doll. The aim with these objects was insertion of the boy's fingers into her vagina.[3] On one occasion she attempted such an exploration herself, but the experi-

[3] See again Kestenberg (1956) on the thesis that intromission is an essential step in defining vagina.

ence was too frightening: she had the impression of a limitless space.[4] It was more suitable to use the male partner and to note carefully the absence of distress in him. That is, he and she were as uninjured as she and the doll had been. She was skillful in choosing rather doll-like, passive partners, the playthings of their own mothers, willing to remain under her control. This play produced orgasm also, but it must be noted that the presence of the doll was never an indispensable condition for experiencing sexual pleasure.

Phenomenologically, her object choices were colored by identification, and in particular, an identification with one of the idealized self-images. A deeply repressed body-as-phallus fantasy was discovered. She regarded herself as mother's penis, and on this fantasy she established a skill in presenting herself to slightly effeminate men as the penis which they hoped to find in every object. It is pertinent in this connection that the transitional object was also one of the objects of identification—the doll was lonely, empty, and phallicized, like herself. The essential difference between the doll and the heterosexual objects lies in the fact that to the doll attributes could be merely assigned; in the men they had to be conceptualized. The preservation of reasonably good empathy and reality testing constrained her to *observe* her partners. In a word, they were less amenable to illusion. The doll was more adaptable, and this must have constituted an advantage to the psychic economy.

The body-as-phallus fantasy had other connections with the transitional object. When the doll was being utilized as a masturbatory obturator the hand was applied to the doll's hair. This contact with hair was pleasurable in itself, but not required for the genital pleasurable sensations. In late adolescence, her own hair became an object of elaborate manipulation and the matrix of numerous fantasies. The unconscious basis of hairdressing for her was this: the naturally bushy hair had to be subdued into a long straight tress, which had two meanings: it was smoother, and less obstructive to rebirth; it was

---

[4] For a full discussion of the effects upon abstract thinking of difficulty in perceiving the vagina see Keiser (1958). My patient does not fit well into his grouping, probably because the repeated intrusions in childhood made the orifices hypercathected even though distorted in concept.

capable of being "let down" and "put up," analogous in her mind to the penis. The hair of the legs was ruthlessly extirpated. The unconscious purpose of this was to achieve a leg as smooth as the doll's, to be as harmless to mother's vagina as the doll's leg had been to her own.

I have said that acquisition of the doll was followed by a sharp increase in her struggle for independence, but it must not be thought that emancipation proceeded smoothly for her. The mother struggled against her daughter's independence, becoming more and more directive of feeding, clothing, and studying. In a kind of desperate paroxysm of her desire for mastery, the mother demonstrated to the daughter her procidentia—her proof to the child of the child's injuriousness and consequent indebtedness. To the child this was a confirmation of her sometimes conscious assessment of mother as phallic. This new trauma, bringing almost unbearable guilt, was experienced at a time (about eighteen) when the doll had been rather completely decathected and the relationship was not revived in its old form. Interestingly for our consideration of the relationship between transitional object and the later intermediate area represented by art, the child now took to painting. Painting was for her a distinctly phallic act: with the brush she captured the sitter's essence, that is, she penetrated the subject. This was opposite to learning. There she had to "let someone else's knowledge come into" her. In briefest terms, to learn was to have a vagina, and to paint was to have a penis. Evidently the doll was utilized so as to express both issues simultaneously—its essence was perceived (penetrated) and it was also received passively.

In portraiture she showed truly great talent. Here the preconscious processes were better tolerated: she could produce a portrait which everyone thought revealed the sitter remarkably well (though not at all literally) without anxiety at not "knowing" all the steps through which her mind had passed. Painting had also the advantage that it was a grown-up field into which mother could not follow. There was no praise from mother, but also no exhortation or admonition. Gradually a feeling of personal freedom came to be founded largely on painting.

Now during analysis a further informative overlapping of these various strategies of the ego appeared: temporarily, the doll was brought back upon the stage and portraits were made of it. In a series of remarkably warm, luminous paintings the doll was endowed with various emotions. One day a portrait of the doll appeared with a peculiar blue coloration of the neck and of the genital area. This unconsciously related to an earlier dream: "I met a girl in the street. She was wearing a blue scarf and had only one breast. I said to her, 'You better go study.' " Here, then, is neatly played out on the doll a highly condensed version of ideas about body defect, their displacements, and the undoing of them by becoming learned. She can see herself in both roles in the dream figures, but the doll seems to be necessary to permit thinking about these things when awake and for gradually removing the anxiety from them after the well-known method of repetition of traumatic experiences in a disguised and controlled form (Freud, 1920). Ultimately, doll portraits gave way to self-portraits. These, too, without direction from the therapist, contributed significantly to the treatment.

The doll and the paintings of it are, then, among other things, links between her old view of herself as physically defective and lacking emotions which others experience and her new version of herself as something much more human. Certain ego operations upon the doll and its mental representations carry her from a more sub-jective to a more objective view of herself. These ego operations utilize Winnicott's "intermediate area of controlled illusion." This area includes transitional object, play, and art. During the whole evolution, thinking tends to be freer and less anxious in the inter-mediate area. Figuratively, but perhaps with deeper meaning than we know, the gaps in her thinking (representative of preconscious functioning) became more tolerable step by step with her tolerance for the "gaps" in her body and in the mother's body. The transi-tional object enters into both accomplishments, and it does so by being much more than an object of libidinal cathexis—in the pres-ence of this cathexis it also is drawn into thinking and probably also into more emotional operations than are included in the idea of libidinization. Here we are aware of an appearance of inconsistency, for we find that she willingly utilized a "controlled regression in the service of the ego" (Kris, 1952)[5] in certain "creative" matters, but we have evidence that her ego was intolerant of regression to primary-process thinking in other connections. She avoided a preconscious style of *problem solving,* but had less trouble with preconscious processes leading to inspiration. Though highly intelligent and artistically creative, she was not a skilled abstract thinker. Her talent was in graphic arts and writing. She preferred writing and was inclined toward vivid imagery with strict attention to characterization. She was conspicuously lacking in mathematical or philosophical interest. It appears that the more abstract the thought, the less tolerant was her ego of the regressed condition. The probable reason is that such thinking is less adapted to attachment to a concrete (transitional) object. For her, it was less possible to avoid the sensation of there being a "gap" in abstract than in creative[6] thinking.

To return to the relationship of the patient with her mother, this time more from the economic angle: it is evident that she found it painful to give up mother and choose another object because she needed to master the traumatic and frustrated aspects of the relationship with mother, and at the same time to try to salvage a little of the real pleasure which she knew rightfully was hers. Feeling that her love for mother was unrequited and that therefore she was swindled, she sought objects which could represent mother in some way although in distorted form. This was especially evident in her homosexual choices, but also was clear in the males she picked: they were all effeminate, and by being slightly feminized men they adequately represented the masculinized mother. The common ground was that they were devoted to body manipulation without creating affection. Here is precisely the point at which a transitional object was utilized: she selected a doll which represented many things simultaneously. Briefly, the doll was thoroughly overdetermined.

5 Kris's formulation, of course, antedates 1952. I refer here to a collection of his writings which show his development of this now classic idea, on which I rely heavily throughout this presentation.

6 I do not wish to imply that there is no "creativity" in "abstraction." Both terms need better delineation than they now have, but for the present, we cannot avoid an appearance of antithesis.

Stated thus, from the point of view of the vicissitudes of cathexis, the matter is clear enough. But let us see if something is to be gained by considering the events more from the side of thinking. "The two principal, basic functions of thinking are to isolate and to connect" (Eissler, 1959). Within the confines of her own mind, the patient has to reconcile mental representations of both the archaic object from which she is trying to achieve adequate separation (mother) and the new object to which she is trying to find an avenue of attachment (lover). She must carry portions of both these representations pretty much with her: they are both subject to relegation to the preconscious but not to repression. She cannot withdraw attention from one representation and assign it to the other with even the degree of freedom which can be exercised with the withdrawal of attention from the objects themselves. To put it simply, she can leave the actual mother behind when she goes out on a date, but not the complicated representation of mother. Her ego must develop a way to retain concurrently the representations of the old object and the new object. But these objects and their representations are not equivalent, they are merely similar. In fundamental respects they are dissimilar. To make them identical would be an ideal (and impossible) solution. Failing that, the ego is faced with a difficult task. It must learn to tolerate the coexistence of two mutually contradictory object representations. It must both combine and separate various attributes of the objects, together with their distortions. In short, the ego must perform thinking. The patient can, among many possibilities, consider that the effeminate man is *really* mother, or that the masculinized mother is *really* going to provide the penis which she wants from the male. She senses that her wishes are trying to put together things which are hopelessly apart. Her wishes have aggravated a conflict between the representations of the objects. This conflict carries with it a sense of unpleasure, and the ego must seek to change the energic disturbance which is felt as unpleasure. Faced with the task of reconciliation of two incompatible concepts, it brings in a third element, the transitional object. Paying due attention to the representations of the transitional object (rather than the material object itself), we might venture the assumption that *whenever* the ego is faced with reconciling an incompatibility it uses a third concept which is capable of ambiguity. The ambiguous concept is intermediate and overlapping: it is endowed with two or more meanings. Such an ambiguous concept includes, in its very nature, an illusion. This is Winnicott's illusion, but I have tried to couch a description of it in language which indicates that the illusion is not only a transition between two objects: it is a bridge between concepts of them, and it retains an anchorage in both banks. In this double root lies its usefulness both as some sort of compromise about the alternative directions of cathexis and its application as a tool of thought.

I think it important to try to say something about this patient's way of handling her affects, even though this carries us into a territory where no conclusions can be reached at this time. This patient found her affects actually more troublesome than her drives. She intuitively and explicitly distinguished between the two. She took up an attitude of real perspective about her drives, accepting pregenital and nearly genital drives with equanimity, acting upon them not too much and not too little. Aggression was likewise accepted as something to be expected in life, to be given and received without undue guilt or retaliation. Her emotions, on the other hand, were to her something much more akin to the classical view of instincts: they exerted an unrelenting pressure upon her, calling for various discharges or compromise solutions.[7] Besides being a concern as to how to dispose of them adequately, they were used in other ways in the psychic life. Sometimes they afforded real enjoyment, but this normal utilization was secondary and rather fleeting. The commonest use was to manipulate emotions so as to produce a kind of unification or identification. Put briefly, she wanted to have an emotion in common with someone else. This need gave rise to an appearance of projection and at first was mistaken for such. But closer scrutiny showed that she was not trying to project her emotions so as to be rid of them, but so as to install in another her own affect, while retaining a portion of it. Now this striving to have an

---

[7] See Eissler (1953) for a detailed discussion of this use of affects.

affect in common reminds us of the use of her traditional object, which was to belong to or to partake of two persons simultaneously. I am tempted to the speculation that conflict between emotions is sometimes handled by the ego in a manner similar to that used for irreconcilable concepts—by displacement to an intermediate object which is then treated *ambivalently*.

We have then, in this patient, three kinds of entities which were to be held intermediate, mutually possessed by two: material object (and its representations), concept, and affect. How these interrelate, which represents the genetically earlier strivings, and which may represent evolutions under the influence of development—these questions remain for further study to elucidate.

In conclusion, it will be clarifying to review the concepts in Freud's writings which can be applied to these lines of argument. In delineating the work of condensation in the dream work, Freud (1900) found that certain of the elements in the dream's manifest content formed "intermediate common entities" between two experiences of the previous day (i.e., two preconscious ideas) which required representation in the dream. This condensation is the basis of overdetermination in both dreams and symptom formation. We are reminded that overdetermination, which we have observed in the transitional object, is an economic operation in the psychic economy which can be effected only by the primary process. Similarly, in the paper on fetishism (1927), Freud points to the dual meaning of the fetish object, and states that such a compromise could be brought about only by the primary process. A fetish is "constructed out of two opposing ideas." This brings us very close to my thesis about transitional objects; however, I am emphasizing the normality of ambiguous objects in realms of thought rather than stressing their utilization for object seeking.

Freud's view of thinking itself as an experimental, tentative cathectic process has not been superseded. He says:

> It is as though the unconscious stretches out feelers, through the medium of the system Pcpt.-Cs., towards the external world and hastily withdraws them as soon as they have sampled the excitations coming from it [1925a, p. 180].

Thought is to be regarded as an experimental action, a kind of groping forward, involving only a small expenditure of energy in the way of discharge. Let us consider where the ego can have made a previous use of this kind of groping forward, where it can have learnt the technique which it now employs in intellective processes. It was at the sensory end of the mental apparatus, in connection with sense perceptions. For upon our hypothesis perception is not merely a passive process; we believe rather that the ego periodically sends out small amounts of cathectic energy into the perceptual system and by their means samples external stimuli and after every such groping advance draws back again [1925b, p. 184f.].

These formulations tend to make thinking intimately connected with some sort of observing, and the latter passage gives us the hint that what was originally a tentative testing of objects in the outer world becomes gradually applicable to the thought representations of objects in the mind.

SUMMARY AND CONCLUSIONS

Observations on the acquisition and use of transitional objects catch the ego in the act of making a transition. In the case at hand, the transition was delayed by a severe deficiency in ego growth and development. Delay was long enough to bring the whole matter well into the time of speech and of analytic cooperativeness, favoring observation of the transition. I think that a tentative extrapolation to earlier and more normal conditions is justified. I propose that the transitional object and its mental representation are repositories of this experimental cathexis. The clinical material suggests that the ego prefers to use a material object when it first attempts the experimental thinking, and later on, with more development, it can dispense with the material object and utilize a representation which functions in the place of it. The ambiguous nature of both the object and its later representations favors experimentation: the double meaning favors mobility of cathexis, which is experimental through trial and error. The ambiguous intermediate object, which in childhood is a material object, can gradually become a mental object in later life. In observing this evolution we probably catch a glimpse from one angle of the origin of the function of conceptualization— a form of abstract thinking.

When we consider what appears to be a gradual transition from a kind of thinking centered upon a material object to thoughts which are more independent of a material "peg," so to speak, we are reminded of the widespread tendency to use various "aids" in abstract thinking. The mechanical models which we tend to employ when grappling with difficult abstractions probably are related to a developmental phase when a material object was used to represent a combination of more or less irreconcilable hypotheses. Analogy also comes to mind as a tool of thought to which we often resort but about which we are wary and mistrustful, as though we recognized its archaic quality. Now an analogy represents an overlapping of two concepts so that they have a common ground. In forming an analogy we stress the common ground in an effort to make what we know about one concept relieve our sense of ignorance about the other.

I suggest that further observations of the use of transitional objects in development, in disease, and in the analytic situation would be helpful in our slow advance toward an adequate psychoanalytic theory of thinking.

BIBLIOGRAPHY

Eissler, K. R. (1953), Notes upon the Emotionality of a Schizophrenic Patient and Its Relation to Problems of Technique. *The Psychoanalytic Study of the Child*, 8:199-251. New York: Int. Univ. Press.
———— (1959), On Isolation. *The Psychoanalytic Study of the Child*, 14:29-60. New York: Int. Univ. Press.
Freud, S. (1900), The Interpretation of Dreams. *Standard Edition*, 4 & 5. London: Hogarth Press, 1953.
———— (1920), Beyond the Pleasure Principle. *Standard Edition*, 18:3-64. London: Hogarth Press, 1955.
———— (1925a), A Note upon the 'Mystic Writing-Pad.' *Collected Papers*, 5:175-180. London: Hogarth Press, 1950.
———— (1925b), Negation. *Collected Papers*, 5:181-185. London: Hogarth Press, 1950.
————(1927), Fetishism. *Collected Papers*, 5:198-204. London: Hogarth Press, 1950.
Greenacre, P. (1955), Further Considerations Regarding Fetishism. *The Psychoanalytic Study of the Child*, 10:187-194. New York: Int. Univ. Press.
———— (1959), Play in Relation to Creative Imagination. *The Psychoanalytic Study of the Child*, 14:61-80. New York: Int. Univ. Press.

——— (1960), Regression and Fixation. *J. Amer. Psychoanal. Assn.,* 8:703-723.

Keiser, S. (1958), Disturbances in Abstract Thinking and Body-Image Formation. *J. Amer. Psychoanal. Assn.,* 6:628-652.

Kestenberg, J. (1956), Vicissitudes of Female Sexuality. *J. Amer. Psychoanal. Assn.,* 4:458-476.

Kris, E. (1938), Ego Development and the Comic. *Psychoanalytic Explorations in Art.* New York: Int. Univ. Press, 1952, pp. 204-216.

——— (1944), Art and Regression. *Trans. N.Y. Acad. Sci.,* 6:236-250.

——— (1952), *Psychoanalytic Explorations in Art.* New York: Int. Univ. Press.

——— (1955), Neutralization and Sublimation. *The Psychoanalytic Study of the Child,* 10:30-46. New York: Int. Univ. Press.

Mittelmann, B. (1955), Motor Patterns and Genital Behavior: Fetishism. *The Psychoanalytic Study of the Child,* 10:141-263. New York: Int. Univ. Press.

Rosen, V. H. (1958), Abstract Thinking and Object Relations. *J. Amer. Psychoanal. Assn.,* 6:653-671.

Stevenson, O. (1954), The First Treasured Possession: A Study of the Part Played by Specially Loved Objects and Toys in the Lives of Certain Children. *The Psychoanalytic Study of the Child,* 9:199-217. New York: Int. Univ. Press.

Weissman, P. (1957), Some Aspects of Sexual Activity in a Fetishist. *Psychoanal. Quart.,* 26:494-507.

Winnicott, D. W. (1953), Transitional Objects and Transitional Phenomena. *Int. J. Psychoanal.,* 34:89-97.

The Evaluation of the Intellect of the Brain-Damaged Child: Historical Development and Present Status

• *JOHN DORIS, Ph.D.*

Yale University

Physicians in the nineteenth and early twentieth century frequently observed and commented upon the association of mental retardation and brain damage. In addition, wide differences in achievement by the same child in various intellectual areas were noted; some children, unable to display their intellectual ability because of speech and motor handicap, were suspected of being brighter than their actual achievements would attest. The problem was how to measure reliably the intellectual potential of the handicapped child so that programs of rehabilitation and education might be prescribed with due consideration for individual differences.

With the rapid growth of mental testing in the field of psychology about the turn of the century—given particular impetus and lasting direction by the work of Alfred Binet—the psychologist was called upon to utilize his skills alongside of the physician and educator in the study of the intellect of the brain-damaged child.

162

EVALUATION OF INTELLIGENCE

Before glancing at the historical development and present status of this field from the psychologist's point of view, it is necessary to describe briefly what is involved in the evaluation of intelligence. The first problem that confronts us is one of definition. Before we can measure something, we must know what it is, or at least we must be able to discriminate it from what it is not. Partial definitions of intelligence are readily listed. It is the ability to learn, to make abstractions, to cope successfully with new situations, to make cognitive discriminations, etc. But if pressed, we must admit that we are dealing with a loosely defined, often ambiguous concept. Even the partial definitions contain terms like "learning" and "abstraction" which are lacking in precise, universally acceptable meaning. It is, of course, possible for certain purposes of theory or investigation to make tight, explicit definitions of intelligence which can, within the framework of the theory or investigation, be used consistently and profitably. But such definitions lose in richness and practical utility as they gain in explication until they are reduced to something of the order of "intelligence is that hypothetical construct which is measured by a properly standardized intelligence test." The clinician involved in the diagnosis, prognosis, and treatment of individuals with specific problems is likely to have little use for this type of definition. He finds it preferable to think of intelligence in looser but more flexible and general terms. The rub comes when he tries to communicate with his colleagues on the results of his observations or investigations. Likewise, he may find himself confused when he tries to make use of the literature. There he finds the I.Q.'s of athetoid children compared with spastic children and the epileptic or the deaf with the normal. He has a right to ask what is being compared and whether the data on which the comparisons were made are comparable.

Fortunately, for clinical purposes, the process of evaluation can be conceptualized in a way which circumvents the knotty problems of the nature of intelligence and the comparability of its techniques of measurement. In this conceptualization I view the evaluation of intelligence as a process of prediction. It maintains that a psychologist on the basis of a subject's performance in certain standardized situations is predicting the subject's potential for achievement or level of performance in certain learning or problem-solving situations that are posed by our culture. The psychologist may be predicting a child's ability to meet successfully the intellectual demands of the classroom, his ability to learn a trade, or his ability to cope with any one of the myriad problem-solving tasks that the culture may pose to him—from learning to communicate his bodily needs to splitting the atom.

If the evaluation of intelligence is conceptualized as a process of prediction, we are in a better position to consider what goes into such a process. We must consider the problem-solving behavior which the clinician must predict, the sample behavior he chooses to observe, and, finally, how he infers from the observed behavior the predicted behavior.

In a sense this conceptualization is an extension of Binet's original approach to the evaluation of intelligence. The practical problem facing Binet was to devise a technique for predicting school performance. It goes beyond that in recognizing that the school situation is only one problem-solving situation that the culture presents to the child. There are many other problem situations the mastery of which are far more crucial to the child's adjustment to his culture. For example, the mastery of language or at least some form of symbolic communication is a problem posed to the child long before school age, and it is one on which most subsequent success in adjustment is based.

Unfortunately, as intelligence tests multiplied and theories of intelligence flourished, the psychologist and the users of psychological tests, even in clinical settings, were all too prone to neglect the original purpose of intelligence testing. I.Q. scores and estimates of intellectual levels were utilized as if they were attributes of the child rather than predictive statements about the child. Intelligence testing in a clinical situation requires, in my view, that specific questions must be posed for a particular child or group of children. The referral for testing must ask either explicitly or implicitly: can this child function in a regular classroom situation, does he need special education, can he learn to read and write, can he learn a skilled trade, or with altered motivation could he function better in school than he now does? It is to this kind of question that the psychologist makes his prediction. Now, in actual practice, it may be that the psychologist hedges or leaves these questions unanswered. He may leave them unanswered simply because they were not explicitly stated in the referral. In such cases, the psychologist can only surmise what questions might be asked about this child and give information which he thinks might be relevant. In other instances, a psychologist may be tempted to hedge, because a sense of insecurity or inadequacy deters him from risking a prediction which the future may prove ridiculous. But the nature of clinical work is such that the situation requires us to predict whenever our observations and our experience combine to give us the assurance that the probability of our prediction is sufficiently higher than chance to warrant its inclusion in the decision making of the patient, his parents, the educator, or the physician. Not to predict in such a situation is a defection of professional responsibility. To point out the positive aspects of this risky business of prediction, it should be remembered that there is nothing more conducive to the growth of clinical skill than to give full consideration to all the relevant data and then see one's prediction go awry because of some overlooked implication of one's observations. It should be further noted that when one does not make the needed predictions or fails to point out that predictions cannot be made on the basis of available knowledge, others will, under the pressure of events, be forced to make the prediction, perhaps, on the basis of less information than the psychologist had at his disposal. These considerations underline the importance for a referring physician or educator to make as explicit as possible the questions which prompted the referral and for the psychologist to address himself to those questions.

To put some of these considerations in more formal terms, we cannot estimate the validity of our intelligence evaluations unless we know the criteria by which the evaluations shall be judged. An estimate of the validity of our evaluations is in turn a prerequisite for any efficient attempt at improving our clinical procedures.

When we turn to an examination of the behavior samples utilized by the psychologist in prediction, the first to consider is the test performance. This may be expressed in the form of an over-all mental age, an intelligence quotient, or it may be expressed in a pattern of scores on different kinds of tests or groups of test items. But the psychologist does not usually base his prediction solely upon a test score or pattern. He draws upon other sources of information such as his observations of the child, the pediatrician's and teacher's reports, and interviews with parents.

All of these may confirm the prediction the psychologist would make on the basis of the test scores; but they may also cause him to qualify or completely revise it. Whether he uses the test score alone or whether he combines it with other sources of information, he is involved in a process of measurement. He is assigning individuals to a place on a scale of test scores or to a place on a subjective judgment scale which he formulates as his clinical opinion. It is therefore pertinent to determine how consistent his measurements are. Would he assign the same test score if he retested the child a week later? Would two psychologists obtain the same test score if they tested the child independently? Would a psychologist's clinical judgment be the same if he formed it on two different occasions? Would two psychologists observing the same behavior and with access to the same information form the same clinical judgment? Obviously all of these questions are concerned with the reliability of measures and judgments. The importance of reliability derives from the fact that we cannot hope for the validity of our diagnostic instruments and techniques if they provide unreliable measures. Of course, it is possible to make reliable measures that are not valid in the sense that scale position does not predict the degree of success on the criterion. But it is hopeless to expect success on prediction if the measures on which the predictions are based do not consistently discriminate between individual differences in ability.

In this discussion of intelligence evaluation I am concerned with two kinds of reliability. The first is the reliability of the test instruments used in the evaluation. Here I am asking if the scores obtained by the same individual on different occasions or with equivalent forms of the same test (e.g., Forms L and M of the Stanford-Binet) will be consistent. The second kind of reliability is that of the psychologist's clinical judgment concerning the child's problem-solving potential. Obviously, since the psychologist's judgment is not solely determined by the test score, the reliability of his judgment can differ from the reliability of the test score. But to the extent that the psychologist depends on the test score in forming his judgment, there is a communality between these different measures, i.e., between the test score and the clinical judgment. Even if, as is the case in a clinical situation, we are mainly concerned with the reliability of the clinical judgment, we can see the necessity for knowing the reliability of the test instrument which contributes to the formation of that judgment.

The inferential procedures by which the psychologist goes from his sample observations of behavior to a prediction are exceedingly complex and do not lend themselves easily to description or to formal analysis. If the psychologist used the test score directly for prediction —as may be done in certain personnel-selection procedures in industrial psychology—the problem would be simple. But instead, the psychologist takes the test score and his observations of how that test score was achieved, and combines it with a multitude of observations on factors such as attention span, attitudes toward being tested, distractibility, perseverance, motivation, and emotionality. He then adds material from the patient's history, parental interviews, school reports, and pediatric examinations. In the end he combines this highly diverse and sometimes contradictory information to form a clinical judgment. While I recognize the complexity of this process, I would still feel that it behooves the psychologist not only in his formal research but in his individual casework to be as explicit as possible about this inferential process. As I shall illustrate later, explicitness in this inferential process permits us to examine in retrospect the reasons for our success and failure in prediction.

My description of what is involved in intelligence evaluation may seem more or less different from what appears in the literature. I believe many investigators and clinicians involved in work with brain-damaged children have explicitly or implicitly conceptualized the problem in a manner not very different from my own. But many workers seem to consider themselves involved in making absolute measures of a clearly delineated, unambiguous, and tangible faculty of the mind.

While different ways of conceptualizing the process may recommend themselves for different purposes, it is my contention that the conceptualization I advocate has special value for clinical work. The essence of such work is that an individual comes to a clinician with a problem. It is the job of the clinician to diagnose the problem, to determine what the prognosis will be without intervention, and to decide what kind of intervention will make what kind of change in the prognosis. Only when he has done this can he rationally offer even a partial solution to the problem. Now, it is seen that intelligence evaluation fits into this scheme in all three ways. In so far as the evaluation is used to predict the child's present level of functioning in problem-solving situations, it participates in the diagnosis of the patient's difficulty. In so far as it is used to predict the child's future level of functioning, it participates in the prognosis. And in so far as the intellectual evaluation predicts differences in functioning according to variations in internal circumstances such as motivation and anxiety, or external circumstances such as environmental and social conditions, it may also participate in determining the kind of intervention that should take place. If we thus keep in mind the roles that the intelligence evaluation is to play in the clinical work, we are in a position to judge effectively its contribution. We can determine its success and failure, and we can analyze the causes for success and failure by re-examining all the steps from the selection of behavior observed through the inferential processes to the predictions and to the final evaluation of the predictions against the appropriate criteria.

REVIEW OF INTELLIGENCE TESTING OF BRAIN-DAMAGED CHILDREN

Having presented a schema for viewing the process of intelligence evaluation, I will now briefly review the development of intelligence testing of brain-damaged children. In this review I will attempt to evaluate the work in this field in the light of this schema.

Early Work

Much of the early work was focused on the child with marked impairment of motor and speech mechanisms. The child with nearly intact speech and motor mechanisms was not viewed as a problem; furthermore, at that time, the diagnostic category of the minimally brain-damaged child with no gross neurological findings was not yet widely accepted. Instead, the problem was the evaluation of the child so severely impaired in speech, movement, or sensory abilities that the usual testing instruments appeared inapplicable. The early workers concerned themselves with the problem of designing or selecting appropriate test instruments and devising suitable methods of administration. Focus was primarily upon deciding what kinds of observations were to be made. The problems of reliability, validity, and interpretation were less in the foreground.

Smith (1926) was one of the earliest to point out the problems and to give practical suggestions for the administration and interpretation of psychological tests with the brain-damaged. These suggestions are for the most part as sound today as when published.

We wish to emphasize, however, the need for careful re-examinations in which the actual intelligence quotient determination plays the least part. We should be extremely careful to note the character of the scattering, the deviations in mental reactions, and the manual performance in the performance tests. If the tests are graded in the manner usually done for other defectives, we are not fair to the child, for they consistently are undergraded rather than being given too high a score. A great deal of difference is noted in individual examinations and much depends upon the interest and perseverance of the examiner. I have found, especially in the group with the associated speech defects, that it is wise to have the teacher or the mother present to interpret the child's answers. Each test must be analyzed in the light of existing defects in the special senses, for defective eyesight, hearing, lack of coordination as well as diminution in sensibility and discrimination, all play a very prominent part.

The "scattering" Smith refers to is the variation in level of performance on different kinds of test items. Thus, the child functioning on verbal tasks at one mental age level may be functioning several years higher or lower on visual-motor tasks. Smith recognized that the scattering "renders the intelligence quotient as being somewhat unreliable in evaluation of the present mental level and as a prognostic indicator of future development." Although Smith here is using the term "unreliable," in current terminology he is obviously discussing the validity of the intelligence quotient.

While Smith touches upon the problem of adapting the testing to the limitations of the child and of taking the pattern of handicaps into account in interpreting the results, Doll and his associates (1932) in their study of mental retardation and birth injury posed themselves the problem of what kinds of test instruments among those available would be suitable for use with brain-damaged individuals. Doll's investigation was undertaken with twelve subjects with a diagnosis of brain injury ranging in age from four to thirty-nine years. All were mentally retarded with marked variation in the degree of motor involvement. In addition to the Stanford-Binet, Doll gave his subjects several other tests of intellectual ability including verbal and nonverbal tests of intelligence and achievement such as the Goodenough Draw-a-Man test, the Healy Picture Completion, the Porteus Mazes, the Witmer form board, and the Ohio literacy test. The Meyer's Mental test included in the battery is of special interest as a forerunner of the Columbia Mental Maturity Scale that recently has come into prominence as a test for cerebral-palsied children.

From a comparison of the performance of the subjects on these tests, Doll concluded that the Stanford-Binet was directly applicable to these subjects without serious modification unless motor and speech handicaps were so severe, as was true of one of his cases, as to inhibit practically all response. For those subjects where other tests proved equally applicable with the Binet, the Binet proved superior in its ability to discriminate levels of ability. Thus on a test like the Goodenough several subjects obtained the same score, although they were sorted out to different levels of ability on the Stanford-Binet. This capacity to make fine discriminations in ability is, of course, a desideratum in intelligence testing. Despite the superiority of the Binet to other tests used in this study, Doll was aware that his brain-injured subjects were handicapped in their performance on some of the individual items of the Binet.

Although this study had shortcomings in design, execution, and interpretation of results, it supported the use of the Stanford-Binet as the instrument of choice in the testing of the brain-damaged child. It is of interest that Schonell (1958), writing some thirty years after Doll and basing herself not only on the mass of clinical and research data accumulated in the interim but also upon her own extensive research and experience in the testing of the cerebral-palsied child, should maintain that the Stanford-Binet is the best single instrument available for the testing of the cerebral-palsied youngster.

Elizabeth Lord (1930, 1937) was another of the early investigators who attempted to develop a psychological method for evaluating the mental status of the child with motor handicap. In her 1930 study she addressed herself to one of the most difficult problems in the area, that of evaluating the motor-handicapped child in infancy and early childhood. In this age group one most frequently encountered what was then referred to as the "inaccessible" child, i.e., the child too handicapped in both motor and speech equipment to permit the use of the standard psychological tests.

The problem which she posed herself was, "to discover whether the child can vicariously acquire through audition and vision the necessary concepts for an interchange of ideas related to objects he cannot handle and to events in which he takes no active part." Lord based her attempts to evaluate the intellect of the handicapped child on Terman's definition of intelligence as "the ability to carry on abstract thought." She sought to measure the capacity for abstract thought in its developmental sequences. In discussing mental development she maintained that:

> It is seen in the alteration from the relatively simple undifferentiated reaction to sound or vision—turning the eyes to any sound or object without further evidence of discrimination—to a response that indicates differentiation in a complex situation. It is also seen in the development from the trick level of behavior

(waving bye-bye or playing pat-a-cake) which in many instances resembles the animal response, to that level of behavior where adjustments are made to words as the essential cues, and finally to the level where verbal situations are solved in language, though the language response be limited to gestures and sounds meaning "Yes" and "No"! It is in brief a change from adjustment on the perceptual level to adjustment on the conceptual level; from an ability to deal with the concrete to an ability to deal with the abstract. This alteration in behavior, which normally occurs in the first six years of life, I have accepted as a criterion of the developmental maturity of the psychic function.

In sharp contrast to many who worked both before and after her, Lord had a commendable concern with making explicit just what she was attempting to measure. One might have some reservation about the mensurability of abstract thought as she defined it or about the particular techniques she used in measurement, but at least with the aim made explicit one can make some judgment about the adequacy with which it was carried out.

From existing tests, such as the Gesell developmental schedule and the Stanford-Binet, and from her experience with preschool children, Lord devised a scale of behavior items to which she could tentatively assign normative values. Part I of this scale dealt with items of body balance, locomotion, manipulation, and vocalization arranged in a developmental series from the first months of life to six years of age. This scale was used to determine the child's level of motor skill which Lord considered a measure of efficiency of reaction. She wished to distinguish this from the child's mental ability which she took to be his appreciation of meaning and his ability to think abstractly. Mental ability was measured in Part II of the scale which began with items concerning the infant's ability to fixate and discriminate one stimulus from another and went on to items of social responses, number concepts, and verbal conceptualizations. An examination of the items in the two parts of the scale raises some questions as to how thoroughly the "efficiency of reaction" has been separated from "the appreciation of meaning." Thus in Part I we find items such as "Builds tower of four blocks," "Secures cube out of reach," or "Uses words in combination," and in Part II "Tries to attain cube placed out of reach" or "The child imitates the tester's vocalization." Nevertheless, compared to preschool tests then available, Lord's scale gave a much better chance for the examiner to distinguish the child's efficiency of motor response from his understanding of situations and his ability to think abstractly.

With this scale, Lord tested a group of thirty-one cerebral-palsied children ranging from thirteen months to nine years of age. Twelve of these children had just one examination; the remaining children had from two to six examinations. With rare exceptions re-examinations were at relatively close time intervals. From the data collected on this group with Part II of her scale, Lord concluded that although several children had a very limited range of response, there was nevertheless a minimum response which each child made with relative precision and stability, and in each case this minimum response could be related to a developmental sequence: "Alteration in adjustment was indicated from examination to examination in spite of the motor disability. There was, in general, a consistency in the developmental quotients from examination to examination on the same case. No child who had a developmental quotient indicating mental deficiency had a significantly higher quotient on later examination."

The importance of this study, then, was that it supported the contention that even severely handicapped brain-damaged children can be discriminated reliably on a developmental scale presumed to measure intellectual ability, and that their performance on the scale at one age level is predictive of their performance at a later age level. A lack of uniformity in the number of retests and the variability in intervals between retests made Lord's data unsuitable for precise and rigorous evaluation, but she bolstered her argument with the presentation of several case studies.

The case-study technique used by Lord has, of course, been repeatedly used by other investigators to demonstrate the reliability and the validity of their assessments of the intellectual endowment of the brain-damaged. Many excellent examples are provided in the writings of Gesell and Amatruda (1947), Doll et al. (1932), and Taylor (1959), to name just a few. The case study is the basic tool of clinical investigation, and furthermore it is undoubtedly indispensable in the teaching and communication of clinical skills. Certainly, the neophyte can be greatly assisted in his acquisition of skill by a perusal of case studies. There he finds descriptions of suitable instruments, techniques of administration, and interpretation that are invaluable. But the limitation of the case study is in its generality. Apparently lawful relationships that hold within an individual case may not hold in another case even when the cases seem quite similar. To determine the generality of a relationship we must examine it in many different cases. This permits us to determine not only how general the relationship is; but, just as importantly, by presenting the exceptions to the rule, it permits us to delineate precisely the nature of the relationship and to discover more important underlying relationships of even greater generality. I do not mean to imply that the clinician in the course of his experience does not check the generality of observed relationships in one case against his observations in the next. I do mean to imply that when his findings are presented as a case study or as a distilled essence of several cases, we are at a loss to know how to estimate the reliability of his observations and the validity of his inferences. We need to know precisely what observations were made, what and how inferences were made from these observations, and how the validity of the inferences was evaluated. With that information we can judge the logical consistency of the clinician's procedure, and we can attempt to replicate his findings. Otherwise we must submit to, or challenge the authority of, the clinician according to the way in which our own experience predisposes us.

Unfortunately, there are few studies in the area of the evaluation of the intelligence of the brain-damaged child that are so designed, executed, and reported that we can know precisely the observations made, the inferences drawn from the observations, and the evaluation of these inferences. This is undoubtedly due in part to the difficulties that are entailed in carrying out a study addressed to some of these problems. But even where the problems are simple and readily amenable to formal investigation, work has been slow in getting underway. For example, it would seem relatively simple to undertake studies of the reliability of test instruments using alternate forms of the same instrument or retests at short time intervals on fairly homogeneous groups of brain-damaged patients, grouped according to age, degree of handicap, and degree of retardation. Yet little has been done and much of that is methodologically suspect.

Recent Reliability Studies

In a 1954 study, Crowell and Crowell correlated the test and retest scores on various intelligence tests for sixty-one cerebral-palsied children. Four different intelligence tests were used, but most of the children were tested with the Stanford-Binet (Form L) or the Porteus Composite Binet. In every case the same test was used on the retest as had been first used with the child. In the majority of cases the second examiner was different from the first. Based on the median of all test-retest intervals two groups were formed. The first group had an average test-retest interval of fifteen months and the second a test-retest interval of forty-three months. Reliability coefficients were reported for each group separately and for the group as a whole. Analysis of the retest scores showed that approximately 51 per cent of the total sample deviated within five I.Q. points of the initial test score and approximately 75 per cent within ten I.Q. points. The Pearson coefficients of reliability for the test-retest mental age scores were .98 for Group I, .78 for Group II, and .92 for the total group. The authors do not state why they chose to report reliability coefficients on the mental age scores rather than the I.Q. scores. Since the paired mental age scores on each of the children were not always obtained at equal time intervals, and since a degree of correlation must exist between mental age and chronological age, the use of mental age scores would appear to be decidedly less desirable than the use of I.Q. scores which would have automatically taken the unequal time intervals into account and which would have partialed out the correlation between mental age and chronological age. Since the authors report that the distribution of I.Q. scores was highly skewed with 50 per cent of the patients classifiable as severely retarded, one might hazard a guess that they felt the distribution too skewed for appropriate application of Pearson's correlation technique, but then one might wonder why they did not undertake a transformation of the I.Q. scores but instead resorted to the suspect use of mental age scores. However, the reported deviations in I.Q. points on retest is much less ambiguous in its implication than the reliability coefficients on mental age scores, and from them one might conclude that there is a considerable degree of test-retest reliability. The authors for their part conclude: "The data suggest that the mental age obtained on the initial examination of a cerebral-palsied child can be accepted as highly reliable for ordinary diagnostic purposes, provided the clinical psychologist has adequate training and experience."

In evaluating this study it must be kept in mind that, like many studies done in this area, it was in the nature of a retrospective investigation. Cerebral-palsied cases having at least two psychological tests with the same instrument were culled from the files of the local board of health and the psychology clinic. The authors attempted to use the data on hand, and as a result many variables were confounded and left confounded in the analysis of the results. For example, four tests were used; were they all equally reliable? In some instances the same psychologist administered the test and retest. Did this make a difference? In the published article, no chronological ages are reported. Did age make a difference in reliability? Mc-Nemar's (1942) analysis of the original standardization norms for the Stanford-Binet indicated that the reliability of the test varied with age groups and with subgroups of intellectual ability, with the younger children and the brighter children showing less reliable test scores. Yet, from the way the Crowells' data are reported we cannot tell how age and intellectual ability affected the reliability. In addition, although this study gives us reliability coefficients for the mental age scores, we do not know how the mental age scores were obtained. Were all tests administered with strict adherence to the instructions of the test manual? These test scores were obtained in clinical settings, and we know that most psychologists functioning in such a setting will modify test administration to adapt to the particular handicaps of the child. How often was such modification necessary for the children in this study, and were the scores obtained from modified test administration as reliable as those obtained from standard administration? The study reports that for 25 per cent of the children there were I.Q. changes of greater than 10 points. One wonders if there were any characteristics in common among the children in this group. Were they the more severely handicapped, the youngest, etc.? I raise these questions not for the sake of carping but rather to point out how much richer such a study can be if it is designed and executed with an eye to obtaining the maximum amount of unambiguous information. In Crowells' defense it must be granted that a much larger sample would be necessary to answer some of my questions, and to their credit it might be pointed out that presumably hundreds of other clinicians working in this area did not think it necessary or worth the effort to obtain any information whatsoever on the reliability of intelligence test scores for cerebral-palsied children. Theirs was a step in the right direction.

The studies of Schonell (1956, 1958) give some answers to the kinds of questions I have raised. In a survey of cerebral palsy in Birmingham, England, 354 children were seen by the psychologist, and for 340 of these between the ages of three and fifteen years it was possible using the Stanford-Binet (Form L) to obtain estimates of intelligence. For each child three scores were obtained. The first of these was the *tested I.Q.*, obtained when the instructions for administration were adhered to irrespective of the child's handicap. The second was the *modified I.Q.*, obtained by scoring as successes those items which the psychologist judged the child would pass except for some special disability which prevented him from carrying out instructions. Schonell includes in her report some details of the ways in which testing was modified to adapt to the child's handicap. The third score was the *estimated I.Q.*, and in each instance in which this *estimated I.Q.* differed from the *tested* and *modified* I.Q.s a short report was written explaining the *estimated* I.Q.

In 253 cases (74%) the three I.Q. scores, *tested, modified,* and *estimated* were identical. With these children the test was administered and scored with strict adherence to the usual procedures. In 87 cases (26%) some modification of test administration was undertaken. It is of interest to note that modification of testing procedure was deemed necessary with more of the athetoid and mixed athetoid-spastic cases than with the pure spastic cases. It is in these groups of athetoid and mixed types that the greatest discrepancies between *estimated* and *tested* I.Q.s occurred. On the whole, differences betwen the *estimated* I.Q.s and the *tested* and/or *modified* I.Q.s were slight. In the 87 cases where the *estimated* I.Q. was different from the *tested* and/or *modified* I.Q., only 38 involved a difference of more than three I.Q. points; 43 involved a difference of only one or two points, which would certainly be considered negligible for all practical considerations. The average difference between *estimated* and *tested* I.Q.s for all 87 cases was only 2.7 points. The six largest differences reported range from 9 to 14 points. All of these latter cases were severely handicapped. Thus, these findings suggest that in the majority of cerebral-palsied cases there is no need for modification of standard test procedures in the use of the Stanford-Binet. They further suggest that when modification of testing procedures are judiciously undertaken by the psychologist or when he makes an estimation of intelligence based upon a modified administration, the results on the average are not greatly different from those obtained by standard administration. However, in some individual cases the differences between the scores were substantial. The question then arises: if a *modified* or *estimated* I.Q. is substantially different from the *tested* I.Q., what evidence do we have for its validity? That is to say, in predicting a child's capacity to profit from education or rehabilitation, should we be guided by the *tested* I.Q. or the *modified* or *estimated* I.Q.? Schonell presents some data which may have some pertinence to this question. Eleven of the children with *estimated* I.Q.s higher than their *tested* I.Q.s were accepted into the day-care program of a cerebral-palsy center. They were retested at twelve-month intervals, one to three retests per child. The author maintains that the retests show that the increase of the *estimated* I.Q. over the *tested* I.Q. was fully or partially justified in all but one case. Unfortunately, it is not clear from her tabled results whether or not all of the retest scores are *estimated* I.Q.s. One column of retest scores is headed as *estimated* I.Q.s, the remaining columns of retest scores are simply headed as I.Q. without specification as to whether they are *tested* or *estimated*. If they, too, are *estimated* I.Q.s—and from the discussion in the text this seems a likely assumption—then the results speak more for the test-retest reliability of *estimated* I.Q.s than they speak for the justification of using *estimated* I.Q.s instead of *tested* I.Q.s for these children. It is my opinion that justification for using either the *estimated* or the *tested* I.Q. should depend upon a demonstration of their predictive value for selected problem-solving tasks.

Schonell presents other data for the reliability of I.Q. scores derived from the Stanford-Binet. In her Birmingham study, a correlation coefficient of .89 was obtained for test-retest scores on 29 children at a twelve-month interval. Another sample of 50 children tested at the Queensland Spastic Center in Brisbane gave a correlation of .96 after twelve months. In both samples the average I.Q. in both the test and retest were within a range of 78 to 82.

These data suggest that in the hands of a competent tester the Stanford-Binet is a reliable instrument for use with cerebral-palsied children even when the tester uses his clinical judgment to make allowances for the child's handicaps in the administration and scoring of the test. This is not to say that certain individuals might not show marked changes in I.Q. scores from test to retest, but it does say that the number of times at which the psychologist's second evaluation will markedly differ from his first are likely to be a small proportion of the total number of children tested. Furthermore, in view of the considerable time interval involved in these studies between test and retest, it is also reasonable to assume that when the two estimates disagree, there is a good possibility that the change in estimate reflects a change in the child's level of functioning rather than an error of the test instrument or psychologist. Some case notes on particular patients used in the reliability study certainly support this latter contention.

Validation Studies

There are relatively few systematic studies of the validity of intelligence testing in the sense in which I am using validity in this paper. One of these attempts at a systematic study was undertaken by Denhoff and Holden (1956). In the authors' words, "This study attempts to show that psychological tests of cerebral-palsied children can actually be used to predict the child's clinical progress." Fifty cerebral palsied children were tested. The revised Stanford-Binet (Form L) was administered to all children who were able to respond at least at a one-and-a-half-year mental level. The Vineland Social Maturity Scale was used to estimate the intellectual level of those who functioned at a lower level. On the basis of the test results,

> ... the psychologist predicted prognosis as "good" if the intelligence quotient was above 85%, "fair" if the intelligence quotient was between 60% and 85%, and "poor" if the intelligence quotient was below 60%. [The mean age at the time of psychological evaluation was three and one fifth years, with a range from four months to twelve years. The mean I.Q. was "60.5%" with a range from "7 to 128%." Two years after the initial testing, clinical progress was assessed by the pediatrician who] rated the child's actual status as "good," "fair," or "poor." "Good" implied developmental progress beyond the child's expected rate over a two-year period with definitely improved physical, mental, and/or emotional status. "Fair" inferred progress within the expected rate, and "poor" was less than expected progress. [It is not clear in the report how the "child's expected rate of development" was deduced. Correlations were then made between the psychological predictions and the clinical progress. The authors report that] there was an over-all agreement of 81% between the initial psychological predictions and the actual clinical progress. [From this the authors conclude:] On the basis of the results presented it would appear that early psychological test predictions are valid indicators of future adjustment.

From my viewpoint, using intelligence evaluation to predict specified problem-solving abilities, I find this validity study difficult to evaluate. The criterion applied is apparently a measure of change from an expected level of "physical, mental and/or emotional status." Logically analyzed, the psychologist was required to estimate the change in "expected rate" of development in mental, physical, and/or emotional status. His estimate was given as "good," "fair," or "poor" ratings which were based on scores from the Vineland or the Binet. Unfortunately, the authors do not give a rationale for making such an estimate on the basis of these tests. The change in

the "expected rate" of development was then independently determined by the pediatrician after two years, and the correlation of
the psychologist's and pediatrician's rating were then taken as a
measure of validity of the psychologist's ratings. This analysis may
seem a little labored, but it is necessary in order to highlight what
the psychologist was supposed to be doing. He was not predicting
from a test score a future level of functioning. He was predicting
the difference between an expected rate of development and an
actual rate of development as it obtained two years after his initial
testing. Now we can see the importance of how the authors arrived
at the "expected" rate of development, yet we are given no information on this point. For the psychologist to be functioning in a rational way in this situation, he would have to know what the
expected rates of development were and he would have to have some
rationale for assuming that the test score was predictive of a change
in that expected rate of development. I suspect that such a rationale
is not only not reported by the authors, but does not exist. What was
undertaken in this study was a correlation between two ratings, one
by a psychologist and one by a pediatrician. This correlation was
statistically significant. The meaning of the correlation from a conceptual point of view is quite unclear. I wonder if the pediatrician's
ratings of change in expected development were not really ratings
of change but ratings of development as it was actually observed
after two years. In this case the correlation between test scores and
pediatric ratings is not so surprising. The original test score probably
correlated to a considerable extent with the child's level of development at that time, and if the test score correlated with the pediatrician's subsequent estimate of level of development, there would
be an acceptable rationale for expecting such a correlation.

This study highlights, I think, the need for the investigator to
state, at all times, precisely what it is that he does. Ambiguities or
omissions in the description can only lead to confusion in the communication of results. As a further illustration of this, I would like
to point out that when the pediatrician's ratings are based on "physical, mental, and/or emotional status" and they correlate with test
scores, we are left wondering what correlated with what? If the

mental evaluation of the pediatrician correlated highly with the Stanford-Binet score we would not be at a loss for an explanation. If the Binet score correlates with an estimate of physical or emotional status we feel in the need of explanation. It is possible in a sample of children with a wide range of physical handicap and neurological damage such as was used in this study that such a correlation would obtain since success on many Binet items depends upon intact motor and sensory equipment. Likewise, a certain degree of over-all emotional stability is necessary for the child to function successfully in a formal test situation. These types of explanation might throw light on the obtained correlation, but it would have been much more cogent and informative if the pediatrician had made three separate ratings of physical, mental, and emotional status and the test scores were correlated with each of these ratings separately.

This study of Denhoff and Holden leaves much to be desired as a validity study. However, it does attempt a formal investigation of validity in an area where formal investigations are notable for their absence.

The work of Taylor and Lord at the Children's Hospital in Boston is of great interest because of its conceptual approach, although it attempts less formally designed investigations of reliability and validity than some others I have considered here. Lord's later work (1937) at the Children's Hospital led her away from the kind of conceptualization advocated in the 1930 study that I have previously discussed. In her 1937 book she is much less interested in the measurement of intelligence as a faculty of the mind, and more interested in the use of psychological evaluation as a way of predicting the child's ability to achieve success in a learning situation. She states that "the practical purpose of the testing program is not to establish a mental status in terms of mental age but to make an analysis of the child's capacity which will be predictive of his educability along various lines." Edith Meyer Taylor (1959) who continued the work of Lord at the Children's Hospital summarized their approach as follows:

> Both of us have recognized the limited merits of intelligence quotients in children with cerebral palsy. In our psychological

studies we have tried to evaluate the child's ability to adjust to his present life-situation, and to adjust to the demands of his environment. Dr. Lord was interested especially in the child's educational potentialities and his prospects to learn how to read and write and do arithmetic. Coming from a slightly different psychological background, I have myself become more and more interested to see the educational problems as symptoms of broader difficulties. We have concentrated especially on the study of reasoning ability, perceptual organization, learning ability, etc., as they pertain to general adjustment of the individual. While the methods have varied and evolved in the past 23 years, the basic philosophy has remained the same; we have tried to judge and to predict how far the child could be expected to adjust to the ordinary demands of his life-situation.

Lord's 1937 publication attempts to summarize the experience gained from the psychological examination and follow-up of more than 300 cases of cerebral palsy. She considers the methodology and techniques of appraising the mental status of the child and gives illustrative case histories. For a number of cases she presents mental estimates based on psychological tests and reports of subsequent school performance, but these data are presented to illustrate the relationship between test results and educational planning rather than formal evidence for the validity of the psychological evaluation. Her illustrations and her discussion of them would indicate that when intellectual development is fairly even in different areas such as vocabulary, comprehension, and visual discriminations, the I.Q. estimate may, in spite of varying degrees of motor handicap and mental retardation, predict school achievement quite well. But when intellectual development is uneven in different areas, success in school is more variable and more difficult to predict.

Edith Taylor (1959) presents more formally some of the findings of the Boston group. In a follow-up study, 214 cerebral-palsied cases, who had been tested for the most part before the age of six years, were re-evaluated three to twelve years later at which time their chronological ages ranged from three to twenty years. As a result of the psychological examination at re-evaluation all cases were classified in the following categories: superior (I.Q. score greater than 110), average (I.Q. 90-110), borderline (I.Q. 70-90), defective (I.Q. 50-70), low-grade defective (I.Q. below 50). Unfortunately, since this follow-up study was not set up at the time of the original testings, the data from the original test reports were not in a directly comparable form and the psychological findings were not expressed in definite quantitative terms. It was therefore necessary for the investigators to classify these reports into categories assumed to be roughly equivalent to the re-evaluation categories set up on the basis of actual I.Q. scores. An examination of the classifications of the subjects on original and re-evaluative tests indicated that of the 214 cases, 157 (73%) were in the same category in both examinations; 33 cases (15%) were in a lower category on re-evaluation and 24 (11%) in a higher category. Only 4 of the cases differed by more than one step in category placement. Repeating this in Taylor's words:

> . . . in 57 cases (those in categories "average" and "superior") the psychologist could assure parents and doctors before the child was of school age that it was of normal intelligence (in 9 cases of superior intelligence). Forty of these children developed as well and two even better than anticipated (a total of 42 children or 72% of the 57 cases). In 107 cases the psychologist believed the child to be mentally defective at an early age. In 91 (85%) of these cases, this evaluation was proved correct by subsequent events. Of 50 children who were originally considered borderline cases (between defective and normal) 6 were better developed when re-examined than they had seemed before; 18 were more noticeably defective than they had appeared when younger; 26 remained in the borderline category.

These findings offer evidence for the reliability of such classifications over considerable time intervals. But in the examination of the causes of disagreement between initial and follow-up categorizations the study gave additional dividends in information that goes beyond this.

> It is not easy to determine for each case the extent to which the differences between original and later examinations result from the child's condition or from incorrect original appraisal. In a number of cases physical deterioration went with decline in men-

tal alertness. In some others it seemed that improved physical condition and increased opportunity for experience had bettered the mental situation also. However, study of the psychological records reveals some other significant causes of possible errors. It appears that most of the disagreements are found in cases where the first examiners tended to place more emphasis on the child's ability to use or respond to language than on other signs of comprehension. For instance, the most flagrant disagreements between original and later estimates are found in the group with pure extra-pyramidal involvement—often among the earliest patients. Of the eleven cases in this group who were originally thought to be defective but turned out to be borderline (6) or average (5) intelligence when examined more than ten years later, five had by then proved to be deaf or hard of hearing. (Medically they belonged to the kernicterus group). The others all had more or less serious speech delays due to dysarthria. In some other instances where the original estimates were lower than the re-evaluations, children classified in other medical groups had difficulty in speaking and learned to talk late. However, errors of prediction probably due to overemphasis on the importance of speech development also occurred with children who talked early. They had earned high ratings as young children because of their verbal fluency; later this facility was not as useful to them, since at higher age level good performance is determined more by reasoning power than by fluency of speech alone.

Brain-Damaged Children Without Gross Neurological Impairment

The studies so far considered have all been concerned with the cerebral-palsied child. Because of the prominent motor, speech, and sensory handicaps existing in this group, the necessity for special study of the problems in the intelligence evaluation of these children is immediately apparent. However, for those children where damage to the central nervous system does not involve gross neurological impairment, the need for special attention to problems of intelligence evaluation, in the sense I have been using it in this paper, has been much less widely recognized. These children with various forms of organic brain dysfunction without gross neurological signs are sometimes referred to as having "minimal brain damage." The term is unfortunate in its connotations, for certainly many children falling in this group are more seriously impaired behaviorally and intellectually than many a child with an obvious cerebral palsy. Probably because of the difficulty in diagnosis in this group through conventional neurological techniques, the use of intelligence testing has often focused on the diagnostic value of patterns of intellectual functioning rather than on the prediction of problem-solving behavior.

Smith (1926) was one of the first to indicate that test patterns might be diagnostic of brain injury. He wrote:

> At the time of birth, too often the minor injuries are overlooked, or later if noted they have spontaneously improved, so that later in life we often see a picture of mental deficiency in which there is no outward expression of brain injury or apparent cause. I cannot help but feel that many of the cases of mental deficiency which present atypical pictures, especially those which do not readily conform to average personality patterns and which show a scattering in intellectual ability, can be explained on such a basis, especially when we realize that the association pathways all develop after such an injury.

In succeeding decades there were more investigations of patterns of scatter as an aid in the diagnosis of brain damage (Bender, 1942; Bradley, 1955; Wechsler, 1944). At the same time there was increased reliance on the use of behavioral and personality factors in the diagnosis of brain damage (Bender, 1942; Bradley, 1955). The typical brain-damaged child was described as hyperactive, irritable, emotionally overactive, anxious, impulsive, and as having a low frustration tolerance and short attention span. This literature on intellectual and behavioral patterns in the functioning of brain-damaged individuals is huge and continues to grow. Despite the great interest in patterns of scores on intellectual tasks involving perception, memory, conceptualization, and reasoning, there has been much less interest in the problem of predicting the level of functioning of the minimally brain-damaged child in such problem-solving situations as are presented by formal schooling.

Strauss and his co-workers (1947, 1955) have been concerned with the relationship between school performance and test patterns in the minimally brain-injured child, but in their publications they tend to lump these children with children with more obvious neurological damage. Doing this, they emphasize similarities in patterns of intellectual and personality functioning in brain-injured children with varying etiology and degree of impairment. They say:

A brain-injured child is a child who before, during, or after birth has received an injury to or suffered an infection of the brain. As a result of such organic impairment, defects of the neuromotor system may be present or absent; however, such a child may show disturbances in perception, thinking, and emotional behavior, either separately or in combination. These disturbances prevent or impede a normal learning process. Special educational methods have been devised to remedy these specific handicaps.

This concept of the "exogenous" mentally defective child was later enlarged to include "the clinical syndrome of the brain-injured child who is not mentally defective, but who in spite of 'normalcy in I.Q.' as tested is still 'defective.'" Strauss et al. were apparently using the term "defective" to mean that the child has a school learning problem related to an uneven development of intellectual skills and/or behavioral difficulties which are presumed to be due to brain injury. In the case studies presented in their last volume (1955), several examples of what might be called minimally brain-damaged children are presented. But in every instance these were children who had already demonstrated their inability to adapt to the intellectual and behavioral demands of a regular classroom situation, and the problem was to prescribe educational procedures to help them overcome their learning problems.

However, my own clinical experience has often faced me with the problem of deciding which child with a syndrome suggestive of minimal brain injury is capable of functioning in a regular classroom and which one needs a special type of educational experience. Conversations with professional colleagues suggest that they are not infrequently faced with the same problem.

Robert is a case in point. He was brought to our clinic at the age of six with a school learning problem. His parents were also concerned about his hyperactivity, his short attention span, his nervousness, and his overexcitability. They described him as a sociable child who related well to adults but had difficulty in relating to children his own age. His low frustration tolerance, his sensitivity, and his inability to assert himself put him at a disadvantage in the give-and-take, rough-and-tumble atmosphere of six-year-old children at play. In addition, other children were likely to view him as "odd." His father explained this in part as Robert's overreadiness to please and to make friends.

Birth and developmental history were as follows. There had been a moderate amount of vaginal bleeding in the fifth month of pregnancy requiring the mother to remain in bed for several days. Birth weight was 4 lbs., 14 oz. and Robert was placed in a premature unit. He was in an incubator and given oxygen during the first few days after birth. He was discharged in two weeks. Colic was present until about eight months. He walked at fourteen months. Simple sentences were used before the second birthday, but the parents considered him a slow speaker and maintained that he did not talk clearly until after his fourth birthday. He was bladder trained at three years, but even at six years he had to be reminded to go to the bathroom. Bowel training was difficult. He would not sit on the potty chair, and training was done by having him stand on newspapers spread upon the floor. Neurological examination at the time he came to our clinic was essentially within normal limits, with the following exceptions: Robert exhibited some difficulty with gross and fine motor coordination. He was unsure of his orientation in space, clumsily bumping into objects. He could skip only on one foot. There was definite difficulty in performing alternating repetitive movements. Even with eyes open he could not sustain his weight on one foot. He grasped a pencil with marked awkwardness and had trouble copying a triangle. The neurologist's impression was that there was no active neurological disease but probably some organic brain deficit, prenatally determined. On psychological examination, Robert obtained a Full Scale I.Q. of 68 on the WISC, a Verbal Scale I.Q. of 79 and a Performance Scale I.Q. of 62. With the notable exception of the vocabulary subtest, scores on all other subtests both Verbal and Performance were markedly below age-level expectation. On the vocabulary subtest Robert achieved a test age of 7-6 which was above his chronological age level of 6-7. On the arithmetic subtest he achieved a test age of 5-2. All other subtests fell below this level. On block designs he was not able to obtain a single raw-score credit. On object assembly he obtained just a single credit but was nevertheless able correctly to recognize and name the puzzles, although he could not put them together. On the Bender Gestalt most of his reproductions were unrecognizable, only the dotted patterns maintaining a semblance of the original Gestalt.

At the time of Robert's initial contact with our clinic, the school was prepared to leave Robert back and was seriously considering his candidacy for a special class. The psychologist who examined Robert and the therapist who was treating him for the emotional aspects of his problem were of the opinion that it was not meaningful to plan for Robert's education in terms of the I.Q. score or his present level of functioning in the class. They were impressed by the fact that the boy had shown some progress in learning to read; that the history indicated no serious retardation in development; that although he could not solve the puzzles in the object assembly test, he had sufficient perceptual skills to recognize what they were; that he showed evidence of considerable social skills in his interactions with adults; and that his vocabulary was fully age adequate not only in the test situation but in his everyday speech. The therapist further felt that Robert's anxiety and short attention span must be a major handicap in the learning situation and was of the opinion that if Robert could be helped with his emotional problems by psychotherapy, or if the teaching situation could be slightly modified to take into account his particular problems, he might perform more efficiently in school. In consultation with the principal and his teacher it was decided that Robert should repeat the first grade instead of being placed in a special class. It was further decided that a teacher would be employed for part-time individual tutoring. Individual tutoring was thought desirable, for it had been observed that Robert worked best in the classroom when the teacher stood beside him. It was not so much a matter of the teacher's offering direct help to him, but rather it seemed that her presence was necessary to keep him oriented toward his work. Why this was so we are not quite certain, but we do know that Robert had a high investment in his interpersonal relationships. For Robert it was important, even more than for the average child, that everybody like him, and since he painfully experienced the rejection that his odd behavior patterns sometimes evoked from other children, he was especially pleased when someone showed an interest in him. The teacher's presence near him when he worked and her expression of approval when he succeeded may have been sufficient for him to overcome the problems in attention span and distractibility that usually interfered with his work. With this program, Robert repeated the first grade successfully. In the second grade he got along so well that the tutoring was not thought necessary, although at times the teacher would keep him after school to give him a little extra help or to permit him to finish an assignment that his slower work patterns had not permitted him to finish with the other children. At the end of the second grade his reading ability was above class average; his arithmetic skills placed him in the lowest quarter of the class but still sufficiently high for promotion. On the last follow-up contact we learned that he had been promoted to the fourth grade, after an adequate performance in the third grade.

In Robert's case, an examination of test patterns, combined with the developmental history and the observations of everyday behavior, led to a conclusion about this child's educability that would not have been reached on the basis of his I.Q. and his actual performance in the first grade. We, of course, still have some concerns about his ability to progress without setback in a regular school program, and we remain in contact with the family in order that we may be alerted as soon as he shows signs of getting into academic difficulty. At such a time we would re-evaluate his status and consider what modifications in the educational program might be necessary. But the fact remains that Robert had demonstrated greater success than would have first been expected and that this level of success had been "predicted" on the basis of test patterns, case history, and behavioral observations. How many cases like Robert exist and how successful the psychologist would be in sorting out the Roberts from the other children with similar I.Q.s who will not succeed in school we do not know. Certainly, we have seen other "minimally brain-damaged" children with test patterns similar to Robert's and with even higher I.Q.s where school success was not achieved. It is precisely because of our lack of knowledge that we express concern that, in their present very active interest in improving skills in the diagnosis of minimal brain damage, the investigators in this field do not overlook the importance of the problems related to the reliable and valid evaluation of the intellectual functioning of these children.

DISCUSSION

In reviewing this brief and selective survey of the literature I would like to draw several generalizations which I hope will give a fair picture of our present state of knowledge and suggest some directions for future research.

On the basis of accumulated clinical experience there would seem to be no question in the minds of the various professional workers in this field that psychological tests administered and interpreted by an experienced clinician provide a sufficiently reliable and valid measure of a child's present level of intellectual functioning and his future potential. These tests, then, in the opinion of experts, are a valuable prerequisite to planning for the education and rehabilitation of the brain-damaged child.

If the purpose of reliability and validity studies by the psychologist is to convince physicians and educators that they have something to gain in the use of psychological testing with brain-damaged children, there would be little need to undertake such investigations. But the psychologist cannot be content with the stamp of approval of his professional colleagues. Basically, his professional orientation is toward developing a science of human behavior. He may be invested in such a science for its intellectual gratifications or he may be invested in it because of its clinical usefulness. Irrespective of the basis of his interest, he cannot be content with partial understanding and sizable errors in his predictions.

In discussing the problem of the evaluation of intelligence in brain-damaged children I have pointed out the necessity of defining intelligence evaluation in an unambiguous and clinically useful fashion. I have done this by proposing that intelligence evaluation be viewed as a process of predicting a subject's problem-solving behavior in specified situations. In assessing a psychologist's success in this predictive process we must consider the behavior he chooses to observe, the reliability with which he observes or measures that behavior, the way in which he infers his prediction from the behavioral observations, and finally the validity of the prediction against the criterion.

Reliability Studies
In the area of reliability of observations, I feel that it is essential to distinguish between the reliability of test instruments and the reli-

ability of the clinical judgments. Schonell (1956, 1958) is the only one of the authors discussed who seems to be directly grappling with this problem. In other publications it is often impossible to tell whether we are dealing with the reliability of the instrument or the clinical judgment. In still other publications authors disregard the instruments altogether and talk about the reliability of the intelligence estimates without detailing the test instruments used. Their position seems to be that the instruments used in a standard fashion are unreliable and it is meaningless to talk in terms of scores. However, if the instruments are completely unreliable for the evaluation of intelligence in brain damage, then one would have to question why the psychologist makes use of them at all. I would suspect that what these authors are not taking into account is that the reliability of a test instrument varies with the kind of population on which it is used and with the way in which it is used. The problem, therefore, is not to disregard reliability but to make studies of reliability with the different kinds of populations that one deals with and with whatever kinds of modifications one wishes to make in test administration. Let us consider some typical problems in this area using the Stanford-Binet as an illustration. It is known that the reliability of the Binet for two specific populations tends to be greater in that population with the greater I.Q. range, other things being equal (McNemar, 1942). Thus if we take a sample of 100 brain-injured subjects with I.Q.s ranging from 30 to 120, we may have a fairly respectable reliability coefficient. But with brain-damaged children the point has been repeatedly made that the problem in estimating the I.Q. rarely occurs in the very bright or the very defective child. Schonell (1958) and others have pointed out that the problem is in estimating the I.Q. in the 50 to 85 range.

I would suggest that the clinician should have greatest concern about the reliability of the Stanford-Binet for brain-damaged children with I.Q.s in this range. Yet, nowhere in the literature are reliability coefficients reported separately for this range. Again McNemar's analysis of the original standardizing data for the Binet indicates that reliability varies with age, with the reliability coefficient increasing with older age groups. This suggests that for the handicapped child we again need reliability estimates on age groups, but they are not to be found in the literature. Case studies and the informal reports of the Boston group would indicate that reliability varies with the type and degree of handicap. Again, the literature provides no precise estimates of reliability for the different subgroups of brain-damaged. The comments made on the deficiencies of our knowledge of instrument reliability could be repeated for the reliability of clinical judgments. Again, we lack precise information on how these vary with age, I.Q. range, and type of disorder.

One further point on reliability is that most of the studies available in the literature involve time intervals of several years between test and retest. Some of the authors have pointed out that this speaks all the more for the reliability of the instruments or the psychologists' judgments. However, it should be noted that when one undertakes a test-retest·estimate of reliability one is ordinarily concerned with determining to what extent random fluctuations of performance will effect the measurements. We either use the same test at relatively short intervals or we use alternate forms of the same test. This is customary procedure in the standardization of instruments. When, as is the case in the studies of brain-damaged children, test and retests are undertaken at intervals of years, we are no longer measuring what is customarily meant by test reliability. A child at four years of age may be given items from the third- through the fifth-year level on the Binet. Retested at seven years he may be given items from the sixth- to the ninth-year level. One can question whether the test is measuring the same thing at these different age levels. Certainly it is known that the Binet becomes more heavily weighted with verbal items and less with visual-motor items as one goes up the age scale. Therefore to present test-retest scores at several years' interval is not strictly speaking a reliability measure. As Anastasi (1954) has pointed out, such long-range retests are best considered as "I.Q. constancy" studies or studies on the predictability of future scores from I.Q. scores obtained earlier in childhood. I would feel that, from the clinical point of view, such studies are in themselves invaluable and much needed, but for the sake of conceptual clarity it is misleading to speak of a test-retest reliability study of the Binet at a two- or three-year interval. In this sense the studies reported in this article have been deficient to a greater or lesser extent in not distinguishing between an "I.Q. constancy" study and a more conventional reliability study. It is of further note that none of the investigators herein reported have availed themselves of the alternate forms of the Stanford-Binet as a readily available tool for a reliability study.

Validation Studies

In the case of the validity studies I feel that there is need for precise specification of criteria with a suitable rationale for the selection of these criteria. The Denhoff and Holden study (1956) is poorly designed from a conceptual point of view. The work of Lord (1937) and Taylor (1959) is much more sound conceptually in that they view the problem as one of prediction of function in educational or other nontest situations. But their results are reported in summarized clinical impressions rather than with detailed presentations of predictions and outcomes. When Taylor resorts to a more formal presentation of findings in the follow-up of cerebral-palsied cases, we are again dealing with prediction of function in one test situation from function in an earlier test situation rather than with what would customarily be considered a validity study. However, although I do not think that this type of study should be confused with a validity study proper, I do think it has demonstrated value in pointing out the need for formal investigations to determine the reasons for success and failure in prediction.

I would hope that future validity studies—which should be designed as validity studies before the initial collection of data— would be as specific as possible in the selection of criteria and would provide suitable rationale for the selection of those criteria. I believe that a distinction should be made between the validity of the test instrument and the validity of the clinical judgment. In making this kind of distinction it may be possible to determine what is involved in the clinical judgment that makes for a greater degree of validity than the test score itself. It may be that the factors going into the clinical judgments can be teased out and standardized in such a way that we may develop better test instruments and so be less dependent upon the clinician with unusual skills.

Behavioral Observations

Finally we must consider the behavioral observations a psychologist makes and the kinds of inferences he draws from them. The studies reviewed have usually been explicit in regard to behavioral observations in so far as they were specific about the test instrument used, but even here detail is often missing. Thus in Taylor's (1959) follow-up we are not given names of specific tests. For the original tests we are only told that the subjects were tested with various instruments, and then the psychologist made his estimate of their intelligence, presumably on the basis of test performance and additional observations. For the retests we have I.Q. estimates, but specification of the tests and the extra test observations are lacking. Schonell (1956) is precise about the test used and gives a general description of ways in which test administration was modified. When *estimated* I.Q.s were different from *tested* I.Q.s, a report was given justifying the difference, but the analyses of these reports or their contents are not presented, and so we cannot know what kinds of observations resulted in a difference between the two I.Q. scores. Many authors in connection with case histories or in giving recommendations for test administration present us with lists of extratest behavior which are used in modifying or in interpreting test results. Until one actually studies the behavioral items in such lists and their relationships to the test results and to the subsequent performance in problem-solving situations, we have no efficient way of assaying their usefulness.

Let us take a concrete example. Early in his training every psychologist is taught that anxiety can affect performance in a test situation; he is therefore told that the anxiety level of the subject and its interaction with performance must be taken into account in interpreting the test results. This does not answer the question of what kinds of behavior on the part of the testee are indicative of anxiety. Are we as clinical psychologists confident that we can reliably measure a subject's level of anxiety while he is taking a test? Surely, when a subject begins to bite his nails, to stammer, to flush, and to express his concern verbally, we can be confident that he is experiencing an anxiety reaction. But does anxiety always express itself so overtly? I once conducted an experiment (Doris and Sarason, 1955) using college students who on the basis of a questionnaire had previously rated themselves as being highly anxious or relatively unanxious in a test situation. These subjects were given various items from intelligence scales under rather stressful conditions of administration. The experimental design was such that I did not know who were the high-anxious and who were the low-anxious subjects at the time of testing. For each subject I had prepared a check list of common signs of anxiety, and in addition I made an over-all estimate of their anxiety level. Neither the scores on the check list nor the over-all subjective judgments were significantly related to the subject's placement in the anxiety groups. This same procedure has been used by other investigators using self-rated anxiety groups and with rare exceptions the results are the same. In our study, one subject still remains vividly in mind. He was a quiet, well-composed youth who seemed to perform with efficiency throughout the test. I rated him low anxious with a high degree of subjective confidence in his rating. In interviewing the boy after the test, it came out that he had actually felt panicky throughout much of the test and that he felt that his degree of upset had interfered with his thinking. Apparently in this case anxiety had been expressed in visceral responses and feeling states unobservable by the tester.

If a clinician must infer the level of anxiety of the tested in order to evaluate properly his performance, we can see the kind of problem that is posed. What kinds of behavior can be used as indicators of anxiety? How reliable are the clinician's observations of such behavior, and what is the relative validity of these different behaviors as anxiety indicators? We face the same problems in the use of extra-test observations as we do in the test itself.

Problems in the measurement of anxiety, motivation, and of all the various attitudinal and situational factors that interact in determining not only the test performance but performance in the criterion situation which the test predicts are not peculiar to the testing of the brain-damaged subjects. Nor are other areas of psychological testing any further advanced in the study of these factors. The clinician faced with the individual patient attempts to assay such factors as best he can and to incorporate them into his prediction. With the present state of knowledge in the field it is unlikely that we can expect otherwise for some time to come. However, studies on anxiety and motivation in test and learning situations have been appearing with increasing frequency in recent years (Atkinson, 1958; Sarason et al., 1960), and they suggest that we shall eventually have a body of experimentally demonstrated knowledge to aid the clinician in his individualized predictions. Meantime, I think it would help investigators in planning studies on extratest factors if the clinicians in reporting their case studies or summarizing their clinical experience could be as explicit as possible as to how extratest factors were assayed.

Test Factors

There is one other aspect of observations and their derived inferences which I would like to touch upon. This concerns the fact that in order to make rational and valid inferences from any observation of test performance we must know what is involved in the test performance. Specifically, what kinds of abilities are necessary for success on a test item and what kinds of disabilities make for failure? Are the abilities involved sensory, perceptual, motor, verbal, associative, conceptual, mnemonic, rational, etc.? In the past, the psychologist has too often relied upon an armchair analysis of the nature of his tests and assumed that the abilities involved in the solution of a test item could be deduced by an inspection of the obvious characteristics of the task. With the advent of factor-analytic techniques and their application to test instruments, it became apparent that even a test of very homogenous make-up might involve factors other than those which are readily apparent from an inspection of the test items, and two tests apparently quite similar in content might in fact be measuring quite different abilities. As an example, we may consider the arithmetic subtest of the Wechsler scale. On the surface one might not consider this test to involve much in the way of a memory factor. However, factor analysis of the adult forms of the Wechsler scales (1958) has indicated that a memory factor accounts for a considerable part of the variance in scores obtained on this subtest. Presumably, although we cannot be certain, the same would hold for the arithmetic subtest in the Wechsler-Intelligence Scale for Children. In the light of such information we re-examine the arithmetic subtest and note that its instructions call for the subject to solve the problem "mentally" without the use of paper and pencil. The question arises, would a paper-and-pencil arithmetic test be so heavily loaded with a memory factor? The evidence to say that this is so is not available, but it does pose the problem for the psychologist trying to predict from the Wechsler to a child's ability to master arithmetic in the school situation. Can he be sure for a particular child that he has a good measure of the child's ability to do arithmetical computations using paper and pencil if he has given him a test which prohibits the use of paper and pencil? For a large group of children it would seem reasonable to expect that the correlation between "mental" and paper-and-pencil computations would be high, but what of an individual child whose brain damage may have selectively impaired memory function?

Cohen's (1952) factor-analytic studies of the Wechsler scale are also of interest because they suggest that the factor loadings of various tests may change with the type of population being studied. Applying the Wechsler-Bellevue test to groups of psychoneurotics, schizophrenics, and brain-damaged patients, he concluded that some of the subtests do not measure the same common factor or combination of factors in different neuropsychiatric groups. He maintains that one must know the patient's diagnosis in order to know what common factor or factors the test is measuring in the case of that patient. To illustrate this, let us consider this study in more detail. Cohen in his factor analysis of the Wechsler-Bellevue identified four principal factors which may be considered as representative of four kinds of psychological functions that underlie performance on the Wechsler. Factor G was considered as *"present* general intellectual functioning." Factor A or the Verbal factor involved richness of vocabulary and verbal-symbolic manipulative ability. Factor B, or the Nonverbal Organization factor, involves the ability to organize visually perceived material into meaningful wholes under conditions of a time limit. Factor C, or the Freedom from Distractibility factor, is a conative factor which makes it possible for problem elements to "register" and to be maintained without loss in the course of manipulation, i.e., the ability to attend or concentrate.

In discussing the arithmetic subtest Cohen maintains, on the basis of his analysis, that "it does not measure a single factor in all the groups. The arithmetic test is found to measure the Freedom from Distractibility factor in the psychoneurotic group, the Verbal factor in the schizophrenic groups, and *both* these factors in the brain-damaged group. The complexity of this test provides a good example of a state of affairs, discoverable only through the comparative factor-analytic technique, whose existence leads to much confusion in pattern-analytic interpretation and research."

The conclusions to be drawn from these factor-analytic studies are obvious. We cannot assume that a test is measuring only what its apparent content would suggest, and we must assume that for different groups of patients the same test may be measuring different kinds of intellectual functioning.

While factor analysis is an important tool for identifying the various abilities or attributes that are measured by tests, there is still a great need for experimental investigation of the nature of our test instruments. The need for this kind of study is nowhere more pressing than in those tests commonly assumed to measure perceptual skills. The reason for this is twofold. On the one hand it is precisely these tests that are so often invoked in the diagnosis of minimal brain damage. On the other hand it is often assumed that the brain-damaged child's difficulty in learning situations is to a considerable degree attributable to perceptual difficulties. If a significant number of brain-damaged children have deficits in perceptual skills not directly attributable to sensory defects or psychological factors such as distractibility, it has implication for our theoretical understanding of the nature of brain functions and for the practical problems of educating these children. Therefore, if brain-damaged patients do more poorly on perceptual tests, we must be certain that the tests are really measuring perceptual abilities or we will be led astray both in our theorizing on brain functions and in our attempts to provide suitable educational and rehabilitative experience for these patients.

As a result of numerous studies, Strauss and his co-workers (1947, 1955) have assumed perceptual differences between brain-damaged and nonbrain-damaged subjects. These findings have led the Strauss group to devise educational techniques designed to surmount the brain-damaged child's perceptual handicaps. Other educators in this area have tended to follow this lead. It is pertinent to ask if the purported perceptual tasks measure only perceptual skills or whether they measure also underlying sensory capacities, complex integrations of perceptual and motor acts, language or other symbolic skills, and factors such as Cohen's "Freedom from Distractibility." If such factors are involved, can we assume that the brain-damaged child's failure on such a test is due to a lack of perceptual skill? Or if one brain-damaged child fails on such a test because of a demonstrable perceptual difficulty, can we assume that the next brain-damaged child failed because of perceptual difficulty, or must we allow in this case that other factors may have been responsible for the failure? If the latter is the case, would we be justified in prescribing the same educational experience for all brain-damaged children who show poor performance on perceptual tests or is it incumbent on us to determine what particular lack of ability underlies each given failure?

Experimental attempts to clarify the nature of perceptual tests have been generally scarce, and it seems that much more research effort goes into the devising of new perceptual tests than in trying to understand the old ones. One exception to this generalization is the study of Bortner and Birch (1960) who attempted to dissociate perceptual and motor factors in the performance of brain-damaged patients on the Wechsler-Bellevue block design test, a test frequently used in clinical practice for making inferences about perceptual skills. In this study brain-damaged and nonbrain-damaged neurological patients were administered the block designs in the usual fashion except that each patient attempted all designs no matter how many he failed. Afterward the patient was presented with the pictured design of each item that he had failed and then shown three models made of blocks. One represented the patient's original unsuccessful attempt to reproduce the design; a second was a standard incorrect reproduction devised by the experimenters; and the third was the correct reproduction. The patient was then asked to select the correct design from the three models. Thus, the authors hoped to separate the perceptual-motor aspect of the task as represented in the subject's original failure from the purely perceptual task as represented by his selection of the design from three alternatives. The results indicated that ten nonbrain-damaged subjects had twenty-eight failures in constructing the designs, but only two failures in correctly identifying the design in an alternative choice situation. For twenty brain-damaged subjects there were fifty-eight failures to construct the designs, but only fourteen failures to identify the designs. The authors conclude, "the inability of brain-injured patients to reproduce block designs is not based upon an inability to accurately perceive the presented model. Rather the difficulty appears to involve an inability to translate a percept into an appropriately organized pattern of acts." In view of the sweeping conclusion of these authors, I think it ought to be pointed out that on the basis of chance alone there is the likelihood of improvement in the choice situation as compared to the reproduction situation. In the alternative choice situation the subject is presented only with designs on which he has previously failed. He is now asked to select the right design from three alternatives. Even if his guesses are purely random guesses he has at least a one in three chance of selecting the right alternative, and hence on chance alone he should have one third less failures in the choice situation as compared to the reproduction situation. Thus with fifty-eight reproduction failures in the brain-damaged group, I would expect that by chance alone there would be approximately forty failures in the choice situation. The only way we could expect fifty-eight failures in the choice situation would be if we maintained that the perceptual disability of the brain-damaged was such that he would always see the blocks distorted in a particular way for a particular pictured design. This is obviously unlikely. Admittedly, the obtained rate of fourteen failures is a considerable improvement; but if we allow for the operation of chance, it is not quite so large an improvement as the authors' presentation would suggest. I would also wonder why the authors minimize the difference in the per cent of error in the choice situation for the two groups. The per cent of errors for the nonbrain-damaged is 7 and for the brain-damaged it is 24. Therefore, even in the "purely" perceptual situation with the block designs, the brain-damaged do more poorly than the controls. A more cautious interpretation of this study would be that it offers support for the contention that at least some failures in the brain-damaged group do not seem to be the direct result of an inability to perceive the designs correctly.

Whatever the specific limitations of this study, it is the kind of study that is badly needed for the effective use of perceptual tests with brain-damaged patients. While the motor components in many standard perceptual tests are obvious, other less obvious considerations such as the degree to which test performance is influenced by factors such as distractibility, perseverance, language skills, and anxiety must also be taken into account. For example, I recall testing a cerebral-palsied boy with the spiral-aftereffect apparatus and some similar apparatus designed to test the perception of illusory motion with varied stimuli. Much controversial research has been reported on this illusion in brain-damaged subjects. My subject reported no illusory movement when asked in the conventional way whether the spiral was moving. However, when the question was asked, "Is it not moving or is it moving a tiny bit?" the subject responded by saying it was moving a little bit, and he demonstrated on repeated trials that he could correctly indicate the varying direction of the illusory movement not only in the case of the spiral but with other stimuli. Here it would seem that the subject's understanding of the frame of reference in which movement was to be described was important for his correct reporting of the illusion. Compared to the rapid and sweeping real movement of the spiral the illusory movement when it has stopped may be indeed a tiny movement for brain-damaged and nonbrain-damaged subjects alike. The subject must understand that the "tiny movement" is what you wish him to report. Therefore, if a group of brain-damaged children differ from nonbrain-damaged children on a perceptual test such as the spiral aftereffect, we must be certain the brain-damaged child comprehends what is required of him just as fully as the nonbrain-damaged child. In addition, other factors such as attention span and distractibility must also be taken into account, for the experiencing of the illusion is dependent in part on the total length of time with which one observes the stimulus. That the brain-damaged child has been exposed to the illusion for the same length of time as the nonbrain-damaged child does not mean that he has attended to it for the same time.

In these perceptual tasks as in all aspects of intelligence evaluation of the brain-damaged child, we are in need of many more thorough, carefully designed and executed investigations. The value of such investigations is certainly not limited to developing our clinical skills for working with the brain-damaged child, as important as that might be. It goes beyond that in contributing to our basic knowledge of brain function and behavior. In that way such studies have general relevance to the fields of neurology, psychiatry, and psychology, as well as a very special importance for those working in the field of child development.

SUMMARY

In this paper it has been proposed that for clinical purposes the evaluation of intelligence be viewed as a process of prediction. In this process the clinician predicts from the subject's performance in certain standardized test situations the subject's potential for achievement or level of performance in certain learning or problem-solving situations that are posed by our culture. This conceptualization has been advocated because it provides a framework which permits the psychologist to apply efficiently his skills to the clinical problem facing him. At the same time it permits the psychologist to evaluate critically his contribution to the solution of that clinical problem. This conceptual framework was then utilized in reviewing the history of practice and research in the intellectual evaluation of the brain-damaged child. Early workers such as Smith, Doll, and Lord addressed themselves to the problems of selection of suitable test instruments and techniques of administration. Because of the state of the field, problems of prediction and the concurrent problems of reliability and validity of measurements were not dealt with in any explicit or rigorous way. In subsequent decades, studies on the reliability of measurements began to appear, reaching their most sophisticated form to date in the work of Schonell. But despite the excellence of this latter work many important questions of reliability remain unanswered. Formal investigations of validity on the other hand are still notably scarce, and the few that exist are far below the standards we might reasonably expect in view of the general knowledge available in the field of tests and measurements. In addition to the obvious need for more formal and more rigorous investigations of reliability and validity of test instruments, it was argued that there is a pressing need for investigating the judgmental process by which the clinician evaluates the extratest behavior of the patient. Finally, the need was pointed out for investigations aimed at determining precisely what abilities are measured in a given patient population by our various test instruments. The results of such investigations are assumed to be relevant not only to our work with brain-damaged children but to our more general understanding of behavior.

BIBLIOGRAPHY

Anastasi, A. (1954), *Psychological Testing*. New York: Macmillan.

Atkinson, J. W. (1958), *Motives in Fantasy, Action and Society*. New York: Van Nostrand.

Bender, L. (1942), Post-encephaletic Behavior Disorders in Childhood. In: *Encephalitis*, ed., J. B. Neal. New York: Grune & Stratton.

Bortner, M. & Birch, H. (1960), Perceptual and Perceptual-motor Dissociation in Brain-damaged Patients. *J. Nerv. Ment. Dis.*, 130:49-53.

Bradley, C. (1955), Organic Factors in the Psychopathology of Childhood. In: *Psychopathology of Childhood*, ed. P. H. Hoch & J. Zubin. New York: Grune & Stratton.

Cohen, J. C. (1952), A Factor-analytically Based Rationale for the Wechsler-Bellvue. *J. Consult. Psychol.*, 26:272-277.

Crowell, D. H. & Crowell, D. C. (1954), Intelligence Test Reliability for Cerebral Palsied Children. *J. Consult. Psychol.*, 18:276.

Denhoff, E. & Holden, R. H. (1956), Prognostic Studies in Children with Cerebral Palsy. *J. Amer. Med. Assn.*, 161:781-784.

Doll, E. A., Phelps, W. M., & Melcher, R. T. (1932), *Mental Deficiency Due to Birth Injuries*. New York: Macmillan.

Doris, J. & Sarason, S. (1955), Test Anxiety and Blame Assignment in a Failure Situation. *J. Abnorm. Soc. Psychol.*, 50:335-338.

Gesell, A. & Amatruda, C. S. (1947), *Developmental Diagnosis*, 2nd ed. New York: Paul B. Hoeber.

Lord, E. E. (1930), A Study of the Mental Development of Children with Lesion in the Central Nervous System. *Genet. Psychol. Monogr.*, 7:365-486.

―――(1937), *Children Handicapped by Cerebral Palsy*. New York: Commonwealth Fund.

McNemar, Q. (1942), *The Revision of the Stanford-Binet Scale*. Boston: Houghton Mifflin.

Meyer, E. & Crothers, B. (1953), Psychological and Physical Evaluation of Patients with Cerebral Palsy Studied for Periods of Ten Years or More. *Amer. J. Phys. Med.*, 32:153-158.

Sarason, S. B., Davidson, K. S., Lighthall, F. F., Waite, R. R., & Ruebush, B. K. (1960), *Anxiety in Elementary School Children*. New York: Wiley.

Schonell, F. E. (1956), *Educating Spastic Children*. Edinburgh: Oliver & Boyd.

―――(1958), Intelligence Testing. In: *Recent Advances in Cerebral Palsy*, ed. R. S. Illingworth. London: Churchhill.

Smith, G. B. (1926), Cerebral Accidents of Childhood and Their Relationships to Mental Deficiency. *Welf. Mag.*, 17:18-33.

Strauss, A. A. & Kephart, N. C. (1955), *Psychopathology and Education of the Brain-Injured*, Vol. II. New York: Grune & Stratton.

―――& Lehtinen, L. E. (1947), *Psychopathology and Education of the Brain-Injured Child*. New York: Grune & Stratton.

Taylor, E. M. (1959), *Psychological Appraisal of Children with Cerebral Defects*. Cambridge: Harvard Univ. Press.

Wechsler, D. (1944), *The Measurement of Adult Intelligence*, 3rd ed. Baltimore: Williams & Wilkins.

―――(1958), *The Measurement and Appraisal of Adult Intelligence*. Baltimore: Williams & Wilkins.

Familial Mental Retardation: Some Possible Neurophysiological and Psychosocial Interrelationships

• *ROBERT B. KUGEL, M.D.*

State University of Iowa

As long as there have been philosophers, there have been questions raised as to whether nature or nurture is the more important ingredient in the development and functioning of man. With the advent of the scientific era and the theories of Darwin and Freud, the issues of heredity versus environment were kindled anew. As the controversy has raged, there often seems to have been little room for any middle ground.

This problem has had a particular twist in regard to mental retardation. Out of the thinking of the nineteenth century, there developed a concept that the human organism was born with a definite quantity of native intelligence which, barring illness or trauma affecting the brain, would essentially remain unaltered during the life of the individual. A series of studies best exemplified by the well-known report of the Kallikaks by Goddard (1912) seemed to show that intelligence was essentially inherited and furthermore was a single unitary trait inherited in much the same fashion as blue or brown eyes. Concomitantly, with the development of intelligence tests by Binet and others and with their ultimate widespread use, the concept of familial mental retardation took clear form. All of this became further strengthened by the application of the statistical principle of a normal curve of distribution. Intelligence tests were usually thought to be imperfect unless they were standardized so that 3 per cent of the population would be considered mentally retarded.

In the first edition of his book, Tredgold (1908) noted that approximately 80 per cent of all mentally retarded individuals would be considered to have familial mental retardation. This figure was revised in the latest edition of Tredgold and Soddy (1956) so that probably no more than 20 per cent of the total are considered to belong to this group. However, Yannet (1959) has indicated that this type of mental retardation still accounts for 60 to 70 per cent of all mentally retarded children in any given community. The change in these estimates has resulted from the increase in knowledge pertaining to specific etiology. Halperin (1946) suggests that familial mental retardation represents a normal but genetically inferior type of person. What type of biological basis there might be for the disorder is not clear.

Benda (1952) has pointed out that there is a significant incidence of central nervous system developmental anomalies occurring in so-called familial mentally retarded individuals. This information was obtained from routine autopsy studies. Most of the attention has been centered on the neuroanatomical defect present which was demonstrable either in a gross or microscopic fashion, with the implication that there was a clear relationship between anatomical defect and psychological malfunctioning. Scant consideration has been given to what possible interrelationships might exist between the neurophysiological background of the individual and the effects of adverse psychosocial existence. Masland, Sarason, and Gladwin (1958) have attempted to show some of the interrelationships that exist between these two factors and some of the several specific medical etiologies which may produce mental retardation. However, they have given very little attention to what interrelationships, if any, might exist with familial mental retardation.

A STUDY OF FAMILIAL MENTAL RETARDATION

With the above considerations as a background, an investigation was launched by a group of workers[1] to study intensively familial mental retardation. In this report we limit ourselves to a consideration of evidences of overt or covert pathology in the central nervous system in children with familial mental retardation and the implications of this association.

The investigation, which has come to be known as the Pine School Project, was planned as being an intensive longitudinal study of children with familial or endogenous mental retardation. The study was also planned so that at the same time deliberate attempts would be made to ameliorate the symptom of mental retardation, if possible, by altering the environment in as many ways as possible, short of removing the child from his home, in an effort to reduce the impact of the variety of forces thought to be responsible for the child's malfunctioning. Every effort was made to keep the children in their own homes. Since studies by Skodak (1939) and Skodak and Skeels (1949) have suggested that children placed in adoptive homes tended to approximate the level of intellectual functioning of the foster parents rather than that of the natural parents, the investigators wished to eliminate this variable. Whether any alteration could take place with these children remaining in the same environment would, of course, have great implication for the type of plans which communities might make in the future for dealing with families having this type of mental retardation.

For the purpose of this study, familial mental retardation was defined as meeting four criteria: (1) as occurring in persons from the lower socioeconomic class as defined by Warner (1957); (2) having at least one sibling or one parent who was mentally retarded; (3) having an I.Q. between 50 and 80 on the Stanford-Binet Test; and (4) having no known or presumed "organic" cause for the mental

[1] This study has been a cooperative venture between the College of Education and the Child Development Clinic, College of Medicine, at the State University of Iowa. The author is indebted to his colleagues Marlin Roll, Ph.D., Theron Alexander, Ph.D., Harry Brown, M.A., Mitchell Greene, M.Sc. (Soc. Admin.), June Triplett, M.P.H., and Mabel Parsons, M.S.

retardation. As an initial sample, there were eighteen children from nine families who were included in this study as shown in Table 2. All but one of these (C-1) met the four criteria. This boy was micro-cephalic. At the inception of this study the children were all between the ages of three and six. The intelligence of the parents is shown in Table 1.

TABLE 1

INTELLIGENCE OF PARENTS

		Retarded	Normal
Family A:	Mother		x
	Father		x
Family B:	Mother		x
	Father	x	
Family C:	Mother	x	
	Father	x	
Family D:	Mother	x	
	Father		x
Family E:	Mother		x
	Father		x
Family F:	Mother	x	
	Father		x
Family G:	Mother	x	
	Father	x	
Family H:	Mother	x	
	Father		x
Family I:	Mother	x	
	Father	?	

The medical evaluation of these children included careful and detailed history of prenatal, perinatal, and postnatal factors which might conceivably influence their later functioning. Not only was information sought from the parents about these facts, but the new-born hospital records were scrutinized whenever possible to eliminate any chance that important data might be overlooked and to verify the information given by the parents. Information was always sought about the history of subsequent illnesses. A detailed neurological examination as well as a general examination was conducted on all of these children in an effort to eliminate any child who might have some neurological deficit, be it ever so slight, which might conceivably contribute to mental retardation. Certain standard laboratory tests were included; a complete blood count, urinalysis, including phenylpyruvic acid determination, etc. No child was accepted who had had a convulsion at any time in his life up to this point. No child was accepted in the study who had any physical defect, such as congenital heart disease, which might reduce his energy potential and thereby alter his intellectual potential. Thus, seventeen of the eighteen children accepted in the study met the four criteria designed to select cases of familial mental retardation.

At a later date, electroencephalograms were obtained on the children. All of the electroencephalograms were performed on the same 15-channel machines. All of the records were run with the children asleep and awake with hyperventilation and with photic stimulation. In most instances sleep was induced with ¾ grain of Seconal. An extensive record was obtained on each youngster with the whole procedure lasting slightly over an hour. None of the children was considered ill at the time the record was taken, and every effort had been made to prepare the child for this experience so that the record would be obtained under optimal situations. Nine of the eighteen had abnormal records, a larger number than would be expected on the basis of distribution in the population (see Table 2).[2] It is this finding that determines the focus of this paper. It suggests that a group of children who were originally regarded as having no neurological or neurophysiological basis for their retardation may in fact have such a basis for this, which indeed may be on an inherited basis. This in no way contests or minimizes the fact that the additional influences of poor environmental circumstances may exaggerate a biological deficiency. It would seem that the combination of the biological and psychosocial handicaps is especially deleterious so far as optimal development of the individual is concerned.

[2] All of the electroencephalograms were interpreted by John R. Knott, Ph.D., Department of Psychiatry, State University of Iowa, to whom the author is also indebted.

TABLE 2

EEG and I.Q. Scores in Subjects

Subject	Age (1958)	I.Q.	EEG
A-1	4	68	14/sec. positive spikes in sleep.
A-2	3	62	Normal.
B-1	7	63	Normal.
B-2	5	70	14/sec. positive spikes in occipital and rt. post. temporal. 6/sec. positive spikes in left temporal in sleep and awake.
C-1	4	68	Normal.
C-2	6	55	No alpha, 20-26/sec. low voltage beta. 14 and 6/sec. positive spikes throughout in sleep and awake.
D-1	6	80	Normal.
D-2	5	60	Slow in rt. parietotemporal in drowsiness ? sharp activity awake.
E-1	5	80	Wave and spike, 3-6/sec. and 14/sec. positive spikes in sleep.
E-2	5	85	Normal.
F-1	5	77	14 and 6/sec. positive spikes. 15/sec. spindles over left hemisphere in sleep.
F-2	4	71	14/sec. positive spikes in sleep.
F-3	3	75	Focal spike process in post. temporal region.
G-1	7	78	4-7/sec. theta in temporal skewing to rt.
G-2	7	68	Normal.
H-1	3	81	14/sec. positive spikes in sleep.
H-2	6	82	Normal.
I-1	6	76	14/sec. positive spikes in sleep.

DISCUSSION

In the last fifteen years there have been many workers who have postulated and cited evidence to support the thesis that environmental deprivation, if occurring long enough and at an early age, may produce devastating results so far as the development of the child is concerned. Such studies as those by Bowlby (1951), Spitz (1945), and Spitz and Wolf (1946) point clearly in this direction. A study by Woodward and Siegel (1957) also shows some of the effects of environmental deprivation as noted in a psychiatric setting, and a report by Coleman and Provence (1957) has demonstrated an example of this as it can be observed in a pediatric setting.

All of these studies would tend to support the hypothesis that there are clear relationships between the development of what is termed intelligence and the milieu of the individual. One might postulate, however, that any child with any sort of a biological handicap or aberration, if put in a psychosocial setting as devastating and destructive as the homes of the Pine School children, would almost certainly not develop his intellectual abilities to the highest level of his capacity. As Rittwagen (1958) has suggested, it is not surprising that children are delinquent when something is known of their backgrounds; it is only surprising that not more of them are delinquent.

In recent years, several people have developed the idea that groups of mentally retarded children could be differentiated on the basis of whether they have "organic" or "nonorganic" etiologies. Much of this thinking has been borrowed from the work of Strauss and Lehtinen (1947) who have elaborated on what they term "brain-injured children." The behavior which is thought to be associated with organic brain involvement is often described as hyperactive, destructive, and perseverative. Although the studies by these workers have certainly added substantially to our knowledge of the behavior of children with impaired functioning, the conclusion that the absence of this type of behavior meant that there was no organic maldevelopment or malfunctioning of the brain seems questionable. This conclusion was apparently not intended by Strauss and Lehtinen, but was reached by others. More recently, studies by Knobloch et al. (1956) in their review of a large number of premature infants have demonstrated further how vulnerable the organism may be to the several adverse factors associated with prematurity and how high the instance of neuropsychiatric sequelae may be.

The term *organic* itself has been abused. For some, this implied gross anatomical abnormality in the brain; for others, certainly a microscopic, histological abnormality. So far few have appreciated the possibility that a physiological abnormality might be present during life but have no demonstrable histological abnormality. There have been some who have claimed that mongolism, for example, does not have an organic basis.

With the rise of our understanding of cellular pathology, spearheaded by Virchow in the latter half of the nineteenth century, there developed a practice that unless something could be demonstrated in a microscopic sense, it was termed idiopathic. As a result there often has been a parting of the ways between research workers who have been concerned with structure as it related to function and those who have been concerned with various pathological manifestations of function. In a sense this epitomizes the unfortunate schism that developed between neurology and pyschiatry.

There has been insufficient attention given to the biochemical aberrations which may have profound effects on the functioning of the individual and yet have no demonstrable histological lesion in the brain so far as microscopic determinations are concerned. One such example would be phenylketonuria. In the light of our present understanding, phenylketonuria clearly may produce profound effects on the functioning of the individual so that at least two neurological symptoms, mental retardation and convulsions, may be present. It is intriguing to note that there are apparently some individuals with phenylketonuria who have no clear neurological symptoms and may be intellectually normal. In phenylketonuria it is recognized that there is an enzyme defect which results in a failure of the body to convert phenylalanine to tyrosine. That there is a Mendelian recessive pattern to the hereditary aspects of this disease is also understood. It remains a perplexing matter, however, to understand the exact pathogenesis of this disorder so that it is not at all clear as to how the symptoms are produced. Although it has been likened to a cellular toxin, this has little, if any, basis of fact. There is no information available as to what type of intracellular malfunctioning is then responsible for the production of the behavioral deficit which is called mental retardation.

An equally intriguing and perplexing example would be the interrelationships between the neurophysiological abnormality and psychological malfunctioning which are presumed to be present in individuals with idiopathic convulsive disorder. Certainly no one would contest the fact that these individuals have a neurological symptom. Electroencephalographic tracings further document the abnormal electrical discharge systems which take place. Some of these individuals, though by no means all of them, may have considerable impairment in the quantity and quality of their intellectual functioning. For some time it has been understood that such children may have a considerable improvement in intellectual functioning, to say nothing of other problems, when the convulsions are brought under control with appropriate medication. Again, repeated efforts at demonstrating histological lesions in the brains of these patients have not been rewarding. In a similar fashion, as with phenylketonuria, one might postulate that the difficulty is a biochemical aberration of an intracellular nature. Many of the varieties of convulsive disorder may well have a biological enzymatic defect which, of course, may be subject to the laws of heredity.

This study might have some particular relevance in at least two directions. Certainly more investigations will be required in order to understand whether there may be some specific biochemical abnormality present in some of the individuals now thought to have familial mental retardation. On the other hand, since on the basis of present knowledge it may be quite impossible to identify or alter structural characteristics of these children's mental subnormality, the social and emotional factors which contribute to the subnormality need to be thoroughly studied to see if it would be possible to reduce these pernicious effects which also contribute to the expression of the symptom of mental retardation. The talents of many individuals may be required, not only to understand the difficulty, but to alleviate the problem. Parsons (1960) has reported some of the contributions made by a home economist, for example, to this type of a problem.

It is certainly quite possible that not all of these children have a biological abnormality as the basis for or even a part of their difficulties. It is likely that familial mental retardation will be found to be due not to a single factor but rather to a combination of many. Therefore, although the biochemical and physiological approach needs greater exploration, there will continue to be need for further investigation of the psychosocial factors.

SUMMARY

This paper utilizes one set of findings from a longitudinal study on familial mental retardation, from which the following points are made.

1. So-called familial mental retardation is not due to a single factor but rather a combination of many.

2. The combination of biological and psychosocial handicaps is especially deleterious so far as optimal development of the individual is concerned.

3. The biological handicap should not be thought of as limited to demonstrable neurological lesions nor to structural defects.

4. An example of a disturbance in enzyme activity as seen in phenylketonuria suggests a biochemical aberration of an intracellular nature. The precise way in which this results in impairment of intellectual functioning is poorly understood. There are probably other comparable biochemical disturbances that are responsible for the biological vulnerability of individuals having so-called familial retardation. Some of these conditions are undoubtedly genetically transmitted.

The most fruitful approach to the understanding of this type of retardation requires the efforts of professional people with varying skills, i.e., chemist, geneticist, biologist, pediatrician, psychologist, psychiatrist, etc.

Some of the efforts of future research will necessarily be in the direction of observations and assessments of the interrelationships between the biological and psychosocial influences. This implies the need for increasingly precise and scientifically sophisticated methods of evaluation of somatic and psychic characteristics of the human organism.

BIBLIOGRAPHY

Benda, C. E. (1952), *Developmental Disorders of Mentation and Cerebral Palsies*. New York: Grune & Stratton.
Bowlby, J. (1951), *Maternal Care and Mental Health*. Geneva: World Health Organization Monographs.

Coleman, R. W. & Provence, S. (1957), Environmental Retardation (Hospitalism) in Infants Living in Families. *Pediatrics*, 19:285-292.

Goddard, H. H. (1912), *The Kallikak Family*. New York: Macmillan.

Halperin, S. L. (1946), Human Heredity and Mental Deficiency. *Amer. J. Ment. Def.*, 51:153-163.

Knobloch, H., Rider, R. V., Harper, P. A., & Pasamanick, B. (1956), The Neuropsychiatric Sequelae of Prematurity: A Longitudinal Study. *J. Amer. Med. Assn.*, 161: 581-585.

Masland, R. L., Sarason, S. B., & Gladwin, T. (1958), *Mental Subnormality*. New York: Basic Books.

Parsons, M. H. (1960), A Home Economist in Service to Families with Mental Retardation. *Children*, 7:184-189.

Rittwagen, M. (1958), *Sins of Their Fathers*. Boston: Houghton Mifflin.

Skodak, M. (1939), Children in Foster Homes. *Univ. Iowa Stud. Child Welf.*, 16.

———— & Skeels, H. M. (1949), A Final Follow-up Study of One Hundred Adopted Children. *J. Genet. Psychol.*, 75:85-125.

Spitz, R. A. (1945), Hospitalism: An Inquiry into the Genesis of Psychiatric Conditions in Early Childhood. *The Psychoanalytic Study of the Child*, 1:53-75. New York: Int. Univ. Press.

———— & Wolf, K. M. (1946), Anaclitic Depression: An Inquiry into the Genesis of Psychiatric Conditions in Early Childhood, II. *The Psychoanalytic Study of the Child*, 2:313-342. New York: Int. Univ. Press.

Strauss, A. A. & Lehtinen, L. E. (1947), *Psychopathology and Education of the Brain-Injured Child*. New York: Grune & Stratton.

Tredgold, A. F. (1908), *A Textbook of Mental Deficiency*. Baltimore: Williams & Wilkins.

Tredgold, R. F. & Soddy, K. (1956), *A Textbook of Mental Deficiency*. Baltimore: Williams & Wilkins.

Yannet, H. (1959), Mental Deficiency. In: *Textbook of Pediatrics*, ed. W. E. Nelson. Philadelphia: Saunders, pp. 1129-1137.

Warner, W. L. (1957), *Social Class in America*. Gloucester, Mass.: Peter Smith.

Woodward, K. F. & Siegel, M. G. (1957), Psychiatric Study of Mentally Retarded Children of Preschool Age. *Pediatrics*, 19:119-126.

The Pediatric Management of the Dying Child: Part II. The Child's Reaction to the Fear of Dying

- *ALBERT J. SOLNIT, M.D.*

  Yale University

- *MORRIS GREEN, M.D.*

  Indiana University

In recent years advances in medical and surgical care have led to a change in the composition of the patient population in many children's hospitals. It is now common for the hospital physician to have as a major part of his work clinical responsibility for children with prolonged and fatal illnesses such as leukemia, chronic glomerulonephritis, or cystic fibrosis. In this circumstance the thoughtful physician is often both curious and troubled about the reactions of a child to his impending death: what is the child's awareness and understanding of this? How does one deal effectively and humanely with those vital questions that may be expressed directly or indirectly?

For a number of obvious reasons data relating to these concerns are seriously lacking. It is not easy to obtain this information about children. Indeed, there is a notable want of reports that attempt to examine at any level this frequent and fateful clinical circumstance

Supported by the Children's Bureau, U.S. Department of Health, Education, and Welfare, and the Connecticut Department of Health.

in childhood (Richmond and Waisman, 1955; Natterson and Knudson, 1960). The present communication ventures to describe the considerations necessary for understanding the child's reaction to his own imminent death and the manner in which he can be helped to cope with this without being psychologically overwhelmed.

The discovery of death is a gradual one and, strictly speaking, the child's concept of death does not crystallize until he is on the threshold of adolescence. Because of his inability to use thought or language effectively, the young child is poorly prepared to cope with the death of a parent, a sibling, or with the threat of his own demise in a serious illness. Every healthy or largely healthy person fears death, and when its threat seems too imminent or too unavoidable there is the characteristic reaction of denying the perception of its threat. (Witness our reaction to the current dilemma in which there seems to be no adequate way of opposing universal destruction from a nuclear war by our knowledge of how to prevent such a holocaust.) The child's tendency to deny the impact of death differs from that of the older person in being dependent, in part, on his expectation that most of his future is in the hands of adults. Whether the predominant tone of this expectation is fearful or hopeful determines the child's psychological vulnerability to the *actuality,* the *threat* or the *fear* of death either of himself or of those whose survival is crucial for his own future development.

Although we have, for purposes of clarity, divided the study of the child's reaction to the fear of dying into the following four parts, these aspects overlap in the usual clinical experience. The first of these situations constitutes the subject of this report; the remainder will be examined in later publications.

1. The child's reactions to his own approaching death as a result of a uniformly fatal illness, e.g., leukemia.
2. The child's reaction to his expectation of dying because of a life-threatening accident or serious illness, e.g., ulcerative colitis.
3. The child's reaction to his expectation of dying because of the death of a parent or sibling. This is one aspect of the

child's reaction to the loss by death of an important human love object.

4. The child's reaction to his parent's expectation that he will die because the child is expected to repeat for the parent something that occurred in the past, or because the child was close to death from a serious illness or accident.

THE DEVELOPMENT OF THE CHILD'S CONCEPT OF DEATH

In order to estimate a child's vulnerability to the fear of dying, it is necessary to understand those developmental steps and perspectives which lead to the establishment of the concept of death. The concept of death becomes established in most children just before puberty or at the beginning of puberty (S. Anthony, 1940; Nagy, 1948). At that time the totality of his experiences, intellectual development, and sense of time, in retrospect and projected into the future, enable the child to conceptualize the implications of inevitability in a number of ways. Just as he finally is able to recognize the inevitability that there is a beginning to life and that certain natal physical characteristics, such as the sexual differences, will persist, the child finally also becomes aware of the inevitability that everyone will eventually die. This awareness of inevitability as a real concept is accompanied by other evidences of perceptual and intellectual development. For example, it is toward the end of latency, nine to eleven years, that the fullest awareness of constancy in size, texture, and weight of inanimate objects develops even when the object is absent (E. J. Anthony, 1960).

Before this crystallization there are many evidences of the child's partial conceptualizations of death. The child under the age of three or four equates death with the absence of the human love object on whom he depends. The four- and five-year-old child is curious about burial, about the characterizations of dead animals and flowers, and about the accidental features of death. Thus, the preschool child experiences the fear of dying as a loss of the love and attention necessary for feeling cared for physically and emotionally. When the child feels furious and frustrated by the limiting, prohibiting, or punishing powerful adult, this developmental experience often becomes associated with the child's wish that the loved adults would go away and never return. It is in this stage of development that the child experiences wishes and thoughts as magically potent. To wish or want strongly carries with it the risk and probability that the thought is father to the act. The child is not yet aware, as the older individual gradually and often painfully learns, that between a wish or thought and a thought-directed act there are many intermediate steps.

Nagy (1959) found that for the child between the ages of five and nine years death is personified. The school-aged child postpones his direct curiosity and expresses through sublimated activities his curiosity about and fear of dying in a superstitious and investigative manner. For example, he jokingly holds his breath when he passes a cemetery in order not to be "spooked." He extends his scientific curiosity to the differences between organic and inorganic substances, and he classifies varieties of life as he equips himself to face the future with hope rather than fear.

In the school-aged child, the time at which most organized religions begin their systematic education of the young, there is sufficient experience and maturation to permit a distance from magical thinking and the development of logical thinking. This permits the child to comprehend the distinctions between death and absence, between dying and going away, and to have an effective awareness of the difference between memory and fantasy. Thus, the school-aged child gradually acquires the basis for conceptualizing the inevitability of death as the end of the human experience. This notion probably receives a significant impetus from the dawning awareness that one is preparing for the unknowns of adolescence with its powerful biological drives, and the reluctant realization that the relative stability of the middle years of childhood are now being replaced by the introduction to adulthood, the end of which is death. The upsurging quality of the sexual and aggressive drives in early adolescence is often experienced as magically powerful and may precipitate a regression to a belief in the magic of thoughts and wishes. If such a regression persists, the adolescent's development may be seriously blocked.

Although this presentation is intended to describe the more usual situation, generalizations have their limitations when attempting to deal with highly individualized responses. The spectrum of reactions is understandably a broad one. For instance, Noshpitz (1960) has pointed out that the disturbed adolescent may demonstrate a complete denial and defiance of dying even when well aware of this possibility. Other adolescents with severe ulcerative colitis, recurrent diabetic coma, or anorexia nervosa have seemed to us to be committed, in a way, to death. Such children appear to derive from this a feeling of power and they resist, often in a passive manner, the physician's efforts to reverse this commitment.

THE CHILD WITH A FATAL ILLNESS

The present paper is concerned principally with the child's reactions to his own dying because of a fatal disease. Few useful observations are available in relation to acute deaths, though it is evident that the young child expresses his wish to be with the parental figure (to feel loved) and to avoid pain. When death comes acutely the child's awareness is often obtunded because of delirium, stupor, or coma. In the more chronic dying experience there is often evidence of depression, withdrawal, fearfulness, and apprehension. Although, in our experience, most children with a fatal illness do not directly ask if they are going to die, this question will be raised by a few patients over the age of four or five. In such cases, the parents (and physicians and nurses) have their own reactions and preferences in how to meet the child's curiosity (Solnit and Green, 1959). It is clear that everyone will die when he is old enough, and it is clear that each young child will have his own idea, notion, or fantasy when he asks if he will die. In back of this are the child's own curiosity and capacity to conceptualize as well as his familial and religious upbringing. When such questions are raised, the physician can ask what the child means by dying, and he can generalize about everyone dying, but it would appear proper not to answer the child's question in the affirmative without discussion with the parents, and only with their permission. They may wish to be the ones who answer this question; they may wish to have help in answering such questions; or they may prefer that the question be unanswered. Generally, the child is expressing three fundamental concerns by his behavior, by direct questions, and by questions expressed indirectly:

1. Am I safe?
2. Will there be a trusted person to keep me from feeling helpless, alone, and to overcome pain?
3. Will you make me feel all right?

Although systematic psychological studies of children suffering from fatal, terminal illness are lacking, our own experience confirms the general assumption that children invariably sense what is happening to them or in their family even when a deliberate attempt is made to shield them from tragic, frightening, or complicated human affairs.

Four-year-old Larry was dying from a widely metastasized neuroblastoma. He had formed a trusting, affectionate relationship with a young intern who cared for him during his repeated hospitalizations. In the first hospitalization, it became clear that this wasted, frail youngster and his young, attractive mother were mutually suffering from a marked depression as they sensed the nature of the diagnosis and prognosis before it had been established. They were experiencing the beginning of a permanent separation soon to occur.

Before receiving anesthesia for a diagnostic laparotomy, Larry became extremely frightened and asked the intern to stay with him if his mommy could not be there. As the induction of anesthesia was to begin, Larry tremulously and in a panic asked the intern to sing him the lullaby that his mother always sang before she tucked him in. There was a moment of silence as the intern overcame his discomfort and then in a quavery voice began to hum Brahm's "Lullaby." Larry relaxed and permitted the anesthesia to be administered. As Larry received radiation treatment and wasted away, the intern frequently wondered what he would say in the event Larry asked whether he would die. The young physician was amply supported by an understanding supervisor with psychoanalytic experience.

The relationship between the mother, father, and Larry remained intimate and affectionate, though the parents' mourning reaction was well underway before their son died. On the day before Larry died he asked the intern to hold him and said that he was afraid to die and that his doctor should promise to come anytime Larry needed him. The intern was astounded, wondering how long Larry had known he was dying. When Larry died twenty-four hours later in a coma, his parents reassured themselves by saying Larry had not known he was dying. The intern and his supervisor knew this was not true, but agreed that it was intolerable for the parents to realize that their only son had sensed his own approaching death.

Although it is difficult to know how Larry would have reacted if his mother or physician had told him he was dying, it does seem clear that Larry's greatest need was to be helped with a profound separation anxiety and depression. His need to understand what was happening to him, his cognitive needs, were less important. It may be that attempts to provide him with cognitive reassurance would have interfered with the assistance from his family and hospital staff that helped him cope with the emotional crisis involved in a final separation. The help provided to the parents in such a tragic situation has been discussed in an earlier paper (Solnit and Green, 1959).

Although in older children the principles of interpretation of fatal illness would be the same, the child's further intellectual and emotional development often introduces other considerations.

Susan, an eleven-year-old girl, had chronic lymphatic leukemia. It became apparent during the course of her hospitalizations that she wanted to know the nature of her illness and, as is frequent with such children, what her future held in terms of getting well. The parents were apprehensive that Susan would discover she had a fatal illness and indicated to her physicians and nurses that the child's questions should be evaded or not answered frankly.

One day during her next-to-last hospitalization, Susan, who had formed a warm and trusting relationship with the pediatric resident, said sadly and with resignation, "I know I'm going to die soon."

When the doctor asked why she thought so, Susan replied, "I've known for a long time that I have leukemia from what people say about my sickness and transfusions; and besides, I've read about it in the newspaper and heard about it on television, but I've been afraid to talk about it." The resident was upset, but, after discussion with the supervising child psychiatrist, he gained Susan's consent to speak with her parents about her understanding of the situation and her wish for permission to talk about what she knew.

The parents were initially shocked and distressed but finally relieved. Their realization that their daughter knew about her impending death was experienced by the parents as permission to prepare themselves more explicitly for her death. While the child and parents were never able (and why should they be?) to discuss the child's questions they could review certain of their feelings and questions more freely with themselves and with the doctors. Each in his own way expressed resentment about Susan's curtailed life, and a fear of what death represented. With supervision the pediatric trainee was able to listen and to answer what he could of Susan's questions. At times the young physician also could say to his patient that he did not know all the answers, but that he did know how to keep Susan comfortable, and how to understand her fears and her wish for closeness with her family. The contribution that such knowledge and understanding can make to the care of the dying child does not always appear sufficiently appreciated; e.g., we have on many occasions noted that the young physician will fail to provide adequate analgesics for the relief of pain in the dying child.

One of the most powerful fears is that which results from the prediction by an authoritative, trusted person that one is going to die soon, before he has lived out his potential. Henry Beecher (1962) in his paper on "Nonspecific Forces Surrounding Disease and the Treatment of Disease," presents evidence that fear itself can kill. This relationship has also been documented by Walter B. Cannon (1942) in the case of voodoo deaths. The unwitting violation of a fatal taboo such as eating a forbidden food was allegedly followed by a psychically determined death, i.e., the individual complied with the consequences that his tribe and family said would follow if one violated a given taboo. Cannon explored the explanation of these deaths on the basis of extreme overactivity of the sympathicoadrenal system. Others (Richter, 1957) have favored an explanation based on overactivity of the parasympathetic system. William Halsted considered these factors to be of such importance that he refused to operate on a patient who was convinced he was going to die.

Thus, the interpretation of a fatal illness is a complicated procedure, often attended with some risk. On the other hand, not to interpret the fatal illness at some level may constitute a disservice to the patient and his family. While there is no one general answer, knowledge of the individual child and family and of the child's developing understanding of death may provide the physician with some feeling for and guide to individual answers in specific situations.

From our clinical experience with dying children and from our supervision of pediatric trainees who were responsible for the care of dying children, it has been difficult to gather systematic data about the behavioral and verbal communications of these children. Many adults will immediately feel relieved and reassured that there is this limitation of knowledge because there are few human experiences so shattering as a child's death. It appears, however, that the adults fear the shattering impact if they allow themselves to see, hear, and respond to the dying child's behavior. Certainly, birth, death, and change are the three constants that every man must eventually recognize and encounter. It seems to us that the adult is devastated by the fear that the child in himself will die. Perhaps the child's death awakens one of man's deepest fears—death before fulfillment.

In a recent newspaper story from London, England,[1] the death of ten-year-old Suzanne Reynolds was reported. The lead sentence was "The Dying Wish of a Gay and Courageous Child Came True Today." This wish refers to the publication of a book of fairy stories, *Snowy and the Christmas Foal*, which the dying girl wrote. The principal character in the book is a pony named Snowy, who finally was

[1] AP release: "Fairy Stories Published: Tiny Cancer Victim's Wish Granted." *New Haven Register*, October, 1962.

able to produce a longed-for foal on Christmas Eve. The newspaper article states:

> Suzanne died of cancer. But not before she finished her life's work. She finished writing *Snowy and the Christmas Foal* the day before she died. . . . Her mother, Eileen Reynolds, said . . . "She never grumbled or spoke of being unwell. She only talked of her pony and cat, and the fairy stories she sat up at night to write." . . . As the dread disease spread, Suzanne wrote faster and faster. It was as if she had to finish the book in a hurry for she never knew she was dying. . . . Suzanne died in late February (1962). But she lives on—in childhood's magic words.

One is free to draw his own inferences, but our experience would indicate that Suzanne's way of knowing about the fatal aspect of her illness is revealed in what she wrote and by the speed with which she wrote in her effort to outrun the last fact of life. Perhaps the adults were blinded by their own fears and anxieties to the demonstrable evidence that Suzanne knew she was dying. In this instance it might very well be that the adults did help Suzanne to weather her last storm in an intuitively reassuring and therapeutic manner. However, this account dramatically demonstrates how difficult it is for adults to let themselves know what the child is trying to convey to them about his perceptions and fears of a fatal illness.

In a recent letter[2] "To the Editor" Mrs. Helen Hageboeck of Moline, Illinois writes:

> I worked in a hospital which treated only patients with malignant diseases—both children and adults. The inevitable accompaniment was pain, suffering and death.
> The ordeals through which these people moved always contained elements of profound tragedy. However, the worst phase of all was one in which patients, families, wives and husbands did not talk or tell what they knew about the disease in order to "protect" each other. The result was the isolation of both parties and this was the most devastating experience of all. Each one "knew" but each one put all his efforts in trying to escape the inevitable. Of course, they did not "escape" but only suffered greater turmoil in their isolation.

[2] "Tragic Silence." *The New York Sunday Times Magazine*, August 5, 1962.

It is our children who suffer most from our evasiveness. They are aware of these matters because their senses are so acute. Yet their questions only bring a reprimand.

I do hope families will talk and doctors will tell what may happen. Then through frankness and the coordination of our efforts we can better handle ourselves and our families in time of crisis.

It should be the aim of future research in this area not only to examine systematically how children express their knowledge or sense that they are dying but also to determine the principles, techniques, and limitations of communicating with these children in a therapeutic manner. Intuition cannot be relied upon, especially in an area so highly charged with anxieties for the responsible adults.

SUMMARY AND CONCLUSIONS

From our observations of dying children and our examination of the child's emotional and cognitive development, we have outlined some of the major considerations in the child's psychological reactions to his own dying. We have illustrated this outline by clinical vignettes. It has become apparent that a more systematic investigation of the child's psychological reactions to his own dying will have to take into account the adult's tendency not to perceive the dying child's behavioral and verbal communications about his own fears because of the anxieties evoked in the adult by the dying child. Only through a more thorough understanding of the dying child's ways of communicating his sense of dying will we be able to know and teach how to help the dying child psychologically, and come to appreciate the limitations of our knowledge and psychological therapy.

BIBLIOGRAPHY

Anthony, E. J. (1960), An Experimental Approach to the Psychopathology of Childhood —Micropsia. In: *Child Development and Child Psychiatry,* eds. C. Shagass & B. Pasamanick. In Tribute to Dr. Arnold Gesell on His Eightieth Year. Psychiatric Research Reports, 13.
Anthony, S. (1940), *The Child's Discovery of Death.* New York: Harcourt, Brace.
Beecher, H. K. (1962), Nonspecific Forces Surrounding Disease and the Treatment of Disease. *J. Amer. Med Assn.,* 179:437-440.

Cannon, W. B. (1942), Voodoo Death. *Amer. Anthropol.*, 44:169.

Nagy, M. H. (1948), The Child's Theories Concerning Death. *J. Genet. Psychol.*, 73:3.

——— (1959), The Child's View of Death. In: *The Meaning of Death*, ed., H. Feifel. New York: McGraw-Hill.

Natterson, J. M. & Knudson, A. G., Jr. (1960), Observations Concerning Fear of Death in Fatally Ill Children and Their Mothers. *Psychosom. Med.*, 22:456-465.

Noshpitz, J. D. (1960), Discussion of: Psychology of Physical Illness, by S. Little. *Pediat. Clin. No. Amer.*, 7:85-96.

Richmond, J. R. & Waisman, H. A. (1955), Psychologic Aspects of Management of Children with Malignant Diseases. *Amer. J. Dis. Child*, 89:42.

Richter, C. P. (1957), On the Phenomenon of Sudden Deaths in Animals and Men. *Psychosom. Med.*, 19:191-198.

Solnit, A. J. & Green, M. (1959), Psychologic Considerations in the Management of Deaths on Pediatric Hospital Services. I. The Doctor and the Child's Family. *Pediatrics*, 24:106-112.

The Adolescent in a Suicidal Crisis: Collaborative Care on a Pediatric Ward

- *MELVIN LEWIS, M.B., B.S. (London), D.C.H.*
  - *ALBERT J. SOLNIT, M.D.*

Yale University

INTRODUCTION

Suicidal attempts and behavior are at a high peak in adolescence compared to other periods of childhood. It could be said that, just as the individual becomes capable of orgastic discharge and ejaculation during his adolescence, he similarly becomes capable of an effective discharge of aggression through homicidal and suicidal behavior. That he sometimes acts on this urge is an expression of an upset in the precarious balance between his drives, his values, and the demands of reality at this time.

The pediatrician who can exploit his ongoing relationship with his young patient by remaining an effective physician during adolescence, especially the early phase of that period, is in an advantageous position to observe the presence of factors that may give warning of an impending imbalance. Further, collaborative work between pediatricians, child psychiatrists, nurses, and social workers

Supported by the Children's Bureau, U.S. Department of Health, Education, and Welfare, and the Connecticut Department of Health.

can be shown to be of value in the management of adolescents who actually attempt suicide.

The aim of this paper is to discuss our understanding of adolescence and the measures that have proved useful in the collaborative care of adolescents in a suicidal crisis. The key to such care lies in the close cooperation between pediatrician and child psychiatrist at every stage.

DEFINITION AND INCIDENCE

For present purposes the group of patients under consideration will be defined as those adolescents who carry out harmful, or potentially harmful, acts upon themselves with the conscious attempt, in part, to end life. This is mentioned at the beginning because there is another group of adolescents who indirectly jeopardize their lives while having no conscious thoughts about suicide. An example of this second group would be a diabetic who foregoes his insulin and thereby endangers his life.

The actual incidence of suicidal attempts in adolescents is hard to ascertain for several reasons. Many suicidal attempts are not diagnosed as such for statistical purposes, but are found under such headings as accidental poisoning, inhalation pneumonia, automobile accidents, etc.; and of course many suicidal attempts are simply not reported.

Nevertheless, suicide was rated as the sixth cause of death in the age range fifteen to twenty years in the Vital Statistics of the United States (U.S. Department of Health, Education, and Welfare, 1958). Bakwin (1957) asserted that suicide was one of the leading causes of death in teenagers. More recently a study by Toolan (1962) at Bellevue Hospital in New York City showed that 11 per cent of all cases admitted under the age of sixteen years had presenting symptoms of suicidal thoughts and actions.

REVIEW OF THE LITERATURE

Since the classic sociological studies of Durkheim (1897) and the psychoanalytic studies of Freud (1917), the literature on the subject of suicide in general and adolescents in particular has grown immensely, with outstanding contributions especially from Bender and Schilder (1937), Moellenhoff (1939), Rook (1959), Schilder and Wechsler (1934), Zilboorg (1936, 1937), Farberow and Schneidman (1961), and many others. A comprehensive review is beyond the scope of this paper. References will be made to the relevant aspects of some of these contributions in the sections that follow.

THE PERIOD OF ADOLESCENCE

Basic to collaborative care of the adolescent in a suicidal crisis is an understanding of the psychological problems, or developmental tasks, facing all adolescents.

Vicissitudes of love (object) relationships. Adolescents often have strong but mixed feelings about separating themselves from their parents and attaching themselves to different adults (A. Freud, 1958). Infatuations and disappointments are common enough in normal adolescents. However, sometimes the task is beyond the capacity of the adolescent, and catastrophic reactions may occur.

Cathy, aged fifteen years, became involved with her twenty-four-year-old boy friend. He was a person given to violence, with a criminal record involving holdup. She became pregnant, and had a miscarriage at three months. One month later, after an argument with her mother in which Cathy was told to get out of the home and leave with her boy friend, Cathy attempted suicide by swallowing an overdose of aspirin.

Cathy's father was an alcoholic. He was violent at times and frequently threatened Cathy's mother. Incest took place when Cathy was nine years old.

Increased instinctual drives and self-regulation. Beginning in puberty, the sexual and aggressive drive derivatives begin to thrust themselves into the awareness of the adolescent. At the same time a maturation of the adolescent's physical capacities provide him for the first time with a possibility of a realization and gratification of these increased urges. However, the adolescent does not yet possess the control and judgment we expect in mature adults. The result may be that, without adequate support from the environment (i.e., parents and other adults), the adolescent may still feel like a young child inside a large and relatively unfamiliar body, threatened by urges whose strength is also relatively unfamiliar to him. The adolescent may then try many maneuvers to deal with this problem, some successful, some not. Occasionally the adolescent will feel overwhelmed and will act impulsively.

Betty, aged fifteen years, had grown rapidly in a few months, and felt quite conspicuous. She sometimes felt waves of discomfort and embarrassment, but could not pinpoint what this was about. She also found herself increasingly irritated with her mother. One evening Betty had apparently been sitting with her skirt riding a little high, and her mother had asked her to pull it down. Betty flared up and an argument, one of many, started between Betty and her mother. Betty ran upstairs to the bathroom and swallowed some aspirin in a suicidal gesture.

Later, Betty stated she did not know why she had suddenly done this, and was horrified at the act.

Identity crisis and reintegration of personality. The attempt to gain —or rather, regain—mastery of his increased psychological drives and physical capacities is a continuous, if fitful, process during adolescence. As this occurs the adolescent is very much aware of the changes that are taking place, and he is curious as to what sort of person he is and what sort of person he wants to be. At the same time there are pressures on him to narrow his choice of interests, make decisions, and arrive at an identity for himself. Sometimes he will, so to speak, try on certain roles to see if they fit. The values of important adults in his life provide him with the models for these part identifications. Occasionally the role adopted is more like a suit of armor. And if the role is too rigid and fixed, it may occasionally fall apart under pressure.

Daniel, a fifteen-year-old boy, had been conscientious and shy in his earlier years. He had grown up in a family disturbed by marital discord. In the year and a half before his suicidal act he had a spurt of growth. He forced himself to socialize more and to go out for school teams. In spite of these experimental attempts to change, his work at school began to slip and he had repeated angry outbursts against his mother and older sister. As far as his parents were concerned he appeared to be doing well. However, he began talking with his peers of the hopelessness of the world situation, how rotten people were, and that he might as well die. There were periods of attempts at proving himself by engaging in strenuous physical and academic work that alternated with other periods filled with moods of sadness and desperation. Although his work improved and he decided to run for an important school office, in retrospect it was noted that he appeared harassed and filled with remorse and hopelessness about his shortcomings. One day, following an important social event at school which he had attended just before the school election, he took a large dose of rat poison. He felt he could not go on. He was brought to the hospital several hours after he had ingested the poison.

The adolescent who attempts suicide has the additional problem of the consequences of his act. Attempted suicide by poisoning may be complicated by an alteration of the sensorium caused by the drug toxicity. During the recovery period the adolescent will also experience a reaction to his having attempted suicide. This reaction may be influenced by the problems with which he was previously struggling, e.g., if he had been particularly concerned with the matter of control over himself, the act may be regarded by him as a manifestation of the hopelessness of ever gaining control. The attitude of those attending the adolescent in this crisis, including his family and the caring staff, will also significantly affect the future path of the adolescent's development.

MANAGEMENT

The diagnosis of attempted suicide is not always immediately apparent. The differential diagnosis includes psychotic states, inadvertent drug intoxication, brain injury, acute infectious processes, and brain tumors. Where there is any possibility that a suicidal component is present in any of these diagnoses, suicidal precautions must be considered in the management and admission to hospital may well be the safest course.

The Adolescent Patient

The suicidal act can be understood as a cry for help by a patient who feels unable to act in a less destructive manner. For the adolescent the act may be an attempt to extricate himself from an intolerable dilemma or to relieve himself of such acute inner discomforts as intense anger, guilt, depression, or threatened disintegration. Sometimes the suicidal attempt is a move to manipulate the family into changing their attitudes. At other times the behavior is determined by unconscious wishes, such as a desire to join a dead relative. It is virtually an act of rescue to admit to hospital the adolescent caught in this web of difficulties.

The immediate management of the adolescent who has made a suicidal attempt and who has been admitted to hospital is essentially a problem of resuscitation and emergency care. At this stage the foremost consideration to occupy the pediatrician is the safeguarding of the patient's life. The goals of the measures to be instituted at this stage are twofold, consisting of efforts to limit and counteract the effects of the particular method of suicide (e.g., poisoning, laceration, etc.) and the prevention of repeated attempts.

In cases of poisoning, in addition to any antidote that may be required, it is obviously important to consider carefully what drugs, if any, should be prescribed to sedate an anxious patient, particularly when there is some doubt as to what drug was taken initially. The safest plan is to use no drug at all until the exact diagnosis is known, or at most to use a relatively uncomplicated pharmacological agent such as chloral hydrate or paraldehyde if sedation becomes necessary.

The immediate prevention of repeated attempts can be guaranteed only by continuous observation of the patient, whether by nurses, aides, selected relatives, or other persons. Statements from patients, such as "I've learned my lesson," "I'm all right now," etc., should not deter the physician from his resolve to take preventive measures until he knows more about his patient. Many adolescents are persuasively charming one moment, but rebelliously or defiantly impulsive at the next moment. The patient may rebel against the order, or ridicule it. In many of these instances the adolescent is carrying his conflicts into the ward setting and may be testing the strength of the physician's resolve. In spite of his protestations, the patient will usually feel comforted by the security of the environment now offered by the pediatrician, and his psychiatric and nursing colleagues. As far as the patient is concerned, apart from feelings of relief at finding himself still alive, or satisfaction at having brought about changes within the family, the adolescent is likely to have feelings of helplessness, fear, and ignominy arising out of his serious act.

The duration of the twenty-four-hour surveillance order is based on an assessment of the patient's psychological state and on a collaborative study of the patient and his environment. Generally, when a suicidal attempt has revealed signs of careful planning and more or less thorough execution, the risk of a repetition is high. Conversely, when the act appears to be impulsive and careless, the subsequent risk of a second attempt may be lower, provided there is evidence of a change in the adolescent and his environment. If the adolescent expresses concern that he may do it again, this should be taken as an indication that he still requires the extra support that continuous surveillance offers him. Further, if he shows evidence of a thought disorder (psychotic reaction), or any impairment of his faculty of judgment, observation should of course be maintained.

The child psychiatrist assists the pediatrician in a number of ways. At many points in their collaborative work the child psychiatrist imparts to the pediatrician an understanding, derived from psychoanalysis and psychiatry, of children, their reaction to crises, and the response of the environment. In more specific terms this will include a psychiatric assessment of a particular patient.

At the same time the pediatrician will impart to the child psychiatrist an assessment of the child's physical condition and an understanding of the child and his family gained from many years of continuous pediatric care.

This enables pediatrician and psychiatrist to share the responsibility for the care of an adolescent in a suicidal crisis. With increasing experience in such collaboration the pediatrician is able to extend further his domain in child and adolescent care. At the same time the special psychological assessments needed will ideally require the services of a child psychiatrist.

Another important guide in the assessment of the need for continued surveillance is the affective state of the patient. The child psychiatrist can utilize the observations and reactions of the pediatrician and the ward staff as he looks for evidence of depression and anxiety. Thus a lightening of mood in the patient is often recognized by the ward staff, who feel more comfortable as they sense a regaining of equilibrium in the adolescent.

Usually the patient who attempts suicide is in a state of conflict, confusion, and anxiety. The act itself (e.g., drug intoxication, self-inflicted wounds, etc.) may result in physical depletion and added confusion, thus further handicapping the patient. He may therefore also be more vulnerable to psychological stress. The pediatrician's task here is to alleviate the patient's immediate and pressing concerns about his condition by deed as well as word. He will want to convey to the patient the expectancy and planning for continued physical safety and the avoidance of unnecessary psychological stress, such as unsuitable visitors, the fear of possible medical or surgical procedures, or anxiety about the future.

The patient's first concern is usually about what is happening to him. If he has taken a drug such as atropine, he may be alarmed at the toxic reactions he experiences. If he has physically harmed his body by corrosive fluid or laceration, he may be worried about the extent of the damage. The pediatrician's explanations of the patient's physical state are an important part of the support the patient needs.

The patient may also react to the event itself with the feeling of bewilderment and fright at his near dissolution. Sometimes the fact of amnesia is upsetting to the adolescent, since it represents to him a period of his current life which is beyond his control. He may want to reconstruct what happened, and he should be encouraged to do so. The tactful repetition of explanations that fill in memory gaps help the patient master his feelings of helplessness. These procedures demonstrate to the patient that his problems can be described, clarified, and understood.

Sometimes the impact of the suicidal attempt is frightening to the extent that the idea of a further attempt becomes alien to the adolescent. The pediatrician can strengthen such a position by clarifying the reality of what has happened and offering further help to the patient. The actual sequence of events may be recounted, the bodily sensations caused by the toxic agents can be accounted for, and the reasons for his being in hospital can be described and outlined to the adolescent. Furthermore, the physical care and protection are reassuring to the patient, provide him with additional support, and point the way to a more satisfactory outcome.

The usefulness of hospitalization is clear: the patient is protected from a stressful environment, while physical and psychological care is being offered and the diagnosis confirmed. Once the complete diagnosis is established, the pediatrician uses his understanding of the problems involved to help the adolescent comprehend the crisis and participate in planning pediatric and psychiatric treatment.

After a period of time has elapsed, usually one or two days, some adolescents may repress or deny the whole problem and close themselves off as they attempt to regain control. At this stage the pediatrician and psychiatrist can usefully have the attitude of accepting the adolescent where he is, refraining from intruding and penetrating his defensive efforts. For example, if the adolescent indicates that he is not prepared at this stage to talk about an important relationship he has with another person, his physicians should not press him to do so at this time. Rather, they should direct their efforts at conveying to the adolescent the understanding care and protection that are being offered. One thus tries to help the adolescent understand what happened, and as far as possible why it happened. At the same time one suggests that there might be more constructive and less dangerous ways of resolving his conflicts, as one helps him toward planning for the future, which will include psychiatric evaluation whenever feasible.

More complex reactions related to the patient's presuicidal problems are also present. The fear of being overwhelmed by one's impulses (instinctual drives) is partially realized in the suicidal attempt. Also, guilt over such an excessively rebellious act may be prominent. Many adolescents also worry about the effect of the drugs they have taken on their sexual functions. Nearly all adolescents are concerned about what others will now think of them.

The Family

The adolescent is also sensitive to the reactions of his family. Most parents feel quite upset and at a loss to understand the event. The manner in which they deal with their own feelings is complex and varied. Solicitous reactions may occur in which the parents ask what they have done wrong. Their anxiety may be expressed as anger, which then is often displaced onto other persons. Withdrawal of the parents from the situation sometimes occurs. Occasionally the suicidal attempt is seized upon as a weapon in a marital conflict. The pediatrician in collaboration with the social worker can recognize and learn to understand these reactions. The social worker's help to the parents assists the pediatrician in the care of his patient.

Interviews with the parents will yield information about the patient's life and the immediate events preceding the suicidal act. The nature of the relationship between the patient and his family is best understood when firsthand observations of the patient with his parents are available. These observations in the hospital are of course mostly made after a suicidal crisis. Any discrepancies between observations made during the crisis and reports of the relationship before the suicidal effort are important data for gauging the degree to which the suicidal act was a reaction to a family situation, and the extent of the parental understanding and tolerance of the adolescent. Depending on the individual situation, the parents are asked at the beginning of or during these interviews for permission for the child psychiatrist to talk further with the adolescent.

The Ward As Therapeutic Environment

Finally, the pediatric ward staff is now a part of the adolescent's environment, and as such it requires adaptation to the needs of the patient and his family. It should be said that in most cases the pediatric ward offers the unique advantage of an environment combining the psychological and medical care of a teenager more readily than can be arranged on most adult psychiatric wards. Surgical intervention, general medical treatment, and psychological management appropriate to the needs of an adolescent are generally more easily mobilized on a pediatric ward. However, the pediatrician and child psychiatrist together may sometimes decide that the behavior of the adolescent is exceeding the limits in which he can safely and judiciously be managed in a pediatric setting, and a transfer of the patient to a psychiatric setting which has full facilities for control and restraint is indicated. Again, the pediatrician may sometimes have to decide that such a transfer of the patient is necessary because, for various reasons, the particular pediatric ward is unsuitable for such care. For example, his ward may be unable to provide the safe, flexible, therapeutic environment that such patients require. This may be particularly true if he does not have the collaborative services of a child psychiatrist available to him. Also, the continued adaptation of this ward to the needs of the adolescent in a suicidal crisis may deplete the resources of the ward personnel, thus running the risk of diminishing the quality of the care available to the other pediatric patients.

Where it is possible for the ward to make this adaptation, efforts should be made to apprise all the ward staff of what measures are indicated. A short briefing conference led by the pediatrician and child psychiatrist for all the key personnel helps to ensure consistent ward management. It is sometimes necessary, for example, to give special instructions to avoid unqualified personnel probing into the patient's motives at a time when he is relatively defenseless.

The continued regulation of the ward environment is best managed by sharing information with the ward staff (Lewis, 1962). Planned sessions for the total key ward staff, which may include pediatricians, nurses, social workers, child psychiatrist, and clinical psychologist, provide an opportunity to learn about the patient and his family, to discuss and understand the care that is being recommended, and to ask questions. More particularly, such points as the need for extra help, definition of duties, the reaction of other patients on the ward, and so on, require clarification and planning. It is important, for example, that visitors to the patient should be screened, since the visit of a particular person may provide the motive, if not the actual means, for the patient to make a second attempt.

Plans After Hospitalization

Later in the hospital care of the adolescent, when the issues are at least more or less clearly recognized if not resolved, a definitive plan involving sustained care should be made before the adolescent leaves the pediatric ward. Sometimes psychiatric hospitalization must be arranged, but more commonly some kind of ambulatory help is indicated. This may take the form of a referral for psychiatric evaluation and treatment, or a continuation of the care offered by the pediatrician, with the collaboration of a child psychiatrist. At all events, the planning should be consolidated before the patient leaves the ward. If follow-up arrangements are not made secure before the adolescent leaves the hospital, there is often a recurrence of the pre-suicidal situation, a denial of the need for follow-up or treatment, and the possibility of a repeat attempt at suicide. The pediatrician will of course take into account the wishes of the adolescent, but the actual recommendations for further care, whether pediatric or psychiatric, should not be left to the judgment of the adolescent.

The need for aftercare is obvious. In one study (Farberow and Schneidman, 1961), nearly half the persons (adolescents and adults) who were in a suicidal crisis, and subsequently committed suicide, did so within ninety days and after they seemed to be on the way to recovery. The aftercare of adolescents who have attempted suicide involves both the adolescent and his family. The pediatrician has as his continuing responsibility the care and protection of the development of the child. By working collaboratively with the psychiatrist and social worker, the pediatrician can perform an essential service to the suicidal adolescent and his family. For example, other siblings are affected by the suicidal act and the shift in family relationships that occurs. The pediatrician can observe these changes and offer guidance to the family.

If there has been no significant shift in the family dynamics, the conditions for a repeat attempt at suicide may still be present. One tries to help the adolescent and his family see the need for an alteration in the circumstances which have allowed a suicidal attempt to occur. One offers assistance in finding such help, making use of whatever community and private resources are available. Psychiatric treatment, family service agencies, child guidance clinics, residential treatment centers, pediatric outpatient facilities, educational programs, etc., may be variously used. If the risk of suicide rises and the family or patient are unable to take appropriate action, one may have to consider active intervention in the form of commitment to a psychiatric hospital.

In the event that the risk is not high and where the family and patient will not accept or are not able to seek psychiatric help, the pediatrician can provide some form of surveillance, keeping himself available to the patient and his family for at least the critical period of the succeeding three or four months. Such a continuing responsibility is expected from the child's physician. However, in such situations the pediatrician will feel more secure in offering such supervision when he can discuss such a patient regularly with a psychiatric colleague. The surveillance of the patient is no guarantee of prevention, but it may enable the pediatrician to anticipate a possible recurrence of a suicidal attempt.

DISCUSSION

Is there any way in which a suicidal attempt could have been anticipated and prevented?

Sometimes there are simply no obvious premonitory signals, as in the cases reported by Stearns (1953). At other times, of course, troubled adolescents may express overt threats of suicide or show major signs (e.g., depression, anxiety, thought disorder, etc.) of impending breakdown. There is, incidentally, no consistent relationship between the presence or absence of premonitory signals and the outcome of the suicidal act. Also, one cannot rely on the suicidal attempt being simply a "gesture." Impulsive "gestures" have ended in death.

Yet, at the same time, it is normal for adolescents to be beset with problems. It is beyond the scope of this paper to discuss the diagnostic criteria of deviations in adolescent development. However, the previously mentioned basic developmental tasks of this period may be useful as an aid to diagnostic thinking. Moreover, the factors in deviant adolescent development that are likely to culminate in suicidal behavior will require a great deal of further clinical investigation before criteria for predicting this self-destructive form of behavior can be established. However, there are certain guides that are helpful in determining at what point psychological imbalance is likely to become life threatening, and what manifestation might indicate that this point is being approached.

When there has been a death in the family or of a friend, the teenager who is already disturbed may often identify with and attempt to rejoin the "lost" person through a suicidal act. For example, Zilboorg (1936) and others have consistently noticed that if a boy or girl, particularly during their early childhood or at puberty, is deprived through death of a loved person with whom he or she is deeply identified, there is an increased likelihood of suicide if such a child is subjected to additional stress.

In situations of direct sexual and aggressive physical violence such as rape, murder, and catastrophic events such as war or airplane crashes, the already disturbed adolescent may act against himself in kind. Also, the characteristics of the young man's or woman's relationship with parents and with peers, and their own views of themselves, will often provide a clue to the possibility of suicidal behavior. Balser and Masterson (1959) have also suggested that a high proportion of adolescents who commit suicide are schizophrenic.

An impression of the adolescent's self-image can often be gleaned from observations of his appearance, mannerisms, language, and behavior. It also becomes clear as one studies these patients that their reaction toward their own body tends to become exaggerated in two directions. At one extreme is the denial of the body and its demands, which may lead to a denial of the adaptive fear of dying; and at the other extreme is the indiscriminate submission to the body's demands in the form of impulsive behavior that permits the direct discharge on the self of murderous impulses. The adolescent who overvalues or undervalues his body and its demands requires assistance in correcting these distortions of reality, both in immediate concrete terms and in a gradual understanding way.

Other more general factors that may indicate self-destructive behavior would include the adolescent's general functioning and working toward future goals. Are his goals realistic, or at least understandably idealistic, or are they quite inappropriate, or even harmful? Lastly, one views the internal turmoil of the adolescent against the background of the forces (i.e., his parents and his life circumstances) which may either be helping him toward integration or be making things more difficult for him.

A detailed account of the assessment of self-destructive potentiality is described in the comprehensive schedule of the Suicide Prevention Center in Los Angeles (Litman and Farberow, 1961; Tabachnick and Farberow, 1961). The clinical observations and assessments that form a composite picture suggesting suicidal behavior can often be ascertained by the pediatrician because of his long-term relationship with the adolescent and his family. When the pediatrician senses or is concerned about suicidal behavior in his adolescent patient, a discussion with his colleague in child psychiatry can be helpful.

Whenever there is doubt in the physician's mind—and certainly when overt threats of suicide are spoken in desperation or in jest— the adolescent and his family should be studied further by the pediatrician and child psychiatrist. Hospitalization on a pediatric ward might here be considered as a prophylactic measure and a means to study the family in more detail.

Certainly the hospital ward provides an opportunity for further investigation and care. Sifneos et al. (1956), in a study of adults in the Massachusetts General Hospital, state: "Hospital care is undoubtedly useful in preventing suicidal attempts. It gives a dramatic background to the patient's appeal for help from his friends and relatives, removes him from the acute situation, provides physical care, offers psychiatric treatment, and offers help in solving practical problems." The same conclusions would appear to apply to children. Solnit (1960) more recently has discussed the positive use of pediatric hospital admission during developmental crises, and Laybourne and

Miller (1962) have reported the close collaboration that was achieved between pediatrician and child psychiatrist in the treatment of certain children on a pediatric ward.

Today, with the increasing awareness of the prevalence of emotional disturbances in children and adolescents, there are probably many situations in which the pediatrician, working in collaboration with the child psychiatrist, can make use of short-term hospital care as a method of treatment of such children. This appears to be the case where adolescents who attempt suicide are concerned.

However, a further complication does arise in these cases. The act of attempting suicide and its implications regarding proximity to death often frightens the physician as well as the patient. The physician must deal with his own anxiety when confronted with this crisis in his patient's life. He may, for example, experience a feeling of alarm which can interfere with his efforts at useful therapeutic action. When an adolescent actually makes a suicidal attempt, the physician sometimes experiences a reaction which at first sight appears paradoxical; he may find himself upset at the frightening proximity of death, yet at the same time relieved at having something concrete and physical with which to deal, e.g., the resuscitation of the patient. In some instances the physician will occupy himself completely with the medical treatment, excluding the psychological aspects from his domain. A satisfactory way of dealing with such anxiety is to call for help in a way that one would have wished the adolescent to have done—namely, seek the advice and collaboration of colleagues in pediatrics and psychiatry who are familiar with the problems involved. Further, the knowledge of a useful plan of action is as reassuring to the physician as it is to the patient.

SUMMARY

The use of pediatric hospitalization in the collaborative care of the adolescent in a suicidal crisis has been described. The foundation for such care rests on an understanding of the problems with which the adolescent is faced. The value of such hospital care in the total management has been discussed.

BIBLIOGRAPHY

Bakwin, H. (1957), Suicide in Children and Adolescents. *J. Ped.*, 50:749-769.
Balser, B. & Masterson, J. F. (1959), Suicide in Adolescents. *Amer. J. Psychiat*, 116: 400-404.
Bender, L. & Schilder, P. (1937), Suicidal Preoccupations and Attempts in Children. *Amer. J. Orthopsychiat.*, 7:225-234.
Durkheim, E. (1897), *Suicide: A Sociological Study*, tr. J. A. Spaulding & G. Simpson. Glencoe, Ill.: Free Press, 1951.
Farberow, N. L. & Schneidman, E. N. (1961), *A Cry for Help*, ed. N. L. Farberow & E. N. Schneidman. New York: McGraw-Hill.
Freud, A. (1958), Adolescence. *The Psychoanalytic Study of the Child*, 13:255-278. New York: Int. Univ. Press.
Freud, S. (1917), Mourning and Melancholia. *Standard Edition*, 14:237-258. London: Hogarth Press, 1957.
Laybourne, P. C. & Miller, H. C. (1962), Pediatric Hospitalization of Psychiatric Patients: Diagnostic and Therapeutic Implications. *Amer. J. Orthopsychiat.*, 32:596-603.
Lewis, M. (1962), The Management of Parents of Acutely Ill Children in the Hospital. *Amer. J. Orthopsychiat.*, 32:60-66.
Litman, R. G. & Farberow, N. L. (1961), Emergency Evaluation of Self-destructive Potentiality. In: *A Cry for Help*, ed. N. L. Farberow & E. N. Schneidman. New York: McGraw-Hill.
Moellenhoff, F. (1939), Ideas of Children About Death. *Bull. Menninger Clin.*, 3:148-156.
Rook, A. (1959), Student Suicides. *Brit. Med. J.*, 1:599-603.
Schilder, P. & Wechsler, D. (1934), The Attitudes of Children Toward Death. *J. Genet. Psychol.*, 45:406-451.
Sifneos, P. E., Gore, C., & Sifneos, A. C. (1956), A Preliminary Psychiatric Study of Attempted Suicide As Seen in a General Hospital. *Amer. J. Psychiat.*, 112:883-888.
Solnit, A. J. (1960), Hospitalization: An Aid to Physical and Psychological Health in Childhood. *A.M.A. J. Dis. Childh.*, 99:155-163.
Stearns, A. W. (1953), Cases of Probable Suicide in Young Persons Without Obvious Motivation. *J. Maine Med. Assn.*, 44:16-23.
Tabachnick, D. & Farberow, N. L. (1961). The Assessment of Self-destructive Potentiality. In: *A Cry for Help*, ed. N. L. Farberow & E. N. Schneidman. New York: McGraw-Hill.
Toolan, J. M. (1962), Suicide and Suicidal Attempts in Children and Adolescents. *Amer. J. Psychiat.*, 118:719-724.
U.S. Dept. of Health, Education, and Welfare (1958), *Vital Statistics of the United States*, 2. Washington, D.C.: U.S. Government Printing Office.
Zilboorg, G. (1936), Differential Diagnostic Types of Suicide. *Arch. Neurol. Psychiat.*, 35:270-291.
—— (1937), Considerations on Suicide, with Particular Reference to That of the Young. *Amer. J. Orthopsychiat.*, 7:15-31.

Toward an Understanding of Psychosomatic
Concepts in Relation to Illness in Children

• *DANE G. PRUGH, M.D.*

University of Colorado

> There seems to be no case in which the soul can act
> or be acted upon without involving the body.
> Aristotle (*De Anima*, Book I)

Contemporary pediatrics has accorded increasing recognition to the importance of the psychological aspects of illness in children. The concept of comprehensive pediatric care rests upon two basic assumptions: (1) both somatic and psychologic factors may act as predisposing, contributory, precipitating, and perpetuating forces in illness, calling for appropriate diagnostic and therapeutic measures; (2) the prevention of disease and the promotion of healthy growth and adaptation must include attention to all aspects of the developing child's psychobiological equipment, as well as the psychosocial setting in which he exists.

Such concepts are of course not new ones. Perceptive clinicians studying children's diseases have been aware of pertinent psychological implications at least since the latter part of the nineteenth century. The work and writings of Milton Senn (1946, 1948), in particular, have contributed in large and significant measure to the modern pediatric understanding and growing implementation of the comprehensive approach, as have also the contributions of Winnicott (1931), Bakwin (1951), Shirley (1954), Aldrich (1945), Powers (1948),

Spock (1938), Richmond (1952), and many others. The pediatrician of today is facing the fact that he must acquire knowledge and skill in the psychological aspects of pediatrics in order to keep pace with current changes in pediatric practice, brought about by the decline in infectious disease partially as the result of antibiotics and by the rise in parental concern regarding child rearing, among other developments.

Although an increasing number of articles dealing with psychological topics have been appearing in recent pediatric literature, the term "psychosomatic disorder" is often employed rather loosely. Abundant publications dealing with this particular topic exist in the psychiatric literature, but these are not familiar to many pediatricians. The present communication attempts to summarize what is known and unknown in this important but at times elusive area, with particular emphasis upon the features especially relevant to child development and behavior.

MODERN CONCEPTS OF DISEASE

The history of medicine can be characterized by the changing concepts of causality in illness which have marked its progress. Prehistory produced the magical and supernatural beliefs of primitive witch doctors and priests. Beginning naturalistic observations were made by philosopher physicians in ancient Greece and later in Arab lands. Following the rise of Western methods of scientific inquiry in the seventeenth and eighteenth centuries, Virchow's demonstrations of cellular pathology and Pasteur's pioneering work opened the way for the development of the late nineteenth-century concept of bacterial causation of disease.

In spite of the therapeutic revolution based on this concept, leading to the sweeping twentieth-century advances in the control of infectious disease, the thoughtful physician of today cannot be satisfied with explanations of disease which are based upon a single etiological factor. His increasing knowledge of immunology leads him to recognize the importance of the state of the "immunity of the host," in addition to the "virulence of the organism," in regard to infectious disease. Recent contributions from the field of human ecology (Corwin, 1949; Hinkle and Wolff, 1958) emphasize the interrelatedness of man and his environment in states of health and disease. Contemporary understanding of psychological forces, opened up by Freud, has added emotional conflict to the growing list of factors which may be involved in the precipitation or intensification of disease. Multiple causality has become an established concept in the medicine of today.

In the broadest sense, all disease may be said to be "psychosomatic," if mind and body are considered as "integrated forces in the organization of function and in the disorganization of disease" (Grinker and Robbins, 1954). Thus, in contrast to popular misconceptions, there can be no room for a medical specialty or scientific discipline called "psychosomatic medicine." Nor is there a place, in this view, for a special field of investigation of one particular discipline. In reality, the psychosomatic approach is a conceptual one, involving a consideration of physiological, psychological, and social factors concerned in the onset and perpetuation of disease, together with appropriate therapeutic measures drawn upon according to the weighting of these various factors. Thus psychosomatic concepts fit comfortably within the purview of "comprehensive pediatrics."

In the literature of recent years, the term "psychosomatic disorder" has often been employed to designate those disease pictures in which psychological and social factors appear to play predominant roles of predisposing, precipitating, or perpetuating character. "Somatopsychic disorder" has been the term utilized by many writers to indicate those disease syndromes in which pathophysiological factors seem to be the predominant or primary influence, with contributory psychological factors or secondary psychological reactions involved. Such terms, however useful operationally, have the obvious limitation of implying the selective involvement of psychological or somatic factors in certain syndromes only. Obviously both are involved in *any* disease picture in varying degrees.

In the discussion to follow, emphasis will be laid arbitrarily upon those disorders of bodily function in children in which psychological or social factors are importantly implicated. It is important first, however, to put this discussion into perspective by presenting current conceptualizations regarding all disease states, considered in relation to the state of health, now recognized as representing more than the absence of disease.

Unitary Theory

The modern unitary theory of health and disease derives from the seminal influence of Bernard (1865), Cannon (1929), and Freud (1940), and has been most explicitly stated by Romano (1950) and G. Engel (1953), among others. In this view, health and disease are regarded as "phases of life" which are dependent upon the balance maintained by the organism, through the use of genically and experientially determined devices, in fulfilling its needs and in mastering stresses from within or from without (Romano, 1950). Health thus represents the phase of successful adaptation (and, in children, of growth and maturation) in which the organism is able to master its environment and is reasonably free from pain, disability, or limitations in its social capacity. Disease represents the phase of failure in adaptation or of breakdown in the attempts of the organism to maintain an adaptive equilibrium or "dynamic steady state" (Engel, 1953). In the phase of disease, failures or disturbances may occur in the growth, development, functioning, or adjustment of the organism as a whole or of any of its systems.

In such a conceptual framework, the concept of "stress" plays a central role. As Engel (1953) has pointed out, a stress for the organism may be the result of any influence, internal or external, which interferes with the satisfaction of basic needs or which disturbs the adaptive equilibrium. Stress is relative, not absolute, since the capacity of the organism will determine whether it can deal successfully, at any given moment, with any particular stimulus of potentially noxious nature. Environmental forces of physical or interpersonal nature may interfere directly with the satisfaction of such needs, ranging from the intake of oxygen to sexual expression, or may damage or disturb in function organs or parts of the body, indirectly interfering with need satisfactions and with the maintenance of the dynamic steady state. Changes in internal dynamics of physiological or psychological character (the latter including, for example, instinctual impulses arising during psychosexual development, enhanced by physiological changes during puberty) may operate individually or, more commonly, conjointly, sequentially, or summatively with environmental forces to act as significant stresses which may upset the current adaptive equilibrium.

Stressful stimuli of various kinds thus may function among multiple etiological forces in the production of disease states, acting to limit the capacity of systems concerned with growth, development, or adaptation, or directly producing damage in cells or parts of the body. The nature of the individual's past experience, of physical, psychological, and social character, interacting with his genic endowment, will determine largely what stimuli may constitute significant stresses which may place a strain upon his current adaptive capacities (Engel, 1953).

In Engel's view (1960), stressful stimuli of *physical nature* include noxious agents which "injure" by virtue of physical or chemical properties. Such stimuli may also occur when external substances are insufficiently available for respiration, nutrition, and other processes, or when insufficiency states arise from a failure of the body to produce essential substances, as in hormone deficiencies. The effects of microorganisms and parasites involve multiple considerations, relating to the virulence of the organism and the resistance of the host, the latter being influenced by past immunologic experience, among other variables, and possibly by psychological or social factors. All of these factors affect first the operation of the biochemical or physiological systems, at the level of molecules, cells, tissues, or organs, and may call out physiological defenses or compensatory mechanisms in an attempt to maintain or re-establish the physiological homeostatic equilibrium.

Stressful stimuli of *psychological* nature involve thoughts or feelings which are unacceptable to the individual because of past experience or current situational factors. They operate, in the older infant, child, or adult, through their effect on the central regulating system (brain and mental apparatus). Such stimuli are usually closely interrelated with stressful influences of *social* or interpersonal significance, involving intrapsychic responses to the loss or threat of loss of key persons, the occurrence of real or fantasied external danger, or intense frustration of sexual or aggressive drives or impulses (Engel, 1960).

Stimuli of these latter two types must be registered by the perceptual systems, and receive conscious or unconscious central representation of symbolic nature in the mental apparatus. Whether these representations (and the mental associations, memory traces, or emotions evoked by them) achieve stressful significance is a highly individualized matter, depending upon the nature of past experience, the level of personality development, and the current situation, including the availability of psychological support from other persons, as well as the intactness of the central nervous system and other factors.

When such stimuli become stressful, the central representations aroused appear to produce a danger signal, anxiety, in the ego, the executive "organ" of the mental apparatus. Such basic anxiety appears to signal to the ego an incipient or potential disruption of its dynamic steady state and may evoke psychological defense mechanisms, such as projection and denial, in an attempt to maintain the equilibrium (Engel, 1960). Other unpleasant and frequently conflicting emotions, including fear, anxiety, or guilt, may be aroused also. Behavioral and social adaptive devices, such as withdrawal or aggressive attack, may be invoked, appropriately or inappropriately, in an attempt to modify the environment in order to alter the source of noxious stimulation or otherwise to resolve the conflicting emotions.

Physical stimuli may of course affect the mental apparatus directly through alterations in the brain tissue or indirectly through changes in its perceptual threshold (Engel, 1960). These may involve external damaging forces, such as trauma or infection, or changes within the organism, as in states of hormonal excess or deficit. Disturbances in the mental representation of the body image may also be produced as a result of gross damage to the brain or to organs or body parts. It is unlikely, however, as Greene (1956) has pointed out, that central symbolic representation is accorded to changes taking place on the cellular level in internal organs involved in maintaining physiological homeostasis. Thus physical stimuli may produce, intensify, or compound stressful stimuli of psychological character, with resulting employment by the organism of physiological, psychological, or social defenses or adaptive behavior selectively or simultaneously. Psychological or social stimuli may bring about changes in function of physiological systems, with consequent effects upon growth, development, or adaptation.

Levels of Organization

The foregoing considerations have led Engel (1960), Greene (1956), Mirsky (1957), Grinker (1959), and others to advocate a conceptual approach to the organism which recognizes three basic levels of organization, *physiological, psychological,* and *social.* In this view, the physiological level can be said to embrace biochemical processes taking place in molecules, cells, or organ systems, which appear to communicate with psychological and social levels of organization in a "transactional" or mutually and reciprocally interacting fashion. Such transactions within the field of forces involve multiple feedback operations at "nodal" (Greene, 1956) points of interaction among the three levels of organization, carried out through the neuroendocrine system and its interrelationships with the brain and mental apparatus as well as the various organ systems (Engel, 1960). Biological systems of the nature involved in such transactions appear to be "open" ones (von Bertalanffy, 1957) in contrast to "closed" systems of the physical universe. Alterations in function taking place at any level of organization may thus produce reciprocal reverberations "up" and "down" the interlocking and transacting open systems.

Such complex feedback operations among the three basic levels of organization appear to be constantly involved in the maintenance of health and adaptation. Variations in the *adaptive capacity* of the organism, brought about by *genic, constitutional, developmental,* or *experiential* factors, may influence its vulnerability to potentially stressful stimuli of physical, psychological, or social nature. Depending upon the organism's adaptive capacity at the time of stressful experience and, within broad limits, the nature, duration, and intensity of the stressful stimuli, a variety of outcomes may ensue, as Engel (1960) suggests. A *new and successful adaptive equilibrium* may be established, with the help of physiological, psychological, or social defense mechanisms, operating in their differing but individually lawful fashions; a *state of partial restriction of function* (or of growth or development) may result, with varying degrees of weighting of somatic or psychological components; marked *decompensation* may occur temporarily, in predominantly physiological or psychological spheres or both; or complete *adaptive breakdown* may follow, leading ultimately to death from damage or depletion or from psychological malfunctioning, as in self-starvation or suicide.

Disease Pictures

Restriction of function (or of growth and development), decompensation, or adaptive breakdown of the organism can be said to represent disease states, deriving from multiple etiological factors as indicated above. In this view, many of the symptoms or signs manifested by the sick person, from fever to regressive behavior, may actually be the result of attempts by the organism to maintain adaptation, to achieve compensation, to effect restitution, or to obtain satisfaction of basic needs, of physiological or psychological nature, rather than specific results of the stressful stimuli and their direct effects (Engel, 1960). Other signs or symptoms may reflect restriction of function, decompensation, or adaptive breakdown. In overwhelmingly stressful situations, the organism may go through phases of response, resembling impact, recoil, and restitution, with particular defenses of physiological, psychological, or social nature employed in each successive phase (Prugh and Tagiuri, 1954).

If the major stressful stimulus is of predominantly physical nature, the resulting changes in physiological systems may produce significant transactional influence upon psychological and social levels of organization, with reverberating responses often occurring in other physiological systems than the one originally involved. When predominantly psychological or social stimuli are experienced as stressful, the signal anxiety or other emotions involved may result in concomitant physiological changes in a variety of organ systems. Such changes are ordinarily reversible, although they may persist as long as the emotional conflict remains unresolved. Bodily changes of this nature may, however, exert undue strain upon an already-damaged organ, such as the heart (Chambers and Reiser, 1953) or may precipitate, accelerate, or enhance pre-existing or latent pathological processes at a biochemical or at an organ-system level, resulting in the clinical pictures of peptic ulcer, asthma, or diabetes, for example (Engel, 1960; Prugh, 1963). These in turn may affect the mental apparatus, either directly, as in diabetic coma, or indirectly, with the arousal of psychological or social defenses in reaction to the presence of illness or disability. Failures in such adaptive maneuvers may lead the individual to inappropriate usage of psychological defenses producing further decompensation, as in the child who denies he is ill with diabetes and overeats heavily, or the negativistic child who refuses to take badly needed medications for his asthma.

If an emotional conflict remains unresolved and unpleasant emotions persist, the attempts by the organism to employ psychological or social defense mechanisms may continue to unhealthy and maladaptive extremes. Such may lead, in individuals predisposed experientially and constitutionally, to the psychopathological pictures customarily referred to as the neuroses or milder personality disorders, or to the psychoses which represent severe decompensation or adaptive breakdown. In infants and young children, such crystallized psychological states are rare, with a variety of symptomatic behavioral or psychological reactions occurring. Maladaptive behavior associated with efforts to deal with stressful stimuli may result in physiological reverberations. These may be seen in the nutritional deficiency resulting from marked food refusal in a chronically depressed child, or the repeated exposure to physical injury seen in certain children struggling to cover up and to deny intense fears.

From the foregoing, it may readily be seen that the symptoms experienced by the patient and even the signs noted by the physician may bear little apparent relationship to the stressful stimuli first experienced and the level of organization first affected. Indeed, the symptoms as reported subjectively by the patient (or, with younger children, by the parents) may vary widely even in response to similar initial stresses at similar levels of organization. Characteristic patterns of response, traditionally designated as syndromes, do commonly occur. Nevertheless, the individual character of response to potential stresses, ranging from the invasion of the hemolytic streptococcus to the loss of a loved person, must constantly be kept in mind in the attempt to understand and evaluate the disease picture.

In the clinical study of disease states, our customarily arbitrary designation of illness as predominantaly physical or "somatic" or as principally "psychological" in character derives from the major point of impingement of significantly stressful stimuli upon the organism, and implies a weighting of emphasis which takes into account the level of organization most prominently involved in adaptive breakdown or in the attempts to maintain or regain equilibrium.

From the approach described, there is no room for artificial dichotomies of wholly somatic or completely psychological disease, no true characterization of illness as "functional" or "organic," no valid diagnosis of psychological disturbance by "ruling out" somatic influences. Rather there must be an active diagnostic search for predisposing, contributory, precipitating, and perpetuating factors of physiological, psychological, or social nature. The weighting of such positive evidence will thus lead to a treatment plan which achieves the appropriate balance of somatic, psychological, or social or environmental methods of therapy or management.

Developmental Factors

In children, the dynamic steady state, reflecting the adaptive equilibrium, is only a relatively stable one, existing at hypothetical cross-

sectional points on a time continuum during the process of growth
and maturation. Within this developmental framework, certain
critical phases in the child's biological progress appear to predispose
him to greater vulnerability in response to stimuli of potentially
stressful nature. Intra-uterine infections occurring during the early
months of embryonic development, for example, seem to produce
congenital anomalies more readily than those occurring at later
stages. Gastrointestinal disturbance leading readily to severe dehydration has its highest incidence in early infancy. Infants in the
second half of the first year of life appear to be particularly susceptible to the effects of significant and prolonged lack of adequate
mothering, with serious depression, marasmus, or marked personality
distortions frequently resulting. Recent animal and human research
suggests that certain patterns of social behavior, if not "triggered off"
sufficiently by interpersonal stimuli during appropriate developmental phases, may be seriously blunted (Bowlby, 1958), leading at
times to irreversible defect in intellectual or other parameters of
development. The greater tendency of the central nervous system
in infancy and early childhood to respond with seizures to a variety
of stimuli is widely recognized. The changing nature and severity
of allergic responses, the differing types of response to tuberculosis
and other infections, and the variations in incidence of rheumatic
fever and other collagen diseases, in relation to age level, are further
examples.

Considered from the viewpoint of health and positive adaptation,
the organism in certain early developmental stages may tolerate
certain stresses more readily than during the later phases. The capacity of the fetus to withstand hypoxia during delivery and the
immediate postnatal period is a case in point, as are the milder
effects of contagious diseases in young children in contrast to adults.
The inborn impetus toward growth and maturation characteristic
of the human organism seems to provide the child with remarkable
resiliency and recuperative powers, even in relation to exceedingly
serious illnesses.

Among factors influencing the child's patterns of development and his adaptive capacity are those of "constitutional" nature. The contemporary concept of constitution is a dynamic, not a static one, as was formerly the case. Constitutional characteristics thus include the sum total of the structural and functional qualities or potentialities of the individual, interacting with his physical environment and his different varieties of experience, beginning with the intra-uterine environment. Hereditary endowment is modified by experiential factors throughout development to produce the individual's basic physique, his intellectual capacity, his immune response patterns, and possibly certain temperamental qualities, among other features. Constitution is a process—not a "given" (Witmer and Kotinsky, 1952).

Developmental differences in reactivity to noxious stimuli thus appear to have numerous sources. These may range from changing patterns of anatomic structure, metabolic activity, organ-system maturation, tissue tropism, and immunologic response to the stage of neuroendocrine integration, the patterning of neural organization, or the level of development of the mental apparatus. Other influences may include genic potentialities, constitutional factors, sex differences, and the nature of environmental exposure to previous stimuli.

THE SOCIAL FIELD OF ILLNESS

Although the social or interpersonal level of functioning of the individual has been mentioned, some elaboration of this concept is indicated, particularly in regard to the psychosocial field of forces within which the child may fall ill. Adults of course exist in a network of interpersonal relationships, changes in which can produce shifts in adaptive equilibrium at psychological or physiological levels of organization. Children are more dependent upon the immediate caretaking figures in their environment, however, and are more vulnerable to a variety of socially stressful stimuli than are adults.

At birth, the human infant is equipped with reflex mechanisms of behavior, operating principally at a subcortical level, and does not appear to exhibit conscious psychological and social levels of organization. For the first several months, the physiological level appears to be predominant, with the mothering figure serving as the external representative of the psychological level. Social interaction between mother and infant takes place largely in terms of contact around the infant's physiological needs, communicated to the mother by the infant's crying or restlessness. Recent research (Richmond and Lipton, 1959) suggests that certain physiological systems of the infant in the neonatal period exhibit rather sensitive responses to feeding and other contacts with the mother, principally in the areas of autonomic functioning and motor behavior.

As true social transactions between parent and infant become possible, beginning in the second or third month with the first social response, the smile, the infant's rapidly developing capacities soon bring him to the point, at least by the second half of the first year, where he may perceive and respond sensitively to social stimuli of positive or negative character.

Parent-Child Relationships

The interpersonal contacts of the infant and young child involve the initial two-person sets of relationships, mother-child, father-child, sibling-child, and the like. The importance of these diadic sets of relationships, particularly the mother-child, for the psychological aspects of the development and adaptation of the young child has been recognized for many years. More recent investigations have implicated actual, threatened, or symbolic disruptions of the early mother-child relationship, as well as other vicissitudes in parent-child interaction, in the predisposition toward or the precipitation of a variety of childhood disease pictures. These may range from predominantly psychological disorders, such as depression (Spitz, 1946), "environmental" retardation in psychomotor development (Coleman and Provence, 1957), psychoneuroses (Cramer, 1959), psychoses (Mahler et al., 1959), and antisocial personality disorders (Bowlby, 1951), through illnesses in which psychological and physiological disturbances coexist, as in "hospitalism" (Spitz, 1945), peptic ulcer (Taboroff and Brown, 1954), marasmus or "failure to thrive" (Bakwin, 1949), ulcerative colitis (Prugh, 1951), asthma (Jessner et al., 1955), and numerous others.

The scope of the present communication does not permit detailed consideration of the specific nature of disturbances in the parent-child relationship which may contribute, *among other variables,* to the appearance of various disease pictures. Indeed, our knowledge of the precise character and degree of such influence is still limited. The deleterious effects of such gross disturbances as marked over-protection (Levy, 1943), or, more rarely, open rejection or neglect (Newell, 1934), occasionally leading to willful injury (Kempe et al., 1962) or inadequate nutrition, are well documented, however. Evidence is accumulating to support the view that markedly unhealthy parental attitudes, often unconscious ones, are more significant in their crippling effects upon the child's personality development and his state of health than any single child-rearing technique.

Although the concept of the parent or parents "doing" something or "failing to do" something for the child has been a popular one, the current view is that of a *transactional relationship between parent and child.* In this view, the developmental characteristics of the child at particular points, beginning with his first feeding response in the neonatal period, may affect the parents as "feedback" operations, with the nature of the relationship between them being at least partially influenced by the child's contributions to the transactional and reverberating parent-child unit (Benedek, 1949). Thus the individual personality structures of the parents, the nature of their previous experience, their attitudes toward child rearing and the particular child, the influence of intercurrent events during the pregnancy and neonatal period, their ability to work together harmoniously as parents, and their capacities to perceive the child's needs as a developing individual, interact with the child's physical and behavioral characteristics, his unfolding genic potentialities, and with various fortuitous events, such as illness or accident, to determine the quality of the parent-child relationship, as well as the nature of its contribution to the child's adaptive capacity and, consequently, his state of health or disease.

Although the tone of the parent-child relationship may be set by the early transactional events, such experience may be formative

rather than fixative in its effect upon the child's personality development and ultimate state of psychological health and maturity. Later
events may offset initial difficulties. Indeed, as Erikson (1950) has
pointed out, subsequent psychosocial interactions may at times compensate in large measure for earlier deficiencies or distortions. In
spite of initial problems, parents may develop in their capacities as
parents or in their ability to deal constructively with a particular
child.

Family Influences

The relationship between child and parents of course takes place
within the context of the nuclear family, common to all societies
in spite of some differences in organization and function. The transactional interpersonal equilibrium between parent and child therefore must be enlarged to include other members of the family, in
regard to their transactions with each other as individuals, pairs, or
other subgroup combinations, as well as in relation to the transactional operations of the total family as a unit or a group of persons.
The character of the marital relationship between the parents bears
importantly upon their handling of a particular child, for example,
as may the physical or behavioral characteristics of a sibling which
call out preferential responses in one or both parents. The degree of
intactness and cohesiveness of the family, its over-all patterns of communication, role operations, and leadership, its value orientations,
and the nature and extent of its integration into the external community, together with significant subgroup operations among its
individual members, appear to be involved in the maintenance of a
family adaptive equilibrium or a balance of familial interpersonal
forces.

Disruptions in this equilibrium may affect parent-child relationships and, indirectly, the adaptive capacity of a particular child,
acting as a stressful stimulus at the social level of organization. Withdrawal of support by one parent as a result of physical illness or
depression may serve as a stressful stimulus for one child in a vulnerable phase of development, producing reverberations at psychological or physiological levels or both. The altered behavior of the

child may then operate as a feedback mechanism to affect unfavorably in turn one or both parents or other family members. The illness and hospitalization of one child, followed by regressive behavior, may alter parental patterns of handling on the basis of their anxiety, guilt, or other emotions. The resultant overprotectiveness or over-permissiveness by one or both parents may arouse jealous or regressive behavior in a sibling with a predisposition toward psychological or somatic illness patterns, producing adaptive breakdown and the appearance of a disease picture in the sibling.

In a healthy family unit, such "crises" may temporarily alter patterns of communication, interpersonal transaction, and role operations. The flexibility and cohesiveness of the family unit is not lost, however, and a new and different family adaptive equilibrium is soon established (Caplan, 1961). This may be either temporary or permanent in nature, resulting in some emotional growth at times for individual family members and often in a higher, more flexibly adaptive level of "family development." In the family which fails to achieve such a new and balanced equilibrium, decompensation and disorganization may ensue, or various types of "schism and skew" (Lidz et al., 1957) may result in regard to role operations or subgroup patterns. The child who falls ill may be made a scapegoat for family tensions, or the temporarily sick member may unconsciously be kept in the role of a chronically invalided person, permitting a tenuous and unhealthy family equilibrium to be maintained at the cost of the psychological health of the family member so dealt with. Actual family breakdown or disintegration may of course occur from a variety of sources, including death or marital incompatibility. Such situations often, although not invariably, result in serious repercussions for the personality development or state of health of young children (Maas and Engler, 1959).

Individual family members with serious psychological illnesses may influence adversely family patterns of response and may serve as "carriers" of disturbed behavior over several generations through their influence on a specific child (Fisher and Mendell, 1960). In certain deeply pathological and precariously poised family equilibria, involving seriously disturbed persons, unhealthy relationships of intensely complementary nature may occur between parent and child or may involve other two-person units, triangular relationships, or even the whole family. In such families, the adjustment of the persons involved is so deeply dependent, in an interlocking fashion, upon that of the specific partner or partners that the death, illness, or even improvement during psychological treatment of one of the partners may disrupt the adjustment of the other or others. Decompensation manifested by illness at a physiological level, marked depression, or even psychosis may occur in the individuals concerned (Ackerman, 1958). Such situations are rare; they occur frequently enough, however, to contraindicate active psychotherapeutic treatment or at least to warrant caution in the approach to treatment of one member without careful concomitant treatment of others.

Sociocultural Factors

In addition to such immediate reverberations within the social "field" of the family unit, other phenomena involving social interaction within the community, state, and national society must be considered in regard to the response of the individual to significantly stressful stimuli at the social level of organization.

That social contacts outside the home can influence the form of psychological illness has long been known. Historical accounts indicate that epidemics of "dancing frenzy" or other group behavior have occurred periodically in particular subcultural groups. In modern times, small epidemics of hysterical conversion symptoms have been observed on pediatric wards, with the "contagion" touched off by the death of one patient, for example. Until recently, epidemics of weakness or paralysis of hysterical nature in adolescent girls were common during the poliomyelitis season. A variety of symptomatic manifestations, including asthma, increased respiratory difficulty, and respiratory infections, has been noted in a group of patients in a respiratory poliomyelitis center, following immediately upon the discharge of a particularly beloved and supportive adult patient (Prugh and Tagiuri, 1954).

Patterns of child rearing have been shown to be strongly influenced by socioeconomic and social class background (Sears et al., 1957), although it is difficult to attach value judgments to such differences except under extreme circumstances. Attitudes toward feeding and discipline may vary among families from differing ethnic or national origins, with feeding problems (Brim, 1955) occurring more frequently in particular subcultural groups.

Recent observations support the impression that socioeconomic or social class factors may play a role in the incidence of various disease states. Although the explanation is not clear, a higher incidence of mental illness and certain types of psychosomatic disorders have been reported in lower socioeconomic groups in North American society (Rennie et al., 1957; Rennie and Srole, 1956). Some available evidence suggests that population shifts or migrations from rural into urban areas may be associated, at least temporarily, with an increased appearance of psychophysiological disturbances (Seguin, 1956). Known levels of incidence in diseases such as hypertension and diabetes, which vary among differing ethnic groups, perhaps partially as the result of inbreeding, may apparently be altered or accentuated upon first exposure to the differing stresses of urbanization and industrialization (Opler, 1959). Certain investigators entertain the hypothesis, as yet unproved, that families in transition from lower-class to middle-class socioeconomic status may be more susceptible to psychological disturbances among their members (Kluckhohn and Spiegel, 1954).

Other epidemiological observations of pertinence include the higher incidence of rheumatic fever in the lower socioeconomic segments of the North American population (Nelson, 1959), perhaps involving more frequent exposure and even lowered resistance to streptococcal infections as a result of poorer living conditions. Differing attitudes toward prenatal care as the result of more limited education may be in part responsible for the fact that complications of pregnancy occur more frequently in women from lower socioeconomic backgrounds (Yankauer et al., 1953). Since the turn of the century in Western society, for reasons which are obscure, a change appears to have taken place in the incidence of disease pictures

(Halliday, 1948), with a decrease in hysterical pictures and an increase in disturbances in function of cardiovascular, gastrointestinal,
and other organ systems.

The causal significance of the apparent relationships among the
variables mentioned above remains to be clarified. Whatever the
contributions of sociocultural factors to the etiology of illness, however, they appear clearly to play a role in regard to attitudes toward
the occurrence of illness, the role of the physician and other helping
persons as well as community agencies. Current research suggests
that families from varying sociocultural backgrounds react differently to the experience of illness in their children (Spiegel, 1954).
Healthy patterns of reaction generally predominate, but unhealthy
patterns may range from overprotection of the ill child to isolation
and even ostracism from the family group. Differences of this nature
appear to exist also in the reactions of families to the need for medical treatment and, in particular, for hospitalization. Immigrant families from rural parts of Southern Europe, for example, may resist
the admission of a child to the hospital, regarding it, in terms of their
experience, as a "death house" to be utilized for terminally ill persons only.

Attitudes toward the sick person may vary from society to society.
In Western society, the "role" of the patient is more comfortably
assigned to the physically ill person than to the obviously disturbed
or mentally ill (Parsons, 1951). Evidence exists also that stereotypes
of social class groups held by physicians may unconsciously affect the
nature of the treatment offered, particularly for mentally ill patients
(Hollingshead and Redlich, 1958).

The Family As the Unit of Study

In summary, it can be said that consideration of the social level of
organization must include the forces which impinge upon the individual as a result of his membership in the family, the particular
social class and ethnic group, the local community, the region, and
the national society, with all the historical and cultural forces which
come to bear upon society and are transmitted down through these

various social institutions to the individual. It is clear then that *the clinician must accept the family rather than the individual alone as the essential unit for the study and treatment of health and disease.* The genic potentialities and the personality characteristics of individual members, the past history of the individuals and the stage of development of the family, the nature of the physical environment, and the current pattern of group interaction within the family, with reference to the sociocultural setting, must be regarded as pertinent to the incidence of disease in one or more family members (Titchener et al., 1960). Thus the falling ill of a child with acute or chronic disease both affects and is affected by the interpersonal family equilibrium in its particular community, society, and culture.

TOWARD A NEW PHYSIOLOGY

Mention has been made of the influences upon the physiological level of organismic functioning by stressful stimuli impinging initially upon the psychological or interpersonal levels. Once the stimulus has been registered, perceived, and accorded central symbolic significance in the mental apparatus, the arousal of emotional responses ordinarily follows. Cobb (1950) and others have pointed out that there are three characteristic components of an emotion: (1) the emotion's *subjective* mental content, which may be consciously registered or may remain unconscious; (2) the *physiological* component, involving a set of changes in nerves, viscera, glands, and muscles; (3) the *behavioral* expression, which may involve various actions of adaptive nature, including communication of the emotion to other persons by verbal or nonverbal means. The behavioral patterns of expression may be facilitated, altered, or inhibited by the mental apparatus. Responses from other individuals may be aroused, as a result of the individual's behavior or communication of emotional content, which may act as a feedback mechanism, producing modification in the subjective emotional experience, behavioral expression, or physiological state.

In the present communication, it is impossible to summarize the extensive literature dealing with the nature and variety of human emotional responses. Darwin (1872) was among the first to point out the adaptive character of emotions, in animals and man. As Cannon (1929) later suggested, certain human emotions, such as anger or fear, presumably had greater adaptive significance in primitive society, where the associated physiological preparation for the behavioral action of "fight" or "flight" was essential to survival. In civilized society, such "emergency" responses are ordinarily less necessary from an adaptive point of view. Emotions, however, are universally aroused in situations involving the experience of a need or drive, with intensification under conditions of frustration of a drive state or in conflict situations, as Freud's (1940) work showed. The signal quality of anxiety, an emotion characterized by a vague awareness of tension and apprehension (without specific conscious content, in contrast to fear) has already been discussed in regard to its significance for the mental apparatus.

No attempt will be made here to discuss the classifications of the subjective components of emotions which such writers as Cobb (1950) and Engel (1962) have offered. Emotions appear to fall along a continuum, from the more pleasurable ones of love, joy, contentment, and sexual satisfaction to the more negative or unpleasant emotions of anxiety, anger, fear, sadness, helplessness, depression, and hopelessness. In recent years, the physiological components or concomitants of emotions have been brought under intensive investigation. Most of the reports dealing with the physiological concomitants have been derived from laboratory situations with presumed psychologically stressful significance, ordinarily of conscious nature, for normal subjects, usually adults. For various reasons, the negative emotions have been scrutinized most carefully, with the principal exception of Stevenson's (1950) studies of pleasurable experience and Cobb's (1950) summary of his impressions of the physiological concomitants of sexual attraction or heterosexual love. The numerous investigations along these lines of Harold Wolff (1953), Stewart Wolf (1951), and their colleagues, as well as those of many other workers (summarized by Applezweig, 1957) have added greatly to our current understanding.

The Physiology of Emotions

A brief mention of some of the physiological concomitants of emotions must suffice, listed in relation to the various organ systems, rather arbitrarily subdivided.

Cardiovascular: variations in heart rate and rhythm, stroke volume, cardiac output, arterial blood pressure, peripheral resistance, and arteriovenous oxygen difference (Hickam et al., 1948; Stead et al., 1945); electrocardiographic patterns (Stevenson and Duncan, 1950; Blom, 1951); exercise tolerance (Duncan et al., 1951); capillary activity (Graham, 1955); and coronary blood flow (Adsett et al., 1962).

Respiratory: variations in respiratory rate, rhythm, and amplitude (Finesinger and Mazick, 1940); tidal volume, CO_2 tension, and oxygen exchange (Engel, 1948); bronchiolar action (Faulkner, 1941); the activity of the diaphragm and the accessory muscles of respiration (Wolf, 1947); and secretory responses, associated with changes in vascularity, of the mucous membranes of the nose (Holmes et al., 1949) and other portions of the respiratory tree (Stevenson and Wolff, 1949).

Gastrointestinal: alterations in motor, vascular, and secretory activity of the esophagus (Rubin et al., 1962), the stomach, including the cardiac and pyloric sphincters (Wolf and Wolff, 1947), and the large intestine (Grace et al., 1951); changes in the level of production of hydrochloric acid (Engel et al., 1956), pepsin (Margolin et al., 1950), and lysozyme (Grace et al., 1948); alterations in function of the external anal sphincter (Prugh, 1954); fluctuations in pH, viscosity, and total amount of secretion of the salivary glands (Bogdanoff et al., 1961); changes in the bacterial flora of the oropharynx (Kaplan et al., 1957); and variations in the absorption of iron (Grace and Doig, 1954).

Genitourinary: alterations in vesical function (Straub et al., 1949) and external sphincter control (Prugh et al., 1953); shifts in renal blood flow and filtration rate (Pfeiffer and Ripley, 1947); changes in uterine muscular activity (Mann, 1957) and menstrual functioning (Menzer, 1953).

Hemic and lymphatic: variations in the blood level of leukocytes (Milhorat et al., 1942); lymphocytes (Farris, 1938), and circulating eosinophiles (Dreyfuss, 1956); relative blood viscosity, clotting time, hematocrit, and sedimentation rate (Schneider, 1950); changes in pH values and oxygen saturation (Wolff et al., 1950).

Musculoskeletal: fluctuations in muscle electrical potentials (Meyer and Noble, 1958); alterations in coordinative activity of various muscle groups (Wolf, 1947).

Skin: changes in skin temperature (Mittelmann and Wolf, 1943); psychogalvanic skin responses (Tong and Murphy, 1960); thermal sweat production (Wolff et al., 1950); sebum secretion (Robin and Kepecs, 1953); cutaneous vascular responses and patterns of wheal formation (Graham, 1950) and exudation (Kepecs et al., 1951); and shifts in vulnerability to inflammatory reactions (Chapman et al., 1956).

Endocrine: variations in the levels of steroids secreted by the *adrenal* cortex, including plasma hydrocortisone (Persky et al., 1958), urinary hydroxycorticosteroids and 17-ketosteroids (Hoagland et al., 1953); fluctuations in the output of male and female hormones from the *gonads* (Cleghorn, 1957); changes in *thyroid* activity, as reflected in alterations in plasma-bound iodine (Hetzel et al., 1952); changes in levels of aldosterone (Venning et al., 1957).

Central nervous system: alterations in electroencephalographic measurements of cortical activity (Barker and Barker, 1950); nerve reaction time (Appelzweig, 1957); sedation threshold (Shagass and Naiman, 1955); pain perception and response (Wolff and Wolf, 1958); activity level (Fries and Wolf, 1953); the response to various drugs and anesthetic agents (Wolf, 1950); variations in perceptual accuracy (Tong and Murphy, 1960), and in cognitive functions such as memory and reasoning (Rapaport, 1942).

In addition to these more specific responses in individual organ systems, more broadly *metabolic* changes have also been observed, some of them related to shifts in hormonal balance, including variations in the urinary excretion of water and electrolytes (Schottstaedt et al., 1956b), catecholamines (Goodall and Berman, 1960), ketone bodies (Hinkle et al., 1950), creatinine (Schottstaedt et al., 1956a), hippuric acid (Persky et al., 1952), and coproporphyrins (Luby et al., 1959), as well as changes in basal metabolism (Coppen and Mezey, 1960), body temperature (Goodell et al., 1950), fluctuations in blood glucose levels (Hinkle and Woolf, 1950), and alterations in the values of serum lipids such as cholesterol (Grundy and Griffen, 1959; Sherber and Marcus, 1957).

Little is known as yet of possible immediate alterations in enzymatic activity or other metabolic processes of biochemical nature taking place at the tissue, cellular, or molecular level. Chapman (1957) and colleagues have described changes in tissue vulnerability produced by hypnosis, but the mechanisms involved in these remains unclear. The physiological levels of gastric pepsin and lysozyme, as mentioned above, do show fluctuations in relation to emotions. These appear, however, to derive from shifts in the secretory activity of the exocrine cells in the mucosal wall of the portions of the gastro-intestinal tract from which such enzymes are released. That stressful stimuli of interpersonal or psychological nature do exert such influences at the cellular level seems likely, from the conceptual approach outlined earlier and from clinical data. Documentation must await the development of new and more refined methods of psychophysiological investigation.

Among the studies cited, some are decidedly preliminary, with the use of exceedingly small samples of subjects. In addition, it has been possible in many instances to study only one or two physiological parameters simultaneously in response to stressful psychological stimuli. Thus the complex and constantly fluctuating interrelationships among the reactions of various organ systems and metabolic processes can often only be inferred. The recent development of polygraphic techniques, involving multiple physiological parameters, has much to offer, although the analysis of such large and complex amounts of data is difficult and at times misleading. Problems have arisen also from the difficulty in defining the stressful stimulus. In some instances, this may be the laboratory situation and not the experimental psychological stimulus, while in other instances, the stimulus or the situation may represent a significant stress for some individuals and not for others (Reiser et al., 1955). For all of these reasons, it seems difficult at present to categorize the exact degree and nature of such psychophysiological events, even though their occurrence seems to be indubitable, from the work at hand.

Mention should be made also of the effects upon psychological functioning of certain physiological phenomena, such as the hormonal changes during the menstrual cycle as studied by Benedek and Rubenstein (1942). The effects of other stressful stimuli of predominantly physical origin must also be considered. Pain from a traumatized part of the body or malaise as the result of a viral infection may produce certain physiological changes which may be intensified or altered by the physiological concomitants of emotions aroused by the experience of becoming ill, with all its individualized significance. Many of the changes in physiological function cited above may be produced by intense muscular effort during exercise in response to a crisis situation and might be mingled with those caused by the emotional response in such situations.

The question of the specificity of physiological concomitants of particular emotions remains still relatively open. Some investigations have shown results which conflict with others, in regard to the effects of particular emotions. Such discrepancies may be the result in part of difficulties in categorization of the particular emotional response under scrutiny. The emotions focused upon in artificial laboratory situations are, as mentioned, largely conscious ones and may appear to be "pure" emotional responses of single nature. In most life situations, however, emotions are mixed, involving strong elements of conflict, with unconscious feelings often at odds with conscious ones. Margolin's work (1951) suggests that, at least in certain situations, unconscious emotions may exert a predominant effect on physiological functions. Data from animal studies, while of basic value in stimulating human investigations, can of course cast no light upon this question.

The association of blushing with shame or embarrassment and of nausea with disgust has long been known. Certain workers still hold that particular physiological changes occur in individual organs or organ systems in relation to specific emotions such as anger or fear. The data presently available would seem to support the conclusion, at this juncture, that there is no specific physiology which corresponds regularly with each emotional state (Kubie, 1957a). Exceptions such as shame and disgust do exist, however, and certain broad patterns of response do seem to occur.

The first of these is the "emergency reaction" to real or fantasied danger, which seems to involve the pattern of physiological preparation for "fight or flight," associated with the emotions of anxiety, fear, or rage. Increased mental alertness, heightened muscular activity, and physiological changes, including increased cardiac rate and output, a rise in blood pressure, the redistribution of blood flow to essential areas, a rise in leukocytes, the mobilization of glucose, an increase in respiratory rate and amplitude, and other phenomena are known to be characteristic of this pattern (Cannon, 1932). Some of these changes occur as the result of the action of epinephrine, secreted by the adrenal medulla, while others involve the broader activities of the sympathetic nervous system. Recent work, summarized by Engel (1962), suggests that epinephrinelike effects are more characteristic of situations in which anxiety or anger are held in check, with no action directed toward outer danger. Norepinephrinelike effects seem to predominate in situations where anger is directed outward and some behavioral action taken. More long-range metabolic preparations for repair of tissue injury, involving the action of corticosteroids, are initiated in the emergency phase, as Selye (1946), F. Engel (1953), and others have indicated.

The second major biological pattern of response has been delineated by Engel and Reichsman (1956) and has been recently termed by Engel (1962) the "withdrawal-conservation" pattern. Although specific physiological data are still limited, emotional states involving feelings of helplessness and hopelessness, arising in situations involving the loss of a significant figure or an inability to deal with real or fantasied threats, are apparently characterized by a general slowing of physiological activity. Such changes include reduced motor activity, diminished secretory activity of the gastrointestinal tract, and increased sleep, and appear to be related to the clinical phenomena of slowed motor responsiveness, poor appetite, constipation, and other physiological manifestations of prolonged grief or depression (Cleghorn and Curtis, 1959).

Much further work remains to be done in these and related areas, in refining the reported observations and in more extensive study of pleasurable emotions and of mourning or grief reactions, among other emotional states. Thus no full physiology of the emotions as yet exists (Engel, 1954a). A beginning has been made, as mentioned earlier, in the investigation of physiological responses to social interaction, as in the newborn infant (Richmond and Lipton, 1959). In addition, Malmo (1957) and others (DiMascio et al., 1957) have reported variations in muscle tension, skin temperature, and electrocardiographic tracings in patient and therapist during interviews, reflecting an "interpersonal physiology." Shottstaedt (1960) has described changes in heart rate and in the patterns of renal excretion of water and electrolytes in the context of vicissitudes in the doctor-patient relationship, while Wolf (1950) and others (Lasagna et al., 1954) have shown variations in the response of patients to drugs in similar situations. Patterns of nonverbal as well as verbal communication appear to operate in these interpersonal emotional exchanges and their physiological concomitants.

Important clinical implications of all these findings for the pediatrician lie in the necessity to consider emotional states in assessing mild deviations in physiological values, such as blood pressure, heart rate, or plasma-bound iodine, thus avoiding iatrogenic effects from overcautious handling. Success or failure in producing certain expected drug effects in child patients may be related partly to alterations in thresholds of response produced by emotional influences, which may include the reactions of parents and child to various events surrounding the illness, as well as the degree of their confidence in the pediatrician.

Mechanisms Involved in Psychophysiological Interrelationships

Although the foregoing material contributes to the documentation of the transactions taking place between psychological and physiological levels of organization, the exact nature of the psychophysiological mechanisms involved has not been discussed. Full knowledge of such mechanisms is not yet completely available. Recent investigation, however, has provided an understanding of many of these inter-relationships, which have been well summarized by Cobb (1950), Cleghorn (1957), and Engel (1962).

The physiological effects of stressful stimuli of psychological nature, resulting from interpersonal or intrapsychic events of emotional or symbolic significance, appear to be mediated by neural interconnections between the cerebral cortex and the hypothalamus, in which lie controls for the autonomic and endocrine systems, with their close relationship in function. Recent studies by MacLean (1958) suggest that the limbic cortex or "visceral brain," in its intimate relationships with the temporal cortex, plays an important role in the integration and regulation of external and internal perceptions and in ultimately determining whether nervous impulses are inhibited or are transmitted to the hypothalamus. Magoun's (1958) work indicates that the reticular activating system acts as an alerting center, with rich interconnections with the cerebral cortex, permitting effects upon motor and autonomic responses involved in states of consciousness or arousal. The direct effects of the hypothalamus upon the activity of the sympathetic and parasympathetic components of the autonomic nervous system have been well summarized by Gellhorn (1943), including their neurohumoral actions upon the cardiovascular system and respiratory mechanisms, the gastrointestinal system, and other internal viscera, as well as certain aspects of carbohydrate metabolism. Although sympathetic and parasympathetic effects appear to operate reciprocally upon the viscera, much overlap occurs. Oversimplified concepts of sympathetic or parasympathetic "overactivity" thus seem no longer tenable (Engel, 1962). Hypothalamic influences upon temperature regulation, appetite control, fat metabolism, the extrapyramidal system, and the reactivity of the somatic musculature under voluntary nervous control have been described (Grinker, 1939; Cleghorn, 1957), among other functions, although some of these effects are incompletely understood.

The posterior pituitary is apparently influenced by the hypothalamus through nervous interconnections, thus affecting water balance, renal mechanisms, thirst, lactation, and parturition phenomena. The influence of the hypothalamus upon the anterior pituitary appears to be mediated both directly, through the action of an adrenergic humoral agent, and indirectly, through the peripheral release of epinephrine (Cleghorn, 1957). By means of these interrelationships, psychological stimuli from the cerebral cortex can bring about the release of ACTH, with its known effects upon the adrenal cortex and the consequent secretion of adrenal cortical hormones. Effects may also be exerted in this way upon the action of the other trophic hormones affecting the gonads (FSH and LH) and thyroid (TSH). Regulating action is furnished by neural and humoral feedback mechanisms (Engel, 1962). Little is known of the factors affecting the rate of secretion of the nontrophic hormones of the anterior pituitary, such as the growth hormone.

Developmental Considerations

The work cited so far has been carried out principally on adults, and its validity for infants and young children remains to be determined. Newborn infants are of course equipped with potential patterns of neural organization and regulation of the type mentioned above. For the first several months, however, smooth integration of physiological components of emotional responses and of reactions to various stressful stimuli does not seem to occur, particularly as regards autonomic functioning (Stuart and Prugh, 1960). As Migeon (1959) has shown, the enzyme systems of the neonate which are involved in the catabolism of cortisol appear to be less active than in adult subjects. Other studies indicate that neonates exhibit an increased thyroxin uptake (Marks et al., 1961) compared to adults. Such findings, however limited, suggest that neuroendocrine patterns of response to stressful stimuli may be somewhat different at birth than at later stages of development.

Richmond and Lipton (1959) have well summarized what is known of the neurophysiology of the newborn, including autonomic activity, motor, and sensory response patterns. Their own work, dealing principally with heart-rate responses to air stream, stroking, and thermal stimulation, indicates that for a single physiological parameter reflecting autonomic activity, a normal distribution curve can be obtained among a group of healthy infants, with the use of regression coefficients and with due regard for the "law of initial values." Such studies permit the identification of individual differences among infants within the first few days of life, in regard to one particular physiological parameter, an observation confirmed by Bridger and Reiser (1959). The work of Grossman and Greenberg (1957) indicates that individual newborn infants may show variations in responsiveness within partitions of the autonomic nervous system, without necessary correlations even among valid indices of individual parameters of functioning. They suggest that each newborn infant may have at least one "vulnerable" component of the autonomic nervous system whose response to environmental stimulation, beginning with the mother-infant contacts, may show a capacity for greater lability and thus for more intensive participation in later emotional response of normal or pathological degree. Whether such reactivity bears any relationship to prenatal conditioning, as Sontag (1944) has suggested, or to the passage of neurohumoral or hormonal substances across the placental barrier remains to be investigated.

In addition to such autonomic investigations, studies of activity level have been carried out by Fries (1953), who found individual differences in responsiveness to a standard stimulus evoking the startle response. Wolff's (1959) observations on the apparent effect of endogenous neural stimulation on patterns of activity in newborn infants are pertinent also, as are Brazelton's (1961) regarding patterns of reaction in normal newborns. Bergman and Escalona (1949) have observed differences in sensitivity of response to external stimuli in very young infants, raising the question of the existence of an individually characteristic "stimulus barrier" or threshold. Individual differences in sleep and sucking patterns have also been described (Bergman and Escalona, 1949; Pratt, 1954), as have apparent differences in drive endowment (Alpert et al., 1956), biochemical patterns (Williams, 1956), and stable reaction patterns in regard to mood responses, biological rhythms, and other parameters (Chess et al., 1959).

The emotional responses of the infant in the first several months of life are less well studied. These appear to be relatively undifferentiated, with a range from apparently pleasurable to unpleasurable states, with a number of autonomically innervated organ systems participating in a more or less global type of physiological concomitance. As the infant develops psychological and interpersonal levels of organization, beginning with the first social response at two to three months of age, more fully differentiated emotional response patterns, associated with voluntary behavior, become gradually available to him. By the beginning of the second year, emotional states of joy, contentment, anger, fear, and depression are clearly characteristic of the infant. Although research data are not available, the impression of many workers is that the physiological concomitants of such emotions become more limited and less global, involving fewer organ systems. The work of Engel and Reichsman (1956) indicates changes in hydrochloric acid secretion in an infant in the second year of life, in association with emotions aroused during interpersonal contacts, with a rise in gastric HCl in states of positive relatedness and of anger and a fall during depression-withdrawal phenomena.

In young children, Tjossem (1955) and colleagues have systematically demonstrated skin-temperature changes in relation to the anxiety generated by separation from the mother. A consistent rise in blood pressure associated with the experience of hospitalization in preschool children has also been reported (Clayton and Hughes, 1952). In contrast to newborn infants, Lacey (1953) and his colleagues have described, in older children and adults, an over-all pattern of autonomic responsiveness (or an index of autonomic activity) as a characteristic of each individual, perhaps influenced by genic factors, as suggested by Jost and Sontag (1944).

From the few available data, there is some indication of progression from less organized to more organized modes of psychophysiological response during development from early infancy onward.

Individual differences in autonomic and other parameters of response apparently exist in the neonatal period and at later points. Much work remains to be done, however, before a full understanding of developmental psychophysiology is possible.

SPECIFIC CLINICAL AND THEORETICAL CONSIDERATIONS REGARDING PSYCHOSOMATIC CONCEPTS

Reference was made earlier to the psychosomatic-somatopsychic continuum often employed in referring to disorders of bodily function in children and adults. In spite of the limitation of such terms, the concepts underlying them require discussion as they relate to clinical syndromes. In order to apply the psychosomatic approach consistently, consideration would have to be undertaken of all possible disturbances of adaptation in the developing child in his family and social setting, a project obviously not within the scope of this communication. Instead, discussion will be focused upon those disorders in which *disturbances in bodily function* are prominent, either as the result of predominantly psychological or interpersonal stressful stimuli or of primarily physical stimuli with accompanying psychological reactions. *All the foregoing considerations regarding multiple factors in etiology apply, in spite of the artificial separation of categories for purposes of discussion.* Thus the term "predominantly" should be read wherever psychological or physical disorders are mentioned. The following breakdown of categories is an arbitrary one, with much unavoidable overlapping.

A. *Psychological Reactions Leading to Self-inflicted Injury or Illness*
   1. Bodily injury or mutilation
   2. Suicidal attempts
   3. Accident proneness

B. *Psychological Reactions with Associated Changes in Bodily Function*
   1. Anxiety reactions
   2. Depressive reactions

    3. Conversion reactions

    4. Symptomatic reactions of young children

C. *Psychophysiological (Vegetative) Reactions*

D. *Mixed Conversion and Psychophysiological Reactions*

E. *Psychological Reactions to Physical Disorders*

    1. Reactions to physical disorders involving primarily the central nervous system

    2. Reactions to physical disorder outside the central nervous system

        a. Reactions to acute illness or injury

        b. Reactions to chronic illness or handicap

In the material to follow, the *physiological concomitants of emotions,* already discussed, will be mentioned only as they occur in anxiety states or as they pertain to the precipitation, intensification, or perpetuation of other disease pictures. Such phenomena of course occur in healthy as well as psychologically or physically ill children. They are ordinarily reversible and, under usual circumstances, involve no structural or permanent change in organ systems or metabolic processes.

Predominantly psychological reactions with associated *preoccupation with bodily functions,* in the absence of disturbance in physiological function, can be mentioned only in passing. Such may be seen in severely disturbed children, usually of school age or beyond, with obsessive fears of body dysfunction or abnormality, the compulsive need to touch body parts to reassure themselves of their intactness, hypochondriacal reactions, somatic delusions, and other trends. Such preoccupation may be seen transiently in less disturbed children, who fear some abnormality of the genitals or stomach or who are troubled by noticing extrasystoles or borborygymi, in the face of some temporary threat to their adaptive equilibrium.

A. *Psychological Reactions Leading to Self-Inflicted Injury*

1. *Bodily Injury or Mutilation.* Disorders of this nature are rare in childhood. They may appear during adolescence in the form of

bizarre self-mutilation or injury in the course of psychotic pictures (Offer and Barglow, 1960), deep personality disorders, or acute and sweeping psychological decompensations. In less severe forms, they may occur in preschool children who bite their own hands or arms, often in association with conflicts over the handling of aggressive impulses toward their parents. Certain children with severe psycho-neurotic pictures may pick open wounds, often in association with unconscious needs for self-punishment or unhealthy enjoyment of pain, thus interfering with the healing process and preventing their return to competitive or other conflict-producing situations.

2. *Suicidal Attempts.* Actual suicide in childhood is uncommon, although occasional attempts are accidentally successful (Bakwin, 1957; Bender and Schilder, 1937). Suicidal attempts, often but not always of dramatic or manipulative nature, are common in adolescents, particularly girls (Balser and Masterson, 1959). Suicidal threats in school-age children are frequent, and often involve the child's need to frighten or punish the parent with the fantasy of suicide, without understanding the meaning of death.

3. *Accident Proneness.* This syndrome has been widely discussed, but relatively few systematic studies exist. Impulsive or hyperactive children with poorly organized personalities or with strong needs to rebel against parental figures may exhibit such patterns (Langford et al., 1954; Marcus et al., 1960; Bakwin and Bakwin, 1953), as may occasional children with unconscious needs to punish themselves for deep guilt feelings. Some very active but relatively healthy children may exhibit such trends temporarily, in the face of family crises.

B. *Psychological Reactions with Associated Changes in Bodily Function*

1. *Anxiety Reactions.* Such pictures in children are ordinarily less clear-cut and more fluctuating than those seen in adults. Most preschool children exhibit fears of unknown situations or objects. Phobias, representing fears unconsciously displaced from the original person or conflict situation within the family onto animals, school, or other ordinarily nonfrightening aspects of everyday life, are

encountered normally in children as developmental phenomena of adaptive nature during the late preschool period. With such fears or phobic patterns, if intense and prolonged, temporary and reversible physiological changes related to fight-flight preparations are frequent.

In older school-age children with true anxiety neurosis, anxiety, without a conscious external object involving appropriate danger, may be more or less constantly present. Such anxiety may be "free-floating" in nature and may attach itself to a bewildering variety of situations or events, representing a reaction to internal dangers arising from possible loss of control of aggressive or sexual impulses, with a need to be constantly "on guard."

Physiological concomitants related to the fight-flight biologic patterns may be frequently evident in children with anxiety reactions. Startle reactions, tremors, elevations in blood pressure and heart rate, marked sinus arrhythmia, slight increase in sedimentation rate, changes in respiratory rate and tendencies toward hyperventilation, slight to moderate elevations in body temperature, increased perspiration with cold, moist palms, and nightmares or other sleep disturbances, are often clinically apparent, leading at times to diagnostic confusion with essential hypertension, rheumatic fever, and thyrotoxicosis. Such changes are ordinarily reversible during more relaxed periods.

2. *Depressive Reactions.* Clinical signs of depression in children may be protean. Overt depression may be masked by eating disturbances, hyperactivity, or other phenomena more commonly in young children than in adults. Marked grief reactions or prolonged depression, however, may be seen in infants (Spitz, 1946) as well as in preschool and older children, with clinical features resembling the slowing of physiological responses characteristic of the withdrawal-conservation patterns. Apathy, anorexia, slowed motor activity, constipation, and other features may be present, at times complicating mild physical illness associated with emotionally significant events within the family.

3. *Conversion Reactions.* The tendency for so-called conversion reactions to occur in persons with psychoneuroses of hysterical nature

has been known for many years. Conversion reactions involve changes in function, ordinarily in the direction of diminution or loss, of parts of the body which are innervated by the voluntary components of the central nervous system, including principally the striated musculature and the somatosensory apparatus (Grinker and Robbins, 1954). Clinical manifestations include the following types:

a. *Disturbances in motor function:* weakness, paralysis, choreiform or other uncoordinated movements, disturbances in gait, posture, convulsivelike phenomena (often without complete loss of consciousness), tics, aphonia, difficulties in swallowing, and disorders such as cataplexy and astasia-abasia, have been described in children as well as adults.

b. *Alterations in sensory perception:* in this category fall disturbances in function of the organs of special sense, as in conversion blindness or tubular vision, deafness, anosmia, and loss of taste. Absent gag and corneal reflexes are common. Intense pain may be perceived from individual parts of the body, particularly the abdomen and the head; anesthesia, hypesthesia, paresthesia, hypersthesia, and severe itching also may occur.

c. *Disturbances in mental functions and consciousness:* these include dissociative phenomena, such as amnesias and fugue states, as well as certain types of syncope, fatigue states, catelepsy, narcolepsy, and stuporous or pseudo-delirious states.

d. *Disturbances in specific organ systems:* other types of disturbances in bodily function occur in which conversion mechanisms may play a role. These may involve *disorders of the upper end of the gastrointestinal tract* (including the throat and mouth), as in vomiting, trismus, globus hystericus, dysphonia, disorders of appetite (anorexia, hyperphagia, and bulimia), and abdominal distention; *disorders of the lower end of the gastrointestinal tract,* such as encopresis and certain types of constipation; *disorders of the voluntary components of respiration,* as in hyperventilation, certain types of dyspnea, breath holding, respiratory tics, certain types of coughing and hiccoughs, yawning and sighing respirations; *disorders of the genitourinary tract,* including certain types of urinary retention or sudden incontinence, as well as certain types of enuresis, dysuria, and frequency (disorders of genital function, such as impotence, frigidity, and dyspareunia are seen only in adolescents and adults).

Most of the last-mentioned disorders of the voluntary components of specific organ systems involve some overlap with involuntarily innervated components. These are discussed in a later section, as are certain severe and generalized types of weakness, paralysis, or other manifestations of marked psychological invalidism.

Space permits only brief discussion of conversion phenomena in childhood, treated more extensively by a number of writers, including Senn (1959), Brazelton (1953), Proctor (1959), and others (Kaufman, 1962; Finch, 1960; Chess, 1959; Kanner, 1948). A few words are appropriate, however, in order to underline the clinical distinction between *conversion reactions* and *psychophysiological (or vegetative) disorders,* a distinction importantly emphasized by Alexander (1950) and others and recognized in the current A.M.A. Nomenclature.

Conversion disturbances, as clinicians are aware, do not ordinarily follow patterns of anatomical distribution of motor or sensory innervation. Rather they are related to the central symbolic representation of a particular bodily function, as in walking, hitting, speaking, and seeing, or to the individual's (often erroneous) subjective concept of the boundaries of a body part. The exact neurophysiological mechanisms involved in the conversion phenomenon are not yet known. Presumably some functional alteration in the activity of the cerebral cortex takes place in response to psychological or interpersonal stimuli, as a result of which the individual muscular components or the particular organ of special sense act "as if" its function were suspended or blocked. Local changes of structural nature are not demonstrable in the body parts involved. Distortions in perception of pain, touch, and other senses may occur "in reverse," as if such stimuli were perceived centrally without the existence of specific sources in the local sites involved. Secondary changes in structure can of course occur, with the development of contractures from long-continued conversion paralysis or of changes in calcium metabolism and excretion as the result of a chronic bedridden existence.

The psychodynamic significance of the classical hysterical conversion symptom has been made abundantly clear through the work of Freud (1940). The symptom, whether it be paralysis of an arm or blindness, appears to carry an unconscious symbolic meaning for the individual, involving, for example, punishment for a wish to hit a loved person with the arm or the inability to see certain disturbing sexual sights, respectively. The emotional conflict between the wish to hit and the fear of punishment or loss of love (or between the wish to see and the fear of seeing) is automatically repressed out of conscious awareness by the mental apparatus. The symptom appears to resolve the conflict temporarily, albeit unhealthily and with the cost of suffering attached. The intrapsychic conflict is thus *unconsciously* "converted" to a somatic dysfunction or a disturbance in innervation, and the anxiety aroused by the conflict is apparently "bound" with the symptom. The individual possesses no conscious insight into the origin and the significance of the symptom, and little or no anxiety is experienced subjectively, leading to *la belle indifference* described in the nineteenth-century French literature on hysteria.

Conversion symptoms may often be removed (or at times produced) by suggestion, hypnosis, or narcohypnosis. Unless the underlying conflict can be resolved in some fashion, however, the symptom may, although not invariably, return or be replaced by another symbolically equivalent one (Seitz, 1957). In this fashion, the maintenance of a balanced though unhealthy adaptive equilibrium is apparently possible over a period of time, with the avoidance of an unbearable degree of tension or anxiety which might cause decompensation and subsequent adaptive breakdown.

The specific psychological determinants of the form and content of the conversion symptom appear to arise from the previous experience of the child and the current conflictual interpersonal setting. As Engel (1962) has emphasized, such determinants may have their origin in: (1) a translation into *body language* of the unacceptable wish and the defense against it (unconsciously, "I wish to see; I should not see; therefore, I cannot see"); (2) the revival of a *memory trace of a previous bodily experience,* involving generally some painful sensation, often arising from a mild physical illness, or a sexually exciting contact; (3) *identification with an important figure,* most often the parent, who has suffered from a particular symptom now experienced by the child in the distorted fashion in which children perceive such symptoms and their own bodies; (4) *punishment for an unacceptable wish or impulse* directed against a loved person, usually a parent, with the child himself suffering magically what he wished upon the other.

Differing combinations of these determinants may occur, and other influences may also play a role in the genesis of the symptom. Unconscious conflicts, found to some extent in all children, appear to be intensified in these children by a variety of disturbing experiences of *predisposing and contributory nature* within the family and in their social contacts outside. *Precipitating* events, involving loss or distortion of a key relationship, other emotionally traumatic experiences, or a shift in the family adaptive equilibrium, apparently operate to bring about the adaptive need for such symptomatic manifestations. *Perpetuating* forces within the family and the child's social life often act to render the symptom adaptively necessary on a continuing basis, permitting an unconscious "secondary gain" from the illness, of unhealthy but vital nature.

It remains unclear precisely why one child develops a conversion reaction and others may develop anxiety reactions, depressions, phobias, or patterns of acting out of hostile or rebellious impulses directly against the parents or society. Multiple determinants of the types mentioned earlier are undoubtedly involved. One possible predisposing factor in the development of conversion reactions might be, for example, a constitutionally determined capacity of the mental apparatus for greater repression of unacceptable feelings and impulses. No systematic research has as yet been undertaken in this area.

In my experience, true conversion reactions of the type described are not encountered commonly in childhood until at least seven or eight years of age. Earlier ones do occur, and disorders in bodily function of predominantly psychological nature are seen frequently in preschool children. These earlier disorders appear to have important differences, however, perhaps related to the fact that the mental apparatus of the child, including the capacity for effective repression necessary for the development of the conversion symptom, does not seem to be sufficiently developed until the early school-age period.

The clinical impression exists that conversion symptoms develop mainly in children (and older persons) with established hysterical personality disorders, principally females, with tendencies toward overdramatic and easily suggestible behavior, conflicts over sexual adjustment, and the propensity for expression of conflict in bodily disturbances. My experiences and that of others (Chodoff and Lyons, 1958; Engel, 1962) would indicate that such is not necessarily or consistently the case. Conversion reactions may be seen in personality pictures of widely varied nature, including neuroses, personality disorders, and psychoses, and may occur in males, albeit less commonly than in females.

As Brazelton (1953) has pointed out, the pediatrician in his daily work sees a large number of transient conversion symptoms, of mild to moderate degree, in school-age, prepubescent, or early adolescent individuals, occurring frequently during convalescence from a predominantly physical illness. Such an illness may, for example, block temporarily a child's currently intense developmental need to achieve scholastically, athletically, or socially, or may precipitate conflict between a regressive wish to continue to be cared for dependently by the mother and the pressure to return to the competitive peer-group arena. Frequently the symptoms of the physical illness are unconsciously incorporated into the conversion symptoms, as in the continuance of pain, vomiting, headache, or, in a more general sense, weakness or easy fatigability. Many of these conversion reactions resolve in a few days or weeks, either "spontaneously" (i.e., through the working out by the child of lesser conflicts or by his taking a maturational step) or "therapeutically," with the planned support of the parents and physician. In these, as in other instances, the reasonably healthy child's developmental capacities and the inherent impetus toward maturation may give him great flexibility of adaptive response, even in the face of relatively great situational stresses of interpersonal nature.

4. *Symptomatic Reactions of Very Young Children.* As mentioned in the previous section, infants and preschool children show a wide variety of disturbances in bodily functions in response to psychological or interpersonal stressful stimuli. Presumably because the adaptive capacities of the mental apparatus (including fully developed ego functions, such as repression, and the intrapsychic operations of the superego or conscience) do not seem to be crystallized until the end of the preschool-age period, these reactions tend to be more fluctuating and protean in character, without the more structuralized quality of true neuroses or personality disorders which may appear later. In general, they occur predominantly in response to situational stimuli from the environment, including principally external and largely conscious conflicts between the child's impulses or wishes and those of the parent figures. In contrast to older children, such disorders only rarely involve internalized or intrapsychic unconscious conflicts between the child's wishes or feelings and the prohibitions of his conscience. These symptomatic reactions in younger children may disappear readily when the external conflict with the parents is resolved. In older children, internalized conflicts may continue in self-perpetuating or repetitive fashion even after significant changes in the interpersonal situation.

For the above and other reasons, such disturbances in bodily function in young children rarely occur in isolation but are ordinarily associated with other reactive responses in various aspects of the child's behavior. All such disturbances can only be summarized briefly and descriptively as follows: (1) *Disturbances related to bodily functions,* such as eating (as in food refusal, rumination, pica, vomiting, and failure to thrive); sleeping, bowel and bladder control; speech; patterns of motoric activity; rhythmic patterns (such as rocking, head rolling, and head banging); various habit patterns (such as thumb sucking, nose picking, and masturbation); and sensory disturbances. (2) *Disturbances related to cognitive functions,* including learning failure of various types, distortions of perception, and disorders in thinking. (3) *Disturbances in social behavior,* as in overaggressive patterns, negativistic or oppositional behavior; disturbed sexual behavior; isolated or withdrawn behavior; and overly dependent or overly independent behavior. (4) *Disturbances in emotional behavior,* as in chronic anxiety, marked fears, acute panic states, depression, and feelings of inadequacy. (5) *Disturbances in integrative behavior,* as in repeated tantrums, impulsive behavior, or disorganized behavior.

In addition to the above, in which much overlapping occurs, one sees other manifestations, including stereotyped behavior of compulsive, ritualized, or overperfectionistic nature, and transient hypochondriacal behavior. All of these may of course be seen in older children, occurring in response to situational stresses or continuing from earlier stages of development. In the present discussion, the focus will be held briefly on the disturbances in bodily function, although these often overlap and fuse with reactive manifestations in the other areas mentioned.

Although bodily disturbances of this nature may resemble superficially conversion reactions, they appear to me to exhibit important differences, in addition to those already mentioned. Because of the less fully developed capacities of the mental apparatus, the symptoms do not appear to have such a strongly symbolic quality as in conversion symptoms. Many of them occur in the context of *regression,* and appear to represent adaptively a temporary giving up of more highly developed functions (as in the infant of one and a half years who ceases to speak and to walk in the face of a physical illness) or a falling back upon earlier, more familiar modes of satisfaction (as with the three-year-old who begins to suck his thumb again upon the arrival of a new sibling). Other disturbances may represent *physiological concomitants of anxiety.* The cardinal anxiety of the child under four is that of separation from the mother. Under conditions of prolonged or frightening separation, the resultant anxiety and frequently associated regression may call out any one or, more frequently, several of the above-mentioned disturbances in bodily function, from loss of bowel or bladder control to fearful behavior with its physiological concomitants (Prugh et al., 1953).

Developmental capacities may also influence the type of picture seen. In the infant under six or seven months of age, true separation anxiety does not yet occur (Spitz, 1945), as the infant does not have available the capacity to distinguish between himself and the outside world. Eating and sleeping disturbances, as well as gastrointestinal disorders, are common at this level, as responses to inappropriate stimulation by the mother, in keeping with the very young infant's tendency to respond in relatively undifferentiated and global fashion. In the older infant, rumination (Richmond et al., 1958) may occur in the face of marked maternal tension or neglect, permitted in part by the capacity, beginning around three months, to employ voluntary hand-to-mouth activity, as well as movements of the tongue, pharynx, and abdominal musculature which make ruminative operations possible. By the second half of the first year, with the growing capacity of the infant to relate to the mother and to perceive himself as separate from her, sudden or prolonged separations may produce *depression* (Spitz, 1946). Associated disturbances in eating, sleeping, gastrointestinal function, growth patterns, and other bodily functions may proceed at times to the point of marasmus (Lourie, 1955) or failure to thrive.

In addition to the effects of anxiety, regression, and depression upon bodily functions, certain disturbances may arise from a *persistence of developmental patterns* beyond their usual point of disappearance. Head rolling and rocking occur normally by the end of the first year and are usually given up before the third year, as is the intense motoric activity of the infant which begins in the second year. In the face of unhealthy parent-child relationships or disruptions in family balance, any of these may persist well beyond the preschool period. *Delay in the appearance of maturational patterns* may occur in other children from similar circumstances, including lags in psychomotor development (Provence and Coleman, 1957), as well as memory, reasoning, and other learning capacities (Eisenberg, 1959). Uneven or fragmented development may appear also, involving variations in inherent capacities interacting with inconsistent parental handling, with overstimulation toward development in some areas and understimulation or blockage in others. Whether precocity of psychological development may be stimulated constructively by parental or other influence remains an open question. The child who is markedly advanced in physical growth (Meiks and Green, 1960), sexual maturation (Mason, 1949), or intellectual development (Haggard, 1957) certainly has important adaptive challenges, as do his parents.

Symptomatic reactions of the type described may produce secondary reverberations at the physiological level, as in the young child who fails to grow (Fried, 1950) or develops nutritional anemia (Pollock and Richmond, 1953) because of food refusal based on strong negativism or depression. Pica in emotionally deprived infants and young children may occur in such intensity as to lead to lead intoxication (Millican et al., 1956), or, in association with thumb sucking, to such conditions as trichobezoar (Langford, 1955). Physical illness may also precipitate or intensify such symptomatic reactions, as in the young child with chronic infection who becomes irritable and hyperactive. All of the symptomatic reactions arising predominantly from interpersonal stimuli may disappear as the stressful circumstances are resolved or as the child, with the help of his parents, moves forward in a developmental step which enables him to employ newly available adaptive mechanisms of more appropriate nature.

C. Psychophysiological or Vegetative Reactions

In contrast to conversion phenomena and the symptomatic reactions of young children are the so-called psychophysiological disorders. With some exceptions to be considered later, these disorders, in which psychological and interpersonal factors are prominently involved, ordinarily occur in involuntarily innervated visceral organs or organ systems, generally supplied by the autonomic nervous system, particularly the parasympathetic branch. In such disorders, no symbolic significance appears to be attached to the symptom of disturbed bodily function, since these operate at a vegetative level (Alexander, 1950) and thus presumably do not receive central symbolic representation. Structural change often occurs in the course of these disease pictures. Such changes are sometimes reversible in nature but at times may result in chronic and irreparable damage to the organ or organ system in question. Physiological reverberations frequently are seen in other systems, and seriously deranged homeostatic functioning of the organism may result.

The term "psychophysiologic autonomic and visceral disorder," now employed in the official A.M.A. Nomenclature, has certain conceptual limitations. To some, the term seems to imply that psychological factors, through the action of the physiological concomitants of the emotions, are the major etiological influences in such disease states. This was indeed a conceptual position taken by certain of the early proponents of the psychosomatic view, who assumed that such alterations in physiological function, if long continued in the face of unresolved emotional conflicts, could result in the appearance of structural change. More recent information supports the impression that predisposing physiological factors are necessary in order to permit the appearance of the particular disease state, with physiological concomitants of emotions operating only as precipitating, intensifying, or perpetuating influences. Some workers, such as Engel (1962), have thus come to call these "somatopsychic-psychosomatic disorders," emphasizing the importance of the physiological predisposition. Since all such terms have limitations, as discussed earlier, the term "psychophysiological or vegetative disorder" will be employed herein, with the understanding that the disorders referred to are characterized by prominent involvement of *both psychological and physiological components,* in contrast to predominantly psychological or predominantly physical disorders, each with their train of reverberations at other levels of organization.

In recent years, numerous disease pictures have been reported as being strongly influenced by psychological and interpersonal factors. No listing of such syndromes can be absolutely complete or up-to-date. The following list is made up according to organ systems, even though such a method of organization fails to depict the complex interrelationships and the considerable overlapping of the bodily processes involved. For more specific discussion of the individual syndromes, the reader is referred to the original references.

Cardiovascular: A variety of syndromes (Ham, 1962), most of them studied in adults, including essential hypertension (Reiser et al., 1957); eclampsia (Kroger and Freed, 1951); vasodepressor and related syncopal reactions, as distinct from hysterical fainting (Engel, 1948; Engel and Romano, 1947; Romano and Engel, 1945); various peripheral vascular disorders, from central angiospastic retinopathy (Wagener, 1957) to Raynaud's disease (Millet et al., 1953); also angina pectoris and coronary thrombosis (Arlow, 1952; Grinker and Robbins, 1954); in children as well as adults, migraine (Katz et al., 1950; Engel et al., 1953) and paroxysmal tachycardia (Falstein and Rosenblum, 1962; Duncan et al., 1950).

Respiratory: Such syndromes as asthma (Alexander, 1950; Gerard, 1946; Long et al., 1958; Creak and Stephen, 1958; Dubo et al., 1961); allergic rhinitis (Miller and Baruch, 1948), and certain types of chronic sinusitis (Holmes et al., 1949) in children and adults; breath-holding spells (Bridge et al., 1943; Bakwin and Bakwin, 1953) in children.

Gastrointestinal: Such disorders, in adults and children, as peptic ulcer (Alexander, 1950; Chapman et al., 1956; Taboroff and Brown, 1954); certain types of gastritis (Wolf and Wolff, 1943, 1947; Warson et al., 1949); cardiospasm (Winkelstein, 1944); ulcerative colitis (Sperling, 1946; Engel, 1954b, c; Prugh, 1951b; Finch and Hess, 1962); mucous colitis (White et al., 1939; Sperling, 1955; Grace et al., 1951) and certain types of chronic noninfectious diarrhea (Prugh and Shwachman, 1955); certain types of constipation (Davidson, 1958; Engel, 1962; Prugh, 1954); regional enteritis (Grace, 1953; Crockett, 1952); certain types of dental malocclusion (Massler and Wood, 1949), bruxism (Bakwin and Bakwin, 1953; Prugh, 1956), and peridontal disease (Moulton et al., 1952); certain types of food sensitivity (Kaufman, 1954); anorexia nervosa (Lesser et al., 1960; Nemiah, 1950; Falstein et al., 1956; Berlin et al., 1951); obesity (Bruch, 1957; Bakwin, 1959; Hamburger, 1958; Heald, 1960); pernicious vomiting of pregnancy (Guze et al., 1959).

In children, megacolon (nonaganglionic type) (Garrard and Richmond, 1952; Pinkerton, 1958); certain types of polydypsia

(Nelson, 1959); idiopathic celiac disease (Prugh, 1951; Campagne, 1959; Grinker and Robbins, 1954); marasmus (Lourie, 1955; Bakwin, 1949a) and colic (Stewart, 1953; Wessel et al., 1954); certain disorders in salivation (Lourie et al., 1942).

Genitourinary: In adolescents and adults, disturbances in menstruation, including dysmenorrhea (Menzer-Benaron and Sturgis, 1957), amenorrhea (Reifenstein, 1946), functional uterine bleeding (Heiman, 1956), and premenstrual tension (Bickers and Woods, 1951); in adults, certain types of sterility (Morris and Sturgis, 1959; Benedek et al., 1953), certain types of urethral and vaginal discharges (Kroger and Freed, 1951; Ross, 1947); habitual abortion (Mann, 1959); certain types of polyuria (Nelson, 1959); and vesical paralysis (Engel, 1962).

Hemic and lymphatic: Most of the vegetative disturbances studied so far in this category are reversible ones and have been listed earlier under the physiological concomitants of emotions. Leukemia and lymphoma, in which psychological factors appear to play a contributory or at times precipitating role, are discussed later in relation to chronic illness.

Musculoskeletal: In adults and children, rheumatoid arthritis (Blom and Nicholls, 1954; Johnson et al., 1947); certain types of low back pain (Holmes and Wolff, 1950); "tension" headache (Wolff, 1948).

Skin: In adults, seborrheic dermatitis (Wittkower and McKenna, 1947); neurodermatitis (Cleveland and Fisher, 1956; Marmor et al., 1956); psoriasis (Wittkower and Russell, 1953; Graham, 1954); certain types of pruritis (Rosenbaum, 1945); certain types of alopecia (Greenberg, 1955; Kaplan and Reisch, 1952) and rosacea (Wittkower and Russell, 1953). In adults and children, certain atopic reactions such as eczema (Wittkower and Russell, 1953; Rosenthal, 1952), urticaria (Graham, 1950; Saul and Bernstein, 1941), and angioneurotic edema (Stokes and Beerman, 1940; Lorand, 1936); also verucca vulgaris (Ullman, 1959; Ullman and Dudek, 1960); herpes simplex (Blank and Brody, 1950); and acne (Wittkower, 1951).

Endocrine: In adults and children, thyrotoxicosis (Ham et al.,

1951; Mandelbrote and Wittkower, 1955; Lidz and Whitehorn, 1950); diabetes (Hinkle and Wolf, 1952; Mirsky, 1948; Fischer and Dolger, 1946; Falstein and Judas, 1955; Bruch, 1949); hyperinsulinism (Romano and Coon, 1942; Portis, 1950); pseudocyesis (Greaves et al., 1960; Fried et al., 1951); disorders of lactation (Newton and Newton, 1951); acute intermittent porphyria (Luby et al., 1959). In children, certain types of growth disturbances (Talbot et al., 1947; Fried, 1950; Rosenbaum, 1960).

Central nervous system: In adults and children, idiopathic epilepsy (including petit mal, grand mal, psychomotor, and other equivalents) (Berlin and Yaeger, 1951; Gottschalk, 1953; Robertiello, 1953; Barker, 1948); narcolepsy (Yoss and Daly, 1960; Smith and Hamilton, 1959); sleep disturbances (Anthony, 1959; Spock, 1957); dizziness and vertigo (Engel, 1948); asthenic reactions (Weiss, 1952; Laughlin, 1954); motion sickness (Bakwin and Bakwin, 1953); and recurrent fever (Bakwin and Bakwin, 1953; White and Long, 1958; Renbourn, 1960; Goodell et al., 1950). In children, hyperactivity (Laufer and Denhoff, 1957; Bakwin and Bakwin, 1953).

Organs of special sense: In adults, glaucoma (Ripley and Wolff, 1950); asthenopia (Senn, 1959); phlyctenular keratitis (Wolf and Messier, 1950); Ménière's syndrome (Fowler and Zeckel, 1952); certain types of tinnitus and hyperacusis (Coleman, 1949; Knapp, 1953).

The above list is not to be taken as an exhaustive one, for literally hundreds of reports in a variety of journals could be drawn upon. Representative studies only are cited, principally the more recent ones, largely in the English literature. The reader is referred to compilations of original papers edited by Harold Wolff (1950), Alexander (1950), Wittkower and Cleghorn (1957), Deutsch (1953), and Jores and Freyberger (1961), the latter covering recent European studies, as well as to monographs by Dunbar (1946), Weiss and English (1943), Grinker (1953), Schottstaedt (1960) and others, for more detailed surveys of the individual areas covered. Most of these deal largely with investigations carried out on adults. Reviews dealing with the general topic of psychophysiological disorders in childhood are more rare, although publications by Sperling (1957), Finch

(1952), Sontag (1953), Carpentieri and Jensen (1949), Garner and Wenar (1959), Bruch (1945) and others (Gerard, 1953; Wolff and Bayer, 1952; Mohr et al., 1955) touch importantly upon various aspects.

1. *Psychological Observations.* Over the past forty or more years, a great many data have been collected by varying clinical methods of investigation, regarding the psychological aspects of the various disorders listed. The earliest workers, particularly those in the psychoanalytic field, viewed the physiological disturbances as conversion reactions involving the visceral organs, with a kind of "organ language" being substituted for feelings which for various reasons could not be expressed verbally or behaviorally. Although the verbal associations of certain patients would seem to support this view, continued work has, in my opinion and that of others (Mirsky, 1960; Engel, 1962), failed to demonstrate symbolic meanings which can be imputed to the physiological disturbances at the organ level. Exacerbations of symptoms, however, may be associated with fantasies of symbolic nature which derive from conflict situations.

Personality profiles: Later studies by Dunbar (1946) and others suggested that specific personality profiles were associated with individual clinical pictures, such as peptic ulcer, ulcerative colitis, arthritis, or idiopathic epilepsy, arising out of a set of common developmental experiences. Personality patterns of a particular type do appear to be present with some consistency in certain disorders (Gildea, 1949), as, for instance, in the passive-dependent, somewhat compulsive child (Prugh, 1951) or adult (Engel, 1954b) with ulcerative colitis. Such patterns do not seem to be present in all cases (Kubie, 1957), however. In addition, the personality disorders reported by many writers, including the "infantile personality" described by Ruesch (1948), do not appear to be type-specific, appearing also in individuals with other psychophysiological disorders, in disturbed persons without physiological disturbance, and, to some extent, in children or adults with chronic illness of predominantly physical nature, as Neuhaus (1958) has indicated. In some instances, in my experience and that of others (Brown, 1958; Wittkower, 1951;

Buck and Hobbs, 1959), as many as three or four disorders of this general type have developed in the same patient, often occurring in sequence but at times appearing simultaneously.

Young children may develop some of these disorders prior to the crystallization of a specific personality structure, which ordinarily does not take place until at least the early school-age period. Finally, since the studies mentioned have been retrospective ones, real difficulty lies in distinguishing between the influence of personality patterns upon disease pictures and the effect upon the personality of the presence of a chronic disease in a particular family setting.

Conflict situations: More recent work by Alexander (1950) introduced the possibility that specific, largely unconscious conflict situations, in individuals made vulnerable by dissatisfying early life experiences (as well as by some type of physiological predisposition), were involved in the precipitation of various clinical disorders. Conflict over wishes to receive dependent gratifications, developed around feeding in infancy, was thought to be specific for peptic ulcer, for example, with a concomitant "vegetative" discharge of tension through secretory activity of the stomach, as if in preparation for the original feeding, occurring later in situations of frustration and heightened conflict. Conflicts over wishes to hold back or to extrude the stool, developed during early toilet training, were said to involve "vectors" which characterize individuals with later constipation or diarrhea, often associated with particular personality traits of stinginess or generosity, respectively, as suggested by earlier psychoanalytic workers (Fenichel, 1945).

Although some validity may reside in this point of view, more recent investigations, designed to test the vector-specificity concept, have not been confirmatory (Mednick et al., 1958). Such conflict situations do seem frequently to be involved in the disorders cited, but they are apparently present also in many individuals who do not show such clinical pictures. The occurrence of multiple disorders simultaneously in a single individual and the need to consider the effects upon the personality of a chronic illness would seem to be additional stumbling blocks. Work is still going on in this area, principally by Alexander and his co-workers. Although the confirmation of the hypothesis in any strict sense seems to me unlikely at this juncture, important stimulation has been given to the field by this work, leading to derivative conceptualization of vital significance.

Parent-child relationships and early experience: Workers with children have described conflicts in the early relationship between the mother and the infant who later develops a psychophysiological disorder. For example, Gerard (1946) believed that asthma occurs in children with demanding and controlling mothers who foster over-dependence in their children, with the symptoms of asthma appearing in the child at times of threat to such unhealthily enhanced dependent needs. Other investigators have seen maternal rejection as the characteristic feature in the family background of children with asthma (Miller and Baruch, 1951) and eczema (Spitz, 1951). The mother's reaction to a particular symptom, such as vomiting or diarrhea, has been thought to be relatively specific, with further enhancement of the symptoms apparently occurring as the result of some unconscious symbolic response by the child (Gerard, 1953). Early and coercive toilet training was thought by a number of workers (Prugh et al., 1956) to be the most important etiological factor in bowel disorders. Sperling (1949) has suggested that the mothers of children with psychophysiological disorders handled their infants in an overanxious fashion, enveloping them in a type of "symbiotic" relationship because of their own needs to deal in this way with more serious underlying emotional or mental disturbances of their own. Unconscious needs of parents to keep their children ill in order to care for them and thus ward off unconsciously hostile or destructive feelings have been described (Sperling, 1957). Family patterns, involving more dominating mothers and passive, retiring fathers, have also been said to be characteristic of children with psychophysiological disorders of varying kinds, including asthma (Gerard, 1946), peptic ulcer (Cole and Taboroff, 1955), and ulcerative colitis (Mohr et al., 1958; Prugh, 1951a, b).

Studies of parent-child and family relationships are exceedingly complicated; very few have as yet been carried out with the use of instruments of measurement which permit even semiquantitative comparisons or contrasts to be made. The difficulties in separating, by largely retrospective study, the original parental attitudes and child-rearing teachniques from those produced by the child's illness are also formidable. Garner and Wenar (1959), for example, have shown some significant differences in the reactions and attitudes of mothers of children with ulcerative colitis and other disorders, as systematically compared with those appearing in control groups of mothers of physically ill and healthy children, a finding supported by Richmond et al. (1955). These trends, however, do not seem to be specific for families of children with psychophysiological disorders. Parents of children with ulcerative colitis and peptic ulcer have been observed to show relatively similar personality patterns (Prugh, unpublished). Fitzelle (1959), in a controlled study, was unable to demonstrate significant differences in maternal attitudes in the study of comparison groups of children with asthma and with chronic physical illness. My own investigations indicate that parental attitudes and handling of the child may change somewhat from the point of initial impact of the illness to its later chronic stages (Prugh, 1951a).

The studies published certainly support the impression of definite pathology in the parent-child relationships, early child-rearing practices, the nature of family equilibria, and other factors prominent in the early experience of children with marked psychophysiological disorders of certain types. Considerable similarity exists in the early experience of many children with psychoneurotic reactions without vegetative disorders, however. With future refinement of research instruments now being developed for measuring family interaction, parent-child relationships, and the like, certain more type-specific features may emerge. Such is not yet the case.

Considerations regarding specificity: The studies in the various areas mentioned, with few exceptions, have been retrospective in nature, and the majority have involved small patient samples, with relatively little attempt to make comparisons with other sick or healthy groups of subjects. Admittedly, anterospective and controlled studies are exceedingly difficult for a variety of reasons to carry out in this or other clinical areas. Nevertheless, in my opinion, it cannot be said at this point that hypotheses implicating specific pathogenic emotions, personality profiles, conflict situations, early developmental experience, parental attitudes, child-rearing techniques, or family patterns as the exclusive causative factor in the etiology of specific psychophysiological disorders have been even partially confirmed.

Although some competent investigators, such as Graham (1962), still feel, on the basis of their own observations, that specific emotions or attitudes are characteristically associated with particular disease states, Kubie (1957a), Grinker (1953), Mirsky (1957), G. Engel (1953), and others have seriously questioned the validity of the specificity hypothesis in its strict form, a view supported recently by critical reviews by Mendelsohn (1956), Wittkower (1960), and Brown (1958). The ubiquity of the observations cited, however, supports the impression that all of the variables cited can be significantly involved in predisposing, contributory, precipitating, and perpetuating fashion. Thus they may be *"necessary but not sufficient conditions"* (Engel, 1962) for the development of a psychophysiological disorder.

2. *Theories Regarding Physiologic Mechanisms.* A number of theories or "physiologic models" have been put forth in attempts to explain the nature and degree of structural change seen in colitis, peptic ulcer, rheumatoid arthritis, and other syndromes, as these may be influenced by psychological and interpersonal stimuli. The earlier concepts, postulating hereditary influences, the existence of constitutional types, or the operation of a "locus minoris resistentiae" as principal causative factors, have largely been abandoned as too general and insufficiently explanatory by themselves. Although some workers still seem to adhere to the early psychoanalytic view that visceral organs may express conflicting emotions symbolically, as in conversion reactions, most investigators today recognize that physiological phenomena cannot be explained in psychological terms and that the two levels of organization, although interrelated through

the mental apparatus and neuroendocrine pathways, exhibit differing laws of operation.

Mention has been made of the model developed by Weiss and English (1943) and others from Cannon's theory of emergency responses and the fight-flight patterns. In this view, the physiological concomitants of emotions, if long continued in states of unresolved conflict, could lead to the development of structural end-organ changes and the characteristic disease pictures, as the result of persistent activation of the sympathetic or parasympathetic components of the autonomic nervous system. Other workers have invoked Pavlov's (1928) concept of conditioned reflexes to explain local changes. More recently, Selye's (1947) formulation of the "general adaptation syndrome" and the "diseases of adaptation" has seemed a fruitful model to many, on the basis of the production in animals of disease states resembling colitis, arthritis, nephritis, and other syndromes by means of the injection of ACTH or cortisone.

Although each of these three models, dealing with response patterns at the autonomic or hormonal level, has been of some help in a conceptual sense, the available evidence, lucidly summarized by Engel (1954c) in regard to ulcerative colitis and by Mendelsohn (1956) in a broader context, does not permit full support of any single one. Cannon's emergency responses explain little more than the anxiety reaction and such phenomena as certain types of diarrhea or other end-organ disturbances of reversible nature. A variety of changes in end organs innervated principally by the parasympathetic component of the autonomic nervous system can be produced in animals by stressful experiences or by injection or local application of parasympatheticomimetic substances (Cobb, 1950). Such experimental situations, however, do not seem to reproduce the structural changes characteristic of many human vegetative disorders. Pavlov's conditioned responses also do not explain local structural change. Recent studies have indicated, however, that many physiological phenomena in human beings as well as animals, including vasomotor responses (Dykman and Gantt, 1958; Menzies, 1937), diuresis (Toth, 1956; Gerbner and Altman, 1959), electroencephalographic patterns

(Gastaut et al., 1957), and bronchiolar constriction (Dekker et al., 1957), may be conditioned to various types of stimuli. Selye's theory remains unconfirmed, in the eyes of many. The studies on which it was based were exclusively animal ones, and the local and systemic changes as produced are apparently not identical with human disease states of chronic nature. Although mechanisms related to each of the three models are undoubtedly involved in predisposing, precipitating, contributory, or perpetuating ways, none appears to serve as an adequate explanation for the disease phenomena.

Several additional theories should be cited. Deutsch (1939) long ago suggested that physical disease in a particular organ, such as the lung, occurring at a time of significant emotional conflict during early personality development, might somehow sensitize the organs to later dysfunction, as in asthma, in the face of reappearance of the conflict. Michaels (1944), Szasz (1951), Margolin (1957), and others have believed that a type of physiological regression or "regressive innervation," coincident with psychological regression, may take place under conditions of conflict to the level of physiological functioning of the neonate. They see in the symptoms of the illness the emergence of responses of undifferentiated, fluctuating, primitive nature, appropriate to the infant's physiological state but productive of pathological organ function in the child or adult.

Approaching the problem from another viewpoint, other psychoanalysts (Fenichel, 1945) have endorsed the view that fixations of conflict at early points of psychosexual development, engendered by traumatic experiences, may provide focal points to which physiological regression may occur in response to later stresses, with the inappropriate involvement of organs prominent in functioning at the time of the original fixation. Hendrick (1947) has put forth the suggestion that a state of "physiological infantilism" may persist in individuals who subsequently develop psychophysiological disorders. Garner and Wenar (1959) feel that a disruption in patterns of physiological integration, occurring as the result of a disturbed mother-infant relationship, may be in part responsible for the vulnerability to such disorders.

Margolin (1957) and others tend to see individuals who develop ulcerative colitis or certain other vegetative disorders as severely disturbed persons, regressing psychologically in the face of stress to infantile levels bordering on psychosis. This view is close to that of Sperling (1949) who has suggested that vegetative disorders, with their roots apparently in very early physical and psychological development, may serve adaptively to ward off a psychotic illness. Other observers have the impression that psychosis may alternate with such disorders as asthma, peptic ulcer, and colitis (Ross, 1957) in the same individual, indicating a kind of substitutive or interchangeable set of adaptive operations between psychological and physiological levels of organization. Kepecs and his colleagues (1951) have suggested, in regard to skin disorders, that shifts in the fluid compartments of, the body in states of exudation or transudation may be correlated with psychological changes. Engel (1956) has observed headaches appearing when the gastrointestinal symptoms of ulcerative colitis begin to subside during treatment. He feels that such headaches may represent conversion mechanisms, involved in a shift of the patient to dealing with conflicts at a higher adaptive level, in contrast to the more primitive conflicts mobilized originally in response to the interpersonal stresses which helped precipitate the illness.

Further observations have not yet confirmed certain of the above theories. Psychological and behavioral regression certainly are present in many patients; as mentioned earlier, they may be influenced by the impact upon the organism of the pathophysiological states themselves as well as the precipitating psychological and interpersonal stressful stimuli. There is still no substantial evidence, however, that a physiological regression does indeed occur in such disorders. Even if it did occur, such a phenomenon would not explain the abnormal tissue responses in peptic ulcer, ulcerative colitis, or rheumatoid arthritis, for example, for which there is no physiological paradigm in the healthy human infant, even at the neonatal level, as Grossman and Greenberg (1957) have shown. Fixation of psychological conflicts at early psychosexual levels undoubtedly plays a significant role in the shaping of the individual's later personality patterns. Disease states in an organ during early development might well sensitize the organ in some fashion to produce an abnormal type of tissue response. Repeated environmental stimulation, as from frequent suppositories or enemas, often administered during toilet training by bowel-conscious parents of children exhibiting later bowel disorders (Prugh, 1954), might predispose to conditioned reflex responses of the end organ in the face of reactivation of conflicting emotions experienced at this early level. Such experiences, however influential, would not of themselves explain the total pathophysiological picture, including the development of chronic structural change. Many of these latter observations can also be made in individuals who may not develop vegetative disorders.

Although a number of patients with ulcerative colitis, peptic ulcer, and other disorders indubitably show serious psychopathology, even of psychotic proportions, a number may show varying degrees of personality disorder of milder nature. Most of the patients reported upon in many articles have been seen following referral for hospital study, which undoubtedly skews the sample in the direction of more severely ill persons. Some evidence suggests that practicing physicians may see a large number of children and adults outside the hospital who exhibit milder degrees of pathophysiological disturbance, with more ready response to supportive therapeutic approaches than the ones ordinarily described in the literature. Alternation of psychotic pictures with states of psychophysiological disorder does seem to occur. Statistical studies by Ross (1957) and others, however, do not firmly support the frequent occurrence of such phenomena nor the related suggestion that psychotic patients necessarily show fewer such disorders than the general population. There appears to be no convincing evidence of any precise correlation between the severity of the psychological disturbance and the pathophysiological process, even though the work of Knapp (1957) and others, including my own, would suggest that this may be the case in certain instances.

Family interaction: A variety of other theories could be cited, including that of Ruesch (1950). His studies of verbal and nonverbal communication have led him to believe that a breakdown in verbal communication between two persons (or in a family system) may result in bodily symptoms which subserve communication on a physiological level. Berblinger and Greenhill (1954), working along the same theoretical lines, have reported apparent phenomena of this nature in the family relationships of patients with ulcerative colitis, as has Coolidge (1956) with asthmatic children. Communication through nonverbal bodily patterns does seem to occur significantly in conversion reactions, as Engel (1962) has emphasized. Such communication appears also to be involved in some of the psychological and behavioral manifestations of psychosis (Jackson, 1959). Conceptualizations of this nature, greatly helpful at the psychological and interpersonal level, are difficult to substantiate at the physiological level.

Although symbolic communication in bodly terms between the sick person and members of his family may not be involved in psychophysiological disorders, some evidence exists (Lindemann, 1950; Grinker, 1953) that shifts in the family balance or adaptive equilibrium can serve as precipitating influences in ulcerative colitis. Our work (Prugh and Tagiuri, 1954) supports the impression that, in patients with damaged respiratory systems, bronchial asthma may be precipitated by somewhat similar shifts in interpersonal forces, involving other patients and staff persons, in a small hospital ward unit. Observations of this kind do not necessarily support the communication theory at the somatic level and also leave open the question of the nature of the pathophysiological process itself.

In recent years, Wolff (1950) has elaborated his earlier postulations of "protective patterns" of somatic response to stressful stimuli of varying kinds. He cites patterns of riddance of noxious agents by vomiting, defecation, secretion of mucus in the respiratory tree, and other mechanisms. In his view, hyperemia, hypersecretion, and hypermotility are characteristic of all vegetative disorders. He feels that such riddance patterns, involving these physiological mechanisms, have become associated with particular attitudes and feelings and as such may be characteristic of the individual, possibly deriving from constitutional or genic factors. Wolff's concepts deal with physiological phenomena in appropriate terms. The generality of his views, however, lays them open to some question, and the problem of chronic and abnormal tissue responses is not explained.

3. *A Comprehensive View of Psychophysiological Disorders.* In the foregoing overcondensed summary of psychological observations and theories regarding the etiology of pathophysiological processes, the major concepts of biological predisposition (of genic or constitutional nature), early developmental experiences of influential character, and precipitating forces of psychological and social nature recur frequently, given differing weighting by different workers. Today, most workers in this field agree that *multiple etiological factors of somatic, psychological, and social nature* are involved in these disorders (and, indeed, in all disease states, as the unitary theory postulates). Engel (1960), Mirsky (1960), and Grinker (1959), the latter with his "field theory," have recently elaborated this view with especial cogency and originality. Of these, Mirsky has developed a comprehensive theory which, from his conceptual framework, has led to the development of testable hypotheses.

Mirsky's work with patients with peptic ulcer has demonstrated that the large majority of such persons exhibit high levels of blood pepsinogen, apparently reflecting increased gastric secretory activity. His work further indicated that a normative distribution of blood pepsinogen values characterizes the general population, beginning in early infancy. Mirsky noted also, as Alexander (1950) has done, that ulcer patients, both by observation and by history, characteristically exhibit strong wishes to be fed and taken care of by others, even though these wishes may be unconscious and unacceptable to the individual. Drawing upon these physiological and psychological data, Weiner, working with Mirsky and others (1957), set up a hypothesis predicting that peptic ulcer would develop in those individuals, among a large group of men in Army basic training, who showed high blood pepsinogen levels (hypersecretors) and, in this potentially stressful situation, high levels of conflict over dependent wishes (the latter tapped by psychological tests). Their findings appeared to confirm this hypothesis. Later studies by Mirsky (1958) indicated that children who later develop peptic ulcer are gastric hypersecretors from infancy. Ader's (1960) studies with animals lend support to Mirsky's general thesis.

Mirsky's conceptual model includes the postulate that all physiological values follow a normal distribution curve from birth or very early infancy. He hypothesizes that newborn infants with high pepsinogen levels and thus high gastric secretory activity may have more intense needs to be fed (oral needs) than infants in the middle or lower ranges of gastric activity. Such infants may be more demanding than others in regard to feeding, and this feedback may affect mothers differently. Some mothers may respond comfortably to such demands and may actually be gratified by such a need for their ministrations. Others may be significantly frustrated and conflicted by the infant's constant demands. Thus a cycle of transactional responses between mother and infant may be set which may be positive or negative in nature. Depending upon the marital relationship and family situation at the time of the infant's birth, as well as later events, conflict over the satisfaction of dependent, receptive needs may be a feature of the child's development. Although anterospective study along these lines remains to be carried out systematically, Mirsky's ideas have added conceptual clarity to the attempt to understand the interaction of inborn biological characteristics and the early experience of the child who later develops peptic ulcer, with implications for the study of other psychophysiological disorders.

The work of Mirsky and his colleagues has not filled in certain gaps in regard to peptic ulcer and its etiology. Not all adults developing ulcer have high blood pepsinogen values. Not all those with either high pepsinogen values or increased levels of conflict over dependent wishes will necessarily develop peptic ulcer. The sex difference in incidence of gastric vs. duodenal ulcer has not been explored, although this may represent simply a biological difference in response patterns between men and women. Finally, as he recognized, Mirsky's investigations have not fully explained the pathophysiological processes by which such individuals actually develop a chronically ulcerative lesion. In addition to hypersecretion of acid and pepsin, these may include such contributing factors as mechanical trauma to the gastric mucosa, the effects of diet or smoking, and others, including the petechial hemorrhages and minute ulcerations shown by Wolff and Wolf (1947) to occur, in the course of gastric hyperemia, hypersecretion, and hypermotility, as a response to intense emotions.

In spite of the limitations mentioned, Mirsky's work has confirmed the operation of predisposing biological and psychological factors which act predictably and with some specificity, *if both are present,* to produce the clinical picture of peptic ulcer in the face of significantly stressful events. In addition, the way has been opened for other anterospective studies in disease syndromes for which biological "tags" can be obtained. These may include persons who, as Doniger (1956) has shown, show a high uptake of radioactive iodine without signs of thyrotoxicosis. Other groups suggested for study by Mirsky (1960) include those persons with low pepsinogen levels who might later develop pernicious anemia, individuals without clinical diabetes who show diabetic glucose-tolerance curves after a standard dose of corticosteroids, and women who develop diabetes in high incidence within some years after giving birth to infants over ten pounds in weight. Some evidence from his studies is available to suggest that individuals in these as yet nondiseased groups exhibit psychological characteristics which are relatively similar to those of patients who have developed these diseases.

In addition to the type of somatic predisposition related to the distribution curve of physiological values (which may include activity level and other values not yet studied), other types have been implicated. The allergic diathesis involved, together with psychological factors, in the picture of bronchial asthma (Long et al., 1958) is a familiar example to clinicians, as in the lowered convulsive threshold in epilepsy (Engel, 1948). Inborn errors of metabolism, many with a hereditary background, have been brought under ·intensive recent scrutiny. It now seems likely that a variety of disease states may have their biological roots in such sources, with some individuals exhibiting the metabolic defect but failing to develop the disease, apparently without sufficiently stressful experience. Diabetes of course represents such a defect, with strong hereditary influences, which may be brought to light by metabolic changes in response to stressful stimuli (Hinkle and Wolf, 1952). A presumed enzymatic defect in the handling of the gliadin fraction of wheat glutens appears to combine with psychological determinants and interpersonal stresses to precipitate and perpetuate the clinical course of certain children with the picture of idiopathic celiac disease (Prugh, 1951; Campagne, 1959). Although the basic mechanisms are still poorly understood, the impression is gaining, from recent work in animals, that marked obesity is often predicated upon a derangement in the dynamics of fat metabolism, in addition to the psychological and interpersonal factors identified by Bruch (1957) in the syndrome of overeating and underactivity. Finally, it is conceivable, although not yet proved, that such diseases as ulcerative colitis, rheumatoid arthritis, and others, which may be precipitated by stressful stimuli of psychological and interpersonal nature, may have their pathophysiology rooted in enzymatic abnormalities which could lead to autoimmunization (Najjar and Robinson, 1959; Goldgraber et al., 1960), with resulting abnormal tissue responses.

A comprehensive view of this nature can include consideration of some of the types of predisposing or contributory factors mentioned earlier, such as the innate patterns of autonomic response, the operation of conditioned reflexes, and other factors which may affect immediate end-organ functioning, as well as the more long-range neuroendocrine changes already described. Contributory factors, such as concurrent bacterial infection, mechanical trauma, and others, may combine with any of the predisposing or precipitating factors mentioned.

A variety of forces, such as secondary infection or lowered resistance to infection, may reinforce the perpetuation of the lesions once established. Increased secretion of hormonal substances, triggered off by psychological factors in biologically predisposed individuals, may, as in thyrotoxicosis or hyperinsulinism, exert effects upon behavior which may further disrupt the dynamic steady state and increase susceptibility to stressful stimuli of physical, psychological, or social nature. The general debilitation arising from other psychophysiological disorders may also contribute to such a circular phenomenon. Finally, the exact features of the typical lesion itself may be in part determined by the patterns of response to noxious stimuli of the particular end organs, as with the characteristic appearance of a discrete ulcer in the stomach and duodenum, in contrast to disseminated small ulcerations in the large bowel. Certain diseases, such as ulcerative colitis, of course appear to have generalized features, affecting many organ systems, suggesting that a vascular or immunological defect may be the basic somatic one.

4. *Factors Peculiar to Children.* Most of the disorders mentioned, when appearing in children, resemble in general those pictures seen in adults. Peptic ulcer and ulcerative colitis have been reported, though rarely, in infants and have even occurred at birth or in the neonatal period. Disturbances such as this at birth would seem to represent a response of the organism to predominantly physical stressful stimuli, invoking neuroendocrine mechanisms, and would appear to support the concept of a characteristic end-organ reaction to nonspecific stimuli.

Developmental factors may influence organ response. Infantile colic, in which "family tension" appears to be involved, together with allergy and other factors, ordinarily disappears by the third or fourth month of life at least, perhaps indicating some integrative step in autonomic functioning. Failure to thrive, often associated with depression, is seen predominantly in early infancy, when more global responses are common. Bronchial asthma, without associated infection, rarely appears until after the latter part of the first year, following ordinarily the subsidence of eczema in allergic infants. Whether such a shift in response patterns is simply a result of a developmental difference in the capacity for sensitization of these two organ systems or may be related also to the effect on the respiratory system of the appearance of anxiety over separation from the mother, normally seen toward the end of the first year, remains to be determined. Chronic diarrhea of psychophysiological origin seems often to have its onset around this period also, as does idiopathic celiac disease.

Although comparative statistics are difficult to obtain, it is the impression of many that the majority of severe disorders in this general category occur somewhat less frequently in young children than in adults. Most of them seem to appear first in significant numbers in the middle school-age period. If true, this may be the result of changing patterns of tissue response, perhaps associated with developmental changes in the mental apparatus, involving increased repression of emotions and internalization of conflict and other features. Other considerations raised in the section on the developmental aspects of the physiology of emotions may bear upon these issues. Disturbance in growth patterns, still little understood but apparently involving neuroendocrine responses as well as insufficient nutrition based on food refusal, of course are specific to childhood. Mention has been made earlier of the possible effect upon the child's behavior and the emotional feedback in the parent-child relationship of inborn or developmental biological characteristics.

D. *Mixed Conversion and Psychophysiological Reactions*

Although the distinction between conversion reactions and psychophysiological or vegetative disorders generally holds true, symptoms of both types may occur in the life of the same individual, sometimes simultaneously. Examples are to be found in the child with asthma who develops a coughing tic or the child with idiopathic epilepsy who shows also episodes of fainting of conversion nature. In such examples, the psychological determinants of the conversion symptoms may lie in the physical sensations subjectively experienced during the active phase of the vegetative disorder, although this may not always be the case.

As mentioned earlier, there seems to be a certain overlap of symbolic and nonsymbolic mechanisms in organ systems which contain components innervated by both the voluntary and involuntary portions of the central nervous system. Kubie's (1957b) classification of the types of involvement of bodily functions in psychological conflicts is helpful in conceptualizing these phenomena.

Organs which implement the relationship to the external environment: In this category fall the exteroceptive sense organs, the striated muscles with their proprioceptive controls, and the organs of speech. These are the organs which facilitate external relationships, subserving orientation in space, the ability to communicate with others, the reception and organization of sensory impressions from the outside world, and the conscious orientative faculties. All of these organs have central representation in the mental apparatus, occupy a place in conscious thought, and are innervated predominantly by the voluntary somatomuscular and somatosensory apparatus, with the involuntary nervous system playing only a secondary synergic or supportive role. Such organs are the objects of complex ideational processes, which the organs themselves can represent symbolically. At times of conflict, the symbolic significance of these organs can lead, in predisposed individuals, to conversion reactions in the manner described earlier.

Organs of internal economy: These organs lie within the interior of the body, are innervated by the autonomic or involuntary nervous system, and thus have extremely limited central representation. Their place in conscious thought is often based on misconceptions, such as those seen in young children who presume a direct connection between the stomach and the uterus, permitting a "seed" to be swallowed and produce a baby. Disorders of these organs in response to psychological conflict are ordinarily of the vegetative type.

Organs of instinctual function: These are the organs which have direct apertural connections with the outside world, including the organs for the intake and output of food, air, and excrement, the swallowing mechanism, the organs of appetite and of genital function. Such organs operate reflexly in early infancy. In later development, however, their functions are initiated under the guidance of the voluntary nervous system. At some point in their physiological operation, the autonomic nervous system takes over the more automatic secondary steps of these organ functions. Thus the combined voluntary and involuntary innervation of these organs permits disturbances in their function to involve both symbolic and vegetative components.

The involvement of the body image as a whole: In this category, including distortions in the total body image, disturbances are diffuse, as in chronic invalidism with widespread conversion paralyses, states of extreme weakness or marked fatigability. Many patients exhibiting this type of disturbance pass through phases in which involvement of each of the other organ groups is represented. Conscious central representation is present, with the somatosensory and the higher conceptual and symbolic systems playing the primary role.

Kubie suggests that the relationships between the temporal cortex, studied experimentally by Penfield (1953), and the visceral brain are responsible for the integration of the symbolic process, providing a mechanism for integrating the past and present, as well as the external and the internal environments of the central nervous system (subserved by the phylogenetically and ontogenetically "new" and "old" parts of the brain respectively). In this way, all of the data which link the organism to the world of experience, both external and internal, may presumably be coordinated. Through these mechanisms, in his view, is mediated "the translation into somatic disturbance of those tensions which are generated on the level of psychological experience."

Kubie's concepts are supported by the work of MacLean (1958) and Penfield (1953). Much further investigation remains to be carried out in this area, however, before full understanding and knowledge are available. His formulation remains of value in the comprehension of the balance of symbolic (voluntary) vs. vegetative (involuntary) components in the disorders of the various organs or combination of organs described.

As mentioned above, disturbances in bodily function associated with psychological conflicts which involve the organs implementing external relationships and those systems associated with the maintenance of the body image as a whole are in general of symbolic nature and appear to be characterized by conversion reactions. An exception may lie in rheumatoid arthritis, in which symbolic components—the inhibition of an angry wish to hit—may be involved initially, with involuntarily innervated structures participating in the response, in concert with bacterial infection or sensitization phenomena. Disturbances of the organs of internal economy ordinarily are of the nonsymbolic vegetative or psychophysiological type summarized in the preceding list. Disturbances in function of what Kubie terms the organs of instinctual function have been puzzling to psychosomatic theorists. I shall discuss these in more detail, employing his conceptual approach.

The organ functions (in these instances, not necessarily identical with organ systems) which can easily be included in this latter category are those of swallowing or deglutition, the act of respiration, the acts of urination and defecation, and the functions of the external genitalia. In my view, the functions of the skin should be also included, for reasons to be mentioned. Disorders of each of these organ functions will be briefly discussed. Some of the disturbances to be mentioned have already been listed under either conversion or vegetative disorders, but such listing does not represent a fixed or arbitrary categorization.

Deglutition: Disorders in swallowing of conversion nature, such as globus hystericus, appear to arise in those portions of the swallowing mechanism included in the somatomuscular system, such as the tongue, the myohyloid and associated muscles. Other disturbances in the swallowing mechanisms, however, such as vomiting (Laybourne, 1953) and cardiospasm (Winkelstein, 1944), may involve the esophagus, the upper two thirds of which contains striated musculature, with the lower third composed entirely of smooth muscle. In these instances, symbolic conversion reactions may apparently be involved in relation to the upper two thirds of the esophagus, with associated involuntary components arising possibly from incoordination of the automatic movements of the lower third of the esophagus and the cardiac sphincter.

Thus psychological stimuli may produce vomiting by a true

conversion mechanism, by the hypersensitivity of the gag reflex under conditions of excitement, or possibly by a conditioned reflex effect upon the involuntary components of the swallowing mechanisms. In cyclic vomiting (Barbero, 1960), infection or disease in another organ may act as an initial stimulant to vomiting, with later conversion mechanisms, together with enhanced dependence upon the parents and other secondary gains, operating to perpetuate the pattern, sometimes to points of serious dehydration and alkalosis. In rumination (Richmond et al., 1958; Gaddini and Gaddini, 1959), occurring in emotionally deprived infants as a substitute for more basic satisfactions, an initial voluntary hand-to-mouth movement may lead to regurgitation, with later both voluntary and involuntary components, the latter perhaps rendered more feasible by the physiological chalasia of young infants. In disorders of appetite, food may be ingested for symbolic reasons unrelated to hunger, contributing, together with the physiological predisposing factors, to obesity. In anorexia nervosa, the initial suppression of appetite may be a voluntary symbolic act, with certain psychophysiological reverberations arising from neuroendocrine changes, in addition to the effects of starvation.

Respiration: The voluntary component in the control of respiratory movements is well known, arising through the action of the accessory muscles, including the abdominal musculature, all of striated nature. Changes in the rate and amplitude of respiration may arise as physiological concomitants of emotions or may acquire symbolic conversion significance as in the hyperventilation syndrome (Engel et al., 1947; Engel, 1962), with its associated metabolic changes leading to tetany. Respiratory coughing, snorting, or barking tics (Mahler, 1949), often arising originally from the reflex response to respiratory infection, may be predicated upon an unconscious symbolic meaning, such as the attempt to cough up or breathe out some fantasied harmful substance. Breath-holding spells (Bakwin and Bakwin, 1953), common during the second year of life, appear to involve an initial voluntary component, related to intense crying over frustration. An involuntary component then appears to "take over," leading to cyanosis, syncope, or even convulsive phenomena, the latter perhaps occurring more frequently in infants with a lowered convulsive threshold.

In bronchial asthma (Long et al., 1958), the basic response is at the level of the terminal bronchioles, predicated upon an allergic diathesis. Psychological stimuli may apparently intensify this response through cortical-hypothalamic-parasympathetic interconnections (Cobb, 1950), through the triggering of a conditioned reflex (Dekker et al., 1957), or by means of conversion disturbances in the accessory muscles, as in suppressed crying over feared separation from the mother (Gerard, 1946).

Urination: Reflex voiding in the young infant is gradually supplemented by voluntary control, involving the contraction of the external sphincter muscle in the male and the perineal muscles in the female, associated with inhibition of the action of the detrusor muscle of the bladder. Enuresis (nocturnal or diurnal) represents a failure to maintain such voluntary muscular tonus, which ordinarily can be maintained even during sleep with the assistance of conditioned reflexes. Failure in function of the external sphincter mechanisms, based on originally conscious and later repressed feelings of rebellion toward the parents (Bostwick and Shackleton, 1951) or deeper conflicts over sexual development (Gerard, 1939), may thus be symbolically involved in enuresis, often associated in the nocturnal form with conflictual dreams. This symptom frequently though not invariably appears in children who have experienced coercive bladder training (Bostwick and Shackleton, 1951). It may also involve a developmental lag in capacities for voluntary control (Bakwin, 1961) or, more rarely, other physiological predisposing or contributory factors. Enuresis may appear in a wide range of personality pictures and family patterns, ranging from a relatively encapsulated symptom in children with little personality disturbance (Bakwin and Bakwin, 1953) to one of a constellation of symptoms in deep personality disorders or psychoses (Michaels, 1935). It may occur as a failure to develop control (Gerard, 1939) or as a regressive manifestation (Prugh et al., 1953).

Conscious disregard of the pressure of a distended bladder in negativistic preschool children may occur during the daytime. In states of recurrent anxiety, involuntary physiological concomitants may predominate, as in many cases of urinary frequency, urgency, or inhibition of urination. Conditioned reflex responses may play a role in situations involving specific fears.

Defecation: In young infants, the defecation reflex operates automatically, although conditioned response to the use of suppositories can be achieved in the first few weeks of life (Watson, 1925). Voluntary control, which can be achieved before the end of the first year, involves the volitional maintenance of the tone of the external anal sphincter, assisted by the levatores ani muscles, resisting the defecation reflex as it builds up from the increasing pressure of a fecal mass within the rectum.

In the preschool child who consciously resists training, the stool may be extruded or withheld, with feelings of rebellion often associated with pleasurable stimulation of the anorectal mucous membrane (Stuart and Prugh, 1960). Unconscious conflicts of this nature persisting or recurring in the older child may lead to soiling apparently based on conversion mechanisms of the external musculature (Prugh et al., 1956a). Encopresis, like enuresis, may represent a developmental failure to achieve control (Vaughan and Cashmore, 1954) or a regressive manifestation in the face of stressful stimuli, as in the response of the preschool child to the separation from the mother involved in hospitalization (Prugh et al., 1953). Coercive bowel training (Anthony, 1957) may represent a predisposing factor of experiential nature. Developmental lags in control mechanisms, local disease during the training period, or overfrequent stimulation of the anorectal region with suppositories or enemas may also be involved. Temporary loss of bowel control, as a result of infectious diarrhea, for example, may arouse anxiety and guilt in the young child and may at times serve as a precipitating factor in persistent soiling. Encopresis, even more than enuresis, may readily provoke resentment or guilt on the part of the parents, leading to a struggle for control with the child which may spread from the bowel into other areas of behavior.

If the child, during the training period or later, suppresses the action of the defecation reflex, the bowel may become unresponsive for a time (Best and Taylor, 1961). In some children, such suppression may continue, in response to coercive toilet training, the pain of an anal fissure, the fear of explosive release associated with hostile fantasies, or the need to obtain unhealthy substitute satisfactions from the pleasurable local sensation of beginning extrusion of the stool followed by withholding. Voluntary withholding of this sort, combined with the involuntary readjustments necessary in peristaltic activity and the action of the internal anal sphincter, may lead to chronic constipation, even though the associated conflict no longer remains conscious (Prugh, 1954). In certain children with predisposing experiences of these types, distention of the sigmoid can occur, with alterations in its propulsive activity as seen in the nonaganglionic type of megacolon (Garrard and Richmond, 1952; Pinkerton, 1958).

Diarrhea related to psychological conflict ordinarily involves physiological concomitants of anxiety, with perhaps the operation of a hyperactive gastrocolic reflex (Szasz, 1951) or increased motility resulting possibly from the overwhelming of sympathetic by parasympathetic discharges in the emergency response (White et al., 1939). Situations involving the arousal of symbolic fantasies may, however, evoke conditioned responses triggering off the defecation reflex and invoking involuntary mechanisms, as in certain cases of ulcerative colitis (Prugh, 1954).

The external genitalia: In childhood these organs rarely show disturbance in function. In adolescents and adult males, priapism or impotence (Fenichel, 1945) would appear to represent in large part a conversion reaction arising from sexual conflicts, involving disturbances in the action of the bulbocavernosus muscle, with associated alterations in function of the involuntarily innervated urethra, seminal vesicles, and venous supply. Frigidity (Marmor, 1954) in sexually conflicted females may derive in large part from spasm of the striated perineal musculature, although involuntary mechanisms may also be involved.

Skin: The skin is innervated by the sympathetic portion of the autonomic nervous system, with the exception of the sebaceous glands, which apparently receive no autonomic innervation (Seitz, 1957). Thus the vascular, sweating, and pilomotor functions of the skin would, in accordance with the conceptual view employed herein, appear to carry no central representation, although such representation is accorded to the responses of the skin to heat, cold, pain, and touch.

In the usual sense, only the disturbances in sensory perception (Engel, 1959) in relation to psychological or social stimuli would be regarded as conversion reactions. Eczema, urticaria, and so-called neurodermatitis would be considered vegetative disorders, for example, with predisposing physiological factors of allergic nature in the first two. In addition to its functions of protection, sensation, and excretion, however, the skin appears to serve as an organ of sexual attraction and of expression of emotions (Seitz, 1957). As such, its external appearance is incorporated into the body image. The work of Seitz (1951) and Barchilon and Engel (1952), among others, would support the view that certain cutaneous changes seem to serve discharge functions which may be symbolically expressive of psychological conflicts and thus may represent intermediate phenomena between vegetative disorders and conversion reactions. The production long ago of various skin lesions through hypnosis (Dunbar, 1946), as well as Seitz's (1951) substitution by hypnosis of cutaneous disorders for symbolically equivalent nondermatological psychological syndromes, would seem to add weight to this view. Clinical studies (Seitz, 1957; Obermayer, 1955; Wittkower and Russell, 1953; Woodhead, 1946) of various chronic skin disorders with psychological components have indicated the presence in such individuals of symbolic conflicts over unconscious exhibitionistic and self-punitive needs, some of the latter being subserved by the painful scratching (Zaidens, 1951). The effectiveness of hypnosis, as well as other methods involving suggestion, in the treatment of verrucae vulgaris in children and adults (Ullman and Dudek, 1960), a lesion known to involve a filtrable virus, is also pertinent, although poorly understood at present.

Although the overlap of conversion reactions and psychophysiological disorders has been emphasized in this section, mixtures with other types of psychological reactions often appear. The majority of more severe and chronic psychophysiological disorders appear to occur, among older children and adults, in individuals with chronic personality disorders, of obsessive-compulsive, passive-dependent, or other types. In my own observation, vegetative disorders may be seen, however, in children with more mild psychological problems, perhaps involving greater somatic predisposition, or, more rarely, in children with near-psychotic pictures.

E. *Psychological Reactions to Predominantly Physical Disorders*

Abundant observations have been reported in recent years in this general area. For the sake of convenience, somatic disorders involving primarily the central nervous system and those affecting principally the rest of the body will be dealt with separately, although the artificiality of this distinction is clearly evident. Reference will be made to key articles dealing with particular aspects of these problems, since only brief discussion of broad principles can be included here.

1. *Reactions to Physical Disorders Involving Primarily the Central Nervous System.* In the current A.M.A. Nomenclature, disease pictures of this type are referred to as brain syndromes, acute and chronic. Many such disorders of course affect other organ systems. Diseases such as poliomyelitis, which affects primarily the motor neurones of the spinal cord, and mumps, causing prominent pathology in the salivary glands, also ordinarily produce some degree of meningoencephalitis, occasionally of severe degree. In addition, the disturbances in behavior arising from brain syndromes, such as hypothalamic lesions (Bakwin and Bakwin, 1953), may at times bear great similarity to those arising from psychological conflict, with admixtures frequently occurring.

Acute brain syndromes: Relatively little can be found in the literature regarding the reactions of children to acute insults to the central nervous system, with the exception of head injury (Fabian and Bender, 1947; Bakwin and Bakwin, 1953). Romano and Engel (1944) some years ago pointed out that in adults the essential feature of the acute brain syndrome is a state of delirium, representing a disturbance in awareness as the result of disordered cerebral metabolism, brought about by noxious stimuli of infectious, traumatic, toxic, metabolic, or other nature. In my experience, delirious pictures occur commonly in children, in response to head injury, meningitis, or encephalitis, and as a result of cerebral metabolic changes arising in pneumonia, heart disease, and other illnesses outside the central nervous system. As Romano and Engel indicated regarding adults, delirium in children which arises from sources other than direct insult to the brain may frequently involve subclinical pictures, discoverable only on careful examination to be mildly stuporous or confused states. Such are in contrast to the more familiar and full-blown delirium, with disoriented and markedly stuporous or agitated behavior, together with hallucinatory experiences based on misperceptions of visual or auditory stimuli.

Clear-cut delirium in older school-age children or in adolescents is easily recognized and bears much similarity to the picture seen in adults. Subclinical delirium, which may, for example, persist during early convalescence from measles encephalitis or may arise in patients with respiratory polio remaining too long out of respirators, is more obscure, and may present itself simply as difficult or excessively demanding behavior. In preschool and younger school-age children, the disturbance in awareness may be masked by markedly withdrawn or intensely anxious behavior or by aggressive attacks on adults who are misperceived as hostile persons ("ghosts, killers," etc.). Any of the symptomatic reactions discussed earlier may be seen, enhanced by the very young child's ready confusion between reality and the vividness of his own fantasies. In early school-age children, the occurrence of amnesia for parts of the delirious period may lead to fears that bodily mutilations may have occurred. Electroencephalographic abnormalities are characteristically present in older children as in adults, returning to baseline as the cause of the disturbance in cerebral metabolism is reversed therapeutically (Engel and Romano, 1944).

Delirious reactions to drugs represent one special feature of childhood, in keeping with the variability of response to pharmacological agents in relation to developmental level (Nelson, 1959).

Older infants and preschool children, for example, may respond paradoxically to certain barbiturates, with overstimulation and a delirious state resulting at times, in opposition to the expected sedation. The possibility exists, as Laufer (1957) has indicated, that children with hyperkinetic activity patterns may respond especially in this fashion to such drugs. Delirious reactions to high doses of dilantin and to sedative or hypnotic agents are well known. The influence of age level upon the incidence of delirium in reaction to the more recent tranquilizing agents is unclear, although such reactions do occur not uncommonly in children.

Although children often respond with great resiliency to central nervous system insults, disturbances in perceptual or visuomotor function may persist for some time, even in the absence of demonstrable delirium or of gross neurological lesions. Crothers and Meyer (1946) have described such difficulties in perceiving and arranging patterns or forms, shown up clearly on the Bender-Gestalt or similar tests, lasting as long as several months after meningitis or encephalitis without apparent neurological sequelae; they may appear also following pneumonia and other diseases not involving the central nervous system directly. Resulting delays or lags in developmental achievement of such perceptual-motor tasks, compounded by regressive manifestations, may lead to learning difficulties in the early school-age child, if these are not recognized and dealt with in planning for the child's gradual return to full academic performance.

Chronic brain syndromes: Space does not permit extensive discussion of this topic, dealt with by so many workers (Bradley, 1957; Bender, 1956; Goldstein, 1954; Laufer, 1962; Bakwin, 1949b; Eisenberg, 1957). Insults to the central nervous system leaving persistent structural change may occur during intra-uterine existence, as the result of such entities as viral infection, toxoplasmosis, erythroblastosis, eclampsia, or placenta previa; during the birth process, as the result of hemorrhage and anoxia; or following birth, in consequence of infectious, traumatic, toxic, neoplastic, heredodegenerative, vascular, metabolic, or other noxious influences. In some instances gross neurological lesions are present, as in the cerebral palsies. In others, only electroencephalographic abnormalities, perceptual-motor defects, and certain behavioral changes may be identifiable, rendering diagnosis difficult at times. Mental retardation may accompany such defects. The majority of children with more mild and diffuse damage to the cerebral cortex do not show this feature, however, in spite of significant diminution in learning capacity (Graham and Berman, 1961; Eisenberg, 1959; Strauss and Lehtinen, 1947; Doll, 1951).

Developmental considerations are important in regard to these types of disorders. In older children and adolescents, signs of disturbance in function from recent brain injury may be seen which are similar to those described in adults by Goldstein (1954). Damage to the brain at different levels of development may have differing effects; these are not always predictable, however. The brain of the newborn infant can withstand considerable hypoxia during and immediately after the birth process (Mabry, 1959; Keith and Gage, 1960). It is also capable of remarkable compensation, by undamaged parts, for diffuse damage occurring as the result of petechial hemorrhage or hypoxia. Thus significant improvement in the clinical signs may occur with maturation (Graham et al., 1962), even though tissue regeneration does not occur in the brain. Extensive lacerations of the cerebral cortex, sustained in infancy, congenital porencephalic cysts (Taylor, 1959), and congenital absence of the corpus callosum (Ford, 1952), for example, have been at times compensated in remarkable fashion, with, in occasional children, very little evidence of cerebral dysfunction on psychological testing. Older children show such capacities for compensation in less marked fashion, although perhaps still more frequently so than adults.

In spite of such observations, some questions remain unsettled. Although the above clinical impressions exist regarding the capacities of newborns, it is still possible that certain functions not yet developed might be affected more markedly in young infants than in older children sustaining brain damage, as Graham (1961) has indicated. Functions recently developed might be in a critical or vulnerable phase in contrast to more solidly established ones, as Hebb (1949) and others have suggested. Longitudinal and controlled studies now going on (Thurston et al., 1960; Graham et al., 1962); should give some answers to such questions. Answers need also to be found to the related questions regarding the long-term outlook in premature infants, who do show some differences from full-term infants in psychological functions for several years at least (Harper et al., 1959).

Early investigations suggested the existence of specific personality disorders associated with postencephalitic states (Bond and Appel, 1931), head injury (Kasanin, 1929), and other conditions. More recent investigations do not support such specificity (Fabian and Bender, 1947; Teuber, 1960). The impression exists today among numerous workers that the degree of effect of gross neurological defects, congenital or acquired, upon the total personality development of the child depends upon several variables, in addition to the severity of the defect and the level of development at which the defect was acquired. These include the child's previous adaptive capacity, the nature of the parent-child relationship, the psychological meaning of the defect to parents and child, the current family equilibrium, and other intercurrent influences, including the quality and character of medical management, educational planning, and other factors. Of these, probably the most important is the capacity of the family to accept and nurture the child in ways appropriate to his capacities (Garrard and Richmond, 1957), with institutionalization necessary only in specific instances. The reactions of parents, which bear some similarity to those seen in relation to other chronic physical disorders, have been well summarized by Garrard and Richmond (1957), with cogent suggestions for management. With contemporary antibiotics and other medical and surgical measures, many children are now able to survive tuberculous meningitis (Nickerson and MacDermot, 1961) and other previously fatal brain diseases, including brain tumors (Langford and Klingman, 1942; Bakwin and Bakwin, 1953). Their serious brain damage poses rehabilitative and habilitative problems for the pediatrician and the representatives of many other disciplines who may collaborate in their care and education.

One particular syndrome has frequently been described as resulting from brain damage or "cerebral dysfunction." This is seen in older preschool and younger school-age children with cortical damage of moderate and diffuse nature, resulting from cerebral insult at birth or in early childhood. The picture is characterized by hyperactivity, distractibility, and impulsivity (Graham and Berman, 1961; Bakwin and Bakwin, 1953; Laufer, 1962), among other features. Diffuse abnormalities are ordinarily present in the electroencephalogram, together with difficulties in perceptual-motor functions and cerebral integrative or organizational capacities. Problems in employing symbols in reading or writing and in abstract concept formation have been described as appearing on psychological testing of such children by Taylor (1959) and others. Specific neurological lesions are rarely demonstrable, and the diagnosis must be made on the basis of the history together with the above findings.

Since the older infant or young preschool child shows normally many of these characteristics, due caution must be employed in making such a diagnosis. Young children with predominantly psychological disturbance may also show difficulties in impulse control, distractibility, and hyperactivity, together with delayed perceptual-motor development, in the absence of any history or signs of brain damage (Stuart and Prugh, 1960; Childers, 1935). The concept of "minimal" or undetected brain damage, put forth strongly by certain workers (Knobloch, 1958; Knobloch and Pasamanick, 1959), does not seem to me to be justified in many instances by the limited evidence available. It thus does not seem appropriate to use the "hyperkinetic syndrome" (Laufer, 1962) by itself as a diagnostic criterion for the presence of brain damage. Young children with hyperkinetic behavior have been shown by Bradley (1950), Bender (1942), and others to respond paradoxically to the amphetamines or related drugs, with a depressant or quieting and organizing effect resulting rather than the stimulant response seen in older children or adults. Although the impression has existed that such a response was specific for brain damage, a controlled investigation by Koret (unpublished) indicates that the hyperactivity and not the brain damage is the variable susceptible to such a paradoxical effect.

The problems involved in the evaluation of mental retardation, with its impact on the family unit, have been discussed by Wolf and Lourie (1953), Masland, Gladwin, and Sarason (1958), and others

(Woodward and Siegel, 1957; G.A.P. report, 1959). The predictive limitations of developmental tests for infants and the need for caution in the interpretation of intelligence tests in the face of psychological disturbance have been well emphasized (Bayley, 1958; Sontag et al., 1958; Eisenberg, 1958a). The psychological problems encountered by children with gross neurological lesions, such as those cerebral-palsied children with athetoid, choreiform, or other extrapyramidal pictures, have been well described by Little (1949) and by Crothers and Paine (1959). Benda (1952, 1955) has discussed extensively a variety of neurological and psychopathological syndromes associated with developmental disorders of mentation. The influence of anxiety or other emotions upon the difficulties in motor coordination of such children is well known (Crothers and Paine, 1959), with marked intensification often resulting. Similar responses have been delineated in adolescents and adults with Parkinsonism (Riklan et al., 1959), multiple sclerosis (Philippopolous et al., 1958), and other pictures.

The frequent admixture of brain syndromes, conversion reactions, and other patterns, including chronic personality disorders in older children, has already been commented upon. Children with uncontrolled idiopathic epilepsy may develop brain damage as a result of status epilepticus, with later conversion mechanisms complicating the picture. Sydenham's chorea, whether or not it represents a "rheumatic encephalitis" on a hypersensitivity basis (McCulloch, 1938), does not ordinarily leave residual brain damage. Such patients, in whom the syndrome may have its onset in relation to psychological stress (Chapman et al., 1958), may show conversion mechanisms of dystonic or other type, superimposed upon the choreiform movements and perpetuating the disability.

2. *Reactions to Physical Disorders Outside the Central Nervous System.* In this section, mention will be made only of certain broad patterns of response, overlapping somewhat with those discussed in the previous section. The reader is referred to Senn's classic article, "Emotions and Symptoms in Pediatric Practice" (1948b), to Richmond's cogent discussion of "The Pediatric Patient in Illness" (1958),

and Korsch's excellent survey, "The Pediatrician and the Sick Child" (1958), together with other basic references (Bellak, 1952; Winnicott, 1931; Langford, 1948; Little, 1960; Barker et al., 1953), for fuller discussions of the reactions of children and families to predominantly physical illness. Again, an arbitrary division of topics will be employed.

a. *Reactions to acute illness or injury:* In recent years, a number of studies of the emotional reactions of children and families to illness have been published by child psychiatrists, pediatricians, and other professional workers. Beverly (1936), Senn (1946), Jackson (1942), Langford (1948), Jensen and Comly (1948), Bakwin (1951), Anna Freud (1952), Little (1960), and many others have contributed important knowledge in regard to psychological responses to acute illness, while Senn (1945), Liss (1948), Barker, Wright, and Gonick (1953), Romano (1943), and others have cast light upon the process of convalescence. Since many children in Western society today encounter hospitalization in the course of treatment for serious illness, the effects of illness upon the child and family are often difficult to separate from the impact of the hospital experience.

Mention was made earlier of the possible decompensating effect of any illness or injury, mild or severe, upon the child's dynamic steady state or upon the family equilibrium. Among the factors determining such an effect are: (1) the *developmental level* of the child, in regard to stage-appropriate biological capacities but also in relation to the stage of psychosexual and psychosocial development; (2) the *previous adaptive capacity* of the child; (3) the prior nature of the *parent-child relationship;* (4) the existing *family adaptive equilibrium;* (5) the *nature of the illness or injury,* including the type of organ system affected, the degree of prostration or pain, type of treatment or home care necessary, and any residual defect or handicap; (6) the *meaning of the illness* to child and parents, in terms of immediately antecedent events and their actual or fantasied connection with the illness or injury, the nature of previous experience of parents or child with such illness, the nature and degree of impact upon the child's social patterns, and other factors.

Space does not permit full discussion of each of these variables, fully dealt with elsewhere. If, for example, a girl who has been previously rather dependent upon the mother and anxious over separation from her develops an acute gastroenteritis a few days after beginning the first grade, the intensification of anxious clinging to the mother brought about by temporarily regressive trends may prolong the disability beyond the point of physical recovery. If the mother has had considerable apprehension over the child's health, related to a pneumonia in infancy, for example, she may blame herself for the child's illness and fear to let her return to school for at least several weeks. In such a situation, the child may derive some unconscious secondary gain from the increased dependence upon the mother but may also feel guilty about missing school and fearful of falling behind in her work. Depending upon the nature of the marital relationship and family balance, as well as the advice of the physician, the father may support the mother to encourage the child's return to school as soon as possible. He may be unable to offer such support, however, and the family dynamics may promote a prolongation of the child's dependency and fear of separation, leading to the picture of school phobia (Eisenberg, 1958b; Waldfogel et al., 1957), associated with abdominal pain or vomiting of conversion nature. Thus predisposing, precipitating, contributory, and perpetuating forces may operate to determine the outcome of even a relatively mild illness.

In the example cited, regressive symptomatic reactions were involved, which may include all the types seen in young children as situational responses. Misinterpretation of illness or accident as punishment, the tendency to fear bodily mutilation as the result of medical or surgical procedures, and other "magical" theories regarding pain or disability are of course characteristic of the preschool and early school-age child. There is a consistent tendency for parents in such stressful situations to personalize the "blame" for the illness and to show self-blame or to project this onto teachers, physicians, or a hostile world. Regressive manifestations in the young child, such as a return to bed wetting or soiling, may arouse guilt or anxiety on the part of the child, with anger or guilt occurring on the part of the parents. The increased care necessary for the ill child may impose a heavy burden upon the parents, with resentment sometimes underlying willingness, while rivalry or other reverberations may occur on the part of siblings. As in the example cited, convalescence may be slowed or otherwise interfered with by such mechanisms, in response to respiratory (Richter, 1943; Brodman et al., 1947) or other diseases.

The most universally important factors thus appear to be those related to the way in which the environment (parental, family, social, and physical) helps the child, at his developmental level, to deal with the physical consequences and the symbolic meaning of the illness or injury. Within broad limits, however, the nature of the illness and its attendant treatment are of significant influence. This is especially true in overwhelming or catastrophic types of illness. In such situations, there is some evidence of a generic type of human organismic response related to the adaptive mechanisms involved in the handling of the phases of *impact, recoil,* and *restitution.* Such a phasic type of response is seen most clearly in children of school age or beyond; preschool children tend to show less clear-cut but somewhat similar patterns. Prugh and Tagiuri (1954) have described, in children, adolescents, and adults suffering from respiratory polio necessitating the use of a tank respirator: (1) an initial *realistic fear,* of suffocation or death, associated with difficulty in breathing and often complicated by delirium, arising from the meningoencephalitis combined with oxygen lack; (2) a phase of *regression,* associated with sweeping denial of the paralytic implications of the illness, the use of primitive fantasy in coping with the enforced helplessness, and various symptomatic regressive manifestations; (3) a later phase of *depression,* warded off for a time by eating disturbances or hostile behavior but gradually involving the appearance of "mourning for the loss of the self," as the long-term implications of the disease became inexorably apparent; (4) a phase of gradual *adaptation,* involving the acceptance of the situation, whatever its outcome, and beginning attempts at mastery, during which occurred gradually the emergence of individual personality needs and adaptive patterns. The first two phases appeared related to the impact, the third phase to recoil, and the fourth to mechanisms of restitution in the attempt to handle such overwhelming stress, with weeks or at times months occupied in the progress from one stage to the next.

A somewhat parallel set of phasic responses have been described in adults by Hamburg (1953), in regard to serious burns, by Wittkower (1947), in relation to spinal cord injuries, and by Shands (1951), in reaction to cancer and other diseases with grave prognostic implications. Generally similar reactions of children and adults to civilian or military disaster (Silber et al., 1956; Cobb and Lindemann, 1943) have been observed as well. In adults, with more firmly established ego structures, the regressive manifestations may be less marked than in children, with denial and disbelief predominating. The biological signs of depression may be more clinically apparent in adults, although strenuous attempts may be made to ward off feelings of helplessness and hopelessness (Schmale, 1958). In some respects, such phasic patterns are also characteristic of the "work of mourning" involved in the handling of grief over the death of a loved person, as described by Freud (1917), Lindemann (1944), Engel (1961), and others. The approach to management of catastrophic illnesses requires cognizance of such phasic patterns and appropriate adaptation of treatment and rehabilitative techniques (Prugh and Tagiuri, 1954), in addition to the awareness of individual personality patterns and needs.

The parents of the children described above exhibited a somewhat parallel phasic set of reactions in assimilating the significance of their child's physical state and grim outlook. Initial realistic fear was often followed by attempts to deny the situation, giving way to depression and self-blame, and finally leading to constructive action, involving individual personality patterns of adaptation. Richmond (1958) has summarized such stages, experienced by parents of children with a variety of disabling and serious illnesses, as: (1) *denial and disbelief,* at times rising to extremely illogical heights and occasionally persisting for months or longer; (2) *fear and frustration,* associated with feelings of depression, guilt, and self-recrimination, with intensified marital strife occurring in some families; (3) intelligent *inquiry and planning,* involving the need to live with some uncertainty.

Although the above phases shade into the stage of chronic illness, they are discussed in relation to acute illness or accident since they begin at the outset of serious illness or injury, at a point when the outlook may not be clear for some weeks or months, even if complete recovery finally ensues. In large measure, the lack of anticipation of or preparation for such overwhelming stress experiences seem to be responsible for the sweeping character of the immediate impact. Parents or children have had no time to organize their defenses in advance, a situation which, as Freud (1940) pointed out, can lead to the development of a "traumatic neurosis," such as the neuroses of war. They may gradually resolve or may merge into a chronic picture of psychological as well as physical difficulties in adaptation, depending upon predisposing, contributory, and perpetuating factors.

No more than brief mention can be given to the precipitating factors in acute illness or injury, already alluded to earlier. Various psychological influences may play a role in the precipitation of disease states involving infections, toxic or traumatic noxious stimuli. The current concern of pediatricians over accidents and poisoning in childhood (Wheatley and Richardson, 1960), including lead intoxication related to pica (Millican et al., 1956; Cooper, 1957), reflects an awareness of the confluence of forces arising from the child's developmental stage, degree of activity, and biological capacities, the type of supervision or disciplinary control offered by parents, and the internal psychological conflicts shown by the child who is frequently involved in accidents (Langford et al., 1954) or self-injurious behavior. A variety of predominantly physical illnesses have been observed to occur in chronological relation to significantly stressful stimuli of psychological or social nature. Such illnesses range from infectious hepatitis (Papper and Handy, 1956) and the common cold (Despert, 1944; Saul, 1938), in individuals undergoing acute emotional conflict, to streptococcal infections, in certain families experiencing stressful events (Haggerty and Meyer, 1961). The phenomenon of lowered immunity or resistance to disease resulting from such stimuli, although apparently operative, is still poorly understood in regard to the psychophysiological and immunological mechanisms involved (Bakke and Wolff, 1950). Animal studies of Ader (1959) and

Rasmussen (1957) tend to support though not to substantiate the occurrence of such a phenomenon in human beings.

Reactions to hospitalization: For a fuller discussion of these important topics, the reader is referred to other sources. The influence of short-term hospitalization, distinguished as far as possible from the results of illness, has been investigated systematically in young infants by Schaeffer and Callender (1959), in older infants and preschool children by Robertson (1958) and Ainsworth and Bowlby (1954), and in preschool and school-age children by Jessner (1959) and by Prugh and his colleagues (1953), among others. Extensive reviews of studies on the effects of short-term hospitalization have been published by Robertson (1958) in his important monograph, and by Dimock (1960), Blom (1958), and Langford (1961) as well. Bowlby (1951) has dealt exhaustively with the field of long-term hospitalization, drawing upon earlier work by Chapin (1908), Bakwin (1949a), Spitz (1945), and others.

From the investigations cited above, certain generalizations can be drawn. The various factors discussed in relation to acute illness or injury are also involved in the determination of the nature and severity of the response of child and family to hospitalization and operation. The character of the necessary treatment, particularly the separation from the family, assumes greater importance, however, with certain differences related to developmental level in particular.

Most, if not all, older infants and children show some observable reaction to the experience of hospitalization and attendant treatment procedures, as distinct from the effects of the illness itself. The majority of children exhibit reactions of the symptomatic type and manifestations of anxiety, depression, or specific fears. In most instances, these are relatively self-limited in character though often persisting for several weeks or months following discharge. Children under four years of age appear to be most susceptible to such circumstances, showing the most severe and persistent reactions. Older children with previously limited capacities for adaptation are also vulnerable.

Infants in the first several months of life show relatively little adverse reaction to hospitalization if adequate substitute mothering is provided (Schaffer and Callender, 1959). They may, however, react temporarily and rather globally to stimuli arising from different methods of feeding or other handling. In the infants of six to eight months who can begin to distinguish strangers and in the younger preschool child, separation from the mother, often misinterpreted by the young child as punishment or desertion, appears to pose the chief threat to a still immature and dependent ego. Such "separation anxiety" appears also to some degree in children of early school age, being strongest and most devastating in disturbed children. In older infants and preschool children, struggling to develop a "sense of autonomy" on the foundations of a "sense of trust" (Erikson, 1950), the reaction to separation appears to transcend the effects of the nature of illness and the type of diagnostic or therapeutic measures employed. The absence of the mother, as a type of substitute ego, lays the child open to "objective anxiety" (A. Freud, 1952), calling out feelings of helplessness and mistrust in a strange environment and fears of abandonment or overwhelming attack, arising from his limited capacities for testing of reality and greater tendencies toward regression. The sequence of *protest, despair,* and *denial* of feeling, the latter often associated with withdrawal and depression, which has been described by Robertson (1958), is frequently seen after a few days of hospitalization, even in well-adjusted children, and may be most troubling to parents.

For the child from four years through the early school-age period, the psychological meaning of the illness and its treatment appears to have greater potential traumatic effect than the actual separation from the parents. Reality factors, inviting misinterpretation as punishment, and fears of bodily mutilation appear to combine with unconscious anxieties, guilt feelings, and fantasies to invest certain treatment procedures and the involvement of particular organs with especial significance for the child from four to six or seven years, in the stage of development of the "prerogatives of masculine or feminine initiative" (Erikson, 1950) and the evolution of the conscience or superego. Procedures calling for manipulation of the genitals, head, eyes, and mouth are most likely to evoke such "subjective anxiety," associated still with some regressive tendencies. Confusions in body image are characteristic of this stage (Bender, 1934), particularly in regard to internal organs, with abundant opportunities available to children for frightening fantasy and misinterpretation of operative or other procedures. Some differences in reactions between boys and girls begin to appear in this age group (Prugh et al., 1953).

In the older school-age and preadolescent child, working developmentally on a "sense of industry" (Erikson, 1950) and accomplishment, greater capacities for reality testing, and other more mature characteristics of the mental apparatus, appear to result in fewer misinterpretations and much more limited regressive tendencies. These can still occur with considerable intensity, however, in the face of marked stress or in the previously disturbed child. Although conscious awareness of the body image is better established, some gaps still remain, with individual variations and sex differences in symbolic investment of particular body parts. Anxiety over the functioning of certain organs is frequently seen, together with fears of genital inadequacy, muscular weakness, and loss of body control or mastery, associated with the feelings of inferiority so readily mobilized in this stage. Loss of self-control is feared; dependence upon others may be both resented and enjoyed. In adolescents, many of the same trends are seen, although in muted fashion, with struggles to establish a "sense of identity" (Erikson, 1950) and independence sometimes interfering with cooperative tendencies in treatment.

The reactions of parents follow somewhat the same pattern already described. Denial and disbelief may be less marked with less serious illness, with significant exceptions. The contacts with hospital staff and blaming them for minor difficulties. Although a few parents their competence but may feel left out or unwanted. Some parents may thus exhibit strong rivalry with nurses or physicians, reacting anxiously or defensively in fear of criticism for their role in the child's illness or at times projecting their own guilt onto the hospital staff and blaming them for minor difficulties. Although a few parents require special psychotherapeutic measures of supportive nature, the better adjusted parents are able, if handled without criticism and with patience and understanding, to deal with this situation comfortably and realistically. If opportunity is made available and they are considered a part of a "therapeutic alliance" with the hospital staff, most parents can make vital contributions to the hospital program through their participation in the care of their own (or at times other parents') children.

Posthospitalization reactions are of significance. Some children may show marked regression or outbursts of anxiety only after return home, after maintaining control rigidly throughout the hospital experience (Prugh et al., 1953). Help for parents in understanding in advance these inherent tendencies of the young child can aid them in reacting less personally to such behavior and in "weaning" the child gradually back to his previous level of adjustment, thus preventing spreading or deepening of significant interpersonal reverberations within the family unit.

In summary, although some reactions of the types described appear to be virtually universal, the majority of children are able to adapt successfully to the experience of hospitalization, with the disappearance of immediate reactions within two or three months. The possibility of emotionally traumatic reactions is great enough (Prugh et al., 1953), however, particularly in preschool and in previously disturbed children, to require careful thought to be given to the actual indications for the use of hospitalization in every instance. Such possibilities also warrant the application, by various members of the hospital staff, of special preventive psychological measures of preparatory and supportive nature, discussed by many of the workers mentioned above, and shown, by controlled investigations, to be effective in minimizing severe emotional reactions of immediate nature in child and family (Prugh et al., 1953; Robertson, 1958). With such an approach and the improvement in physical condition resulting from medical treatment, hospitalization can be a relatively constructive experience for many children.

Reactions to surgical procedures: Surgical experience by the child in hospital has been studied most systematically by Jessner, Blom, and Waldfogel (1952), Faust and colleagues (Faust, 1952; Jackson et al., 1953), and Goldman and Crain (1957), in regard to tonsillectomy, and by Jackson (1951) in relation to anesthesia. The earlier observations by Langford (1937) and Levy (1945), on reactions to tonsillectomy, and Pearson's (1941) and Jensen's (1949) perceptive discussions of the effects of operative procedures provided seminal influences on the more recent work. The general field has been surveyed by Loomis (1956), Prugh (1958), and others regarding younger children, and by Tichener and Levine (1960) in relation to older children and adults. Observations on adolescents and adults undergoing mitral surgery have been reported by Fox and his co-workers (1954) and by Kaplan (1956). Other surgical procedures, principally in adults, have been studied by Deutsch (1942), Linde-mann (1941), Herring (1956), and others (Meyer et al., 1955).

Reactions to surgical procedures overlap greatly with those described in relation to hospitalization. In the study of Jessner, Blom, and Waldfogel (1952), observations were made regarding the fear of loss of self-control while undergoing anesthesia, in addition to individual fantasies in the older age group about what would be done under narcosis to the various organs of the body. The work of Jackson (1951) has demonstrated the effectiveness of techniques of psychological preparation in smoothing anesthetic induction and in minimizing the amount of anesthetic agent required, under condi-tions involving less fear and apprehension, with easier postoperative recovery. Such findings are supported by the work of Shagass (1955), indicating that the sedation threshold may be higher in patients with greater anxiety. For patients with serious heart disease or other debilitating conditions, the use of such psychological methods and the smaller amount of anesthetic agent employed may help to pro-vide a vital margin of safety in long and difficult operative proce-dures (Titchener and Levine, 1960), which can be a seriously stressful experience, with widespread neuroendocrine reverberations (Price et al., 1957). The developmental considerations cited earlier also apply to the response to preoperative sedation.

Special problems may arise in relation to certain operations with necessarily mutilating effects, such as amputation. The tendency in the younger child to misinterpret the procedure as a hostile act or as a punishment for past transgressions may, as with other proce-dures, lead to aggressive behavior in fantasied self-defense. Although phantom-limb phenomena, as seen in adults (Kolb, 1954), are encountered more rarely in children in crystallized form, strenuous denial (Weinstein and Kahn, 1955) occurs frequently, leading at times to difficulties in prosthetic steps (Bechtol, 1955). Again the parental responses and the other factors mentioned are of vital significance. In older children and adolescents with hysterical personality structures, the unconscious need to suffer because of deep-seated guilt over hostile or sexual feelings may lead to the phenomena of recurrent pain, at times leading to diagnostic confusion with appendicitis (Blanton and Kirk, 1947), or to so-called "polysurgical addiction" (Menninger, 1934) described in adults. Psychological and developmental considerations should be included in the evaluation of patients for reparative procedures, as in cosmetic surgery for facial deformities (MacGregor et al., 1953) and the surgical approach to pseudohermaphroditism (Money et al., 1955). Such indeed should be the case with any elective procedure, such as operation for undescended testicle. Paradoxical reactions by child and parents occur at times, with complaints rather than gratitude or with an exacerbation of neurotic symptoms (Ruesch et al., 1951), related to the need to deal with shifts in attitude toward the child with his new appearance.

b. *Reactions to chronic illness or handicap:* For a full discussion of this topic, the reader is referred to the review monograph by Barker, Wright, and Gonick (1953), the recent review article by Korsch (1958), the chapter by Richmond (1958), Ruesch's studies (1951), the work of Meng (1938), and the writings of Witmer and Kotinsky (1952), Kubie (1945), and Grayson (1952), among others (Richmond, 1954; Martmer, 1959; Szurek, 1951; Gates, 1946; Jensen, 1956; Allen and Pearson, 1928). Over the years, studies have been made of children and adults with rheumatic heart disease (Brazelton et al., 1953; Josselyn et al., 1955), pulmonary tuberculosis (Dubo, 1950; Rosenblueth and Bowlby, 1955; Holmes et al., 1957), tubercular meningitis (Nickerson and MacDermot, 1961), poliomyelitis (Crothers and Meyer, 1946; Seidenfeld, 1949; Prugh and Taguiri, 1954), nephrosis (Korsch and Barnett, 1961), nephritis (Persike and Lippman, 1948; McCrory et al., 1959), hemophilia (Browne et al., 1960), malignant diseases of varying types (Bozeman et al., 1955;

Richmond and Waisman, 1955) including leukemia (Greene et al., 1956), and orthopedic problems requiring immobilization (Bergman, 1945; Korsch, 1958; Blom, 1958). Other chronic diseases, including some with vegetative components such as asthma (Jessner et al., 1955), epilepsy (Gottschalk, 1953; Bridge, 1949), rheumatoid arthritis (Brazelton et al., 1953), obesity (Bruch, 1957), and diabetes (Bruch, 1949), have been reported on. Neurological syndromes such as cerebral palsy (Crothers and Paine, 1959), muscular dystrophy (Morrow and Cohen, 1954), and dystrophia myotonica (Wallerstein and Rubin, 1954), myasthenia gravis (Brolley and Hollender, 1955), and familial dysautonomia (Riley, 1957; Freedman et al., 1960), as well as others already mentioned, have been investigated from a psychological approach, as have disorders of metabolism affecting growth, such as nonpituitary dwarfism (Talbot et al., 1947; Fried, 1950), cretinism (Bruch and McCune, 1944), and precocious puberty (Mason, 1949). Reports have been published dealing with children and their parents with blindness (Hallenbeck, 1954; Cole and Taboroff, 1955), deafness (Sharoff, 1959; Bakwin, 1950), and with a variety of congenital anomalies, among them cleft palate and harelip (Tisza et al., 1958), genitourinary abnormalities (Fineman, 1959; Gates and Weinberger, 1955), facial deformities (MacGregor et al., 1953), congenital heart defects (Chazan et al., 1951; Landtman et al., 1960); hermaphroditism (Money et al., 1955; Bayer, 1947), and others, including congenital amputation (Gurney, 1958).

Although significant effects on personality development and social adjustment have been pointed out by all these writers, the inescapable conclusion, from a perusal of the above studies and the views of Kubie (1945) and Wittkower (1947), among others, is that many children and adults with chronic diseases or congenital or acquired handicaps make a surprisingly adequate adaptation to their problems. Again, of the variables mentioned earlier, those relating to the child's adaptive capacity and the parent-child-family balance appear to be more influential than the nature of the specific disease or handicap. In regard to handicap, the timing of its onset does raise special issues, as in sensory handicaps, such as blindness or deafness, of congenital versus acquired nature (Cole and Taboroff, 1955;

Bakwin, 1950). Even these factors may evoke different responses in child and parents, however. Several special problems only can be included in this section.

For a number of years the concept of specific personality malformations resulting from particular diseases or handicaps was strongly entertained, including notably the "organ inferiority" concept of Adler (1927). Although special challenges do arise with different disorders, the evidence available would appear to render this concept no longer tenable. The personality disorders found in such patients may resemble closely those seen in children with no physical illness (Barker et al., 1953). The fear of loss of control of the environment in the blind child (Norris et al., 1957), the apprehension over losing balance and falling in those with cerebral palsy (Little, 1949), and the suspicion of what is being said about themselves by the deaf are frequently present (Myklebust, 1960) but do not appear specific to these disorders.

The personality pictures seen in many children with a variety of chronic diseases or handicaps appear rather to fall along a continuum. These may range from overdependent, overanxious, and passive or withdrawn patterns, with strong secondary gains from illness, to overindependent and at times aggressive modes of behavior, with frequently associated tendencies to strongly deny illness, even to markedly unhealthy extremes. In the middle of the continuum are a group of children who show realistic dependence, within the limits of the degree of incapacitation imposed by the illness, with relatively outgoing social patterns, and with relatively little need for major secondary gain or for unhealthy control of the external world, including the parents. Such children may show some denial of the serious implications of their disease, perhaps necessary for the maintenance of hope and guarded optimism. They can apparently accept their limitations fairly adequately, however, and can find compensatory satisfactions in activities appropriate to their physical state.

Parental reactions seem also to group themselves along a continuum of response. One group appears to respond with overanxiety, overprotectiveness, or overindulgence, and with inconsistent or over-permissive discipline, finding it difficult to control or limit the child, even for realistic reasons, as in diabetic management. At the other end of the continuum falls a cluster of parental responses which involve great difficulty in accepting realistically the child's illness because of his intensely personal significance to them in terms of their own unconscious emotional needs, because of extreme guilt, or because of their own current problems, economic or otherwise. Such parents may deny the extent of the child's illness, may project the blame onto the child or hospital staff, may "shop" medically, may refuse appropriate treatment, and may overcontrol or push the child unconsciously to physical and emotional lengths far beyond his capacities. A few of these latter parents may openly reject, stigmatize, or isolate the child within the family unit, as a result of individual conflicts, marital problems, or social and cultural patterns. A middle group of parents appears to be able, after the initial impact and recoil, to use realistic methods of inquiry and planning, with a capacity to accept the child's illness, to permit him appropriate dependence, and to help him exploit his capacities constructively, within the limits of his disability.

At present, there appears to be little correlation possible between types of unhealthy parental and family reactions and specific types of personality distortion on the part of the chronically ill or handicapped child, as was indicated earlier in a more general sense. Conversion mechanisms (Young and Hermann, 1951) or other psychological reactions may at times lead to invalidism in less handicapped children. The impression prevails also that even a small and virtually unnoticeable defect may carry overwhelming significance in certain families for unconsciously overdetermined reasons. For some parents, the inability of a child with cerebral palsy to learn well academically may be more threatening than the neurological defect (Crothers and Paine, 1959). Although visible cosmetic defects may be most troubling in some families, in others the occurrence of a hidden metabolic handicap may be even more mysterious and threatening, without relation to its actual severity.

Space does not permit discussion of numerous pertinent issues. The problems in sexual development for the child with pseudohermaphroditism (Money et al., 1955)) or extrophy of the bladder (Fineman, 1959), the nature of responses to movement restraint (Bergmann, 1945) or prosthetic devices (Bechtol, 1955), and other challenges to adaptation are discussed in specific reports.

In a general sense, difficulties in the establishment or maintenance of body image are present for most children with chronic disease or handicap (MacGregor et al., 1953; Barker et al., 1953; Watson and Johnson, 1958; Bender, 1934; Bender and Silver, 1948), whether inside or outside the central nervous system. The role of the parents in the development of the child's conscious and unconscious awareness of his body and its characteristics is of course most fundamental. Although problems of this nature are frequent, however, they do not seem to be specific for such children, as such difficulties may be seen without physical disfigurement of any sort (Schilder, 1935). Size, strength, and physical attractiveness do play some role in the child's confidence and social adjustment. As Barker and his colleagues (1953) have pointed out, however, there are overlapping variables, and various studies have failed to attribute great significance to these particular somatopsychological factors except in individual cases in particular family situations. Reactions to differences in body image, related to residual functions and capacities, in comparison to other patients in groups with similar problems, have at times interfered with rehabilitative procedures in school-age children and adolescents (Prugh and Jaguiri, 1954), in line with their needs for acceptance by the peer group.

In addition to observations on the types of adaptation made by child and family within the community, studies have been made, over a number of years, of the reactions of chronically ill or handicapped children to long-term hospitalization or institutionalization. The impressions of Bakwin (1949a), Bibring (1949), and others, in regard to the effects of long-term hospitalization for orthopedic or other physical disorders, have resulted in strong agreement with those of Lowrey (1940), Goldfarb (1943), Bender (1941), A. Freud and Burlingham (1944), and others, carried out in orphanages, and with the results of Bowlby's world survey (1951) in both areas. Serious emotional deprivation frequently, although not always

(Bowlby, 1951; Glaser and Eisenberg, 1956; Ainsworth, 1962), results from long-term institutionalization of children for any reason. Chronic depression, shallow social relationships, distorted time concepts and capacities for learning, difficulties in impulse control, rebellious or antisocial behavior, and lowered resistance to disease, with high morbidity and mortality rates, seem to result frequently, together with other psychopathological pictures (Prugh and Harlow, 1962), from experiences in large groups by older infants or young children with limited contacts with parental figures or their substitutes. "Masked" emotional deprivation, with similar types of personality distortion, can of course occur in relatively intact families, in which parents, preoccupied with their own needs, cannot meet their children's basic requirements for emotional warmth (Prugh and Harlow, 1962). As a result of such studies, a revolution in methods of planning for long-term care of children has been in process in all parts of the world (Bowlby, 1951).

The handling of terminal illness and the death of a child presents challenging problems, well discussed by Richmond and Waisman (1955) in regard to malignancy, and by Solnit and Green (1959), Korsch (1958), and others (Sherwin and McCully, 1961; Natterson and Knudson, 1960; B. Cobb, 1952) in a more general sense. The child's concept of death is not fully developed, in the sense of realistic comprehension, until nine or ten years of age or later (Mahler, 1950), and thus children may fairly adequately deny fears of death. Parents often carry out "mourning in advance," requiring much support from medical and nursing staff, as well as that from other parents facing similar problems (Richmond, 1958; Friedman, unpublished).

Certain chronic diseases must be mentioned in which psychological factors have been observed to play contributory or at times precipitating roles, although physical predisposing or perpetuating factors may predominate. These may include the collagen diseases, particularly lupus (McClary et al., 1955); infectious diseases such as tuberculosis (Holmes et al., 1957), chronic respiratory or sinus infections (Holmes et al., 1949), and brucellosis (Harris, 1950); certain degenerative diseases such as multiple sclerosis (Philippopolous et al., 1958), and Parkinsonism (Booth, 1948), and a variety of others, among them pernicious anemia (Lewin, 1959), herpes simplex (Blank and Brody, 1950), and fungus infections (Harris, 1944). The onset of leukemia and lymphoma in adults and older children in a setting of depression over actual or symbolic loss of importantly supportive figures has been reported by Greene et al. (1956), while Schmale (1958) has made similar observations in a number of diseases. The impressions of Grinker (1953) and others regarding the rapid failure and death of patients with cancer, infectious hepatitis, and other diseases, in the face of depression or lack of motivation to recover, are also pertinent. In most of these situations, the mechanisms apparently involved remain obscure.

One last point remains to be discussed. Although many children with chronic illness or handicap respond with great benefit to the positive effects of recent drugs or surgery, a small group may show paradoxical responses. Such children may find difficulty in using new-found capacities suddenly, and may respond, temporarily at least, with psychological decompensation or may show a variety of symptomatic reactions. In such instances it appears that the tenuous balance of adaptive forces set up over a long period by child and family may be upset rather than helped by the sudden "precipitation into health" of the child. A child and family who have adapted to his role as an invalid may find it difficult quickly to readapt, especially if deep-seated emotional conflicts and an unhealthy family equilibrium have been present. In adults, psychoticlike pictures, usually transient, have been reported occasionally in such situations (Meyer, 1956). These are rarely seen in children, in my experience. A variety of conversion reactions and other symptoms may occur, however, calling for a gradual rehabilitative approach in the encouragement of the child's return to a healthy role within the family. A somewhat parallel response may be seen in older school-age children or adolesments who, like adults, may develop psychotic reactions to ACTH or cortisone during treatment for arthritis or other diseases. The direct effect of cortisone on the brain certainly seems to account for part of the effect (Rome and Braceland, 1952; Goolker and Schein, 1953). Problems in realignment of intrapsychic and interpersonal balance may also be involved (Quarton et al., 1955; Fox and Gifford, 1953), as well as premorbid personality problems.

IMPLICATIONS FOR TREATMENT, PREVENTION, AND RESEARCH

The focus of this presentation has been upon a conceptual framework underlying the psychosomatic approach to the understanding of states of health and disease in childhood. Implications for diagnosis and treatment by pediatricians, alone or in collaboration with child psychiatrists, have perforce been mentioned at only a few points. Fuller discussion may be found in many of the foregoing references or in discussions focused on technical adaptations of the approach to infants (Lourie, 1955), children (Rose, 1960; Mittelmann, 1949), parents of chronically ill or handicapped children (Milliken, 1943; Korsch et al., 1954; Richmond, 1954), and adults (Richmond, 1958, unpublished; Engel, 1952; Margolin, 1957). One of the most fundamental discussions is offered in Milton Senn's paper on "The Psychotherapeutic Role of the Pediatrician" (1948a). The principles involved in the therapeutic use of the physician's relationship with the child and parents, as set forth by him, appear to underlie all other steps, including hospitalization, the use of drugs, and other measures. In addition, the modern pediatrician's comprehensive approach to management of the ill child in the family requires him to act as a coordinator and integrator of the diagnostic, therapeutic, rehabilitative, and educational skills of many medical subspecialties and a host of other highly trained professional persons newly available to child and family in hospital and community.

Of most vital significance for the future is the preventive approach applied to psychological as well as physical aspects of development and behavior. Only brief mention of this field of endeavor has been possible. The extent of our still limited knowledge regarding preventive psychological considerations is well summarized elsewhere (Caplan, 1961; Richmond, 1952; Stuart and Prugh, 1960). Although large segments of this field require considerable illumination, based on systematic investigation yet to be done, the pediatrician's potential contribution to the prevention of unhealthy psychological reactions by child and family to illness and hospitalization seems straightforward and vital (Senn, 1946; Prugh, 1959).

In the area of research, many large gaps in our knowledge remain to be filled, as has been indicated at various points in the foregoing discussion. The need for longitudinal investigations of modest but well-designed nature has been emphasized in regard to the collection of normative data dealing with various parameters of personality development. Follow-up research is urgently necessary in many areas, in order to increase our understanding of the natural history of disease states and their psychological and social components. The importance of anterospective methods, with the help of biological "tags," in psychophysiological investigation appears to be growing, as are the opportunities for rigorous and well-controlled studies, difficult as these may be to erect. As pediatricians and their collaborators acquire increasing competence in psychophysiological investigation, but newly established as a proper field of pediatric endeavor, new ideas and new knowledge will add immeasurably to the effectiveness of treatment, the lodestone of today, and prevention, the talisman of tomorrow.

BIBLIOGRAPHY

Ackerman, N. (1958), *The Psychodynamics of Family Life*. New York: Basic Books.
Ader, R. (1959), The Effects of Early Experience on Subsequent Emotionality and Resistance to Stress. *Psychol. Monog. No. 472*. Washington: American Psychological Association.
───── Beels, C. C. & Tatum, R. (1960), Blood Pepsinogen and Gastric Erosions in the Rat. *Psychosom. Med.*, 22:1.
Adler, A. (1927), *Practice and Theory of Individual Psychology*. New York: Harcourt.
Adsett, C. A., Schottstaedt, W. W., & Wolf, S. G. (1962), Changes in Coronary Blood Flow and Other Hemodynamic Indicators Induced by Stressful Interviews. *Psychosom. Med.*, 24:331.
Ainsworth, M. C. (1962), The Effects of Maternal Deprivation: A Review of Findings and Controversy in the Context of Research Strategy. In *Deprivation of Maternal Care. A Reassessment of its Effects*. Geneva: World Health Organization.
───── & Bowlby, J. (1954), Research Strategy in the Study of Mother-Child Separation. *Courrier Centre International de L'Enfance*, 4:2.
Aldrich, C. A. (1945), The Relation of Pediatric Preventive Medicine to Mental Hygiene. *Psychosom. Med.*, 7:368.
Alexander, F. (1950), *Psychosomatic Medicine: Its Principles and Applications*. New York: Norton.

Allen, F. H., & Pearson, G. H. J. (1928), Emotional Problems of the Physically Handicapped Child. *Brit. J. Med. Psychol.*, 8:212.

Alpert, A., Neubauer, P. B., & Weil, A. (1956), Unusual Variations in Drive Endowment. In *The Psychoanalytic Study of the Child, 11:125.* New York: Int. Univ. Press.

Anthony, E. J. (1957), An Experimental Approach to the Psychopathology of Childhood: Encopresis. *Brit. J. Med. Psychol.*, 33:146.

—— (1959), An Experimental Approach to the Psychopathology of Sleep Disturbances. *Brit. J. Med. Psychol.*, 32:19

Appelzweig, M. H. (1957), *Psychological Stress and Related Concepts: A Bibliography.* New London, Conn.: Connecticut College Press.

Arlow, J. A. (1952), Anxiety Patterns in Angina Pectoris. *Psychosom Med.*, 14:461.

Bakke, J. L., & Wolff, H. G. (1950), Life Situations and Serum Antibody Titers. In *Life Stress and Bodily Disease,* ed. H. G. Wolff, S. G. Wolf, & C. C. Hare. Baltimore: Williams & Wilkins.

Bakwin, H. (1949a.), Emotional Deprivation in Infants. *J. Pediat.,* 35:512.

—— (1949b), Cerebral Damage and Behavior Disorders in Children. *J. Pediat.,* 34:371.

—— (1951), The Hospital Care of Infants and Children. *J. Pediat.,* 39:383.

—— (1957), Suicide in Children and Adolescents. *J. Pediat.,* 50:749.

—— (1959), Obesity in Children. *Pediatrics,* 54:392.

—— (1961), Enuresis in Children. *J. Pediat.,* 58:806.

—— & Bakwin, R. M. (1953), *Clinical Management of Behavior Disorders in Children.* Philadelphia: Saunders.

Bakwin, R. M. (1950), The Deaf Child. *J. Pediat.,* 36:668.

Balser, B. H., & Masterson, J. E. (1959), Suicide in Adolescents. *Amer. J. Psychiat.,* 116:400.

Barbero, G. J. (1960), Cyclic Vomiting. *Pediatrics,* 25:740.

Barchilon, J. & Engel, G. L. (1952), Dermatitis: An Hysterical Conversion Symptom in a Young Woman: Psychosomatic Conference. *Psychosom Med.,* 14:295.

Barker, R. G., Wright, B., & Gonick, M. (1953), *Adjustment to Physical Handicap and Illness: A Survey of the Social Psychology of Physique and Disability.* New York: Social Science Research Council.

Barker, W. (1948), Studies on Epilepsy: The Petit Mal Attack as a Response Within the Central Nervous System to Distress in Organism-Environment Integration. *Psychosom. Med.,* 10:73.

—— & Barker, S. (1950), Experimental Production of Human Convulsive Brain Potentials by Stress-Induced Effects upon Neural Integration Function: Dynamics of the Convulsive Reaction to Stress. In *Life Stress and Bodily Disease,* ed. H. G. Wolff, S. G. Wolf, & C. C. Hare. Baltimore: Williams & Wilkins.

Bayer, L. M. (1947), Pseudo-Hermaphrodism: A Psychosomatic Case Study. *Psychosom. Med,* 9:246.

Bayley, N. (1958), Value and Limitations of Infant Testing. *Children,* 5:129.

Bechtol, C. O. (1955), The Juvenile Amputee. *Pediat. Clin. No. Amer.,* 2:1121.

Bellak, L. (1952), *Psychology of Physical Illness: Psychiatry Applied to Medicine, Surgery, and the Specialties.* New York: Grune & Stratton.

Benda, C. E. (1952), *Developmental Disorders of Mentation and the Cerebral Palsies.* New York: Grune & Stratton.

—— & Farrell, M. J. (1955), Psychopathology of Mental Deficiency in Children. In *Psychopathology of Childhood,* ed. P. H. Hoch & J. Zubin. New York: Grune & Stratton.

Bender, L. (1934), Psychoses Associated with Somatic Diseases that Distort the Body Structure. *Arch. Neurol & Psychiat.*, 32:1000.

—— (1956), *Psychopathology of Children with Organic Brain Disorders.* Springfield, Ill.: Thomas.

—— & Cottington, F. (1942), The Use of Amphetamine Sulfate (Benzedrine) in Child Psychiatry. *Amer. J. Psychiat.*, 99:116.

—— & Schilder, P. (1937), Suicidal Preoccupations and Attempts in Children. *Amer. J. Orthopsychiat.*, 7:225.

—— & Silver, A. (1948), Body Image Problems of the Brain Damaged Child. *J. Social Issues*, 4:84.

—— & Yarnell, H. (1941), An Observation Nursery. *Amer. J. Psychiat.*, 97:1158.

Benedek, T. (1949), The Psychosomatic Implications of the Primary Unit: Mother-Child. *Amer. J. Orthopsychiat.* 19:642.

—— Ham, G. C., Robbins, F. P., & Rubenstein, B. B. (1953), Some Emotional Factors in Infertility. *Psychosom. Med.*, 15:485.

—— & Rubenstein, B. B. (1942), The Sexual Cycle in Women. *Psychosom. Med. Monog.* 142. Washington: National Research Council.

Berblinger, K. W., & Greenhill, M. H. (1954), Levels of Communication in Ulcerative Colitis: A Case Study. *Psychosom. Med.*, 16:156.

Bergman, P., & Escalona, S. (1949), Unusual Sensitivities in Very Young Children. In *The Psychoanalytic Study of the Child*, 3/4:333. New York: Int. Univ. Press.

Bergmann, T. (1945), Observation of Children's Reactions to Motor Restraint. *Nerv. Child*, 4:318.

Berlin, I. (1954), Some Reasons for Failures in Referral for Psychiatric Care of Patients with Psychosomatic Illnesses. *Ann. Intern. Med.*, 40:1165.

—— Boatman, M. J., Sheimo, S. L., & Szurek, S. A. (1951), Adolescent Alternation of Anorexia and Obesity. Workshop. *Amer. J. Orthopsychiat.*, 21:387.

—— & Yaeger, C. L. (1951), Correlation of Epileptic Seizures, Electroencephalograms and Emotional State. *Amer. J. Dis. Child.*, 81:664.

Bernard, C. (1865), *An Introduction to the Study of Experimental Medicine.* New York: Macmillan, 1927.

Best, C. H., & Taylor, N. B. (1961), *The Physiological Basis of Medical Practice: A Text in Applied Physiology.* Baltimore: Williams and Wilkins.

Beverley, B. L. (1936), Effects of Illness on Emotional Development. *J. Pediat.*, 8:533.

Bibring, G. L. (1949), The Child First. In *Long-Term Care of Children.* Washington, D.C.: Children's Bureau.

Bickers, W., & Woods, M. (1951), Premenstrual Tension. *New Eng. J. Med.*, 245:453.

Blank, H., & Brody, M. W. (1950), Recurrent Herpes Simplex: A Psychiatric and Laboratory Study. *Psychosom. Med.*, 12:254.

Blanton, S. M. D., & Kirk, V. M. S. (1947), A Psychiatric Study of Sixty-One Appendectomy Cases. *Ann. Surg.*, 126:305.

Blom, G. E. (1951), A Review of Electrocardiographic Changes in Emotional States. *J. Nerv. Ment. Dis.*, 113:283.

—— (1958), The Reactions of Hospitalized Children to Illness. *Pediatrics*, 22:590.

—— & Nicholls, G. (1954), Emotional Factors in Children with Rheumatoid Arthritis. *Amer. J. Orthopsychiat.*, 24:588.

Bogdonoff, M. D., Bogdonoff, M. M., & Wolf, S. G. (1961), Studies on Salivary Function in Man: Variations in Secretory Rate as Part of the Individual's Adaptive Pattern. *J. Psychosom. Res.*, 5:170.

Bond, E. D., & Appel, K. F. (1931), Treatment of Behavior Disorders Following Encephalitis, An Experiment in Re-Education. New York: Commonwealth Fund.

Booth, G. (1948), Psychodynamics in Parkinsonism. *Psychosom. Med.,* 10:1.

Bostwick, J., & Shackleton, M. G. (1951), Enuresis and Toilet Training. *Australian Med. J.,* 2:110.

Bowlby, J. (1951), *Maternal Care and Mental Health.* Geneva: World Health Organization.

—— (1958), The Nature of the Child's Tie to his Mother. *Int. J. Psycho-anal.* 39:350.

Bozeman, M. F., Orback, C. E., & Sutherland, A. M. (1955), Psychological Impact of Cancer and its Treatment. III. The Adaptation of Mothers to the Threatened Loss of Their Children Through Leukemia. *Cancer,* 8:1.

Bradley, C. (1950), Benzedrine[R] and Dexedrine[R] in the Treatment of Children's Behavior Disorders. *Pediatrics,* 5:24.

—— (1957), Characteristics and Management of Children with Behavior Problems Associated with Organic Brain Damage. *Ped. Clin. No. Amer.,* 4:1049.

Brazelton, T. B. (1953), The Pediatrician and Hysteria in Childhood. *Nerv. Child,* 10:306.

—— (1961), Psychophysiologic Reactions in the Neonate. I. The Value of Observation of the Neonate. *J. Pediat.,* 58:508.

—— Holder, R., & Talbot, B. (1953), Emotional Aspects of Rheumatic Fever in Children. *J. Pediat.,* 43:339.

Bridge, E. M. (1949), *Epilepsy and Convulsive Disorders in Children.* New York: McGraw-Hill.

—— Livingston, S., & Tietze, C. (1943), Breathholding Spells: Their Relationship to Syncope, Convulsions, and Other Phenomena. *J. Pediat.,* 23:539.

Bridger, W. H., & Reiser, M. F. (1959), Psychophysiologic Studies of the Neonate. An Approach Toward the Methodological and Theoretical Problems Involved. *Psychosom. Med.,* 21:265.

Brim, O. G. (1955), Feeding Problems Among Families Attending Child Health Stations. In *Sourcebook in Marriage and Family,* ed. M. B. Sussman. New York: Houghton Mifflin.

Brodman, K., Mittelmann, B., Wechsler, D., Weider, A., & Wolff, H. G. (1947), The Relation of Personality Disturbance to Duration of Convalescence from Acute Respiratory Infections. *Psychosom. Med.,* 9:37.

Brolley, M., & Hollender, M. H. (1955), Psychological Problem of Patients with Nyasthenia Gravis. *J. Nerv. Ment. Dis.,* 122:178.

Brown, F. A. (1958), A Clinical Psychologist's Perspective on Research in Psychosomatic Medicine. *Psychosom. Med.* 20:174.

Browne, W. J., Mally, M. O., & Kane, R. P. (1960), Psychosocial Aspects of Hemophilia: A Study of Twenty-Eight Hemophiliac Children and Their Families. *Amer. J. Orthopsychiat.,* 30:730.

Bruch, H. (1945), Psychosomatic Approach to Childhood Disorders. In *Modern Trends in Child Psychiatry,* ed. D. C. N. Lewis & B. L. Pacella. New York: Int. Univ. Press.

—— (1949), Physiologic and Psychologic Interrelationships in Diabetes in Children. *Psychosom. Med.,* 11:200.

—— (1957), *The Importance of Overweight.* New York: Norton.

—— & McCune, D. J. (1944), Progress in Pediatrics. Mental Development of Congenitally Hypothyroid Children: Its Relationship to Physical Development and Adequacy of Treatment. *Amer. J. Dis. Child.,* 67:205.

Buck, C., & Hobbs, G. E. (1959), The Problem of Specificity in Psychosomatic Illness. *J. Psychosom. Res.,* 3:227.

Call, J. D. (1959), Emotional Factors Favoring Successful Breast Feeding of Infants. *J. Pediat.*, 55:485.

Campagne, W. V. L. (1959), *Ein Enquete Bij Coeliakpatienten.* Leiden: Luctor et Emergo.

Cannon, W. B. (1929), *Bodily Changes in Pain, Hunger, Fear, and Rage. An Account of Recent Researches into the Function of Emotional Excitement.* New York: D. Appleton.

—— (1932), *The Wisdom of the Body.* New York: Norton.

Caplan, G., ed. (1961), *Prevention of Mental Disorders in Children.* New York: Basic Books.

Carpentieri, J., & Jensen, R. A. (1949), Psychosomatic Medicine and Pediatrics. *Quart. J. Child Behav.*, 1:72.

Chambers, W. N., & Reiser, M. F. (1953), Emotional Stress in the Precipitation of Congestive Heart Failure. *Psychosom. Med.*, 15:38.

Chapin, H. D. (1908), A Plan of Dealing with Atrophic Infants and Children. *Arch. Pediat.*, 25:491.

Chapman, A. H., Loeb, D. G., & Young, J. B. (1956), A Psychosomatic Study of Five Children with Duodenal Ulcer. *J. Pediat.*, 48:248.

—— Pilkey, L., & Gibbons, M. J. (1958), A Psychosomatic Study of Eight Children with Sydenham's Chorea. *Pediatrics*, 21:582.

Chapman, L. F., Goodell, H., & Wolff, H. G. (1957), Changes in Tissue Vulnerability Induced by Hypnotic Suggestion. *Fed. Proc.*, 16:1.

Chazan, M., Harris, T., O'Neill, D., & Campbell, M. (1951), The Intellectual and Emotional Development of Children with Congenital Heart Disease. *Guy's Hosp. Rep.*, 100:331.

Chess, S. (1959), *An Introduction to Child Psychiatry.* New York: Grune & Stratton.

—— Thomas, A., & Birch, H. (1959), Characteristics of the Individual Child's Behavioral Response to the Environment. *Amer. J. Orthopsychiat.*, 29:791.

Childers, A. T. (1935), Hyper-Activity in Children Having Behavior Disorders. *Amer. J. Orthopsychiat.*, 5:227.

Chodoff, P., & Lyons, H. (1958), Hysteria, the Hysterical Personality and "Hysterical" Conversion. *Amer. J. Psychiat.*, 114:734.

Clayton, G. W., & Hughes, J. G. (1952), Variations in Blood Pressure in Hospitalized Children. *J. Pediat.*, 40:462.

Cleghorn, R. A. (1957), The Interplay Between Endocrine and Psychological Dysfunction. In *Recent Developments in Psychosomatic Medicine*, ed. E. D. Wittkower & R. A. Cleghorn. Philadelphia: J. B. Lippincott.

—— & Curtis, G. C. (1959), Psychosomatic Accompaniments of Latent and Manifest Depressive Affect. *Canad. Psychiat. Assn. J.*, 4:13.

Cleveland, S. E., & Fisher, S. (1956), Psychological Factors in Neurodermatoses. *Psychosom. Med.*, 18:209.

Cobb, B. (1952), Psychological Impact of Long Illness and Death of Child on Family Circle. *J. Pediat.*, 49:746.

Cobb, S. (1950), *Emotions and Clinical Medicine. With an Introduction on Semantics and Definitions.* New York: Norton.

—— & Lindemann, E. (1943), Neuropsychiatric Observations. *Ann. Surg.*, 117:814.

Cole, N. F., & Taboroff, L. H. (1955), The Psychological Problems of the Congenitally Blind Child, A Workshop. *Amer. J. Orthopsychiat.*, 25:627.

Coleman, D. (1949), Psychosomatic Aspects of Diseases of the Ear, Nose, and Throat. *Laryngoscope*, 59:709.

Coleman, R. W., & Provence, S. (1957), Environmental Retardation. *Pediatrics*, 19:285.

Coolidge, J. C. (1956), Asthma in Mother and Child as a Special Type of Intercommunication. *Amer. J. Orthopsychiat.*, 26:165.

Cooper, M. (1957), *Pica*. Springfield, Ill.: Thomas.

Coppen, A. J., & Mezey, A. G. (1960), Metabolic Effect of Venipuncture in Man. *J. Psychosom. Res.*, 5:56.

Corwin, E. H. L., ed. (1949), *Ecology of Health*. New York: Commonwealth Fund.

Cramer, J. B. (1959), Common Neuroses of Childhood. In *American Handbook of Psychiatry*, ed. S. Arieti. New York: Basic Books.

Creak, M., & Stephen, J. M. (1958), The Psychological Aspects of Asthma in Children. In *Symposium on Behavior Disorders*. Philadelphia: Saunders.

Crockett, R. W. (1952), Psychiatric Findings in Crohn's Disease. *Lancet*, 1:946.

Cross, B. (1955), Neurohormonal Mechanisms in Emotional Inhibition of Milk Ejection. *J. Endocrinol.*, 12:29.

Crothers, B., & Meyer, E. (1946), The Psychologic and Psychiatric Implications of Poliomyelitis. *J. Pediat.*, 28:324.

—— & Paine, R. S. (1959), *The Natural History of Cerebral Palsy*. Cambridge: Harvard Univ. Press.

Darwin, C. (1872), *Expression of the Emotions in Man and Animals*. New York: D. Appleton: 1896.

Davidson, M. (1958), Constipation and Fecal Incontinence. In *Symposium on Behavior Disorders*. Philadelphia: Saunders.

Dekker, E., Pelser, H. E., & Groen, J. (1957), Conditioning as a Cause of Asthmatic Attacks. *J. Psychosom. Res.*, 2:97.

Despert, J. L. (1944), Emotional Factors in Some Young Children's Colds. *Med. Clin. No. Amer.*, 28:603.

Deutsch, F. (1939), The Choice of Organ in Organ Neurosis. *Int. J. Psycho-anal.*, 20:252.

—— ed. (1953), *The Psychosomatic Concept in Psychoanalysis*. New York: Int. Univ. Press.

Deutsch, H. (1942), Some Psychoanalytic Observations in Surgery. *Psychosom. Med.*, 4:105.

DiMascio, A., Boyd, R. W., & Greenblatt, M. (1957), Physiological Correlates of Tension and Antagonism During Psychotherapy: A Study of "Interpersonal Physiology." *Psychosom. Med.*, 19:99.

Dimock, H. G. (1960), *The Child in Hospital: A Study of His Emotional and Social Well-Being*. Philadelphia: F. A. Davis.

Doll, E. A. (1951), Mental Evaluation of Children with Expressive Handicaps. *Amer. J. Orthopsychiat.*, 21:148.

Doniger, M., Wittkower, E. D., Stephens-Newsham, L., & Hoffman, M. M. (1956), Psychophysiologic Studies in Thyroid Function. *Psychosom. Med.*, 18:310.

Dreyfuss, F. (1956), Coagulation Time of the Blood, Level of Blood Eosinophils and Thrombocytes Under Emotional Stress. *J. Psychosom. Res.*, 1:252.

Dubo, S. (1950), Psychiatric Study of Children with Pulmonary Tuberculosis. *Amer. J. Orthopsychiat.*, 20:520.

—— & McLean, J. A., Ching, A. Y. T., Wright, H. L., Kauffman, P. E., & Sheldon, J. M. (1961), A Study of Relationships Between Family Situation, Bronchial Asthma, and Personal Adjustment in Children. *J. Pediat.*, 59:402.

Dunbar, H. F. (1946), *Emotions and Bodily Changes*. New York: Columbia Univ. Press.

Duncan, C. H., Stevenson, I., & Ripley, H. (1950), Life Situations, Emotions, and Paroxysmal Auricular Arrhythmias. *Psychosom. Med.*, 12:23.

—— Stevenson, I., & Wolff, H. G. (1951), Life Situations, Emotions, and Exercise Tolerance. *Psychosom. Med.*, 13:36.

Dykman, R. A., & Gantt, W. H. (1958), Autonomic Conditioning in Dogs and Humans. In *Physiological Bases of Psychiatry*, ed. W. H. Gantt. Springfield, Ill.: Thomas.

Eisenberg, L. (1957), The Psychiatric Implications of Brain Damage in Children. *Psychiat. Quart.*, 31:72.

—— (1958a), Emotional Determinants of Mental Deficiency. *Arch. Neurol. Psychiat.*, 80:114.

—— (1958b.), School Phobia: Diagnosis, Genesis, and Clinical Management. In *Symposium on Behavior Disorders*. Philadelphia: W. B. Saunders.

—— (1959), Office Evaluation of Specific Reading Disability in Children. *Pediatrics*, 23:997.

Engel, F. L. (1953), General Concepts of Adrenocortical Function in Relation to the Response to Stress. *Psychosom. Med.*, 15:565.

Engel, G. L. (1948), *Mechanisms of Fainting*. Springfield, Ill.: Thomas.

—— (1952), Psychologic Aspects of the Management of Patients with Ulcerative Colitis. *N. Y. State J. Med.*, 52:2255.

—— (1953), Homeostasis, Behavioral Adjustment, and the Concept of Health and Disease. In *Mid-Century Psychiatry: An Overview*, ed. R. R. Grinker. Springfield, Ill.: Thomas.

—— (1954a), Selection of Clinical Material in Psychosomatic Medicine: The Need for a New Physiology. *Psychosom. Med.*, 16:368.

—— (1954b), Studies of Ulcerative Colitis: I. Clinical Data Bearing on the Nature of the Somatic Process. *Psychosom. Med.*, 16:496.

—— (1954c), Studies of Ulcerative Colitis: II. The Nature of the Somatic Processes and the Adequacy of Psychosomatic Hypotheses. *Amer. J. Med.*, 16:416.

—— (1956) Studies of Ulcerative Colitis: IV: The Significance of Headaches. *Psychosom. Med.*, 18:334.

—— (1959), "Psychogenic" Pain and the Pain-Prone Patient. *Amer. J. Med.*, 26:899.

—— (1960), A Unified Concept of Health and Disease. *Persp. in Biol. & Med.*, 3:459.

—— (1961), Is Grief a Disease? A Challenge for Medical Research. *Psychosom. Med.*, 23:18.

—— (1962), *Psychological Development in Health and Disease*. Philadelphia: W. B. Saunders.

—— Hamburger, W. W., Reiser, M., & Plunkett, J. (1953), Electroencephalographic and Psychological Studies of Case of Migraine with Severe Pre-Headache Phenomena; with Comments on Cerebral Vasospasm and Focal Hypertensive Encephalopathy. *Psychosom. Med.*, 15:337.

—— Logan, M., & Ferris, E. B. (1947), Hyperventilation: Analysis of Clinical Symptomatology. *Ann. Int. Med.*, 27:683.

—— Reichsman, F., & Segal, H. L. (1956), A Study of an Infant with a Gastric Fistula: I. Behavior and Rate of Total Hydrochloric Acid Secretion. *Psychosom. Med.*, 18:374.

—— & Romano, J. (1944), Delirium. II. Reversibility of Electroencephalogram: Experimental Procedures. *Arch. Neurol. Psychiat.*, 51:378.

—— —— (1947), Studies of Syncope: IV. Biologic Interpretation of Vasodepressor Syncope. *Psychosom. Med.*, 9:288.

Erikson, E. (1950), Growth and Crises of the Healthy Personality. In *Symposium on the Healthy Personality*, Supplement II. New York: Josiah Macy, Jr. Foundation.

Fabian, A. A. & Bender, L. (1947), Head Injury in Children: Predisposing Factors. *Amer. J. Orthopsychiat.*, 17:68.

Falstein, E. I., Feinstein, S. C., & Judas, I. (1956), Anorexia Nervosa in the Male Child. *Amer. J. Orthopsychiat.*, 26:751.

———— & Judas, I. (1955), Juvenile Diabetes and Its Psychiatric Implications. *Amer. J. Orthopsychiat.*, 25:330.

———— & Rosenblum, A. H. (1962), Juvenile Paroxysmal Supraventricular Tachycardia: Psychosomatic and Psychodynamic Aspects. *J. Amer. Acad. Child Psychiat.*, 1:246.

Farris, E. J. (1938), Increase in Lymphocytes in Healthy Persons Under Certain Emotional States. *Amer. J. Anat.*, 63:297.

Faulkner, W. B. (1941), Bronchoscopic Observations of Changes due to Psychic Factors. *Pacific Coast Med.*, 8:22.

Faust, O. (1952), *Reducing Emotional Trauma in Hospitalized Children: A Study in Psychosomatic Pediatraics.* Albany, N. Y.: Albany Medical College.

Fenichel, O. (1945), *The Psychoanalytic Theory of Neurosis.* New York: Norton.

Finch, S. M. (1952), Psychosomatic Problems in Children. *Nerv. Child*, 9:261.

———— (1960), *Fundamentals of Child Psychiatry.* New York: Norton.

———— & Hess, J. H. (1962), Ulcerative Colitis in Children. *Amer. J. Psychiat.*, 118:819.

Fineman, A. (1959), Preliminary Observations on Ego Development in Children with Congenital Defects of the Genito-urinary System. *Amer. J. Orthopsychiat.*, 29:110.

Finesinger, J. E. & Mazick, S. G. (1940), The Effect of a Painful Stimulus and Its Recall upon Respiration in Psychoneurotic Patients. *Psychosom. Med.*, 2:333.

Fischer, A. E. & Dolger, H. (1946), Behavior and Psychologic Problems of Young Diabetic Patients: A 10-20 Year Survey. *Arch. Int. Med.*, 78:711.

Fisher, S. & Mendell, D. (1960), The Communication of Neurotic Patterns Over Two and Three Generations. In *The Family,* ed. N. W. Bell & E. F. Vogel. Glencoe, Ill.: Free Press.

Fitzelle, G. T. (1959), Personality Factors and Certain Attitudes Toward Child-Bearing Among Parents of Asthmatic Children. *Psychosom. Med.*, 21:208.

Ford, F. R. (1952), *Diseases of the Nervous System in Infancy and Childhood and Adolescence.* Springfield, Ill.: Thomas.

Fowler, E. P. & Zeckel, A. (1952), Psychosomatic Aspects of Meniere's Disease. *J. Amer. Med. Assn.*, 148:1265.

Fox, H. M. & Gifford, S. (1953), Psychological Responses to ACTH and Cortisone: A Preliminary Theoretical Formulation. *Psychosom. Med.*, 15:614.

———— Rizzo, N. D., & Gifford, S. (1954), Psychological Observations of Patients Undergoing Mitral Surgery: A Study of Stress. *Psychosom. Med.*, 16:186.

Freedman, A. M., Helme, W., Havel, J., Eustis, M., Riley, C., & Langford, W. S. (1960), Family Adjustment to the Brain-Damaged Child. In *A Modern Introduction to the Family,* ed. N. W. Bell & E. F. Vogel. Glencoe, Ill.: Free Press.

Fried, P., Rakoff, A. E., Schopbach, R. R., & Kaplan, A. J. (1951), Pseudocyesis: A Psychosomatic Study in Gynecology. *J. Amer. Med. Assn.*, 145:1329.

Fried, R. I. (1950), Socio-emotional Factors Accounting for Growth Failure in Children as Measured by the Wetzel Grid. In *Life Stress and Bodily Disease,* ed. H. G. Wolff, S. G. Wolf, & C. C. Hare. Baltimore: Williams & Wilkins.

Friedman, S. B., Shodoff, P., Mason, J. W., & Hamburg, D. A., Behavioral Observations in Parents Anticipating the Death of a Child. (unpublished material.)

Fries, M. E. & Woolf, P. (1953), Some Hypotheses on the Role of the Congenital Activity Type in Personality Development. In *The Psychoanalytic Study of the Child,* 8:48. New York: Int. Univ. Press.

Freud, A. (1952), The Role of Bodily Illness in the Mental Life of Children. In *The Psychoanalytic Study of the Child,* 7:42. New York: Int. Univ. Press.

———— & Burlingham, D. (1944), *Infants Without Families: The Case for and Against Residential Nurseries.* New York: Int. Univ. Press.

Freud, S. (1917), Mourning and Melancholia. *Collected Papers*, 4:152. London: Hogarth Press, 1925.

———— (1940), *An Outline of Psychoanalysis.* New York: Norton, 1949.

Gaddini, R. D. & Gaddini, E. (1959), Rumination in Infancy. In *Dynamic Psychopathology in Childhood,* ed. L. Jessner & E. Pavenstedt. New York: Grune & Stratton.

GAP Report (1959), *Basic Considerations in Mental Retardation: A Preliminary Report.* New York: Group for the Advancement of Psychiatry.

Garner, A. M. & Wenar, C. (1959), *The Mother-Child Interaction in Psychosomatic Disorders.* Urbana, Ill.: Univ. Ill. Press.

Garrard, S. D. & Richmond, J. B. (1952), Psychogenic Megacolon Manifested by Fecal Soiling. *Pediatrics,* 10:474.

———— ———— (1957), Psychologic Aspects of the Management of Children with Defects or Damage of the Central Nervous System. *Pediat. Clin. No. Amer.,* 4:1033.

Gastaut, H., Jus, A., Morrell, C., Storm, F., Van Leeuwen, W., Dougier, S., Naquet, R., Regis, H., Roger, A., Bekkering, D., Kamp, A., & Werre, J. (1957), Etude Topographique des Reactions Electroencephalographiques Conditionnees chez l'homme. *Electroencephalog anc Clin. Neurophysiol.,* 9:1.

Gates, M. F. (1946), A Comparative Study of Some Problems of Social and Emotional Adjustment of Crippled and Non-Crippled Girls and Boys. *J. Genet. Psychol.,* 68:219.

Gates, P. & Weinberger, J. J. (1955), The Concept of the Damaged Body in Psychosomatic Complaints of the Genito-Urinary Tract. *Psychoanal. Rev.,* 42:17.

Gellhorn, E. (1943), Autonomic Regulations: Their Significance for Physiology, Psychology, and Neuropsychiatry. New York: Interscience Publ.

Gerard, M. W. (1939), Enuresis: A Study in Etiology. *Amer. J. Orthopsychiat.,* 9:48.

———— (1946), Bronchial Asthma in Children. *Nerv. Child,* 5:327.

———— (1953), Genesis of Psychosomatic Symptoms in Infancy. The Influence of Infantile Traumata upon Symptom Choice. In *Psychosomatic Concept in Psychoanalysis,* ed. F. Deutsch. New York: Int. Univ. Press.

Gerbner, M. & Altman, H. (1959), On the Mechanism of the Diuretic Conditioned Reflex. *J. Psychosom. Res.,* 3:242.

Gildea, E. F. (1949), Special Features of Personality Which are Common to Certain Psychosomatic Disorders. *Psychosom. Med.,* 11:273.

Glaser, K. & Eisenberg, L. (1956), Maternal Deprivation. *Pediatrics,* 18:626.

Goldfarb, W. (1943), The Effects of Early Institutional Care on Adolescent Personality. *J. Exper. Educ.* 12:106.

Goldgraber, M. B., Kirsner, J. B., & Palmer, L. L. (1960), The Histopathology of Chronic Ulcerative Colitis and Its Pathogenic Implications. *Gastroenterology,* 38:596.

Goldman, H. B. & Crain I. (1957), Psychologic Aspects of Tonsillectomy. *N. Y. State J. Med.,* 57:232.

Goldstein, K. (1954), The Brain Injured Child. In *Pediatric Problems in Clinical Practice,* ed. H. Michal-Smith. New York: Grune and Stratton.

Goodall, Mc.C. & Berman, M. (1960), Urinary Output of Adrenaline, Noradrenaline, and 3-Methoxy-4-Hydroxymandelic Acid Following Centrifugation and Anticipation of Centrifugation. *J. Clin. Invest.,* 39:1533.

Goodell, H., Graham, D. T., & Wolff, H. G. (1950), Changes in Body Heat Regulation Associated with Varying Life Situations and Emotional Stress. In *Life Stress and Bodily Disease,* ed. H. G. Wolff, S. G. Wolf, & C. C. Hare. Baltimore: Williams & Wilkins.

Goolker, P. & Schein, J. (1953), Psychic Effects of ACTH and Cortisone. *Psychosom. Med.,* 15:589.

Gottschalk, L. A. (1953), Effects of Intensive Psychotherapy on Epileptic Children. *Arch. Neurol. Psychiat.,* 70:361.

Grace, W. J. (1953), Life Stress and Regional Enteritis. *Gastroenterology*, 23:542.
—— & Doig, R. K. (1954), Studies of Absorption of Iron from the Gastro-Intestinal Tract. *Clin. Research*, 2:53.
—— Seton, P. H., Wolf, S., & Wolff, H. G. (1948), Changes in Lysozyme Formation in the Human Colon in Various Emotional States. *Bull. N. Y. Acad. Med.*, 24:390.
—— Wolf, S., & Wolff, H. G. (1951), *The Human Colon*. New York: Hoeber.
Graham, D. T. (1950), The Pathogenesis of Hives: Experimental Study of Life Situations, Emotions, and Cutaneous Vascular Reactions. In *Life Stress and Bodily Disease*, ed. H. G. Wolff, S. G. Wolf, & C. C. Hare. Baltimore: Williams & Wilkins.
—— (1954), The Relation of Psoriasis to Attitude and to Vascular Reactions of the Human Skin. *J. Invest. Dermatol.*, 22:379.
—— (1955), Cutaneous Vascular Reactions in Raynaud's Disease and in States of Hostility, Anxiety, and Depression. *Psychosom. Med.*, 17:200.
—— Lundy, R. M., Benjamin, L. S., Kabler, J. B., Lewis, W. C., Kunish, N. O., & Graham, F. K. (1962), Specific Attitudes in Initial Interviews with Patients Having Different "Psychosomatic" Diseases. *Psychosom. Med.*, 24:257.
Graham, F. K. & Berman, P. W. (1961), Current Status of Behavior Tests for Brain Damage in Infants and Preschool Children. *Amer. J. Orthopsychiat.*, 31:713.
—— Enhart, C. B., Thurston, D., & Craft, M. (1962), Development Three Years After Perinatal Anoxia and Other Potentionally Damaging Newborn Experiences. *Psychol. Monog.*, 76. Washington: American Psychological Association.
Grayson, M., Power, A., & Levi, J. (1952), Psychiatric Aspects of Rehabilitation. *Rehabil. Monogr.*, 2. New York: Institute of Physical Medicine and Rehabilitation.
Greaves, D., Green, P. E., & West, L. J. (1960), Psychodynamic and Psychophysiological Aspects of Pseudocyesis. *Psychosom. Med.*, 22:24.
Greenberg, S. D. (1955), Alopecia Areata: A Psychiatric Survey. *Arch Dermatol.*, 72:454.
Greene, W. A. (1956), Process in Psychosomatic Disorders. *Psychosom. Med.*, 28:150.
—— Young, L. E., & Swisher, S. N. (1956), Psychological Factors and Reticuloendothelial Disease. II. Observations on a Group of Women with Lymphomas and Leukemias. *Psychosom. Med.*, 18:284.
Grinker, R. R. (1939), Hypothalamic Functions in Psychosomatic Interrelations. *Psychosom. Med.*, 1:19.
—— (1953), *Psychosomatic Research*. New York: Norton.
—— ed. (1959), *Toward a Unitary Theory of Human Behavior*. New York: Basic Books.
—— & Robbins, F. P. (1954), *Psychosomatic Case Book*. New York: Blakiston.
Grossman, H. J. & Greenberg, N. H. (1957), Psychosomatic Differentiation in Infancy. I. Autonomic Activity in the Newborn. *Psychosom. Med.* 19:293.
Grundy, S. & Griffen, A. (1959), Effects of Periodic Mental Stress on Serum Cholesterol Levels. *Circulation*, 19:496.
Gurney, W. (1958), Parents of Children with Congenital Amputation. *Children*, 5:95.
Guze, S. B., Delong, W. B., Majerus, P. W., & Robins, E. (1959), Association of Clinical Psychiatric Disease with Hyperemesis Gravidarum: A $3\frac{1}{2}$ Year Follow-up Study of 48 Patients and 45 Controls. *New Eng. J. Med.*, 261:1363.
Haggard, E. A. (1957), Socialization, Personality, and Academic Achievement in Gifted Children. *School Review*. Chicago: Univ. Chicago Press.
Haggerty, R. & Meyer, R. (1961), Streptococcal Infection in Families. Abstract. *Amer. J. Dis. Child.*, 102:71.
Hallenbeck, J. (1954), Pseudo-retardation in Retrolental Fibroplasia. *New Outlook for the Blind*, 48:301.
Halliday, J. L. (1948), *Psychosocial Medicine: A Study of the Sick Society*. New York: Norton.

Ham, G. C. (1962), Psychosomatic Perspectives: The Cardiovascular System. *Psychosom. Med.*, 24:31.

—— Alexander, F., & Carmichael, H. T. (1951), A Psychosomatic Theory of Thyrotoxicosis. *Psychosom. Med.*, 13:18.

Hamburg, D., Hamburg, B., & DeGoza, S. (1953), Adaptive Problems and Mechanisms in the Severely Burned Patient. *Psychiatry*, 16:1.

Hamburger, W. W. (1958), The Occurrence and Meaning of Dreams of Food and Eating. I. Typical Food and Eating Dreams of Four People in Analysis. *Psychosom. Med.*, 20:1.

Harper, P. A., Fischer, L. K., & Rider, R. V. (1959), Neurological and Intellectual Status of Prematures at Three to Five Years of Age. *J. Pediat.*, 55:679.

Harris, H. J. (1944), Fungus Infection of Feet. A Case Report Illustrating a Psychosomatic Problem. *Psychosom. Med.*, 6:336.

—— (1950), *Brucellosis: Clinical and Subclinical*. New York: Hoeber.

Heald, F. (1960), Obesity in the Adolescent. In *Symposium on Adolescence*, ed. L. T. Meiks & M. Green. Philadelphia: Saunders.

Hebb, D. O. (1949), *The Organization of Behavior: A Neuropsychological Theory*. New York: Wiley.

Heiman, M. (1956), The Role of Stress Situations and Psychological Factors in Functional Uterine Bleeding. *J. Mount Sinai Hosp.*, 23:755.

Hendrick, I. (1947), *Facts and Theories of Psychoanalysis*. New York: Knopf.

Herring, F. H. (1956), Response During Anesthesia and Surgery: Effect of Psychological Factors. *Psychosom. Med.*, 18:243.

Hetzel, B. S., De La Naba, D. S., & Hinkle, L. (1952), *Rapid Changes in Plasma PBI in Euthyroid and Hyperthyroid Subjects*. Springfield, Ill.: Thomas.

Hickam, J. B., Cargill, W. H., & Golden, A. (1948), Cardiovascular Reactions to Emotional Stimuli, Effect on Cardiac Output, Arteriovenous Oxygen Difference, Arterial Pressure and Peripheral Resistance. *J. Clin. Invest.*, 29:754.

Hinkle, L. E., Conger, G., & Wolf, S. G. (1950), Studies in Diabetes Mellitus: The Relation of Stressful Life Situations to the Concentration of Ketone Bodies in the Blood of Diabetic and Non-Diabetic Humans. *J. Clin. Invest.* 29:754.

—— & Wolf, S. G. (1950), Studies in Diabetes Mellitus: Changes in Glucose, Ketone, and Water Metabolism during Stress. In *Life Stress and Bodily Disease*, ed. H. G. Wolff, S. G. Wolf, & C. C. Hare. Baltimore: Williams & Wilkins.

—— & Wolf, S. G. (1952), A Summary of Experimental Evidence Relating Life Stress to Diabetes Mellitus. *J. Mount Sinai Hosp.*, 19:537.

—— & Wolff, H. G. (1958), Ecologic Investigations of the Relationship Between Illness, Life Experience, and the Social Environment. *Ann. Int. Med.*, 49:1373.

Hoagland, H., Pincus, G., Elmadjian, F., Romanoff, L., Freeman, H., Hope, J., Ballan, J., Berkeley A. & Carlo J. (1953), Study of Adrenocortical Physiology in Normal and Schizophrenic Men. *Arch. Neurol. Psychiat.* 69:470.

Hollingshead, A. B., and Redlich, F. C. (1958), *Social Class and Mental Illness: A Community Study*. New York: Wiley.

Holmes, T. H., Hawkins, N. G., Bowerman, C. E., Clarke, E. R., Jr., & Joffe, J. R. (1957), Psychosocial and Psychophysiologic Studies of Tuberculosis. *Psychosom. Med.*, 19:134.

—— & Wolff, H. G. (1950), Life Situations, Emotions, and Backache. In *Life Stress and Bodily Disease*, ed. H. G. Wolff, S. G. Wolf, & C. C. Hare. Baltimore: Williams & Wilkins.

—— Wolff, H. G., Wolf, S. G., & Goodell, H. (1949), *The Nose: An Experimental Study of Reactions within the Nose in Human Subjects during Varying Life Experiences*. Springfield, Ill.: Thomas.

Huschka, M. (1942), The Child's Response to Coercive Bowel Training. *Psychosom. Med.*, 4:301.

Jackson, D. D. (1959), Family Interaction, Family Homeostasis, and Some Implications for the Conjoint Family Psychotherapy. In *Individual and Familial Dynamics*, ed. J. Masserman. New York: Grune & Stratton.

Jackson, E. B. (1942), Treatment of the Young Child in the Hospital. *Amer. J. Orthopsychiat.*, 12:56.

Jackson, K. (1951), Psychologic Preparation as a Method of Reducing Emotional Trauma of Anesthesia in Children. *Anesthesiology*, 12:293.

────── Winkley, R., Faust, O. A., Cermak. E. G., & Burtt, M. M. (1953), Behavior Changes Indicating Emotional Trauma in Tonsillectomized Children: Final Report. *Pediatrics*, 12:23.

Jensen, R. A. (1949), The Child, the Surgeon, the Operation. *Minnesota Med.*, 32:616.

────── (1956), Psychiatric Aspects of the Handicapped Child. *Minnesota Med.*, 39:541.

────── & Comly, H. H. (1948), Child-Parent Problems and the Hospital. *Nervous Child*, 7:200.

Jessner, L. (1959), Some Observations on Children Hospitalized During Latency. In *Dynamic Psychopathology in Childhood*, ed. L. Jessner & E. Pavenstedt. New York: Grune & Stratton.

────── Blom, G. E., & Waldfogel, S. (1952), Emotional Implications of Tonsillectomy and Adenoidectomy on Children. In *The Psychoanalytic Study of the Child*, 7:126. New York: Int. Univ. Press.

────── Lamont, J., Long, R., Rollins, N., Whipple, B., & Prentice, N. (1955), Emotional Impact of Nearness and Separation for the Asthmatic Child and His Mother. In *The Psychoanalytic Study of the Child*, 10:353. New York: Int. Univ. Press.

Johnson, A., Shapiro, L. B., & Alexander, F. (1947), Preliminary Report on a Psychosomatic Study of Rheumatoid Arthritis. *Psychosom. Med.*, 9:295.

Jores, A., & Freyburger, H., ed. (1961), *Advances in Psychosomatic Medicine: Symposium of the Fourth European Conference on Psychosomatic Research*. New York: Robert Brunner.

Josselyn, I., Simon, A., & Fells, E. (1955), Anxiety in Children Convalescing from Rheumatic Fever. *Amer. J. Orthopsychiat.*, 25:109.

Jost, H., & Sontag, L. W. (1944), The Genetic Factor in Autonomic Nervous System Function. *Psychosom. Med.*, 6:308.

Kanner, L. (1948), *Child Psychiatry*. Springfield, Ill.: Thomas.

Kaplan, H., & Reisch, M. (1952), Universal Alopecia: A Psychosomatic Appraisal. *N. Y. State J. Med.*, 52:1144.

Kaplan, S. M. (1956), Psychological Aspects of Cardiac Disease: A Study of Patients Experiencing Mitral Commissurotomy. *Psychosom. Med.*, 18:221.

────── Gottschalk, L. A., & Fleming, D. E. (1957), Modifications of Oropharyngeal Bacteria with Changes in the Psychodynamic State. *Arch. Neurol. Psychiat.*, 78:656.

Kasanin, J. (1929), Personality Changes in Children Following Cerebral Trauma. *J. Nerv. Ment. Dis.*, 69:385.

Katz, J., Friedman, A. P. & Gisolfi, A. (1950), Psychologic Factors of Migraine in Children, *N. Y. State J. Med.*, 50:2269.

Kaufman, I. (1962), Conversion Hysteria in Latency. *J. Amer. Acad. Child Psychiat.*, 1:385.

Kaufman, W. (1954), Some Psychosomatic Aspects of Food Allergy. *Psychosom. Med.*, 16:10.

Keith, H. M., & Gage, R. P. (1960), Neurological Lesions in Relation to Asphyxia of the Newborn and Factors of Pregnancy. Long-Term Follow-up. *Pediatrics*, 26:616.

Kempe, C. H., Silverman, F. N., Steele, B. F., Droegemueller, W., & Silver, H. K. (1962), The Battered-Child Syndrome. *J. Amer. Med. Assn.*, 181:17.

Kepecs, J. G., Robin, M., & Brunner, M. (1951), Relationship Between Certain Emotional States and Exudation into the Skin. *Psychosom. Med.*, 13:10.

Kluckhohn, F., & Spiegel, J. P. (1954), *Integration and Conflict in Family Behavior.* GAP Report No. 27. New York: Group for the Advancement of Psychiatry.

Knapp, P. H. (1953), The Ear, Listening, and Hearing. *J. Amer. Psychoanal. Assn.*, 1:672.

——— Nemetz, S. J., with Gilbert, R. R., Lowell, F. C., & Michelson, A. L. (1957), Personality Variations in Bronchial Asthma: A Study of Forty Patients: Notes on the Relationship of Psychosis and the Problem of Measuring Maturity. *Psychosom. Med.*, 19:443.

Knobloch, H. (1958), Influence of Prenatal and Paranatal Factors on Behavior. In *Ross Pediatric Research Conference: Physical and Behavioral Growth.* Columbus, Ohio: Ross Laboratories.

——— & Pasamanick, B. (1959), Syndrome of Minimal Cerebral Damage in Infancy. *J. Amer. Med. Assn.*, 170:1384.

Kolb, L. C. (1954), *The Painful Phantom: Psychology, Physiology, and Treatment.* Springfield, Ill.: Thomas.

Koret, S., The Effect of Amphetamine Sulfate upon the Behavior and School Performance of Hyperactive Children. Unpublished doctoral dissertation, Boston University.

Korsch, B. (1958), Psychologic Principles in Pediatric Practice: The Pediatrician and the Sick Child. In *Advances in Pediatrics*, ed. S. Z. Levine. Chicago: Yearbook Publ.

——— & Barnett, H. L. (1961), The Physician, the Family, and the Child with Nephrosis. *J. Pediat.*, 58:707.

——— Fraad, L. M., & Barnett, H. L. (1954), Pediatric Discussions with Parent Groups. *Pediatrics*, 44:703.

Kroger, W. & Freed, S. (1951), *Psychosomatic Obstetrics, Gynecology, and Endocrinology.* Philadelphia: Saunders.

Kubie, L. S. (1945), Motivation and Rehabilitation. *Psychiatry*, 8:69.

——— (1957a), The Problem of Specificity in the Psychosomatic Process. In *Recent Developments in Psychosomatic Medicine*, ed. E. D. Wittkower & R. A. Cleghorn. Philadelphia: Lippincott.

——— (1957b), The Central Representation of the Symbolic Process in Relation to Psychosomatic Disorders. In *Recent Developments in Psychosomatic Medicine*, ed. E. D. Wittkower & R. A. Cleghorn. Philadelphia: Lippincott.

Lacey, J. I., Bateman, D. E., & Van Lehn, R. (1953), Autonomic Response Specificity. An Experimental Study. *Psychosom. Med.*, 15:8.

Landtman, B., Valanne, E., Pentti, R., & Aukee, M. (1960), *Psychosomatic Behaviour of Children with Congenital Heart Disease.* Helsinki: Mercatorin Kirjapaino.

Langford, W. S. (1937), Anxiety Attacks in Children. *Amer. J. Orthopsychiat.*, 7:210.

——— (1948), Physical Illness and Convalescence: Their Meaning to the Child. *J. Pediat.*, 33:242.

——— (1955), Disturbance in Mother-Infant Relationship Leading to Apathy, Extra-Nutritional Sucking, and Hairball. In *Emotional Problems of Early Childhood*, ed. G. Caplan. New York: Basic Books.

——— (1961), The Child in the Pediatric Hospital: Adaptation to Illness and Hospitalization. *Amer. J. Orthopsychiat.*, 31:667.

——— Gilder, R., Wilking, V. N., Genn, M. M., & Sherrill, H. H. (1954), Pilot Study of Childhood Accidents: Preliminary Report. *Pediatrics*, 11:405.

——— & Klingman, W. O. (1942), Behavior Disorders Associated with Intracranial Tumors in Childhood: Report of Cases. *Amer. J. Dis. Child.*, 63:433.

Lasagna, L., Mosteller, F., von Felsinger, J. M., & Beecher, H. K. (1954), A Study of the Placebo Response. *Amer. J. Med.,* 16:771.

Laufer, M. W. (1962), Cerebral Dysfunction and Behavior Disorders in Adolescents. *Amer. J. Orthopsychiat.,* 32:501.

———— & Denhoff, E. (1957), Hyperkinetic Behavior Syndrome in Children. *J. Pediat.,* 50:463.

Laughlin, H. P. (1954), Psychiatric Aspects of Fatigue: Emotional Fatigue, Fatigue States, and Neurasthenia. *Med. Ann. District of Columbia,* 23:22.

Laybourne, P. C. (1953), Psychogenic Vomiting in Children. *Amer. J. Dis. Child.,* 86:726.

Lesser, L. I., Ashenden, J. F., Dubuskey, M., & Eisenberg, L. (1960), Anorexia Nervosa in Children. *Amer. J. Orthopsychiat.,* 30:572.

Levy, D. M. (1943), *Maternal Overprotection.* New York: Columbia Univ. Press.

———— (1945), Psychic Trauma of Operations in Children and a Note on Combat Neurosis. *Amer. J. Dis. Child.,* 69:7.

Lewin, K. K. (1959), Role of Depression in the Production of Illness in Pernicious Anemia. *Psychosom. Med.,* 21:23.

Lidz, T., Cornelison, A. R., Fleck, S., & Terry, D. (1957), The Intrafamilial Environment of the Schizophrenic Patient. II. Marital Schism and Marital Skew. *Amer. J. Psychiat.,* 114:241.

———— & Whitehorn, J. C. (1950), Life Situations, Emotions, and Graves' Disease. *Psychosom. Med.,* 12:184.

Lindemann, E. (1941), Observations on Psychiatric Sequelae to Surgical Operations in Women. *Amer. J. Psychiat.,* 98:132.

———— (1944), Symptomatology and Management of Acute Grief. *Amer. J. Psychiat.,* 101:141.

———— (1950), Modifications in the Course of Ulcerative Colitis in Relationship to Changes in Life Situations and Reaction Patterns. In *Life Stress and Bodily Disease,* ed. H. G. Wolff, S. G. Wolf, & C. C. Hare. Baltimore: Williams & Wilkins.

Liss, E. (1948), Pediatric Convalescence. *Nerv. Child,* 7:204.

Little, S. (1949), A Note on an Investigation of the Emotional Complications of Cerebral Palsy. *Nerv. Child,* 8:181.

———— (1960), Psychology of Physical Illness in Adolescents. In *Symposium on Adolescence,* ed. L. T. Meiks & M. Green. Philadelphia: Saunders.

Long, R. T., Lamont, J. H., Whipple, B., Bandler, L., Blom, G. E., Burgin, L., & Jessner, L. (1958), A Psychosomatic Study of Allergic and Emotional Factors in Children with Asthma. *Amer. J. Psychiat.* 114:890.

Loomis, E. A. (1956), The Child's Emotions and Surgery. In *Pre- and Post-Operative Care in the Pediatric Surgical Patient,* ed. W. B. Kiesewetter. Chicago: Yearbook Publ.

Lorand, S. (1936), Psychogenic Factors in a Case of Angioneurotic Edema. *J. Mount Sinai Hosp.,* 2:231.

Lourie, R. S. (1955), Experience with Therapy of Psychosomatic Problems in Infants. In *Psychopathology of Childhood,* ed. P. H. Hoch & J. Zubin. New York: Grune & Stratton.

———— Barrers, S. E., & Strongin, E. J. (1942), Autonomic Nervous System Function in Children with Behavior Problems as Measured by the Parotid Secretory Rate. *Amer. J. Psychiat.,* 99:419.

Lowrey, L. G. (1940), Personality Distortion and Early Institutional Care. *Amer. J. Orthopsychiat.,* 10:576.

Luby, E. D., Ware, J. G., Senf, R., & Frohman, C. E. (1959), Stress and the Precipitation of Acute Intermittent Porphyria. *Psychosom. Med.,* 21:34.

McClary, A. R., Meyer, E., & Weitzman, E. L. (1955), Observations on the Role of the Mechanism of Depression in Some Patients with Disseminated Lupus Erythematosus. *Psychosom. Med.*, 17:311.

McCrory, W. W., Fleisher, D. S., & Sohn, W. B. (1959), Effects of Early Ambulation on the Course of Nephritis in Children. *Pediatrics*, 24:395.

McCulloch, H. (1938), Encephalitis Rheumatica (Chorea Minor of Sydenham). *J. Pediat.*, 13:741.

Maas, H. S., & Engler, R. E. (1959), *Children in Need of Parents*. New York: Columbia Univ. Press.

Mabry, C. C. (1959), Prolonged Neonatal Anoxia without Apparent Adverse Sequellae. *J. Pediat.*, 55:211.

MacGregor, F. C., Abel, T. M., Bryt, A., Lauer, E., & Weissman, S. (1953), Facial Deformities and Plastic Surgery: A Psychosocial Study. In *American Lecture Series, Publication No. 174*. Springfield, Ill.: Thomas.

MacLean, P. H. (1958), Contrasting Function of Limbic and Neocortical Systems of the Brain and Their Relevance to Psychophysiologic Aspects of Medicine. *Amer. J. Med.*, 25:611.

Magoun, H. W. (1958), *The Waking Brain*. Springfield, Ill.: Thomas.

Mahler, M. S. (1949), Psychoanalytic Evaluation of Tics. In *The Psychoanalytic Study of the Child 3/4*:279. New York: Int. Univ. Press.

—— (1950), *Helping Children to Accept Death*. New York: Child Study Assn. of Amer.

—— Furer, M., & Settlage, A. (1959), Severe Emotional Disturbances in Childhood: Psychoses. In *American Handbook of Psychiatry*, ed. S. Arieti. New York: Basic Books.

Malmo, R. B., Boag, T. J., & Smith, A. A. (1957), Physiological Study of Personal Interaction. *Psychosom. Med.*, 19:105.

Mandelbrote, B. M., & Wittkower, E. D. (1955), Emotional Factors in Graves' Disease. *Psychosom. Med.*, 17:109.

Mann, E. C. (1957), The Role of Emotional Determinants in Habitual Abortion. *Surg. Clin. No. Amer.*, 37:447.

—— (1959), Habitual Abortion. A Report in Two Parts on 160 Patients. *Amer. J. Obstet. & Gynecol.*, 77:706.

Marcus, I., Swander, D., Southerland, F. & Achulschofer, E. (1960), *Interdisciplinary Approach to Accident Patterns in Children*. Lafayette, Ind.: Child Developm. Publ.

Margolin, S. G. (1951), The Behavior of the Stomach During Psychoanalysis. *Psychoanal. Quart.*, 20:349.

—— (1957), Psychotherapeutic Principles in Psychosomatic Practice. In *Recent Developments in Psychosomatic Medicine*, ed. E. D. Wittkower & R. A. Cleghorn. Philadelphia: Lippincott.

—— Orringer, D., Kaufman, M. R., Winklestein, A., Hollander, F., Janowitz, H., Stein, A., & Levy, M. (1950), Variation of Gastric Functions During Conscious and Unconscious Conflict States. In *Life Stress and Bodily Disease*, ed. H. G. Wolff, S. G. Wolf, & C. C. Hare. Baltimore: Williams & Wilkins.

Marks, J., Wolfson, J., & Klein, R. (1961), Neonatal Thyroid Functions: Erythocyte T_3 Uptake in Early Infancy. *J. Pediat.*, 58:32.

Marmor, J. (1954), Some Considerations Concerning Orgasm in the Female. *Psychosom. Med.*, 16:240.

—— Ashley, M., Tabachnick, N., Storkan, M., & McDonald, F. (1956), The Mother-Child Relationship in the Genesis of Neurodermatitis. *Arch. Dermatol.*, 74:599.

Martmer, E. E. (1959), *The Child with a Handicap*. Springfield, Ill.: Thomas.

Masland, R. L., Sarason, S. B., & Gladwin, T. (1958), *Mental Subnormality: Biological, Psychological, and Cultural Factors*. New York: Basic Books.

Mason, L. W. (1949), Precocious Puberty. *J. Pediat.*, 34:730.

Massler, M., & Wood, A. W. S. (1949), Thumb-Sucking. *J. Dentist. Child.* 16:1.

Mednick, S. A., Garner, A. M., & Stone, H. K. (1958), A Test of Some Behavioral Hypotheses Drawn from Alexander's Specificity Theory. *Amer. J. Orthopsychiat.*, 29:592.

Meiks, L. T., & Green, M., ed. (1960), *Symposium on Adolescence.* Philadelphia: W. B. Saunders.

Mendelson, M., Hirsch, S., & Webber, C. S. (1956), A Critical Examination of Some Recent Theoretical Models in Psychosomatic Medicine. *Psychosom. Med.*, 18:363.

Meng, H. (1938), Zur Social Psychologie der Korperbeschadigten: Ein Beitrag Zum Problem der Praktischen Psychohygiene. *Schweiz. Arch. Neurol. Psychiat.*, 40:328.

Menninger, K. A. (1934), Polysurgery and Polysurgical Addiction. *Psychoanal. Quart.*, 3:173.

Menzer, D. (1953), The Importance of the Psychologic Factor in Gynecology. *New Eng. J. Med.*, 249:519.

Menzer-Benaron, D., & Sturgis, S. H. (1957), Relationship Between Emotional and Somatic Factors in Gynecologic Disease. In *Progress in Gynecology,* ed. S. H. Sturgis & Meigs, New York: Grune & Stratton.

Menzies, R. (1937), Conditioned Vasomotor Responses in Human Subjects. *J. Psychol.*, 4:75.

Meyer, B. C., Brown, F., & Levine, A. (1955), Observations on the House-Tree-Person Drawing Test Before and After Surgery. *Psychosom. Med.*, 17:428.

Meyer, D. R., & Noble, M. E. (1958), Summation of Manifest Anxiety and Muscular Tension. *J. Experimental Psychol.*, 55:599.

Meyer, E. (1956), Acute Psychologic Disturbances in the Course of Hospitalization of Patients with Chronic Illness. *J. Chronic Dis.*, 3:111.

Michaels, J. J. (1935), *Disorders of Character.* Springfield, Ill.: Thomas.

———— (1944), A Psychiatric Adventure in Comparative Pathophysiology of the Infant and the Adult. *J. Nerv. Ment. Dis.*, 100:49.

Migeon, C. J. (1959), Cortisol Production and Metabolism in the Neonate. *J. Pediat.*, 55:280.

Milhorat, A. T., Small, S. M., & Diethelm, O. (1942), Leukocytosis During Various Emotional States. *Arch. Neurol. Psychiat.*, 47:779.

Miller, H., & Baruch, D. W. (1948), Psychosomatic Studies of Children with Allergic Manifestations. I. Maternal Rejection: A Study of Sixty-Three Cases. *Psychosom. Med.*, 10:275.

———— & Baruch, D. W. (1951), *Maternal Rejection Aspects in the Treatment of Bronchial Asthma. Somatic and Psychiatric Treatment of Asthma.* Baltimore: Williams & Wilkins.

Millet, J. A. P., Lief, H., & Mittelmann, B. (1953), Raynaud's Disease: Psychogenic Factors and Psychotherapy. *Psychosom. Med.*, 15:61.

Millican, F. R., Lourie, R. S., & Layman, E. M. (1956), Emotional Factors in the Etiology and Treatment of Lead Poisoning: A Study of Pica in Children. *Amer. J. Dis. Child.*, 91:144.

Milliken, S. (1943), Group Discussion of Parents of Handicapped Children from the Health Education Standpoint. *Amer. J. Pub. Health,* 43:900.

Mirsky, I. A. (1948), Emotional Factors in the Patient with Diabetes Mellitus. *Bull. Menninger Clinic,* 12:187.

———— (1957), The Psychosomatic Approach to the Etiology of Clinical Disorders. *Psychosom. Med.*, 19:424.

———— (1958), Physiologic, Psychologic, and Social Determinants in the Etiology of Duodenal Ulcer. *Amer. J. Dig. Dis.*, 3:285.

——— (1960), Physiologic, Psychologic, and Social Determinants of Psychosomatic Disorders. *Dis. Nerv. System*, 21:50.

Mittelmann, B. (1949), Briefer Psychotherapy in Psychosomatic Disorders of Children and Adolescents. *Nerv. Child*, 8:291.

——— & Wolff, H. G. (1943), Emotions and Skin Temperature. *Psychosom. Med.*, 5:211.

Mohr, G. J., Josselyn, I. M., Spurlock, J., & Barron, S. H. (1958), Studies in Ulcerative Colitis. *Amer. J. Psychiat.*, 114:1067.

——— Richmond, J. B., Garner, A., & Eddy, E. J. (1955), A Program for the Study of Children with Psychosomatic Disorders. In *Emotional Problems of Childhood*, ed. G. Caplan. New York: Basic Books.

Money, J., Hampson, J. G., & Hampson, J. L. (1955), Hermaphroditism: Recommendations Concerning Assignment of Sex, Change of Sex, and Psychologic Management. *Bull. Johns Hopkins Hosp.*, 97:284.

Morris, T. A., Jr., & Sturgis, S. H. (1959), Practical Aspects of Psychosomatic Sterility. *Clin. Obstet. Gynec.*, 2:890.

Morris, R., & Cohen, J. (1954), The Psycho-Social Factors in Muscular Dystrophy. *J. Amer. Acad. Child Psychiat.*, 3:70.

Moulton, R., Even, S., & Thierman, W. (1952), Emotional Factors in Periodontal Disease. *J. Oral Surg., Oral Med., & Oral Pathol.*, 5:833.

Myklebust, H. R., ed. (1960), *The Psychology of Deafness*. New York: Grune & Stratton.

Najjar, V. A., & Robinson, J. P. (1959), Medical Progress: The Mechanism of Antibody-Antigen Reaction and its Implication in Allergic and Immunologic States. *J. Pediat.*, 55:777.

Natterson, J. M., & Knudson, A. G. (1960), Observations Concerning Fear of Death in Fatally Ill Children and Their Mothers. *Psychom. Med.*, 22:456.

Nelson, W. E., ed. (1959), *Textbook of Pediatrics*, 7th ed. Philadelphia: Saunders.

Nemiah, J. C. (1950), Anorexia Nervosa. A Clinical Psychiatric Study. *Medicine*, 29:225.

Neuhaus, E. C. (1958), A Personality Study of Asthmatic and Cardiac Children. *Psychosom. Med.*, 20:181.

Newell, H. W. (1934), The Psycho-Dynamics of Maternal Rejection. *Amer. J. Orthopsychiat.*, 4:387.

Newton, N. R., & Newton, M. N. (1951), Recent Trends in Breast Feeding: A Review. *Amer. J. Med. Science*, 221:691.

Nickerson, G., & MacDermot, P. N. (1961), Psychometric Evaluation and Factors Affecting the Performance of Children who have Recovered from Tuberculous Meningitis. *Pediatrics*, 27:68.

Norris, M., Spaulding, P. J., & Brodie, F. H. (1957), *Blindness in Children*. Chicago: Univ. Chicago Press.

Obermayer, M. E. (1955), *Psychocutaneous Medicine*. Springfield, Ill.: Thomas.

Offer, D., & Barglow, P. (1960), Adolescent and Young Adult Self-Mutilation Incidents in a General Psychiatric Hospital. *Arch. Gen. Psychiat.*, 3:194.

Opler, M. K. (1959), Cultural Differences in Mental Disorders: An Italian and Irish Contrast in the Schizophrenias—U. S. A. In *Culture and Mental Health*, ed. M. K. Opler. New York: Macmillan.

Papper, S., & Handy, J. (1956), Observations in a "Control" Group of Patients in Psychosomatic Investigation. *New Eng. J. Med.*, 255:1067.

Parsons, T. C. (1951), *The Social System*. Glencoe, Ill.: Free Press.

Pavlov, I. P. (1928), *Lectures on Conditioned Reflexes*, tr. W. H. Gantt. New York: Int. Publ.

Pearson, G. H. J. (1941), Effect of Operative Procedures on the Emotional Life of the Child. *Amer. J. Dis. Child.*, 62:716.

Penfield, W., & Jaspar, H. (1953), *Epilepsy and the Functional Anatomy of the Human Brain*. Boston: Little Brown.

Persike, E. C., & Lippman, R. W. (1948), Psychologic Management of Children with Glomerular Nephritis. *Amer. J. Dis. Child.*, 75:540.

Persky, H., Gamm, S. R., & Grinker, R. R. (1952), Correlation Between Fluctuation of Free Anxiety and Quantity of Hippuric Acid Excretion. *Psychosom. Med.*, 13:34.

—— Hamburg, D. A., Basowitz, H., Grinker, R. R., Sabshin, M., Korchin, S. J., Herz, M., Board, F. A., & Heath, H. A. (1958), Relation of Emotional Responses and Changes in Plasma Hydrocortisone Level after Stressful Interview. *Arch. Neurol. Psychiat.*, 79:434.

Pfeiffer, J. B., & Ripley, H. S. (1947), Measurement of Renal Blood Flow and Glomerular Filtration during Variations in Blood Pressure Related to Changes in Emotional State and Life Situation. Abstract from Annual Meeting. *J. Clin. Inves.*, 26:1193.

Philippopolous, S. G., Wittkower, E. D., & Cousineau, A. (1958), The Etiological Significance of Emotional Factors in Onset and Exacerbations of Multiple Sclerosis: A Preliminary Report. *Psychosom Med.*, 20:458.

Pinkerton, P. (1958), Psychogenic Megacolon in Children: The Implications of Bowel Negativism. *Arch. Dis. Child.*, 33:371.

Pollock, G. H., & Richmond, J. B. (1953), Nutritional Anemia in Children: Importance of Emotional, Social, and Economic Factors. *Psychosom. Med.*, 15:477.

Portis, S. A. (1950), Life Situations, Emotions, and Hyperinsulinism. *J. Amer. Med. Assn.*, 142:1281.

Powers, G. F. (1948), Humanizing Hospital Experience. *Amer. J. Dis. Child.*, 76:365.

Pratt, K. C. (1954), The Neonate. In *Manual of Child Psychology*, 2nd ed., ed. L. Carmichael. New York: Wiley.

Price, D., Thaler, M., & Mason, J. (1957), Preoperative Emotional States and Adrenal Cortical Activity. *Arch. Neurol. Psychiat.*, 77:646.

Proctor, J. T. (1959), Hysteria in Childhood. *Amer. J. Orthopsychiat.*, 28:394.

Provence, S., & Coleman, R. (1957), Environmental Retardation (Hospitalism) in Infants Living in Families. *Pediatrics*, 19:285.

Prugh, D. G., Long-term Follow-up Studies of Children with Ulcerative Colitis. (unpublished)

—— (1951a), Role of Emotional Factors in Idiopathic Celiac Disease. *Psychosom. Med.*, 13:220.

—— (1951b), The Role of Emotional Factors in Ulcerative Colitis in Childhood. *Gastroenterology*, 18:339.

—— (1954), Childhood Experience and Colonic Disorder. *Ann. N. Y. Acad. Sci.*, 58:355.

—— (1956), Psychological and Psychophysiological Aspects of Oral Activities in Childhood. *Ped. Clin. N. Amer.*, 3:1049.

—— (1958), Emotional Reactions to Surgery. In *The Non-Operative Aspects of Surgery*. Report of the Twenty-seventh Ross Pediatric Conference. Columbus, Ohio: Ross Laboratories.

—— (1959), The Clinical Examination of the Infant and Child. In *Textbook of Pediatrics*, ed. W. E. Nelson. 7th ed. Philadelphia: Saunders.

—— (1961), Some Psychologic Considerations Concerned with the Problem of Overnutrition. *Amer. J. Clin. Nutrition*, 9:538.

—— (1963), Psychophysiologic Aspects of In-Born Errors of Metabolism. In *The Psychological Basis of Medical Practice*, ed. H. Lief, N. Lief, & V. Lief. New York: Hoeber.

—— & Harlow, R. G. (1962), Masked Deprivation in Infants and Young Children. In *Deprivation of Maternal Care. A Reassessment of Its Effects*. Geneva: World Health Organization.

—— & Shwachman, H. (1955), Observations on Chronic Unexplained Diarrhea in Infants and Young Children. *Amer. J. Dis. Child.*, 90:496.

—— Staub, E. M., Sands, H., Kirschbaum, R., & Lenihan, E. A. 1953), A Study of the Emotional Reactions of Children and Families to Illness and Hospitalization. *Amer. J. Orthopsychiat.*, 23:78.

—— & Jaguiri, C. K. (1954), Emotional Aspects of the Respirator Care of Patients with Poliomyelitis. *Psychosom. Med.*, 16:104.

—— Wermer, H., & Lord, J. (1956), The Significance of the Anal Phase for Pediatrics and Child Psychiatry. In *Case Studies in Childhood Emotional Disabilities*, Vol. II. New York: Amer. Orthopsychiat. Assn.

Quarton, C. G., Clark, L. D., Cobb, S., & Bauer, W. (1955), Mental Disturbances Associated with ACTH and Cortisone: A Review of Explanatory Hypotheses. *Medicine*, 34:13.

Rapaport, D. (1942), *Emotions and Memory*. Baltimore: Williams & Wilkins.

Rasmussen, A. F., Marsh, J. T., & Brill, N. Q. (1957), Increased Susceptibility to Herpes Simplex in Mice Subjected to Avoidance-Learning Stress or Restraint. *Proc. Soc. Exper. Biol. & Med.*, 96:183.

Reifenstein, E. C. (1946), Psychogenic or Hypothalamic Amenorrhea. *Med. Clin. No. Amer.* 30:1103.

Reiser, M. F., Ferris, E. B., & Levine, M. (1957), Cardiovascular Disorders, Heart Disease, and Hypertension. In *Recent Developments in Psychosomatic Medicine*, ed. E. D. Wittkower & R. A. Cleghorn. Philadelphia: Lippincott.

—— Reeves, R. B., & Armington, J. (1955), Effect of Variations in Laboratory Procedure and Experimenter upon the Ballistocardiogram, Blood Pressure, and Heart Rate in Healthy Young Men. *Psychosom. Med.*, 17:185.

Renbourn, E. T. (1960), Body Temperature and Pulse Rate in Boys and Young Men Prior to Sporting Contests. A Study of Emotional Hyperthermia: With a Review of the Literature. *J. Psychosom. Res.*, 4:149.

Rennie, T. A. C., & Srole, L. (1956), Social Class Prevalence and Distribution of Psychosomatic Conditions in an Urban Population. *Psychosom. Med.*, 18:449.

—— Srole, L., Opler, M. K., & Langner, T. S. (1957), Urban Life and Mental Health. *Amer. J. Psychiat.*, 113:831.

Richmond, J. B. (1952), Health Supervision of Infants and Children. *J. Pediat.*, 40:634.

—— (1954), Self-Understanding for the Parents of Handicapped Children. *Publ. Health Rep.*, 69:702.

—— (1958), The Pediatric Patient in Illness. In *The Psychology of Medical Practice*, ed. M. H. Hollender. Philadelphia: Saunders.

—— (1958, unpublished), Goals of Therapy in Psychosomatic Disorders. Paper presented at Annual Meeting of American Psychosomatic Society, April 1958.

—— Eddy, E., & Green, M. (1958), Rumination: A Psychosomatic Syndrome of Infancy. *Pediatrics*, 22:49.

—— & Lipton, E. L. (1959), Some Aspects of the Neurophysiology of the Newborn and Their Implications of Child Development. In *Dynamic Psychopathology of Childhood*, ed. L. Jessner & E. Pavenstedt. New York: Grune & Stratton.

—— & Waisman, H. A. (1955), Psychologic Aspects of Management of Children with Malignant Diseases. *Amer. J. Dis. Child.*, 89:42.

Richter, H. G. (1943), Emotional Disturbances of Constant Pattern Following Non-Specific Respiratory Infections. *J. Pediat.*, 23:315.

Riklan, M., Weiner, H., & Diller, L. (1959), Somato-Psychologic Studies in Parkinson's Disease. I. An Investigation into the Relationship of Certain Disease Factors to Psychological Functions. *J. Nerv. Ment. Dis.*, 129:263.

Riley, C. M. (1957), Familial Dysautonomia. In *Advances in Pediatrics*. Chicago: Yearbook Publ.

Ripley, H. S., & Wolff, H. G. (1950), Life Situations, Emotions, and Glaucoma. *Psychosom. Med.*, 12:215.

Robertiello, R. C. (1953), Psychomotor Epilepsy in Children. *Dis. Nerv. System*, 14:337.

Robertson, J. (1958), *Young Children in Hospitals*. New York: Basic Books.

Robin, M., & Kepecs, J. G. (1953), The Relationship Between Certain Emotional States and the Rate of Secretion of Sebum. *J. Invest. Dermatol.*, 20:373.

Romano, J. (1943), Emotional Components of Illness. *Connecticut State Med. J.*, 7:22.

—————(1950), Basic Orientation and Education of the Medical Student. *J. Amer. Med. Assn.*, 143:409.

—————& Coon, G. P. (1942), Physiologic and Psychologic Studies in Spontaneous Hypoglycemia. *Psychosom. Med.*, 4:283.

—————& Engel, G. L. (1944), Physiologic and Psychologic Considerations of Delirium. *Med. Clin. N. Amer.*, 28:629.

————— ————— (1945), Studies of Syncope. III. Differentiation Between Vasodepressor and Hysterical Fainting. *Psychosom. Med.*, 7:3.

Rome, H. P., & Braceland, F. J. (1952), The Psychological Response to ACTH, Cortisone, Hydrocortisone, and Related Steroid Substances. *Amer. J. Psychiat.*, 108:641.

Rose, J. A. (1960), The Dimensions of Comprehensive Pediatrics. *Pediatrics*, 26:729.

Rosenbaum, M. (1945), Psychosomatic Factors of Pruritis. *Psychosom. Med.*, 7:52.

—————(1960), The Role of Psychological Factors in Delayed Growth in Adolescence: A Case Report. *Amer. J. Orthopsychiat.*, 29:762.

Rosenblueth, D., & Bowlby, J. (1955), The Social and Psychological Background of Tuberculous Children. *British Med. J.*, 1:946.

Rosenthal, M. J. (1952), A Psychosomatic Study of Infantile Eczema. *Pediatrics*, 10:581.

Ross, W. D. (1947), Urethral Discharge as a Symptom of Psychiatric Disorder. *Psychosom. Med.*, 9:273.

—————(1957), Psychosomatic Disorders and Psychoses. In *Recent Developments in Psychosomatic Medicine*, ed. E. D. Wittkower & R. A. Cleghorn. Philadelphia: Lippincott.

Rubin, J., Nagler, R., Spiro, H. M., & Pilot, M. L. (1962), Measuring the Effect of Emotions on Esophageal Motility. *Psychosom. Med.*, 24:170.

Ruesch, J. (1948), Infantile Personality: The Core Problem of Psychosomatic Medicine. *Psychosom. Med.*, 10:134.

—————Christiansen, C., Patterson, L. C., Dewees, S., & Jacobson, A., in cooperation with Soley, M. H. (1947), Psychological Invalidism in Thyroidectomized Patients. *Psychosom. Med.*, 9:77.

—————Harris, R. E., Christiansen, C., Heller, S. H., Loeb, M. B., Dewees, S., & Jacobson, A. (1951), *Chronic Disease and Psychological Invalidism: A Psychosomatic Study*. Berkeley: Univ. Calif. Press.

—————& Prestwood, A. R. (1950), Communication and Bodily Disease. In *Life Stress and Bodily Disease*, ed. H. G. Wolff, S. G. Wolf, & C. C. Hare. Baltimore: Williams & Wilkins.

Saul, L. J. (1938), Psychogenic Factors in the Etiology of the Common Cold and Related Symptoms. *Int. J. Psycho-anal.*, 19:451.

—————& Bernstein, C. (1941), The Emotional Settings of Some Attacks of Urticaria. *Psychosom. Med.*, 3:349.

Schaffer, H. R., & Callender, W. M. (1959), Psychologic Effects of Hospitalization in Infancy. *Pediatrics*, 24:528.

Schilder, P. (1935), *The Image and Appearance of the Human Body: Studies in the Constructive Energies of the People*. London: Kegan Paul.

Schmale, A. H., Jr. (1958), Relation of Separation and Depression to Disease. I. Report on a Hospitalized Medical Population. *Psychosom. Med.*, 20:259.

Schneider, R. A. (1950), The Relation of Stress to Clotting Time, Relative Viscosity and Certain other Biophysical Alterations of the Blood in the Normotensive and Hypertensive Subject. In *Life Stress and Bodily Disease*, ed. H. G. Wolff, S. G. Wolf, & C. C. Hare. Baltimore: Williams & Wilkins.

Schottstaedt, W. W. (1960), *Psychophysiologic Approach in Medical Practice*. Chicago: Yearbook Publ.

——— Grace, W. J., & Wolff, H. G. (1956a), Life Situations, Behavior, Attitudes, Emotions, and Renal Secretion of Fluid Electrolytes. V. Variations in Excretion of Endogenous Creatinine. *J. Psychosom. Res.*, 1:292.

——— ——— ——— (1956b), Life Situations, Behavior, Attitudes, Emotions, and Renal Secretion of Fluid Electrolytes. I. Method of Study. *J. Psychosom. Res.*, 1:75.

Sears, R. R., Maccoby, E. E., & Levin, H. L. (1957), *Patterns of Child Rearing*. Evanston, Ill.: Row Peterson.

Seguin, C. A. (1956), Migration and Psychosomatic Disadaptation. *Psychosom. Med.*, 18:404.

Seidenfeld, M. A. (1949), Psychologic Aspects of Poliomyelitis. *Pediatrics*, 4:309.

Seitz, P. F. D. (1951), Symbolism and Organ Choice in Conversion Reactions: An Experimental Approach. *Psychosom. Med.*, 13:254.

——— (1957), Psychological Aspects of Skin Diseases. In *Recent Developments in Psychosomatic Medicine*, ed. E. D. Wittkower & R. A. Cleghorn. Philadelphia: Lippincott.

Selye, H. (1946), The General Adaptation Syndrome and the Diseases of Adaptation. *J. Clin. Endocrinol.*, 6:117.

——— (1947), The General Adaptation Syndrome and the Diseases of Adaptation. In *Textbook of Endocrinology*. Montreal: Univ. Montreal.

Senn, M. J. E. (1945), Emotional Aspects of Convalescence. *The Child*, 10:24.

——— (1946), Relationship of Pediatrics and Psychiatry. *Amer. J. Dis. Child.*, 71:537.

——— (1948a), The Psychotherapeutic Role of the Pediatrician. *Pediatrics*, 2:147.

——— (1948b), Emotions and Symptoms in Pediatric Practice. In *Advances in Pediatrics*. Chicago: Yearbook Publ.

——— (1959), Psychologic Disorders. In *Textbook of Pediatrics*, ed. W. E. Nelson. Philadelphia: Saunders.

Shagass, C., & Naiman, J. (1955), The Sedation Threshold. Abstract from Annual Meeting. *Psychosom. Med.*, 17:480.

Shands, H. C., Finesinger, J. E., Cobb, S., & Abrams, R. D. (1951), Psychological Mechanisms in Patients with Cancer. *Cancer*, 4:1159.

Sharoff, R. L. (1959), Enforced Restriction of Communication: Its Implications for the Emotional and Intellectual Development of the Deaf Child. *Amer. J. Psychiat.*, 116:443.

Sherber, D. A., & Marcus, M. (1957), Studies on the Physical State of the Serum Lipids under Stress. Abstract. *Circulation*, 16:491.

Sherwin, A. C., & McCully, R. S. (1961), Reactions Observed in Boys of Various Ages (Ten to Fourteen), to a Crippling, Progressive, and Fatal Illness (Muscular Dystrophy). *J. Chronic Dis.*, 13:59.

Shirley, H. G. (1954), *The Child, His Parents, and His Physician*. Springfield, Ill.: Thomas.

Silber, E., Bloch, D., & Perry, S. (1956), Some Factors in the Emotional Reaction of Children to Disaster. *Amer. J. Psychiat.*, 113:416.

Smith, C. M., & Hamilton, J. (1959), Psychological Factors in the Narcolepsy-Cataplexy Syndrome. *Psychosom. Med.*, 21:40.

Solnit, A. J., & Green, M. (1959), Psychologic Considerations in the Management of Death in Pediatric Hospital Services. I. The Doctor and the Child's Family. *Pediatrics*, 24:106.

Sontag, L. W. (1944), Differences in Modifiability of Fetal Behavior and Physiology. *Psychosom. Med.*, 6:151.

———— (1953), Psychosomatic Aspects of Childhood. In *Contributions Toward Medical Psychology*, ed. A. Weider. New York: Ronald Press.

———— Baker, C. T., & Nelson, V. L. *Mental Growth and Personality Development: A Longitudinal Study*. Lafayette, Ind.: Child Developm. Publ.

Sperling, M. (1946), Psychoanalytic Study of Ulcerative Colitis in Children. *Psychoanal. Quart.*, 15:302.

———— (1949), The Role of the Mother in Psychosomatic Disorders in Children. *Psychosom. Med.*, 11:377.

———— (1955), Observations from the Treatment of Children Suffering from Non-Bloody Diarrhea or Mucous Colitis. *J. Hillside Hosp.*, 4:25.

———— (1957), Psychosomatic Medicine and Pediatrics. In *Recent Developments in Psychosomatic Medicine*, ed. E. D. Wittkower & R. A. Cleghorn. Philadelphia, Lippincott.

Spiegel, J. P. (1954), Mental Health and the Family. *New Eng. J. Med.*, 251:843.

———— & Bell, N. W. (1959), The Family of the Psychiatric Patient. In *American Handbook of Psychiatry*, ed. S. Arieti. New York: Basic Books.

Spitz, R. A. (1945), Hospitalism: An Inquiry into the Genesis of Psychiatric Conditions in Early Childhood. In *The Psychoanalytic Study of the Child*, 1:53. New York: Int. Univ. Press.

———— (1946), Anaclitic Depression. In *The Psychoanalytic Study of the Child*, 2:313. New York: Int. Univ. Press.

———— (1951), The Psychogenic Diseases of Infancy: An Attempt at their Etiological Classification. In *The Psychoanalytic Study of the Child*, 6:255. New York: Int. Univ. Press.

Spock, B. (1957), Sleep Problems in the Early Years. *Postgraduate Med.*, 21:272.

———— & Huschka, M. (1938), The Psychological Aspects of Pediatric Practice. *Practitioners Library of Med. & Surg.*, 13:757.

Stead, E. A., Warren, J. V., Merrill, A. J., & Brannon, E. S. (1945), Cardiac Output in Male Subjects as Measured by the Technique of Right Atrial Catheterization. Normal Values with Observations on Effects of Anxiety and Tilting. *J. Clin. Invest.*, 24:326.

Stevenson, I. P. (1950), Physical Symptoms During Pleasurable Emotional States. *Psychosom. Med.*, 12:98.

———— & Duncan, C. H. (1950), Alterations in Cardiac Function and Circulatory Efficiency During Periods of Life Stress as Shown by Changes in the Rate, Rhythm, Electrocardiographic Pattern and Out-Put of the Heart in Those with Cardiovascular Disease. In *Life Stress and Bodily Disease*, ed. H. G. Wolff, S. G. Wolf, & C. C. Hare. Baltimore: Williams & Wilkins.

———— & Wolff, H. G. (1949), Life Situations, Emotions, and Bronchial Mucus. *Psychosom. Med.*, 11:223.

Stewart, A. H. (1953), Excessive Crying in Infants—A Family Disease. In *Problems of Infancy and Childhood*, ed. M. J. E. Senn. New York: Josiah Macy Jr. Foundation.

Stokes, J. H., & Beerman, H. (1940), Psychosomatic Correlations in Allergic Conditions— A Review of Problems and Literature. *Psychosom. Med.*, 2:438.

Straub, L. R., Ripley, H. S., & Wolf, S. G. (1949), Disturbances of Bladder Function Associated with Emotional States. *J. Amer. Med. Assn.*, 141:1139.

Strauss, A. A., & Lehtinen, L. D. (1947), *Psychopathology and Education of the Brain-Injured Child*. New York: Grune & Stratton.

Stuart, H. C., & Prugh, D. G., ed. (1960), *The Healthy Child: His Physical, Psychological and Social Development*. Cambridge: Harvard Univ. Press.

Szasz, T. S. (1951), Oral Mechanisms in Constipation and Diarrhea. *Int. J. Psycho-anal.*, 32:196.

Szurek, A. (1951), Comments on Psychopathology of Children with Somatic Illness. *Amer. J. Psychiat.*, 107:844.

Taboroff, L. H., & Brown, W. H. (1954), A Study of the Personality Patterns of Children and Adolescents with the Peptic Ulcer Syndrome. *Amer. J. Orthopsychiat.*, 24:602.

Talbot, N. B., Sobel, E. H., Burke, B. S., Lindemann, E., & Kaufman, W. B. (1947), Dwarfism in Healthy Children: Its Possible Relation to Emotional, Nutritional, and Endocrine Disturbances. *New Eng. J. Med.*, 236:783.

Taylor, E. M. (1959), *Psychological Appraisal of Children with Cerebral Defects*. Cambridge: Harvard Univ. Press.

Teuber, H. L. (1960), The Premorbid Personality and Reaction to Brain Damage. In *Brain and Behavior*, Session II. Symposium 1959, L. Eisenberg, Chr. *Amer. J. Orthopsychiat.*, 30:322.

Thurston, D., Graham, F. K., Ernhart, E. B., Eichman, P. L., & Craft, M. (1960), Neurologic Status of 3-Year-Old Children Originally Studied at Birth. *Neurology*, 10:680.

Tisza, V. B., Selverstone, B., Rosenblum, G., & Hanlon, N. (1958), Psychiatric Observations of Children with Cleft Palate. *Amer. J. Orthopsychiat.*, 28:416.

Titchener, J. L., & Levine, M. (1960), *Surgery as a Human Experience: The Psychodynamics of Surgical Practice*. New York: Oxford Univ. Press.

—— Riskin, J., & Emerson, R. (1960), The Family in Psychosomatic Process: A Case Report Illustrating a Method of Psychosomatic Research. *Psychosom. Med.*, 22:127.

Tjossem, T. D., Leider, A. R., Deisher, R. W., Ripley, H. S., & Holmes, T. H. (1955), Psychophysiological Studies of Two to Four Year Old Children. Abstract from Annual Meeting. *Psychosom. Med.*, 17:476.

Tong, J. E., & Murphy, I. C. (1960), A Review of Stress Reactivity Research in Relation to Psychopathology and Psychopathic Behavior. *J. Ment. Sci.*, 106:1273.

Toth, L. A. (1956), A Pseudo-water Diuresis in Man. *J. Urology*, 76:206.

Ullman, M. (1959), On the Psyche and Warts. I. Suggestion and Warts: A Review and Comment. *Psychosom. Med.*, 21:473.

—— & Dudek, S. (1960), On the Psyche and Warts: II. Hypnotic Suggestion and Warts. *Psychosom. Med.*, 20:68.

Vaughan, V. G., & Cashmore, A. A. (1954), Encopresis in Childhood. *Guy's Hosp. Rep.*, 103:360.

Venning, E. H., Dyrenfurth, I., & Beck, J. C. (1957), Effect of Anxiety upon Aldosterone Excretion in Man. *J. Clin. Endocrinol.*, 17:1005.

von Bertalanffy, L. (1957), *Semantics and General System Theory*. Lakeville, Conn.: Institution of General Semantics.

Wagener, H. P. (1957), Central Angiospastic Retinopathy and Central Serous Chorioretinitis. *Amer. J. Med. Sci.*, 233:220.

Waldfogel, S., Coolidge, J. C., & Hahn, P. G. (1957), The Development, Meaning, and Management of School Phobia. *Amer. J. Orthopsychiat.*, 27:754.

Wallerstein, R. S., & Rubin, S. (1954), Some Psychosomatic Considerations in Dystrophia Myotonica. *J. Nerv. Ment. Dis.*, 120:277.

Warson, S. R., Turkel, S., & Schiele, H. S. (1949), Pseudopeptic Ulcer Syndromes in Children. *J. Pediat.*, 35:215.

Watson, E. J., & Johnson, A. M. (1958), The Emotional Significance of Acquired Physical Disfigurement in Children. *Amer. J. Orthopsychiat.*, 28:85.

Watson, J. (1925), *Behaviorism*. New York: Norton.

Weiner, H., Thaler, M., Reiser, M. F., & Mirsky, I. A. (1957), Etiology of Duodenal Ulcer. I. Relation of Specific Psychological Characteristics to Rate of Gastric Secretion (Serum Pepsinogen). *Psychosom. Med.*, 19:1.

Weinstein, E. A., & Kahn, R. L. (1955), Denial of Illness, Symbolic and Psychological Aspects. Springfield, Ill.: Thomas.

Weiss, E. (1952), Neurocirculatory Asthenia. *Psychosom. Med.*, 14:150.

———— & English, O. S. (1943), *Psychosomatic Medicine. The Clinical Application of Psychopathology to General Medical Problems.* Philadelphia: Saunders.

Wessel, M. A., Cobb, J. C., Jackson, E. B., Harris, G. S., & Detwiler, A. C. (1954), Paroxysmal Fussing in Infancy, Sometimes Called "Colic." *Pediatrics*, 14:421.

Wheatley, G. M., & Richardson, S. A. (1960), Some Approaches to Research in Childhood Accidents. *Pediatrics*, 25:343.

White, B. V., Cobb, S., & Jones, C. M. (1939), Mucous Colitis. *Psychosom. Med. Monogr.*, I. Washington: National Research Council.

White, K. L., & Long, W. N. (1958), The Incidence of "Psychogenic" Fever in a University Hospital. *J. Chron. Dis.*, 8:567.

Williams, R. V. (1956), *Biochemical Individuality*. New York: Wiley.

Winkelstein, A. (1944), Some General Observations on Cardiospasm. *Med. Clin. No. Amer.* 28:589.

Winnicott, D. W. (1931), *Clinical Notes on the Disorders of Children.* London: W. Heinemann, Ltd.

Witmer, H. L., & Kotinsky, R., ed. (1952), *Personality in the Making.* New York: Harper.

Wittkower, E. D. (1947), Rehabilitation of the Limbless: A Joint Surgical and Psychological Study. *Occupational Med.*, 28:93.

———— (1951), Acne Vulgaris: A Psychosomatic Study. *Brit. J. Dermatol.*, 63:214.

———— (1960), Twenty Years of North American Psychosomatic Medicine. *Psychosom. Med.*, 22:308.

———— & Cleghorn, R. A. (1957), *Recent Developments in Psychosomatic Medicine.* Philadelphia: Lippincott.

———— & McKenna, R. M. B. (1947), The Psychological Aspects of Seborrheic Dermatitis. *Brit. J. Dermatol. & Syph.*, 59:281.

———— & Russell, B. (1953), *Emotional Factors in Skin Diseases.* New York: Hoeber.

Wolf, S., & Lourie, R. S. (1953), Impact of the Mentally Defective Child on the Family Unit. *Clin. Proc. Children's Hospital,* Washington, D. C.: 9:25.

Wolf, S. G. (1947), Sustained Contraction of the Diaphragm: the Mechanism of a Common Type of Dyspnea, and Precordial Pain. Abstract from Annual Meeting. *J. Clin. Invest.*, 26:1201.

———— (1950), Effects of Suggestion and Conditioning on the Action of Chemical Agents in Human Subjects: The Pharmacology of Placebos. *J. Clin. Invest.*, 29:100.

———— Chairman (1951), Report of the Committee on Psychosomatic Relationships in Gastroenterology. *Gastroenterology*, 18:55.

——— & Messier, P. E. (1950), Corneal Vascular Changes in Association with Conflict in a Patient with Phlyctenular Keratitis. In *Life Stress and Bodily Disease,* ed. H. G. Wolff, S. G. Wolf, & C. C. Hare. Baltimore: Williams & Wilkins.
——— & Wolff, H. G. (1943), The Gastric Mucosa, "Gastritis," and Ulcer. *Amer. J. Diges. Dis.,* 10:23.
——— ——— (1947), *Human Gastric Function: An Experimental Study of Man and His Stomach.* New York: Oxford Univ. Press.
Wolff, E. W., & Bayer, L. M. (1952), Psychosomatic Disorders of Childhood and Adolescence. *Amer. J. Orthopsychiat.,* 22:510.
Wolff, H. G. (1948), *Headache and Other Head Pain.* New York: Oxford Med. Publ.
——— (1950), Life Stress and Disease—A Formulation. In *Life Stress and Bodily Disease,* ed. H. G. Wolff, S. G. Wolf, & C. C. Hare. Baltimore: Williams & Wilkins.
——— (1953), *Stress and Disease.* Springfield, Ill.: Thomas.
——— & Wolf, S. (1958), *Pain.* American Lecture in Psychology. Springfield, Ill.: Thomas.
——— Wolf, S. G., & Hare, C. C., ed. (1950), *Life Stress and Bodily Disease.* Baltimore: Williams & Wilkins.
Wolff, P. H. (1959), Observations on Newborn Infants. *Psychosom. Med.,* 21:110.
Woodhead, B. (1946), The Psychological Aspects of Allergic Skin Reactions in Childhood. *Arch. Dis. Child.,* 21:98.
Woodward, K. F., & Siegel, M. G. (1957), Psychiatric Study of Mentally Retarded Children of Pre-School Age. Preliminary Report. *Pediatrics,* 19:119.
Yankauer, A., Goss, K. G., & Romeo, S. M. (1953), An Evaluation of Prenatal Care and Its Relationship to Social Class and Social Disorganization. *Amer. J. Pub. Health,* 43:1001.
Yoss, R. E., & Daly, D. D. (1960), Narcolepsy in Children. *Pediatrics,* 25:1025.
Young, R. H., & Hermann, H. T. (1951), Hysterical Paralysis Associated with Poliomyelitis. *J. Amer. Med. Assn.,* 147:1132.
Zaidens, S. H. (1951), Self-Inflicted Dermatoses and Their Psychodynamics. *J. Nerv. & Ment. Dis.,* 113:395.

Part IV

Pediatric Practice Today

This section reflects many of the problems of and solutions to modern pediatric practice with which Milton Senn has been associated in a crucially influential way for more than thirty years. It is characteristic of Senn as a medical educator that those influenced by him do not represent one point of view. Although all of the authors in this section share the conviction that in this country pediatrics has the responsibility of training physicians to provide optimal medical care for children, each of these authors has developed his own thesis. Morris Green views the future of pediatric responsibility in an imaginative and questioning manner. This is followed by Barbara Korsch's examination of the changing work of the pediatrician in the light of advancing knowledge and the changing conditions of pediatric practice. The next two articles, by Richard T. Cushing and Morris S. Dixon, Jr. respectively, describe different solutions to the problems that are regularly encountered in the private practice of pediatrics. In the last three papers in this section serious efforts are made to define the extent and limitations of our knowledge in three important areas of pediatric practice. Richard E. Wolf maps out the present and future responsibility of pediatric care in the hospital, having identified some of the past failures and triumphs; Norman J. Cohen and Martha F. Leonard demonstrate pediatric knowledge and techniques in the management of children who avoid going to school; and J. Roswell Gallagher describes the principles involved in the pediatric management of expected problems of development in adolescence.

Comprehensive Pediatrics and the Changing Role of the Pediatrician

• *MORRIS GREEN, M.D.*

Indiana University

It is fashionable today to write about *comprehensive* pediatrics. Some educators have the notion that the *comprehensive approach* constitutes a highly desirable goal, while others hold equally fervently the opposite conviction. But on both sides of this ideological fence one senses the unspoken realization that this is a sham polemic: the truly comprehensive pediatrician does not and will not exist. The compassionate pediatrician does and will exist; the pediatrician who has acquired special knowledge and skills in the psychosocial aspects of pediatrics does and will exist; and the pediatrician imaginative enough to develop more effective as well as broader approaches to child health does and will exist. But the all-encompassing physician is yesterday's illusion and today's chimera.

Nevertheless, interest in broadening the scope of pediatrics is real and becomes increasingly augmented. This concern has derived from a number of developments: the increasing preoccupation of the physician with specialized physical aspects of disease appears to be accompanied by a greater difficulty in developing sensitivity to the psychological and social facets of health and disease; the frightfully high incidence of emotional disorders in the child and adult population has made urgent the need for better preventive measures; the increasing desire of parents and others for better understanding of children has created a demand for more accurate information about growth and development; advances in genetics, microbiology, biochemistry, and other basic sciences has expanded tremendously the opportunities for pediatric research and improved management of health and disease. All of this has implications for the future of pediatrics. Although I make no pretense to clairvoyance, I would like to present my thoughts regarding possible changes in the role of the practitioner of pediatrics, the academic pediatrician, and the community pediatrician in the next decade.

THE PRACTITIONER OF PEDIATRICS

The exact role of the pediatric practitioner in the future will depend upon two general considerations: the results of pediatric research and the expectations of society. Any change in role must remain acceptable to the consumer. Today, well-baby and well-child care constitutes the major professional activity of most pediatric practitioners. This role has been traditional and is now somewhat institutionalized. Is this still the most effective arrangement? Would some other approach accomplish the same aims more efficiently and prove more challenging to the physician? Well-baby visits have some features comparable to the mass-survey techniques employed for detection of defects in the adult population. The contribution of such mass surveys can be questioned when considered in terms of the expenditure of time and the most optimal utilization of professional manpower. It might be well, therefore, to look critically at current practices in well-baby and well-child care. Apart from visits necessitated by the giving of immunizations, how frequently should the baby and family be seen? What should be done during these visits?

Pediatrics is enlarging the chronological limits of its interest. It is now becoming accepted in some communities that the pediatrician wishes to see the family prenatally. This practice represents both an early preventive and a positive approach to physical and emotional health by providing anticipatory guidance in the establishment of a healthy mutual adaptation of parents and child, and in providing a basis for close collaboration of parents and physician in the care of the new child. Parents are encouraged to ask questions, and the pediatrician becomes aware of any special health problems that may affect the newborn infant, e.g., erythroblastosis or cystic fibrosis. As more becomes known about pregnancy experiences and the development of neurological or behavioral disorders, and about genetics and inborn errors of metabolism, this practice will become more important.

At the other end of the chronological scale there has been an increase of pediatric interest in the care of the adolescent. This is being reflected both in private practice and in hospital clinics. These developments represent impressive demonstrations at extremes of the age spectrum of the potentiality of pediatrics.

But getting back to current methods of well-infant care, I would like to examine briefly what has come to be termed *anticipatory guidance*. In principle, such guidance can be very helpful. Unfortunately, in some quarters it has become reduced to a recipe in which the pediatrician outlines to the parent, verbally or by means of printed slips, the developmental problems and achievements to be expected before the next return visit, along with recommendations as to how various problems should be managed.

I question the validity and value of much of this practice. I do not believe that anyone is in a position to *tell* others how to rear their children. There is a tremendous difference in the development of individual children, a fact not adequately emphasized in the literature; there are enormous differences in child-care practices in individual families; and most of the interaction between parents and their children is unconsciously determined. This is not to deny that there are certain general developmental phenomena that might be mentioned to parents in anticipation of their occurrence and certain directive advice that may be justified. I do question, however, much of the "standard" advice given about child-care practices and the advisability of attempting to have others conform to the physician's current values and judgments rather than helping parents and their children to be active and resourceful in dealing with their own problems in their own way.

As a substitute for anticipatory guidance, I would recommend that the pediatrician increasingly become the family *conferee*. This implies that the pediatrician is available to listen to the developmental problems which a particular family currently has or which they are anticipating and to help them decide upon the best ways for *them* to manage the situation. At times of family crises, e.g., a death or serious physical or emotional illness, he would help the family master the experience in a way that leads to further integration of the family and psychological growth of the child. The pediatrician would not be completely inactive in this and could give some directive advice, but the active agent would properly be the parent and the child. In experiencing this approach the parent would actually feel that the pediatrician had given more helpful advice than when the physician has done most of the talking.

Although this type of *family monitoring* would require a one-to-one relationship between the physician and the family, the use of group sessions might minimize the need for individual appointments or make these more effective. It would seem of value for parents who are having their first child to have group sessions supervised by a pediatrician with experience in group work. Parents whose children are about the same age could meet in the evenings, perhaps once prenatally, eight times during the first year, and somewhat less frequently thereafter. Each parent would be charged a fee for this series of group sessions, which would compensate the physician adequately for his time. Individual well-baby visits then would be more effective.

PSYCHOTHERAPEUTIC ROLE OF THE PEDIATRICIAN IN PRACTICE

Pediatrics has a major potential contribution to make to mental health. Increasingly, parents come to the pediatrician not because of illness but because they want his guidance in keeping their children physically and emotionally healthy. They wish to discuss with him concerns about problems in child care and rearing. Although much has been written about the psychotherapeutic role of the pediatrician, few physicians are comfortable in this area and many are uncertain about just what their role should be. This is true not only of the practitioner who had little or no formal undergraduate education in psychiatry but also of the more recent trainee who had more formal education in psychiatry but little appropriate supervised experience during his pediatric residency. Psychotherapeutic medicine is similar to organic medicine in that unless one is well trained, one may not know what is being missed diagnostically or therapeutically. The sensitive practitioner feels defeated and discouraged when he finds himself not prepared to understand or manage many of the problems encountered in his day-to-day practice. Ignoring or minimizing the problems seems wrong, while "common sense" appears not particularly helpful. The practitioner who has completed a two-year residency should have achieved a certain awareness and skill in this area; the trainee who has spent a third year in an appropriately designed educational program will have a different kind of competence; and the pediatrician who wishes to pursue this interest in an academic setting will have a still different background. The goals for each must be realistic. It is my impression that often too much is expected by the enthusiast from the first group and too little from the last.

The pediatrician, as any other physician, must be knowledgeable about human behavior. The basic instruction in this should be accomplished during the undergraduate years so that the residency period may be utilized for practical experience, refinement of techniques, and developing the capacity for self-education. The subject matter related to an understanding of human behavior has been steadily increasing in recent years. A familiarity with and use of this content and skills are usually implied in the term "comprehensive" pediatrics. Included here are such basic matters as normal growth and development; some notion about current and past child-care practices; psychopathology of children and child-parent relationships, including symptom formation and family dynamics; and some knowledge concerning the patient-physician relationship. This is the background against which the psychotherapeutic physician utilizes his customary tools—the medical interview, the physical examination, and the like. Although interviewing is probably the most important psychotherapeutic skill that the pediatrician can acquire and utilize practically, few physicians are adequately trained in this.

Since there has been some confusion between the role of the pediatrician and that of the child psychiatrist, it is probably important to emphasize that the pediatrician interested in the psychosocial aspects of his specialty is not substituting for the psychiatrist. Even though the supply of child psychiatrists will never be adequate to provide needed services, the pediatrician's role in psychotherapeutic medicine is not as a second-best substitute for psychiatric services. He is not equipped to practice child psychiatry and should not attempt to do so even if psychiatric facilities are unavailable. He must resist the attempt by others to have him take on the long-term management of children who are seriously disturbed psychiatrically. Pediatric psychotherapeutic care need not be regarded as more or less important or more or less expert than psychiatric care. It has different aims and methods. The pediatrician's contribution ultimately will not be to treat behavioral problems but to attempt to prevent their occurrence. Our present knowledge limits this preventive role, but certainly this situation will not remain static.

Some parents find treatment by a pediatrician more acceptable than that by a child psychiatrist or child guidance clinic. This is especially the case when children present physical symptoms such as headache or abdominal pain, even when these have a psychologic etiology. In part this is because the pediatrician is considered to be competent in the recognition and management of physical illness. Parents are often able to accept his statement that the symptoms have an emotional basis more readily from the pediatrician than from a psychiatrist. The pediatrician must then decide whether the nature of the problem is one that lies within his competence or whether he should help the family accept referral to a child psychiatric facility.

The matter of time and fees always comes up in discussions of this phase of pediatric practice. Many pediatricians feel that they do not have sufficient time to spend with patients who have problems in the psychosocial area. This is unquestionably true in some cases. Many others could probably arrange the time but are uncertain about what to do and are reluctant to charge appropriate fees. There is a custom of a standard charge per office visit rather than for the length of visit. This can be changed if discussed with the parents. Others have the impression that parents currently do not visualize this as something the pediatrician does and that there is no consumer demand for this service. On the other hand, there is some evidence that parents value the opportunity to purchase as much of the doctor's time as they feel they need and to pay a commensurate fee. Many find the quick reassurance given in the "telephone hour" really not very helpful and would welcome an opportunity for adequate discussion.

The time and fee problem is not to be lightly brushed aside because in many instances the pediatrician must interview the child and the parents separately. The use of family group therapy might make this more practicable, but this has been little explored in pediatrics. In this approach the child, usually above the age of eight or nine years, and his parents are first seen individually. In later sessions they are seen as a group. This arrangement has not only time-saving advantages but also special psychotherapeutic possibilities. On the basis of personal experience, this technique appears adaptable to pediatric practice.

It may be that pediatricians in private practice will develop a collaborative arrangement with social workers much as has the child psychiatrist working with patients and families who are experiencing social and emotional troubles related to medical or developmental problems. Those of us who work in the setting of a medical center find it difficult to visualize the management of psychosocial problems by the pediatrician without such ancillary help in many instances. Although this arrangement has been utilized by a few practitioners, the idea has not caught on for a number of reasons. Because of the nature of their profession most social workers are affiliated with social or community agencies. There also is a serious shortage of experienced persons in the field, and the social worker collaborating with pediatricians or other nonpsychiatric physicians in private practice would have to be unusually experienced or have access to supervision.

PHYSICAL HEALTH AND THE PRACTITIONER

Although much of the presentation to this point has been concerned with psychosocial aspects of pediatrics, the primary function of the pediatrician today remains related to physical health. The continuing postgraduate education of the physician in this area represents one of the most serious challenges facing medical education. There is general agreement that the physician should acquire in his undergraduate and residency experience the ability and habit of self-education. But every physician sees patients whose problems he cannot understand on the basis of experience or reading. The opportunity to obtain other opinions offers better medical care for the patient and an excellent educational opportunity for the physician. Such consultations may be obtained from one's colleagues, but this raises problems at times. It would seem that the offering of such consultative services to physicians by university medical centers could represent an important contribution to postgraduate education. The arrangement should be such that patients from all economic groups may be seen promptly upon referral by their physician. Work-up and consultations at the diagnostic center should be completed promptly and the referring doctor sent punctually a letter which outlines concisely the findings, diagnostic impressions, and recommendations made. A diagnostic clinic established in July, 1958, at the James Whitcomb Riley Hospital in part for this purpose has seemed to establish a closer collaborative tie between the teaching hospital and the community practitioner.

The multiply handicapped child also presents a special problem. Although the pediatrician cannot provide the various specialized types of care which such children require, he can help tie together the fragments of medical service that exist when such treatment is given by many persons or facilities. The pediatrician's training and interests should best qualify him as the integrator of rehabilitative services for children and as a liaison person between the family and the complex of specialized services needed. Unfortunately, many pediatricians seem to have little interest in the chronically ill or handicapped child. In many university medical centers, services for the multiply handicapped child are inadequately integrated. Frequently such patients are seen by a different physician at each visit so that the patient and his family have no one whom they can identify as *their* doctor. Advice which seems conflicting to the parents is often given by different specialists. The referring practitioner often tends to withdraw because he does not know what is going on in the child's visits to the community rehabilitation center or at the medical center. Communication needs to be improved. In the medical centers themselves someone must follow the multiply handicapped child so that his care may be properly coordinated and interpreted to the family.

THE COMMUNITY PEDIATRICIAN

Many community agencies concerned with children, for example, schools, welfare agencies, services for crippled children, child guidance clinics, family and parent organizations, or children's institutions, have arrangements for effective pediatric consultation. Other agencies fail to utilize such help. Frequently neither the agency nor the physician sees this as part of the pediatrician's role. Certainly there are many deficiencies in the community that affect child health and development. Unquestionably many children are not securing adequate medical care, especially preventive services. Anyone who has worked in the clinics of a large municipal hospital can attest to this. Child welfare services are not adequately staffed with professionally qualified persons. There is no need to enumerate here all the other deficiencies that exist at the community level in child care. Nor do I propose that all of these problems could be solved even if adequate budgetary support were available. But I do believe that this is an area to which the individual pediatrician and community pediatric groups could give increasing thoughtful attention and that realistic goals and achievements might be forthcoming.

There are many ways in which the problem may be approached.

One obvious approach would be through strong and vocal pediatric representation on various community commissions concerned with youth. Another would be for individual pediatricians to develop a special interest in a specific community problem—e.g., education, adoptions, mental health, retardation, or rehabilitation—and become identified with this interest in the community. In some areas, e.g., medical care, facilities for the handicapped, child guidance clinics, and health and welfare services, the pediatrician has a more obvious professional interest than in others such as schools, recreational facilities, and job opportunities where his involvement is more that of one interested in child welfare.

We have given some thought to an extension of this development by proposing the training and utilization of what might be termed the "community child health specialist." This person, who would have generic training in pediatrics and a background similar to that of maternal and child health officers, would be a member of the municipal health and welfare council or similar organizations now functioning in most metropolitan communities to develop optimal community services on a broad front. The pediatrician functioning as the community child health specialist would represent children's needs in the community. He would utilize the assistance of resource people in his own department as well as practitioners in the community and the various voluntary health and welfare agencies in an effort to advance comprehensive child care at the community level just as the pediatric practitioner attempts to do this at the family level.

This proposal may be regarded as visionary. Perhaps it is. But more and more I am impressed that community services could be greatly strengthened and advanced if persons with the biological and social background, the special proficiencies and capabilities of the pediatrician, would become increasingly involved in the child welfare field. The contribution that the individual pediatrician can make to the mental and physical health of children is impressive, but it is as nothing compared to the contribution that will come with the eventual strengthening of community resources. The availability of such resources will probably precede any massive advance in the field of mental health.

THE PEDIATRIC EDUCATOR

One of the things that can be said with certainty about the future of pediatric education is that it will be different. I shall not presume to deal with all aspects of this but will restrict my remarks to that phase with which I am currently most involved.

Clinical training in ambulatory patient care has generally been inferior to experience in the hospital care of illness. Many practitioners feel that they have not been prepared for practice today, or at least not in a manner that permits them to find in their work a real challenge and an opportunity to grow professionally and intellectually. Undoubtedly, dissatisfaction on the part of some can be ascribed to their being basically misfitted for the practice of pediatrics. This is a personal matter and not especially the fault of pediatric education except perhaps to the extent that such persons are attracted to this field by what they see of pediatrics in the teaching hospital. It may be that something more should be done by the teaching services to help such persons plan careers other than practice. On the other hand, many thoughtful pediatric educators agree that more could be done to prepare persons to become more effective, creative, and satisfied practitioners. Failure to give adequate attention to preparing men for practice has, I believe, done a disservice to pediatrics by undermining the self-esteem and prestige of the practitioner. This in turn has discouraged the interest of medical students and interns in pediatrics as a specialty.

In view of the dissatisfaction expressed by many practitioners with their preparation for the psychosocial aspects of child care, the supposition that adequate skill in this area can be developed after completion of formal training must be considered.

Education is a continuing process in which one learns from clinical experience and from reading. This applies to psychosocial as much as to organic pediatrics. Provided the proper groundwork has been obtained during undergraduate years, the residency period determines whether this nascent interest and competence become an integral part of the physician's diagnostic and therapeutic acumen or whether they are laid aside. Never again is there as convenient an opportunity for gaining this broader competence. The outpatient department, properly staffed and organized, would appear to be the most appropriate setting for education in psychosocial and community pediatrics. It is here that the academic pediatrician interested in "comprehensive" pediatrics can probably best function. He can teach in many ways, but most importantly by serving as a model for identification and through conveying certain expectations of the medical student or resident. The trainee's program should include, if appropriate: attention to psychological, social, and physical considerations; techniques for interviewing parents and children skillfully; awareness of the relationship between physician, parent, and child; and emphasis on the aim of providing personally and with the help of others as complete care as possible. Discussions about disease and disease processes continue to rank high in interest and concern of the well-trained resident, and he is apt to listen to a teacher who continues to be well-informed in the traditional areas of medicine as well as in the psychological and social spheres.

While more medical graduates are seeking pediatric training that goes beyond the traditional, and more teaching centers are attempting to provide this, there are some deterrents. There is the lingering prejudice against psychological considerations. There is the lesser importance placed on the nonorganic aspects of medical care in relation to the organic. And there is the knowledge of how many pediatric practitioners currently avoid or overlook the psychosocial aspects of practice and the rationalization that no change in this pattern is particularly necessary, possible, or perhaps desirable. The concern has sometimes been expressed that increased attention to psychosocial pediatrics would lead to dilution of research and teaching in physical pediatrics. It is difficult to follow this line of thought. Its relevance to the place of the psychosocial considerations in the specialty of pediatrics escapes me. No reflective person wishes to see research and experience in physical illness in pediatrics minimized in any way.

Actually, most leaders in medical education recognize the broad responsibilities of pediatrics and are both informed about and support the new developments. It is the lack of investigative methodology, tradition of research, and atmosphere of scientific curiosity that constitutes, in my opinion, the crucial deterrents to recruitment of imaginative young investigators into this field of psychosocial pediatrics. Potential candidates are interested not only in acquiring a certain body of knowledge and skills but also in developing research competence that permits them to make personal contributions. In the absence of active research of this kind in departments of pediatrics, the young investigator turns to other fields. Besides this intellectual factor, traditional areas of pediatric investigation appear to offer a more certain opportunity for progress from a research fellowship to academic position than does the field of child development. Ideally, this should not be a factor in one's decision, but realistically it may be the decisive factor in career selection in many cases.

Investigative activities in psychosocial pediatrics and child development should be directed by the member of the department of pediatrics who has the appropriate interest and training. It would be hoped that in time such pediatricians could supervise the training of younger investigators within the framework of departments of pediatrics. Currently there are but few structured fellowship programs that provide systematic instruction in research methods applicable to this field and little in the way of fellowship support.

This phase of pediatrics must be, in its own way, as scientific as microbiology or biochemistry. Initially the research methodology used will be that borrowed and modified from the behavioral sciences. But as long as pediatrics depends on other behavioral scientists to conduct investigations in its own sphere of interest, this area of pediatrics will not achieve its potential role.

Furthering our knowledge about children is clearly a responsibility of pediatric research. If investigators interested in child development in its broadest sense are to be incorporated into pediatrics, it would seem the child development and study centers should not only have closer bonds to pediatrics but should be an integral part of university departments of pediatrics. This is not only because of the interest of pediatrics in the over-all aspects of childhood—biological, social, and emotional—but, even more importantly, because the pediatrician has the clinical experience that raises questions and hypotheses deserving of scientific investigation. What is needed is the application of suitable research methodology to pertinent questions. As outpatient departments become better organized and staffed, they will present opportunities for a great expansion of research productivity. They will represent a laboratory for clinical research in a new, developing aspect of pediatrics.

SUMMARY

Modern pediatrics has available an increasing knowledge of psychosocial aspects of child development. In pediatric practice and education, and in the application of pediatric knowledge and perspectives to the community's public health needs, the modern pediatrician has opportunities for advancing our knowledge of child development. It is suggested that pediatrics will increasingly become concerned with all aspects of child health.

The Unique Role of the Pediatrician in Modern Medical Practice

• *BARBARA KORSCH, M.D.*

University of Southern California

Pediatrics has changed most drastically in its short history as a medical specialty. Other professional disciplines, e.g., public health, nursing, social work, have also adapted to changing community needs, but they have not been confronted with the need for such fundamental reorientation or with such a threat to their basic professional identity as are pediatric educators and practitioners.

These urgent demands for self-evaluation and change on the part of pediatricians emanate both from the consumers of pediatric services, the parents of the children that constitute the pediatrician's practice, and from the pediatricians themselves who are dissatisfied with the nature of their practices and also with the manner in which their training prepares them or fails to prepare them for their real functions in practice. There has been a formidable amount of discussion, informal and in print, concerning these problems. No attempt will be made here to summarize or acknowledge all phases of this polemic. Even the appended bibliography contains only a few representative samples of statements of the varying viewpoints on the situation. I shall attempt only to analyze some of the factors that have placed the pediatrician in the position where he must stop and re-evaluate his professional functions at this time, and then proceed to outline what I believe to be some of the specific and unique contributions that the pediatrician can make to the health and welfare of children and their families in the present situation and to speculate on his future contributions.

Why are pediatricians forced to stop and think what they are doing, and what should they be able to do at a time when their colleagues from medicine and surgery are still much more comfortably tending to the sick in the way in which they were trained and living up closely to their professional self-image? Obviously, all the reasons for the pediatrician's conflict are valid for physicians in all forms of general and special practice, but in pediatrics there is something that makes the conflict more acute.

First, *the health needs of children* in the community have changed drastically in the last few decades in the Western world. Acute nutritional disturbances and acute infectious diseases were among the problems that most frequently required the pediatrician's knowledge and services when pediatrics developed as a specialty. Infant mortality due to treatable, preventable, acute illness was a major problem and has now changed quantitatively and qualitatively. Hospital treatment was required for a great many acute disturbances now amenable to ambulatory and home treatment. At present in this part of the world, the pediatrician is more concerned with health supervision, preventive medicine, treatment of minor acute illness, the handling of children with congenital anomalies, handicaps, chronic illness, attention to psychological problems, child rearing, and meeting parental needs that are the most time-consuming and demanding areas.

Aside from the changing needs specifically in the health field, there are *general changes in social philosophy and psychological thought* that have fundamentally affected pediatric practice. The psychosocial aspects constitute an increasingly significant portion of pediatrics. The advent of psychoanalysis and modern psychological and anthropological studies have radically affected the understanding of child development and child-rearing practices. Therefore, community and parental expectations of the pediatricians often have changed. For example, if, as is currently thought, future psychopathology can be causally related to certain early childhood experiences, the pediatrician finds himself in part responsible for their prevention. Also, in our Western society, with its dearth of absolute moral, social, and other objective values, there is an increased tendency to focus on human relationships and on children as the hope for the future. This has been called a "child-centered" age—and that certainly puts the pediatrician into the spotlight.

Perhaps also *the very nature of pediatric work* is such that it forces pediatricians toward introspection and re-evaluation. Pediatricians are accustomed to studying changing, growing organisms. Normal growth and development rather than the restoration to *status quo* are the criteria of health in their day-to-day work and have perhaps become the criteria of health in respect to their own professional performance.

Rather than recapitulating the current "crisis" in pediatrics, or exploring further the "sources of discontent" among pediatricians as they have been expressed repeatedly in recent years (Veeder and Nelson, 1957, 1958), I shall devote the rest of this essay to speculation about the future of pediatrics.

Thoughtful pediatricians and medical educators have proposed a number of alternative courses for the future of pediatrics. In simplified form, these would seem to consist of the following possibilities:

1. No radical revisions should be made in the medical curriculum. There should be a continued attempt to teach both the technical facts required for the conscientious medical care of sick children, and a modicum (or minimum) knowledge of growth and development, behavioral science, and understanding of human relationships needed to function in the role of a physician in contact with patients and parents.

2. A change should be made in the direction of equipping pediatricians better for the task of giving "comprehensive" medical care to growing children, including attention to their psychological and social needs—"the new pediatrics" (Levine, 1960; May, 1959).

This alternative implies acceptance of the changing needs and demands of the community, and increased emphasis on the human
aspects of patient care. It might involve diminished attention to
some of the traditional subjects of pediatric education dealing with
scientific technical facts relating to diagnosis and treatment of disease; or an increased total training period for the pediatrician
might be required. Perhaps a reorientation rather than an augmenta-
tion of the educational program might be sufficient.

3. A change could be made in the opposite direction, that is a
reorientation of medical education and pediatric practice that would
in effect result in the pediatricians functioning more as do other
medical specialists and consultants. They would be responsible for
diagnosis and treatment of disease in children and for research in
relevant fields of the medical sciences. They would have to function
largely in relation to medical centers since an independent individual physician could hardly be equipped to deal adequately with the
complex requirements of modern medicine. This alternative would
be predicated on having general practitioners or family physicians
available to deal with the less technical "common or garden variety"
of problems including the psychological aspects of the care of children and families. The recruiting of these family physicians and
planning appropriate educational programs for them is a problem
that the proponents of this alternative do not face up to.

4. The next alternative represents a combination of the second
and third possibilities outlined above. This might imply that pediatricians in training, after having shared a period of basic education
necessary for all who intend to take care of children, would then be
able to choose between two alternative training programs. One
alternative would prepare them for the consultant or specialist role;
the other would emphasize growth and development, knowledge of
psychosocial problems, and the "art of medicine," and would require
less time being spent on the subtleties of enzyme chemistry, coagulation factors, detailed techniques for diagnosis of congenital heart
disease, and similar topics. Some medical educators would visualize
the specialist as undergoing the same basic education as the family
physician to children, but would then have the specialist continue

beyond this time period while the family physician to children would have a shorter total period of training. Others have suggested that there might also be special areas of study such as behavioral sciences, interview techniques, etc., for the family physician which might not be necessary for the future specialists.

5. Another alternative that has been discussed is to maintain pediatric education and practice basically as they are but to make much more extensive use of ancillary personnel such as psychologists, social workers, public health nurses.

6. Finally, serious thought has been given to the question of whether the specialty of pediatrics, which developed at a time of special needs that no longer exist in the community, might logically be disbanded. This would leave the day-to-day care of children in the hands of the general family physician, and the specialized problems would be delegated to specialists who have no particular pediatric orientation.

In summary then, thought is currently being given to the possibility of having pediatricians very similar to the present ones in training and practice; to having no pediatricians at all; to having pediatricians function as consultants in the community; to having two kinds of pediatricians, the technical expert and the family doctor to children; and to educating pediatricians to serving their present functions better.

I do not intend to explore all these propositions at this time. The current discrepancy between the content of pediatric education and pediatric practice as well as the dissatisfactions and recognized inadequacies on the part of practitioners in pediatrics have led to a need to formulate these alternate solutions. Each one has been defended and each one has features that deserve consideration. A recapitulation of all these features would not be very enlightening. However, there is one aspect of the situation that merits more consideration than it has received in published commentaries on the role of the pediatrician. I am referring to the special contributions that can be made in various frames of reference by a pediatrician and *only* by a pediatrician.

The pediatrician's relationship to the children for whom he

cares and to their parents is unique. There are a number of features of this particular relationship which enable him to perform services that any one of a number of related specialists is not in a position to contribute at the right time and with the same effectiveness, though the latter may also have the required knowledge or interest in a specific area of medicine and human relationships.

Outstanding among these special features is the *continuity* of contact with the child during the period of growth and development and with the parents as they are expected to meet the child's changing needs over a period of time. It is clear that this constitutes a great advantage in dealing with an organism during a period of rapid and dramatic change and that no specialist who might be summoned for one particular episode and has to rely on a cross-sectional approach could approximate.

In addition, the pediatrician relates to the parents as parents, since he is the child's physician and can help the parents in their function in respect to the child more effectively than anyone who has to approach the parents in the role of a psychotherapist, medical doctor, or social worker. Problems in human relationships can be discussed by the pediatrician with impunity when an analogous approach by the parents' own physician would be much more threatening. For example, marital discord is a very personal, highly charged problem which human beings are loath to discuss until they reach the point of decompensation and have to admit to themselves and others that they are in need of outside help. On the other hand, there are situations where a pediatrician can easily, tactfully, and effectively help a couple to discuss and gain clearer insight into a marital disagreement *as it affects* the pediatrician's patient, their child. Indirectly, the marital strife may thus also be relieved, although the pediatrician is apparently only advising about the optimal environment for the child, a topic which many parents are quite willing to discuss and attempt to ameliorate.

The pediatrician, while at certain times being able to fulfill a psychotherapeutic role and using relatively nondirective techniques, also has the possibility not enjoyed to a similar degree by other members of the "helping profession" to use the *authority* that goes with his physical medical role to motivate parents and child patients in a more constructive direction. They expect to be told how many drops of medicine to give or what kind of shoes the child should wear, and although they by no means always do what they are told even in the physical medical sphere, there are occasions when they will accept thoughtful, direct advice on child rearing and minor behavior problems better from the pediatrician than anyone else.

The pediatrician in the framework of his traditional functioning as he offers health supervision, prophylactic immunizations, and sees the child for diagnosis and treatment of acute illness is *on the spot* to see parents and children as problems develop, to fulfill a preventive role, or at least to begin giving attention to a problem as it arises, instead of having to wait for the situation to become sufficiently disturbing and the parents to develop enough insight so that they would seek help on their own.

Due to the fact that under the usual circumstances, the pediatrician is summoned when a baby is just born or in modern practice may be consulted even before the baby arrives, the pediatrician from the beginning works *with* the mother or both parents. Thus, he is able to identify with their attitudes toward the infant and child as it grows and develops. This diminishes the tendency to identify primarily with the child patient and the temptation to defend the child against the parent instead of working for the child with the parents.

The pediatrician by the nature of his work is sensitized and obliged to assume a *broad* view on patient care. Infants and very young children are less differentiated than older individuals, and so the pediatrician of necessity cannot separate his interest in physical factors from psychological and emotional features. An infant can be slow in physical development because he has insufficient kidney function or because he has inadequate mothering. Similarly, the pediatrician, much more extensively than his counterpart in adult medicine, is forced to take into account the family and the community in which the child patient functions. He is required to obtain much of his information from the patient's parents or the school or other responsible individuals in the environment, and must also rely on them to carry out his recommendations.

Physicians who care for adults are always slightly dismayed when faced with a small patient. They are appalled by uncooperative behavior, failure to get adequate histories directly from the patient, the small size of veins for venapuncture, etc., all of which are accepted features of the pediatrician's ambience. Pediatricians acquire techniques in relation to children which yield greatly improved results. They know the range of normal for physiologic and other functions which enables them to evaluate their findings properly. It would be difficult to impart all these techniques to those professional workers who spend only a portion of their time with children patients, and it also would be difficult for medical specialists whose major effort is devoted to the care of adult patients to maintain the facility of handling children which comes with constant use and practice.

Pediatricians are well versed in, and with present emphasis will be even more informed on, all aspects of growth and development— the guiding principle of pediatrics that distinguishes it from all other medical specialties. General understanding of these principles is of course basic to all those professions which serve human beings, but the detailed knowledge which is the foundation of pediatric practice would overburden the training of the general physician.

Since the pediatrician in most instances starts out caring for healthy babies and has the mission of keeping his patients well, he traditionally assumes not only responsibility for health supervision but also for *preventive medical care.* Prophylactic immunizations are one of the best established pediatric services. Advice on prevention of accidents or instructions to prevent contamination of milk feedings are other examples. Thus, his whole orientation is toward safeguarding health and preventing disease and disturbances, two basic approaches which are most central in current medical thinking.

Likewise, the pediatrician tends to have more interest and to be a more active participant in community matters such as public health, education, and social institutions than do most practitioners of medicine and the related professions. It can be seen in many outstanding examples that the broader interest in child health, children, and youth that is prevalent among pediatricians extends beyond national boundaries, and in recent years great contributions have been made by pediatricians to international child health work.

Finally, there is another trend in current medical practice that lends itself well to adaptation of the pediatrician's special skills. The increasing complexity of medical practice with more and more specialization and an ever mounting number of specialized diagnostic and therapeutic techniques has led to a situation in which many child patients can no longer be optimally cared for by an individual physician. Specialists and technicians of various types are required for the child with congenital heart disease, for the cerebral palsy patient, or for the young patient with a hearing defect. Yet, this same patient who needs, for example, a pediatric cardiologist, angiocardiographer, and pulmonary physiologist for his diagnosis, and the multimembered pediatric surgical team for definitive treatment is a single small child who also has some other basic needs. He needs to know a number of things. He must know who is *his doctor,* he must be told what are the functions of the various people who come in contact with him, what does he have to look forward to, will it hurt, how long will he be in the hospital, can his parents come to see him, and why does he have to have his heart fixed when he never did anything especially bad. He needs someone in attendance who knows from past experience that he is allergic to penicillin and will not contribute to his medical problems by ordering this form of treatment.

In addition, the small child with the complex congenital heart lesion has a set of parents who are anxious, who may blame themselves for having had a child late in life, and who have many questions when they are asked to make far-reaching decisions about medical matters they do not really understand. These parents need *their pediatrician* to interpret the statements and maneuvers emanating from the various high-powered specialists in charge of their

child. The parents need someone to facilitate communication between these specialists and themselves and between one specialist
and the other. They need a guide and protector to lead them and the
child through the maze of the modern medical center.

The pediatrician in a situation like this ideally also serves to
interpret the child's psychological and physiological limitations to
the other medical specialists, so that they can give optimal care to
the child patient. Only the pediatrician who is himself trained in
medicine and pediatrics and has a basic understanding of all the
complex medical features of the situation and who is knowledgeable
and interested in parents and child as human beings can fulfill all
these functions together in the optimal way and at the right time.

In view of these considerations, among others, it appears to me
that a strong case can be made for the pediatrician to continue to
serve as the physician to children and indirectly to their families.
This position should not be taken as an argument against some of
the alternatives for changing pediatric education and practice. Having somewhat differential education and experience for different
groups of pediatricians is current practice. Other specialized programs may be developed to good advantage. Pediatric subspecialists
and experts will certainly be increasingly needed in patient care
and research as medical science gets more manifold and complex.
Increased emphasis on the behavioral sciences and the psychosocial
aspects of medicine for all medical students and physicians in training with additional teaching of the principles of growth and development to pediatricians appears eminently desirable. Finally, there
should be increasing utilization of related professional workers such
as public health nurses, social workers, psychologists, and educators,
not to substitute for but to complement the work of the pediatrician.

BIBLIOGRAPHY

Levine, S. Z. (1960), Pediatric Education at the Crossroads. *Amer. J. Dis. Child.*, 100:
    651-656.
May, C. D. (1959), Can the New Pediatrics Be Practiced? *Pediatrics*, 23:253-254.
——— (1960a), The Future of Pediatricians as Medical Specialists in the United States.
    Amer. J. Dis. Child., 100:661-668.

—————— (1960b), In: *Careers in Pediatrics*, ed. R. H. Spitz. Report of the 36th Ross Conference on Pediatric Research. Columbus: Ross Laboratories.

Richmond, J. B. (1959), Some Observations of the Sociology of Pediatric Education and Practice. *Pediatrics*, 23:1175-1178.

Senn, M. J. E. (1946), Relationship of Pediatrics and Psychiatry. *Amer. J. Dis. Child.*, 71:537-549.

Veeder, B. S. & Nelson, W. E. (1957, 1958), Correspondence [on the Dissatisfactions in Pediatric Practice]. *J. Pediat.*, 51:745-747; 52:115-121, 367-370, 490; 53:381-382.

Pediatric Potentials in a General Medical Group

• *RICHARD T. CUSHING, M.D.*

St. Louis Park Medical Center

Pediatrics as a separate medical specialty has been undergoing a re-evaluation and critical review by teachers, practitioners, and others interested in medical progress and education. Many voices have been heard attacking or defending present goals of the specialty and the adequacy of the training of pediatricians. There is a diversity of ideas regarding the role of the pediatrician in private medicine today and how to train him for this role; in fact, there are questions raised as to whether the pediatrician should be concerned with the health of children at all or just with systems or diseases of children. It is interesting to note parenthetically that the physician who further limits or narrows his interest is called a "sub" specialist by some or a "super" specialist by others; it apparently depends on one's point of view.

This essay proposes a broadened concept of pediatric purpose and demonstrates how the climate of a general medical group may promote the achievement of this purpose. Much of the stimulus for these thoughts comes from Dr. Milton J. E. Senn.

Health as a goal to be achieved rather than disease as a state to be conquered is a distinction that is important to make at the outset of this presentation, for this particular emphasis helps differentiate the more comprehensive view of pediatrics from the more limited one. As our knowledge increases many specific diseases will yield to our understanding, but it does not necessarily follow that health in a given individual will be achieved. Health, as defined here, is a state characterized by physical and emotional homeostasis, and this definition implies a potential rather than an actual state, probably never completely achieved by anyone. It is my contention that the basic purpose of pediatrics is to be concerned with promoting the health of both children and families since the health of one largely determines the health of the other. Promoting health implies recognizing health needs and seeking ways and means of meeting these needs. Health needs may be largely physical or largely emotional, largely centered with the individual's internal environment or with his interpersonal relationships.

The practitioner of pediatrics must be concerned with these health needs and, even more importantly, be able to evaluate how well these needs can be met by the family, himself, and the community. To state the point another way, child and family health requires supervision, and the physician concerned with child and family health should be oriented and trained to supply this supervision to the extent necessary in a particular family.

Health supervision includes somatic and emotional evaluation of the family and its members and advice about or treatment of health problems. However, knowledge in all areas of health is advancing well beyond the capability of any one physician to master. Thus, in order to gain the full benefit of current medical knowledge, the patient must trust that his physician will guide him to a consultant if necessary for special health problems. In addition, the pediatrician or family doctor acting as health supervisor must assume the responsibility of interpreting the consultant's findings and recommendations to the patient, using to full advantage his rapport from previous associations. While the importance of this role as medical guide may seem evident, it is disturbing to see how many people do not know how to secure competent medical advice. They become lost in a maze of "ologists" and depend on self-referral based on self-diagnosis. It is the health supervisor's job to see that the patient gets the help he needs and then makes sure that both know what help the patient got.

In the role of health supervisor the pediatrician of today must be prepared to discuss child-rearing problems with parents, for he will be called upon to do so and is in an ideal position to be of real help. The new mother is deluged with conflicting advice on how to "handle" her child, what to feed him, how to dress him, when to train him, how to get him to sleep, how to "make him mind." This advice reaches her through many channels. The first source is the model of her own parents' methods, as she remembers them, and which she may accept or react against. She then may have to deal with advice from her parents in their new role as grandparents, a full generation removed from their own child-rearing years. She must also listen to the next-door neighbor, the lady across the street, the bridge partner, all of whom find it easy to tell her what to do and how to raise her child. Or she may have no one to guide her at all. For various reasons, such as superstition or lack of information and objectivity, this advice of friends and relatives may be worse than useless. Recognizing this, the conscientious mother may then try to clarify the confusion by turning to the written advice of child-rearing experts. To her consternation frequently she finds differences of emphasis or opinion among the experts which may leave her more confused than ever.

What is needed, it would seem, is a professional counselor who is interested, objective, and knowledgeable. Who should do this counseling: the family physician, the pediatrician, the internist, the psychiatrist, the social worker, the minister, the family agency? All these are possible and presently existing sources of child-rearing advice. But the person with medical training is in a particularly advantageous position to do this counseling in view of this knowledge of physical health and his understanding of physical and emotional interrelationships. Even more important is the opportunity to make his interest in child-rearing problems known during the regular visits in the early months of parenthood. This helps the parents seek advice early when the problems may be less complex.

By tradition and interest, and often unhappily by default, the position of counselor has belonged to the family doctor who, in fact, generally has the least training and time to pursue this phase of health care. The pediatrician, however, may have certain unique qualifications which favor his acting as counselor because of his more intensive training in the understanding of children and their needs and his orientation to well-child preventive care. It may be no accident that he has chosen pediatrics as his field because of his sensitivity in this area. But the busy pediatrician finds himself caught in the same hectic swirl as the family doctor, especially when he is in solo practice and is confronted with ever-increasing demands on his time.

How then is the need of families for health supervision and child-rearing advice to be met by the medical profession? The prerequisites to this answer would appear to be physician acceptance of the concept of broad medical responsibility and time available to learn and practice it on an economically feasible basis. The current emphasis on comprehensive and longitudinal care in basic medical teaching may orient the physician in training, but the time factor cannot be answered by teaching, even by arming the physician with techniques which increase his efficiency. The time must be made available for pursuing this interest or it soon may be stifled.

One promising and workable approach to comprehensive care and health supervision exists within the framework of a general medical group with an orientation toward providing total family care. The two main potentials of this type of association lie in the management of the physician's time and the facility of communications between doctors. Patient and physician both are benefited, and the economics can be sound. The remainder of this essay will illustrate the ways in which time management and communications can make practicable the concepts of pediatric purpose previously discussed.

By having well-trained colleagues to call upon for help, the pediatrician will be able to set aside time to pursue a special medical interest without neglecting the urgent physical needs of his patients or jeopardizing his own economic well-being. More importantly, he will be able to be away on a regularly scheduled basis so that he can plan his work in an orderly and progressive way. At these times he knows his practice will be cared for, and his patients know this too. A colleague with access to the child's continuous medical record is available to handle acute problems. For example, in the group of which I am a member, there are five pediatricians among the twenty-four physicians. Currently, our special interests include subspecialty certifications in pediatric allergy and pediatric cardiology, and regular work in endocrinology, bacteriology, and behavior-problem counseling. As the doctor's interests expand or change, his use of time will change, and he expects to have his request for professional time away reviewed periodically by his colleagues. This allows re-evaluation and constructive criticism of his objectives.

The benefits of this use of time are obvious. The physician benefits by continuing his professional growth. His colleagues benefit by having a physician whose knowledge in a special area is current, and the patient benefits for both reasons. Time can thus be made available, too, for the managing of difficult diagnostic or therapeutic hospital problems which can easily submerge the solo practitioner to the extent that he feels compelled to refer this complex problem to others.

The freedom of exchange of ideas and the right to be critical of another physician's work are perhaps the most important factors in the enhancement of medical practice under the group approach. A situation similar to that in a teaching hospital may thus exist in that the group physician may at any time be called upon to discuss and defend his management of a particular case. Questions, comments, and criticism are freely sought and freely given. In this atmosphere of stimulation the problem case is thoroughly discussed, and the group's experience fully utilized. Moreover, the supervisory role of the original physician is maintained. The group member thus continues to learn and teach without threatening his self-esteem or pocketbook or those of his colleagues.

In this climate the pediatrician may truly maintain a flexible and stimulating role, having a practice in which he serves as health supervisor, consultant, teacher, and student concurrently and continuously. At the same time he can count on being with his family and on uncommitted leisure time, knowing that his patients have good medical care. This varied professional life and uninterrupted leisure time tend to avoid the rut of routinization and the treadmill of boredom—two of the most serious problems facing the pediatrician today. Few medical problems, no matter how complex, cannot be expertly managed by the team approach of a general medical group and the group level of medical competence not only maintained but frequently elevated.

In summary, this essay has attempted to demonstrate the need for a comprehensive approach to the practice of pediatrics, and to show how the climate of a general medical group makes this approach feasible.

Group Practice of Pediatrics in a
Rural Community

• *MORRIS S. DIXON, JR., M.D.*

The Wooster Clinic

During the last two decades, group practice has become very popular in most areas of the United States, possibly with the exception of the Eastern Seaboard and New England. There are many reasons for this popularity, and I should like to discuss them from the standpoint of the community, the patient, and the doctor—in particular, the pediatrician.

Today there is much comment in the lay press about a critical shortage of doctors. Some medical surveys report that there is not such a drastic shortage of doctors in the country as a whole, but a concentration of doctors in metropolitan areas and a lack in rural communities. General practitioners have practiced in these communities in the past, but nowadays fewer are being trained. Group practice answers some of these problems because the attraction of practicing with other well-trained men draws physicians, and particularly specialists, to more remote communities, which would probably not be able to entice the individual specialist in solo practice. No good pediatrician would consider practicing in an area that did not have a well-trained surgeon. Therefore, the community is very happy to have a medical clinic established, because it realizes that the clinic will draw sufficient medical personnel to take care of its medical needs.

Patients usually are enthusiastic about a group, after the initial visits. Of course, the individual physician with whom the patient has contact is more important than the group as a whole. The most important advantage from the patient's standpoint is the availability of a doctor at all times to take care of emergencies. "If you are too busy or unavailable, I can always be seen by one of the other doctors in the clinic" is a frequently heard statement. The common bond of practicing under the same roof makes the substitute physician more acceptable than two solo physicians covering each other.

A unit history, with all clinic visits and medical reports written in one chart, is another common bond which increases the patient's rapport with the substitute physician. The patient realizes there is continuity of care, which is less likely when he sees a complete stranger with no background information except the current history. A unit history is obviously an advantage for all physicians seeing the patient, because much of the past history is readily apparent on the chart, complete with laboratory data and therapy given.

Availability of consultation is a service appreciated by patients. Various specialists are in close proximity and frequently will consult on the problem during one office visit. Many times these consultations are brief, and usually are at no extra charge to the patient. If the problem is complex, then formal consultation can be made at a convenient time.

From the doctor's standpoint, there are several major advantages in group practice (Hunter, 1958). First is the proximity of his colleagues. There is a comradeship among physicians in a group that would be difficult to attain in solo practice. Sharing patients and sharing income are fundamental to this relationship. The rivalry which occurs between individual practitioners is seldom seen among members of a group. For the physician first entering practice, the group is a great enticement because of the rapidity of building up a practice. When a new pediatrician started practice twenty or thirty years ago, he would frequently see only a handful of patients during the first year or two. In a group, this is not a problem, because a need is present before a man is hired. He therefore has the framework of a practice provided for him on his first day. After the high level of productivity as a resident, it would be most disconcerting to have nothing to do for a year or two.

Most pediatricians who have just finished a residency have exhausted their financial resources, and so a guaranteed salary for the first year of practice is most welcome. There is usually very little outlay of capital necessary to begin practice in a group, because an office and equipment are provided. If the group arrangement is mutually acceptable, he very likely will have to buy into the group when he becomes a partner; but this is done at a time when income is greater than that necessary to take care of his immediate needs.

A major factor of group practice to me has been the release of the pressures of the business of medicine. Business decisions have to be made by the group or a committee within it. However, this is different from the day-to-day business decisions that are necessary in solo practice. Most groups of any size have a business manager who handles the common problems of personnel and financial matters, thus relieving the physician of this burden and allowing him to devote full time to the practice of medicine, for which he was trained. If a partner has a particular flair for the business of medicine, there is ample opportunity for him to use his ability in setting up policies for the approval of the group.

Few pediatricians have X-ray, electrocardiogram, minor surgery, and laboratory facilities in their offices. This is uneconomical in solo practice, but is an important asset to a group. For example, in working up a patient with a congenital cardiac lesion, it is much more convenient to have the chest X-ray, electrocardiogram, and blood count done during the same office visit; parents appreciate the convenience of accomplishing this in one visit. When a child is acutely ill with pneumonia, it is in his best interest to have a chest X-ray followed by appropriate therapy, with as little moving as possible. Emergency treatment, such as suturing lacerations or gastric lavage for poisoning, can be handled in the minor surgery adjoining the office with colleagues easily available to provide assistance.

A much heralded advantage of group practice is the freedom from need to be constantly available to patients. All groups have a call system to provide the service of a doctor, and yet allow each individual some free time. In my experience, the call system works well in a larger clinic in a larger community, where the pediatrician works with other pediatricians, and his telephone is not listed in the directory. In my personal practice, I am the only pediatrician in a small clinic, and living in a smaller community it is impossible to refrain from listing my telephone; therefore patients frequently call my residence regardless of my "call" status. I therefore must leave town to escape my work.

The result of Dr. Robert Aldrich's "Survey of Pediatricians in the United States" in 1958 (Levine, 1960) corroborates the fact that many pediatricians feel that they are stagnant because they see so few exciting medical problems. I find rural practice most rewarding in this respect because of the variety of the diseases requiring true pediatric training and judgment in their diagnosis and treatment. There are still a great many diseased children in our country who could benefit immensely from good pediatric care. To me, the current discussion among medical educators of pediatrics in the future can be answered emphatically that we need not only well-trained general practitioners but also well-trained pediatric generalists to handle pediatric problems in smaller hospitals (see Levine, 1960; May, 1960; Smith, 1960). Pediatric subspecialists (or superspecialists) will always have a place in large hospitals and medical centers.

Along with advantages of group practice there also are some drawbacks. The most important one is that groups occasionally have internal strife, usually over financial problems or personality clashes. A well-constructed contract, which is fair to all, will usually prevent financial strife. Choosing new colleagues carefully will help prevent personality problems. A rugged individualist will not be happy in group practice because he must share his patients to some extent with other members of the group. Sometimes patients will blame the entire clinic for one doctor's lack of diplomacy or error, instead of showing antagonism only to the individual.

As groups enlarge, they sometimes become impersonal, and patients feel that they are only a number. It is important for all clinic doctors to be aware of this attitude and to stress to all patients that each one should have a personal physician. When patients realize that their doctor feels a personal interest in them, they will learn to accept service from his trusted colleague, in the absence of their own physician. The business manager, receptionists, office, and nursing personnel need to be constantly reminded to regard patients as people with problems.

Earlier I stated that starting practice in a group is generally done at a much faster pace than in solo practice. However, as the physician ages and wants to slow down prior to retirement, this can become a problem in a group because of the shared income. When a man is not producing at capacity, the partnership suffers financially. Most groups have means of allowing the older members to practice more leisurely, but often this can be a problem and source of ill will.

In smaller communities, solo practitioners often resent a group. When a patient is referred to an individual physician in the group and sees the benefits of being a clinic patient, it is frequently difficult to observe medical ethics and make sure the patient returns to the referring physician; thus, the solo practitioners may feel that a group is a threat to their practice.

Other criticisms such as the inability of patients to have consultations outside of the group, abuse of laboratory facilities for financial return, and abuse of consultation within the group, are unjustified criticisms in my experience.

In metropolitan areas today, there is a great demand for general practitioners. Patients want a doctor to make house calls and treat the majority of their illnesses without repeated consultations with the various specialists, and yet he must be reasonably competent. They also want a doctor to listen to their problems and to be interested in them as individuals. I like to think of a medical clinic as the family's general practitioner. It is impossible for an individual physician to be competent in all phases of medicine today, but he can be quite competent in the broader specialties of internal medicine, pediatrics, surgery, and obstetrics. Each patient should have a personal physician (an internist or pediatrician) who will utilize the surgeon and obstetrician when needed.

Taking care of the "whole child" is more easily and possibly better accomplished in a group environment than in solo practice. There is no reason why a group pediatrician cannot be as close to parents and provide as good child care as a pediatrician in single practice. Associates who take care of other members of the family, and often have experienced stress situations with them, may know the family more intimately than the pediatrician; these colleagues can often provide helpful information and advice when counseling on psychological problems. The knowledge that emergency care of lacerations, poisonings, and burns can be given in the clinic by the child's own doctor is a source of comfort to most parents. Too frequently parents who have moved to our community from metropolitan areas tell me that their city pediatrician was happy to take care of their child by appointment when he was well; when an accident occurred, however, the child was usually treated in a hospital emergency room by a complete stranger.

Dr. Senn always stressed the need for the care of the "whole child" in his teaching sessions with the Yale house officers. Although his discussions usually emphasized psychological aspects of patient care, he never underestimated physical sickness. The practice of pediatrics in a multiple specialty group in a rural community offers the doctor opportunity to see large numbers of interesting patients and to care for them with the total concern which Dr. Senn's teachings have demonstrated.

SUMMARY

Some advantages and disadvantages of group practice have been presented from the standpoint of the community, the patient, and the pediatrician. Frequently better family and "whole child" care can be given by a multiple specialty group than by individual practitioners.

BIBLIOGRAPHY

Hunter, A. W. (1958), Joining a Group. *The Physician and Group Practice.* Chicago:
    Year Book Publishers, pp. 40-48.
Levine, S. Z. (1960), Pediatric Education at the Crossroads. *Amer. J. Dis. Child.,* 100:
    651-656.
May, C. D. (1960), The Future of Pediatricians as Medical Specialists in the United
    States. *Amer. J. Dis. Child.,* 100:661-668.
Smith, C. A. (1960), Who Will Take Care of the Children? *J. Amer. Med. Assn.,* 174:
    1373-1376.

The Hospital and the Child

• *RICHARD E. WOLF, M.D.*
University of Cincinnati

For over twenty years there has been a sizable body of pediatric knowledge developing around the subject of the psychological aspects of hospitalization and this has been part of the teaching in medical schools and pediatric centers throughout our country and abroad. Parents, pediatricians, and nurses have heard that every child coming to hospital deserves some preparation. Hospital staff members have known that children continue to need preparation for each new situation within the hospital period. Over the past two decades we have seen hospitals for children "humanized" in an attempt to minimize the emotional trauma inherent in the situation when a sick child is separated from family and is injected into a new and, to him, a very strange and frightening situation.

Why then make hospitalization and children the subject of an essay? I write about this because, despite the recognition by physicians and nurses, hospital administrators, and hospital boards that preparation is necessary, we look around at our children's hospitals and still find children coming to the hospital unprepared or poorly prepared. We still find the child who had been led to believe that he is going on an excursion. We still hear a parent promise that she will remain when there is no possibility of this. Children hear "It will not hurt" when it does hurt. Let us then take a look at ourselves, at the hospital, and at the child to see what the barriers might be to our better functioning in accordance with our own principles. Perhaps we shall gain a better understanding of why it is that knowledge of facts does not necessarily confer the wisdom to use the facts.

Some of the barriers in the way of better functioning in accordance with our principles must be related to the way we act as physicians. Doctors working in a hospital every day think it is a wonderful place, but when the doctor becomes a patient, he hates the hospital and its routine. Imagine how a child must feel! To him, the hospital is often a nightmare. Why is he separated from his mother? There are many things he cannot understand. Hospital care for children has become extremely complicated with intravenous infusions, blood transfusions, drugs, nasal tubes, laboratory studies—all of them necessary, but how can a little child understand this? As hospital care for children has become more complicated, it has tended to become impersonal and, though it quickly becomes routinized to the physicians, unfortunately, just as quickly, a numbness to the effect of the routine sets in. Though it may be routine to delay breakfast until a glucose tolerance test has been performed, it never becomes routine to a child to miss his breakfast. Though it is routine to have a gastrointestinal series extend over the better part of a morning with several trips to and from the darkened fluoroscopy room, this can never become routine to the child who is subjected to this experience.

Perhaps as physicians we expect parents to be preparing the child for some of the experiences he is to have in the hospital. But, if we do, we are assuming a sophistication and ability in the parents that do not necessarily exist. The parent cannot be expected to know the way in which we professionals are going to go about our professional duties where a sick child in the hospital is concerned. Even more important to an understanding of this is the realization of the difference between the child-parent unit when the child is ill at home and when the sick child comes to the hospital. When he is sick at home, he is Mrs. Jones's Johnny and Dr. Smith is a guest in the home when he visits. When Dr. Smith sends Johnny Jones to his hospital, Johnny becomes a guest of the hospital and the patient of Dr. Smith. That he is Mrs. Jones's boy somehow becomes incidental.

We understand the child's dependence upon his parents and we understand something about the building up of the sense of trust which enables him to depend upon other adults when they must substitute for parents. When a child enters the hospital, meeting his dependency needs is relegated to his doctor, the nurse, the house physician, to the other adults who are there to take care of him. This shift to other adults is not easy for the child. No hospital today can offer a child a single adult as his parent substitute for a significant period of time during even one day. It is not unusual for one child in the hospital to be seen for treatment, care, and recreation by more than twelve different adults in a twenty-four-hour period! And this child might be only two years old! We say growth and development must go on despite hospitalization, despite the period of time the child is in the hospital, and we add that a consistent relationship with a relatively few stable adults is a *sine qua non* for the development of personality, of discipline, and for emotional growth. Are these merely modern medical clichés? The more elaborate our children's hospitals become, the more difficult it seems to be to provide continuity of care and consistency in adult relationship for the individual child patient. When our conscience pricks us about this, rationalization and complacency set in. As long as the head nurse on Johnny's ward is a "natural" with children, he will be all right no matter how the lab technician talks to him for the few minutes she is with him. And how can residents and nurses and technicians get their work done if they spend two thirds of their time explaining things to a small child? We talk about teamwork and how everyone plays a part in the care of the child; and yet, do we really see to it that one person introduces the next one before leaving a child? How often does the attending physician introduce the resident to his child patient and say, "Johnny, this is the doctor who is going to take care of you while you are here. He and I work together, but he is here all the time, and I only come to see you once a day"? We say that a child should be admitted to a nurse not a unit, but how often does the nurse who admits a youngster to her ward introduce him to the nurse who will be taking care of him? When does this nurse bring to the bedside the nurse who relieves her when she goes off duty at 3:00 o'clock? Little things, simple things? Yes, but, as a parent, would you leave a child while he was napping, knowing that he would awaken, find you gone, and in your stead, someone whom he had not seen before? And yet, how easy it is to do this to a child in a hospital.

Parents contribute to this barrier to our functioning in accordance with our principles, too. What does hospitalization of a child do to a parent? When a parent lacks information of what to expect in a hospital—just doesn't know the facts—he can hardly support his child through it. Why, then, doesn't he ask? There may be several reasons why a parent does not ask for more facts of hospitalization. First of all, the parent has some mixed feelings about giving over the care of her youngster to the hospital and its staff, and not knowing is like not acknowledging something that is unpleasant. Part of the parent is willing to relinquish the child because she really knows that his best interests dictate this, but another part of the parent resists giving over this care to someone else. Furthermore, as other adults assume helpful and even lifesaving roles with one's child, the parent may feel less and less needed, even to the point of feeling left out and rejected. When this occurs, it is not beyond understanding that the parent counterrejects the child, as if "since you need me less, I'll do less for you."

Parents have their own varying capacities for mastering pain, both psychological and physical, and some would rather not know about painful things. In not having to think of unpleasantness, he may be less likely to communicate some of his own anxiety to his child. A parent may have had prior experience with hospitals, either in his own childhood or as an adult, and this experience may have left a residue of fear and anxiety now worked over and distorted with the passage of years. With his intellect, the parent knows that coming to a hospital does not necessarily mean serious or fatal illness, but with his heart, he feels that something has changed. If the hospital becomes home to the child, the parent will feel left out.

So far, I have been concerned with the behavior of adults in relation to hospitalization, behavior that indicates that we are not functioning in accordance with some of our own principles. But the child himself behaves in a different fashion and his behavior reflects attitudes that he has brought with him into the hospital, though the theme may be varied because of the factors of hospitalization, separation from home, pain or discomfort. These may cause him to behave toward himself in an altered fashion. Sometimes he is not able to separate the sick parts of his body from himself as a psychological unit. Odd behavior in a part of his body confuses his definition of himself. He becomes a different and unfamiliar person to himself. This is not unusual in acute illness, and severe pain changes the boundaries of one's concept of self, so that the self becomes the pain (Josselyn, 1954). If illness is chronic or leaves a permanent handicap, the response is more significant. Certain patients then indicate a loss of identity except in terms of their condition. When a child comments, "I am a polio patient," or "I am a heart case," this may imply a shift of self-identity from being a total person to being primarily a diseased part. Far better if the child says, "I have polio," or "I have a heart condition," than if he refers to himself as "a polio case" or "a bad heart."

The child's needs for physical expression are important. If the physical expression that comes through large muscles is impossible, because of his handicap, what are the other ways in which a child can express himself? The child may be handicapped by his disease, but he need not be further handicapped by the restrictions unnecessarily imposed by his treatment or the treatment milieu of the hospital. Sometimes our hospitals are too quiet for children. Most of the children in hospitals are physically restricted anyhow, and singing and shouting and the use of voice can take the place of physical activity when this is limited. The child physically restricted by paralysis or weakness is often too silent a child and one lacking in spontaneity. It is as if, because he cannot run as he used to, or as others do, he must also dam up other forms of expression. When such a child is encouraged to sing and shout, one often sees an expansion in his intellectual activities, his resourcefulness, and his personality in general. There is a real place for music and singing in a children's hospital.

The social expressions of a child of school age normally dilute the intensity of the emotional attachment to parents through peer attachments and activities. These may be seriously hampered in the hospital setting unless means are taken to prevent this. But there can be things to do and get-well clubs and convalescent activities wherein a group of children can socialize, can set up their own peer code, and make use of the adult only as the counselor as they go about the business of being children, without adult direction. This fosters normal social growth despite handicap and hospitalization.

Although we have school programs in our hospitals and their curricula keep pace with schools on the outside, the child who is in a hospital for a long time misses out on some of the crucial learning experiences of everyday life. Many things cannot be learned in the classroom, but are learned through the many incidents that happen by chance in any family. Consider for a moment the inability of the hospitalized child to have chance exposure (in small doses) to the naked body of another in seeing his parent or sibling of the opposite or of the same sex. This is virtually impossible in the hospital, and our techniques where bathing or toileting are concerned not only respect privacy of the individual child but make it next-to-impossible for a child to have some of this small-dose, easy exposure to the normal "affairs of the body." Yet, in this same atmosphere, he hears a great deal about bodies, sick bodies, and distorted body functions. To this he adds his own fantasies about himself and how his own particular disturbance will affect his function. Unless the staff realizes this and looks for opportunities to discuss with the child things about his body and its function, the normal parts and the normal functions, this will not just happen in the hospital. Education in the affairs of the body, call it sex education if you will, is a responsibility that adults owe children. If a child spends a long period of time in the artificial setting of the hospital, does he need this any less? Parents are less likely to have the chance opportunity to play the role of educator in this way when the child is not living at home, so doctors and nurses must be ready to handle the child's questions about his body, and ready to make use of the educational setting of the hospital ward to explain these things to the questioning child.

How then are we to meet the child's needs in the hospital? To answer this, we must first ask ourselves: what is a hospital? Webster's first definition is: "A place for shelter or entertainment of travelers, strangers." It comes from the French word meaning "guest." "Hospitality" is defined as "hospitable treatment, reception or disposition." What then is a hospital for a child? Certainly it is not a hotel, it is not a home, it is not a school, it is not exactly like anything else that a child has known. To the child, it is a new place in which he finds many new and strange things, new people, strangers, but a place where he finds enough of that which is familiar to him to feel that this is a child's place. If this is so, it becomes a new place where he can have new experiences and in which growth can take place. Toward this end, the physical atmosphere and the physical structure must have some familiarity. There must be furnishings and color and light and toys, an atmosphere that helps a child feel that he is among familiar things. The physical design should have taken the child into account, so that things that he is going to use are close enough so he can get to them. Shelves and cubbies, beds and chairs, steps to get up and down must be scaled down to his size and ability. Equipment must be that which can be handled easily by the youngster. The dishes and cups must be light so that he can hold them, and spoons and forks of a size proportioned to his hand and mouth. Straws for drinking should be flexible so that they do not crack when bent, and food trays constructed so that they will remain level when on a bed. These are the things that all children need in a hospital, and they can be adapted to the need of the individual child and his individual handicap, whatever this might be.

If the place must be designed for a child, it is even more important that the persons in this place be adaptable people. Anna Freud (1950) once said that many medical people act as if they wished that *only the child's body* came to the hospital, that the more troublesome parts of him—his feelings and his mind—remained at home! In a hospital where the child comes with his *body,* his *mind,* and his *feelings,* and where the goal is that all of these parts be ministered to as to the whole, the attitudes of the persons who make up his personal environment are crucial. The attitude of the professional, be this doctor, nurse, attendant, recreation worker or teacher, toward himself, toward the child, toward the disease, will determine the extent to which the child's needs will be met and the amount of growth that will take place.

No discussion of the needs of the child in the hospital would be complete without emphasizing the importance of frequent visiting by parents. Fortunately, the trend over the past ten years has been toward ever-increasing numbers of hospitals allowing daily visiting. In 1954, only 25 per cent of New York City hospitals allowed daily visiting. By 1958 the figure was up to 66 per cent and has risen since (Langford, 1961). The presence of the parent in itself is not enough. The child must feel that his mother approves of what is done to him and approves of the people who are doing it. Ways must be found for the parent to continue to participate in the child's growth and development so that family relationships remain vital ones. Flexibility in visiting hours so that a parent may be encouraged to participate in meals and recreation activities with a child keep relationships vital and sustaining. Visiting regulations that are flexible leave it up to parent and child to make their own plans for frequency of visits, recognizing the fact that some children, particularly older ones, do not need parents to visit daily. In our sweep toward the development of more natural facilities in hospitals, we must avoid "legislation" of naturalness and permissiveness. It is too bad to see a parent feeling compelled to visit an older child every day when neither he nor his child really need this, yet one or the other fears that someone will think less of him if there is not a daily visit since it is permitted.

A word about the future: hospitals have been changing in still another way. In the past twenty years who has not thrilled at the rapid advances of pediatric surgery? In 1940, when I was an intern, pediatric surgery consisted of correction of pyloric stenosis, intussusception, repair of herniae, appendectomies, treatment of osteo-myelitis, and, of course, tonsillectomies. Since then, there has been added the surgical correction of congenital anomalies of the eso-phagus, of congenital cardiac defects, the knowledge of lung cysts, better understanding and treatment of atresia of the rectum, opera-tions for Hirschsprung's disease, and a tremendous improvement in the preoperative, operative, and postoperative care of children. I am certain that during the next twenty years, every leading medical school and large medical center will have a department of pediatric surgery with a chief who will take his rightful place alongside the chief of pediatrics and of all other specialties. What does this mean for the child and what does this mean for the hospital? With the surgical advances in the treatment of congenital anomalies, it means that there will be more neonates and young infants spending sig-nificant periods of time in the hospital. It is challenging to think of the ways and means by which the parent-child relationship can get off to some kind of a healthy start, when the hospital and its corps of adults acting as parent-substitutes are interposed between the newborn and his family. What we have learned during the past twenty years about total care of the child in the hospital, the respect for parents, and the role of the parent in the hospitalization of a child will be drawn upon heavily as we program our hospitals to facilitate and support the technical advances that pediatric surgery heralds.

For the hospital it means that a children's hospital should remain a separate and complete unit staffed by men and women who give most, if not all, of their time, to all the phases of child care. Every activity of the hospital, from its playroom to the instruments used in the operating room, must be geared to the child. In such an atmosphere, the trainee in medicine and nursing—pediatric or sur-gical—absorbs the atmosphere of total child care. Fear has been expressed that, as pediatric surgery develops, our children's hospitals may tend to take on the sterile atmosphere that is associated with the traditional surgical field. This need not happen if we continue to put our knowledge to work. The fascination and reward of the development of pediatric surgery will add another chapter to the advances of medicine which have enabled the modern children's hospital to become a place to heal the child or to keep him well. What greater satisfaction can there be than the correction of a deformity in a newborn who has his whole life ahead of him? A hospital can have as the barometer of its environment the results it is achieving in the ongoing development of the very young child whose congenital condition may require him to spend significant periods of the first year of his life in the hospital.

Who knows in which direction the next dramatic advance in medicine will come? But certain it is that a hospital maintaining a constant creative approach which recognizes that "Yesterday is but today's memory and tomorrow is today's dream" will be ready (Gibran, 1923).

SUMMARY

Despite many advances in the direction of humanizing hospital care of children, and increased knowledge of why it is important, much remains to be done. This paper summarizes various aspects of the child's reactions and needs, the attitudes and concerns of parents, and some of those of the hospital staff members. It indicates some of the ways in which hospital care can be improved and poses questions in regard to the future nature of hospitalization for children. The need for continued work to improve this service to children and parents is stressed.

BIBLIOGRAPHY

Freud, A. (1950), The Role of Sickness and Hospitalization in the Life of a Child. Lecture, Psychiatric Clinic, Western Reserve University, Cleveland, Ohio.
Gibran, K. (1923), The Prophet. New York: Knopf.
Josselyn, I. (1954), Symposium on the Management of Long-term Illness in Children. American Academy of Pediatrics, Chicago.
Langford, W. S. (1961), The Child in Pediatric Hospital. Amer. J. Orthopsychiat., 31:667.

Early Pediatric Management of Acute School Avoidance

• *NORMAN J. COHEN, M.D.*

Rothchild Municipal Hospital, Haifa

• *MARTHA F. LEONARD, M.D.*

Yale University

Among the acute problems confronting pediatricians today is an increasing number of children who are prevented by anxiety from being able to attend school. We refer to this phenomenon as acute school avoidance—a general descriptive term, which may include children with school phobia. Inability to go to school may be attributed by some children to somatic symptoms or to apprehension that such symptoms would occur in school. Other children may experience fear, either diffuse or focused on the school or on some specific aspect of the school situation. When it is time to go to school, the child becomes acutely anxious, often cries, and cannot go. As soon as the parents abandon their efforts to urge or force him to attend school, the symptoms usually subside, and the child may appear comfortable at home until school is mentioned again. Psychiatric knowledge has indicated that the basic difficulty is usually

Supported by a grant from the National Institute of Mental Health.

The authors wish to express their gratitude to Dr. Albert J. Solnit for his advice in the management of these children and his encouragement and assistance in the preparation of this paper.

not in going to school but in leaving home—anxiety in anticipation of or at the time of separation from the parents.

When the parents realize that they are unable to help their child return to school, they often turn first to their family doctor or pediatrician. Usually he already has an effective relationship with the child and family as a trusted counselor who safeguards the child's health. He may be in the best position to expedite the child's early return to school if he is interested and prepared to accept the responsibility for the early recognition and management of this serious disturbance in the child's life. Immediate referral of a child with acute school avoidance to a psychiatrist may cause an unfortunate delay in the return of the child to school, especially if the parents are reluctant to accept psychiatric assistance. This may make his return increasingly difficult. On the other hand, early return of the child to school with the pediatrician's help often permits a more effective psychiatric referral later, if it seems indicated.

The rationale for pediatric management rests on four important assumptions: (1) that helping the child resume learning at school can be accomplished without uncovering the underlying etiological factors and without harming the child; (2) that the resilience of the developing, growing child makes it possible for development to resume if the obstacles can be circumvented temporarily; (3) that sufficient resolution of the obstacles can take place silently and through indirect means to permit the continuation of development and the mastery of future developmental tasks; and (4) that effective psychiatric referral and treatment are more likely if early pediatric care for this condition has been instituted. However, there is little in the pediatric literature (Eisenberg, 1958a; Warren, 1948) to guide the child's physician in the detailed management of this problem. The purpose of this paper is to share our conviction that the interested pediatrician can undertake the diagnosis and early treatment of children with acute school avoidance and to illustrate some of the principles of pediatric management.

This clinical report is based on the experience of two pediatricians in treating six children with acute school avoidance in the general Pediatric Outpatient Department of the Grace-New Haven

Hospital from 1960 to 1962. A large number of children had been helped by similar treatment in prior years, but had not been observed and reported in so great detail as these. The referrals were made by parents or by practicing physicians. A full pediatric evaluation was made and early pediatric management was instituted. The decision as to the appropriateness of psychiatric referral was usually considered only after the child's return to school. The case history of one child is recorded in full in the appendix. Vignettes from the histories of the other children will illustrate salient aspects of pediatric management.

PEDIATRIC MANAGEMENT

The first goal in the management of a child with acute school avoidance is the early return of the child to school. The pediatrician, understanding the importance of school experience for the developing child, will realize the urgency of this first step. The longer the child remains at home, the more he falls behind in his learning and the more difficult it is to catch up. The longer he is out of contact with his peers, the more painful it is to rationalize his absences. Even more serious is the fact that by being at home he elaborates the abnormally strong dependent ties to his mother which often have contributed to the initial separation difficulty. Secondary gains of closeness to the mother and freedom from the structured demands of the school program tend to perpetuate the symptoms and make return to school all the more difficult. Because of this increasingly corrosive influence of being out of school the physician's first attack must be on this symptom, even while the contributory factors are being investigated. Experience shows that successful return to school can be accomplished without full uncovering of underlying etiological factors.

Frequently, both parents and school demand early institution of home teaching. The provision of such instruction at home, even as a temporary arrangement, explicitly conveys to parents and child everyone's acceptance of the fact that he is too sick to return to school. It removes from the child the incentives for return to school

—keeping up with his class and conforming to school-attendance laws. Such an official stamp of approval of his remaining indefinitely at home often fosters his feeling of inadequacy and difference from his peers. Since the very nature of the problem is often separation anxiety, it is most important not to offer any alternative to the mastery of the child's ability to leave the home and return to school.

Sandy, an eleven-year-old adopted girl, was out of school for three weeks because of abdominal pains, nausea, and anorexia each evening and morning before school. She had a previous history from her kindergarten days of short periods of refusal to go to school. Having given up hope of getting Sandy back to school, the parents turned to their pediatrician. A complete medical investigation revealed no organic lesion, and the essentially psychological nature of the problem was noted. The child and her parents were seen separately on each clinic visit, during which the confident expectation and need for an early return to school were stressed. The pediatrician helped them to work out an acceptable way of coping with the anxiety at separation and assisting Sandy's return to school. Ten days later, during which there were two clinic visits, Sandy was back at school. After five additional visits during the next two and a half months, it became clear that a disturbed mother-child relationship had existed at least as far back as Sandy's second year of life. An impending move to a new neighborhood and promotion to a junior high school in this new area, as well as physical signs indicating Sandy's onset of puberty, heightened her anxiety and made her return to school all the more precarious. Referral for psychiatric help was suggested about two months after her successful return to school and was accepted by Sandy and her parents.

The pediatrician, presented with the problem of acute school avoidance, in contrast to most psychiatrists, starts with a complete physical examination in addition to a full history. Sandy is an example of the children in whom somatic symptoms were blamed for the child's nonattendance at school. A six-year-old girl in this series had abdominal pain, diarrhea, and allergic rhinitis, which were used as justification for frequent school absences. Avoidance of school in a thirteen-year-old girl was explained by her inability to stay in class because of frequent loose bowel movements. When each of these girls was allowed to stay at home, the somatic symptoms quickly subsided. The pediatrician, convinced by his evaluations that the child is physically well, or that the symptoms are out of proportion to any possible organic cause, offers reassurance to the child and parents. He explains the way anxiety can express itself in bodily symptoms. He pronounces it physically safe for the child to return to school on the basis of his expert knowledge, examination, and often laboratory assistance. This reassurance of health is important to all children and parents and is especially crucial when inability to go to school is rationalized on somatic grounds.

Sandy's parents had lost hope for her to return to school that year. None of the parents of the six children was able to take his child to school or to convey any real expectation for an early return. Eisenberg (1958a) described such situations: "The child may be urged to leave his mother's side, but she simultaneously tightens her grasp about him. He may be told he has nothing to fear by a father whose physical tremor indicates that some disaster lies in store. He may be 'ordered' to go in a hesitant and wavering voice that lets the child know that the 'order' need not—indeed, should not—be followed" (p. 651). In contrast to these contradictory verbal and behavioral cues of the parents, the pediatrician makes explicit and clear from the first contact his confidence that the early return of the child to school is to be accomplished. At no time is the return to school discussed in term of *if,* but always of *when* and *how.*

The pediatrician's conviction becomes more effective as the relationships develop between him, the child, and the parents. Three of these children were able to talk alone with the doctor from the first visit. The time of the visit is divided about equally between the child and parents, with the child deciding who should be seen first. In order to make the tense and anxious child comfortable, the first visits begin with a little play, using a ball, doll, crayons, or books. Initiating a discussion of the child's hobbies, sports, friends, and other interests, the pediatrician can then lead into more highly charged areas. His purpose is to convey to the child his understanding and acceptance of him in order to increase the patient's trust and enable him to identify with the pediatrician. This special doctor friend is one who can understand the child's difficulties without being critical and without taking sides. He makes it clear to the child that he will help him find a way to get back to school. The other three children were unable to leave their parents' side in the clinic. In the presence of the parents, the pediatrician used part of the time to talk directly with the child in a manner appropriate to his age. This helps to maintain the child's self-respect and strengthen his trust in his doctor. It is also an example to the parents of how the child's feelings and opinions, even in highly charged areas, can be elicited from and discussed with the child.

The parents are all offered an opportunity of discussion alone with the pediatrician. Where separation cannot be accomplished in the clinic, occasional visits are scheduled for the parents without the child. As a sympathetic and noncritical listener, the pediatrician enables them to express their views of the problem and their feelings about the child's being out of school. This often promotes better communication between the parents, who may express their feelings more readily in the presence of a neutral person. The parents are helped to appreciate the seriousness of the child's being out of school, the malignant course of untreated school avoidance, and the importance of the child's need to develop self-confidence and independence. This understanding enables them to collaborate in a plan that helps the child to return to school. With the beginning of this active collaboration the parents are less overwhelmed by the child's complaints and more secure and consistent in their handling of him.

On the day that Kathleen, an eleven-year-old fifth grader, received her first D on a report card, which upset her greatly, she also learned of the sudden death of her paternal grandfather. Her stay at home for the period of grief was then extended by the birth of a baby sister, an attack of cervical adenitis, and the death of the maternal grandmother. After six weeks it became apparent that Kathleen had no intention of returning to school, saying that the thought of school made her feel "creepy" and want to vomit. The mother's difficulty in handling Kathleen was accentuated by her fatigue during her postpartum period and her involvement with the new baby. The school nurse and guidance teacher came to the home one day and took Kathleen to school forcibly, but the mother forbade them to do it again because it was too upsetting to her and the child. The father often accompanied Kathleen to the clinic. After he became convinced of the seriousness to her future of this interruption of her normal school experience, he was able to stay home from work one day and take Kathleen to school in a firm but nonpunitive way. In the meantime, her motivation to return to school and her confidence in her ability to do this had been strengthened by weekly visits to the pediatrician and occasional telephone calls. She went right back to all her classes, and in three days requested to go on the school bus with her friends. She did not miss another day from school during the rest of the year and was able to catch up in studies sufficiently to be promoted.

Although it is not yet clear what part the father-child relationship played in Kathleen's acute school avoidance, inclusion of the father in the plans for her return to school was of crucial importance. With the encouragement of the pediatrician and his help in deciding when Kathleen was ready, the father succeeded after a month of fruitless effort by the mother. Because the intensity of the father-child relationship is often much less than that of mother and child, separation from the father at school may be less conflicted than from the mother. It may also be easier for the child to leave his mother at home rather than to be left by her at school. The child's ability to be active in the separation may aid in his mastery of this difficult task. The father's strength and firmness may be of vital support to both the child and the mother in accomplishing separation which is difficult for both of them. The return of three other children was also facilitated by the participation of their fathers, while the father's involvement was minimal in the case of the other two children. All the parents required explicit permission to take a firm stand instead of their former helplessness and inconsistency.

Kathleen verbalized clearly her determination never to return to school, saying it did not matter if she were not promoted since she was not going to school next year either. The pediatrician tried to uncover and strengthen her unexpressed motivation to separate from her parents and return to her regular school environment. He worked closely not only with the child's parents but also with the educators to construct a plan for this particular child. A visit to the school by the doctor acquainted the teaching staff with his work with the child and family. The teachers were reassured when Kathleen's inability to attend school was explained to them as a problem of separation from home rather than a fear originating in school or deliberate truancy. Possible modification of the school routines to reduce her anxieties on the first days were discussed. Where parents and teachers working alone had been unable to force the child to attend school, coordination of their efforts and understanding to work with that part of the child which wanted to be in school provided an atmosphere in which the child's anxiety could be tolerated, enabling the child to return to school. Though some children need a gradual introduction to school by visiting after hours, or first spending time in the library or the principal's office, others can better tolerate immediate return to the full school day. Kathleen's return was accomplished in three steps: a visit to the teacher after school; one unsuccessful attempt at part-time return; and finally return to the full school program.

The plan for the child's return to school must avoid forcing the child beyond his tolerance. One can be firm without being cruel. This involves a sensitive titration of how much the child can tolerate. It also requires an assessment of how much the environment at home and at school can be adapted to the child's needs, and yet not distort reality to a degree that impedes rather than facilitates healthy adaptation. Her father's staying home to take Kathleen to school gave her the firm direction she needed. However, allowing her to try staying in the principal's office instead of going to class on the first day was not a useful adaptation. For her it was important to go right back to the full school program and be accepted as a regular member of her class.

In the course of helping children to return to school, the pediatrician is often faced with urgent requests for drugs. In this series, none were prescribed after the children were referred to the clinic. The use of drugs often implies illness to the child and makes it more difficult for him and the parents to accept the pediatrician's reassurance that the child is in good physical health. Any lessening of the acuteness of the child's perceptions by a sedative or tranquilizer might interfere with his ability to think clearly about his problem and gain self-confidence. Since the active participation of the child and parents is required to face the psychological nature of the problem and to build inner strength to combat it, dependence on outside panaceas such as drugs seemed contraindicated. There was also less risk of harming the child or exceeding his tolerance of the school situation if drugs were not used.

Life's crises, such as deaths or births, may precipitate or prolong school avoidance, as it did for Kathleen. When such crises occur after the child's return to school, a relapse may demonstrate the precariousness of the first return and the need for continued treatment. Relapses also may occur without obvious crises. The pediatrician's work is not completed with the first return to school.

On her third day in the first grade, six-year-old Jane developed a mild gastroenteritis. Two weeks later after disappearance of the fever, diarrhea, and tenesmus, she would become acutely panicky and complain of abdominal pains and loss of appetite in the morning when going to school was mentioned. The symptoms vanished completely with the family's acceptance of her remaining at home with her mother. The mother was an intense, anxious, often depressed and bitter woman, extremely dependent on and angry at her family. She had strong feelings about her own inadequacy. The father, an interstate truck driver, was often away from home, and the marital problems were severe. Jane was very dependent on and demanding of her mother, who was overconcerned about Jane's symptoms and completely unable to get her to go to school. Jane refused to separate from her mother during the clinic visits. The intensity of the mother's involvement with Jane and a severe marital conflict indicated the need for psychiatric treatment of the mother. Accordingly a psychiatric referral was suggested, but was refused. A single visit of the mother with a social worker precipitated the mother's "prostration," her reaction to the threatened airing of some of her unacceptable feelings. From this time clinic appointments were consistently canceled because of finances, weather, or health. However, Jane was now back in school, perhaps mobilized by her mother's alarm at the psychiatric referral. Occasionally Jane repeated the pattern of absences due to minor physical complaints. Regular telephone contact initiated by the pediatrician with Jane and her mother was maintained. Sixteen months after the initial clinic visit, at the birth of a sister, Jane again was unable to go to school. She returned after a week and achieved satisfactorily in her second grade work. Her attendance at school, together with her increased ability to separate from her mother, assisted her to express more independence; she was less whiny and clinging. She even began to resist her mother when the latter tried to keep Jane out of school.

Three other children had occasional absences from school after their initial return, attributed to vague illness or anxiety over report cards or tests. One demonstrated ability to continue regularly in class even with minor respiratory infections, for which her mother had previously encouraged and would now have allowed her to stay at home.

The efficacy of the contact with Jane was restricted by its limitation to the telephone. Calls were made by the pediatrician to both child and mother. The child was supported in her progressively successful attempts to leave home in the morning. The mother was reassured that she was a good mother in keeping Jane at school and not cruel or harmful to her daughter. She became increasingly able to discuss the personal relationships within the family and her feelings about the child. She displayed moments of awareness of the psychosomatic nature of Jane's symptoms. With her increasing ability to see Jane as a competent seven-year-old, she was encouraged to tell Jane about the pregnancy, answer Jane's questions, and provide the child with basic facts about sex education.

It is important for the physician, parents, and child to understand that separation anxiety of long standing is not quickly dissipated despite symptomatic relief. The child and parents continue to need support and guidance as they learn to handle the anxiety associated with separation. Contact with the pediatrician at longer intervals enables them to discuss many of the factors which were associated with the acute school avoidance. Their fears and apprehensions can be verbalized, and clarified, and become more tolerable with the physician's help. Learning to understand the connection between fear and its physiological manifestations, the child may avoid or be able to understand and tolerate symptoms. For four of the children, continued clinic visits at longer intervals served to strengthen the relationship between the physician and the child. It formed the basis for working with the child in other areas of difficulty and concern, including sex education, sleep disturbances, and recent life's crises.

In all six children there was a disturbed sleeping pattern, which was probably another manifestation of separation anxiety. Teddy, the twelve-year-old boy, whose history is reported in the appendix, showed the most marked sleep problem. From the age of six he spent many nights in his parents' bed. After many discussions, the pediatrician succeeded in convincing parents and child of the importance of Teddy's learning to sleep alone. In a four-and-one-half-year-old boy, who was seen for acute nursery school avoidance, the sleep disturbance consisted of a difficulty in falling asleep, which led to moving his bed into the parents' room and many scenes of anger and spanking. With the support of the pediatrician, the boy surprised his parents by his request to move back to his own room. He then was able to return to school.

RESULTS

Pediatric management of these six children resulted in the return of all to school. The youngest boy had been out of school only a few days, the remainder from three to six weeks before the first visit to the clinic. After the start of pediatric management, the earliest return was accomplished in ten days. Four of the children were back within the first month, and the last after two and a half months. The pediatrician saw the children and parents two to six times, and in four instances made a visit to the school before the child's return. All children were still in school one to two years later. Three have continued to attend school regularly. The other three have had a few brief recurrences of school avoidance, and one had fifty absences in the last year attributed to minor illnesses and the birth of a sibling. Psychiatric evaluation and treatment are indicated for these three, but the parents of only one have so far accepted it. One child, who has attended school regularly since her return which was aided by pediatric management, is awaiting psychiatric treatment. An important factor in the successful return of these children to school was the speed with which pediatric management was instituted.

As a result of the early return to school, these children, all of apparently average intelligence, have been able to fulfill requirements for their respective grades. Even more important is their mastery over their fearful avoidance of school and their acquiring of a degree of independence which may free them for further normal development.

COLLABORATIVE ASSISTANCE

After the establishment of the relationship between pediatrician, child, and parents, and the child's return to school, it is appropriate to consider the need for psychiatric referral. The pediatrician with his positive, directive approach has been able to help the child return to school without jeopardizing his future relationship with the child. Although the pediatrician usually cannot be clear about the underlying conflicts and their compromise functions, he works toward strengthening the child's interest in returning to school. Where the disturbance has not been too severe, the younger and more resilient child may be released by his successful return to school to follow a more normal pattern of growth and psychological development. The pediatrician may be assisted by occasional discussions with a child psychiatrist about his particular patient.

Where the intensity of the parents' involvement and the severity of conflicts indicate the need for further clarifying the underlying factors, and psychiatric help is not accepted by the parents or not available, a social worker can see the parent while the physician continues with the child. The social worker enables the parents to uncover and better understand some of the less obvious aspects of their relationship with the child and each other. The child's rapport with his physician may be enhanced by his not having to compete with his parents for his doctor's time and attention. Frequent sharing of information between physician and social worker aids both in their collaborative management of the problem. A successful social work contact often facilitates psychiatric referral.

Psychiatric treatment of the child is desirable when in the course of pediatric management it has become clear to the pediatrician that despite the child's return to school, the manifest or underlying psychological difficulties persistently interfere with the child's balanced development. The acceptance of the referral may be a measure of the child's and the parents' trust in the physician, and of his preparation of them for this move. He can establish a foundation for an effective psychiatric referral by answering the questions of child and parents and helping them work through their hesitations about this form of treatment.

Some parents are never able to accept or obtain psychiatric treatment for their children. The pediatrician's patient and noncritical support may be important even though all the underlying psychological conflicts which fostered school avoidance are not uncovered. Being back at school provides the child with experience which is essential for the promotion of healthy and balanced development. A more normal peer relationship and release from some of the unhealthy dependency on parents give to both parents and child a measure of increased confidence and independence. As a result of the help received, both children and parents see their pediatrician as a humane and understanding person who is interested in their physical and psychological welfare. If recurrences of school avoidance occur, the foundation established by the previous pediatric management can encourage and facilitate an earlier request for help.

ETIOLOGICAL CONSIDERATIONS

Understanding the dynamics of separation anxiety stems from psychiatric formulations and can be made more meangingful for the pediatrician by occasional discussions with a child psychiatrist. The basic problem in school avoidance has been formulated by Johnson et al. (1941), Eisenberg (1958a, b), and others (Broadwin, 1932; Coolidge et al., 1957, 1960; Davidson, 1961; Estes et al., 1956; Partridge, 1939; Talbot, 1957; Van Houton, 1948; Waldfogel et al., 1957) as a difficulty, not in going to school, but of leaving home—anxiety at separation from parents. This is defined as "a pathological emotional state in which child and parent are involved in a relationship characterized by intense need on the part of both to be in physical proximity" (Johnson et al., 1941). This anxiety may be displaced onto the school. It is usually the mother from whom the child has difficulties in separating. The acute inability of the child to go to school is usually precipitated by some crisis which makes mother and child more dependent on each other. Going to school is often made more difficult because each fears what might happen to the other during their absence. The parents' ambivalence, both fostering and resenting the child's dependence, leads to their giving the child contradictory verbal and behavioral cues. This was well illustrated by the mother who warned her daughter that the nurse and guidance teacher were going to "drag her bodily" to school in a tone which clearly encouraged the girl to resist. The parents' acceptance of the child's remaining at home and the secondary gains to the child— more attention from the mother and reduction of school demands— tend to perpetuate and increase the difficulties of separation and of return to school. Extremely close and involved relationships between parents and grandparents as well as children may be a factor in the development of separation anxiety, as demonstrated in the report of Teddy (see Appendix). Another child's anxiety was heightened by her parents' marital discord.

Serious health problems in the parents may also be important contributing factors. This was especially significant in the history of Bobby.

When Bobby was fifteen months old, his mother had an acute depression, for which she was treated with electric shock therapy while remaining at home. For at least three months her depression and confusion rendered her unable to take any interest in Bobby. He was cared for by a series of maids, and was considered too young ever to have his mother's illness explained to him. About this time he developed severe temper tantrums, sleep disturbance, and an inability to leave his mother. During his first year of nursery school he became increasingly reluctant to attend. At the beginning of the second year, at the age of four and a half, he showed such panic that he could no longer go to school. Although there was no obvious triggering event to precipitate his acute school avoidance, the fears evoked by his mother's withdrawal of interest from him at a crucial stage in his development must have been one of the important underlying factors. As soon as Bobby had been helped to attend another nursery school, his mother wanted to stop his clinic visits because of his reluctance to come.

Some of the other children's histories suggested more definite precipitating causes for their acute inability to go to school. One girl developed acute school avoidance after an attack of gastroenteritis. Promotion of a boy who was extremely short from the top grade of a small elementary school to the lowest grade of a large junior high school seemed to trigger his symptoms. In another girl the combined crises of a death in the family, a low mark on a report card, and birth of a sibling culminated in her withdrawal from school.

SYMPTOMS

The form of the symptoms understandably varied according to the age and developmental levels of the children at the time of onset of the acute stage. A four-and-one-half-year-old boy manifested his separation anxiety by temper tantrums; a six-year-old girl had a mild behavior disturbance, many somatic complaints, and an unjustifiably large number of absences from school. She had a limited ability to verbalize her fear of going to school. The four older children were not considered to be behavior problems, and could verbalize clearly their dread of somatic symptoms and overwhelming fear of the school situation. Thus acting-out behavior and diffuse anxiety seem to predominate in the preschool child; somatic symptoms are more characteristic of early latency children; and as the child approaches puberty, he may have an increasing ability to focus on the problem through verbalization, although his symptoms are often somatic or experienced as a fear of acting like a baby at school.

PREVENTION

Can the pediatrician prevent the development of serious separation anxiety in his early contacts with a family? Anxiety at separation is a normal phenomenon. John Bowlby (1960) states: "I have been

impressed both by the frequency of the separation anxieties exhibited at high levels in neurotic patients and by its ubiquity at more
modest levels of the every-day life of all of us." Knowing this, the
pediatrician can help parents understand and carry out appropriate
steps at each age level. The physician promotes healthy separation
and learning experiences through his guidance in the introduction
of the cup, weaning, self-feeding, sleeping arrangements, and toileting. Mastery of early separation experiences lessens the anxiety of
child and parents, and prepares them for increasing degrees of separation. Nursery games, such as peek-a-boo, bye-bye, and hide-and-
seek, aid the child in coping with separation anxiety. It is believed
that the child's active repetition of what he has previously experienced only passively helps him to master the anxiety. The introduction of dependable substitutes for the parents enables the child to
learn to tolerate the parents' absence for increasingly longer periods.
At the time of crises in the family, such as birth, death, serious illnesses, or operations, the physician collaborates with the parents to
assist the child in understanding these significant events. The parent
and physician can help the child to understand by means of explanations or through providing opportunities to play out his feelings
and questions about these painful and threatening events. The language and play used are appropriate to the child's age and capacity
to comprehend his own experiences. When a crucial event is anticipated, such as the birth of a baby or elective surgery, this educational
approach serves as preparation. When crises are unexpected, explanation at an appropriate level as soon afterward as possible helps the
child to use the experience constructively.

Awareness of expected levels of anxiety at separation in a growing child alerts the pediatrician to the need for concern when the
degree of anxiety becomes excessive. Infantilization of the child and
his inability to show age-adequate levels of independence are danger
signals of future separation anxiety which warrant the physician's
intervention. Another sign of increasing separation anxiety may be
abnormal sleeping patterns, e.g., where the child shares the room
or even the bed of his parents. Other examples include fears of
separation which interfere with the normal activities of child and

parents and frequent absenteeism from school attributed to vague minor illness. Repeated loss of appetite in the morning, crying, and resistance to leaving home, even though school attendance may be accomplished, are all warning signs of fear of separation and potential school avoidance. The pediatrician must realize the seriousness of the implications and tactfully share his concerns about them with child and parent. Instituting a plan of pediatric management on the basis of principles previously described may prevent the separation anxiety from becoming an obstacle to school attendance.

SUMMARY

The rationale for the pediatrician to undertake the early management of children with acute school avoidance is formulated by the description of the pediatric treatment of six children with acute school avoidance problems. In all six children early return to school was stressed as a primary goal and was accomplished in the context of pediatric care with a recognition of the essentially psychological nature of the problem. Reassurance was offered in regard to sound physical health and an explanation of the physiological manifestations of anxiety was communicated to child and parents at an appropriate time. The pediatrician's firm expectation that the child would soon return to school was clearly conveyed to the child and parents. As the physician realistically established a positive relationship with child and parents, he also was able to resolve any pressure from the parents or relatives to treat the child with tranquilizers or to institute homebound teaching prematurely. The father's active participation in any plan for the child's return to school was often essential and always helpful.

Plans for the child's return to school emerged from discussions with the principal and teacher. Such planning, usually at the child's school, took into account the child's and parents' tolerances of anxiety in order to make certain that the return to school was accomplished in a humane and nontraumatic manner. The return to school was viewed as the first step toward helping the child with his anxiety and not as a cure. Our experience indicated that acute school avoidance was usually related to a previous separation anxiety. Thus, pediatric guidance includes the prevention of acute school avoidance through the early detection of untoward separation anxiety and through providing assistance to cope with realistic separation experiences.

APPENDIX

Teddy, a twelve-year-old Jewish boy, was referred to the Pediatric Clinic in October, 1960, by his father's physician, after a month of inability to go to school. His trouble began after he entered seventh grade in a large junior high school, a marked change from the small elementary school in his own neighborhood. Both the size of the school and the size of the students were overwhelming to this boy who was only 51 inches tall. On the fourth day, for no obvious reason, he felt sick in school with abdominal distress and fear of crying, and was allowed to go home. When the symptoms recurred the next day, the school nurse persuaded him to stay in school because it was probably "nerves." The following morning he cried, trembled, and said he could not go to school although he did not know why. Day after day this scene was repeated. The parents' efforts to force, plead, humiliate, bribe, scold, or punish were to no avail. As soon as they gave up helplessly for the day, Teddy relaxed, watched television, rode his bicycle, or helped his father in their clothing store. Hebrew and Bar Mitzvah lessons were also abandoned. Tranquilizers had no apparent effect. Teddy's father's physician recommended forcibly taking Teddy to school. After this was tried once unsuccessfully, he referred the boy to the Pediatric Outpatient Department.

Teddy lived with his parents and sixteen-year-old sister in a small four-room apartment. He had been a placid baby, the delight of his parents and grandparents, who had never been able to deny him anything. He had always been attached to his mother. At three years he had a traumatic experience following herniorrhaphy at another hospital, where he became extremely fearful at being left alone with a net over his crib. From this time he had many nightmares and later began to "sleepwalk" into his parents' bedroom nearly every night. Concurrently with his school avoidance he became fearful of going to bed in the room he shared with his sister. Rather than having him cry or stay awake, his parents allowed him to sleep with them. He was considered a good, respectful, and affectionate boy, but always insistent on getting his own way.

Teddy's father, a forty-six-year-old clothing-store owner, was a small, hard-working, cheerful, but tired-looking man who was subject to spells of unexplained trembling and had recently had a spine operation for a ruptured disk. The patient's mother, forty-four years old, worked part time as a cashier in the store. She was also short, plump, cheerful, and affectionate. Both were angry, perplexed, and helpless at Teddy's acute school avoidance, wondering whether it was motivated by real fear or deliberate avoidance of school demands. Both parents were subjected to family pressures and criticism for their inability to return him to school. Teddy's sister had also had morning crying spells on the first few days of junior high school, but had been able to attend school.

Teddy was a cherubic-looking boy with large round eyes and plump rosy cheeks. Physical examination showed no abnormality except his short stature and moderate obesity, especially of waist and hips.

Teddy and his mother, and occasionally both parents, were seen at first about once a week with the time divided about equally between them. Although Teddy could talk with the doctor alone, he stayed right outside the door when his parents and the doctor were conferring. Teddy's visits began at first with playing tic-tac-toe and making drawings of his house and apartment. Conversations about his friends, hobbies, and interests led to his school experiences and his feelings about returning to school. After the initial visit he talked easily about his dread of going to school, saying that the funny feeling in his stomach and his fear of crying made it impossible for him to try. He declared firmly that he wanted to return to school, but that he could not cope with the panicky feelings which arose at the thought of going. After a complete physical examination he was assured of his good physical health. His trembling and abdominal symptoms were explained as manifestations of anxiety. The pediatrician emphasized the importance of Teddy's return to school and the certainty that Teddy would accomplish this step with help. Teddy was urged to choose a day for his return, but both he and his mother procrastinated about the dates chosen.

The parents were also assured of Teddy's good health and the fact that his crying and trembling would not harm him. They were given an opportunity of voicing their feelings and fears about Teddy's school avoidance. Apprehensive about the loss of school time, they requested a home teacher. The pediatrician explained that it was more important for Teddy's future learning to have him return to school as early as possible. The parents were given permission to be firm with Teddy without being punitive, and were helped to work out a nontraumatic way of returning him to school. The pediatrician made a visit to the school, where it was also necessary to explain the importance of not instituting home instruction. The cooperation of principal and guidance teacher was enlisted to adapt the school program to Teddy's needs when he first returned to school.

About one month after the first clinic visit, a day arrived when, spurred by the lashing remarks of a favorite uncle, his parents were able to take Teddy to school. Since he was unwilling to try to attend a class, he was allowed to stay in the principal's office, filing cards, and running errands for a few hours. After two days of this, he borrowed money from the guidance teacher to stay for lunch. By running errands in the school he became familiar with the building and teachers. From his own teachers he obtained some work assignments and began to do homework. About two weeks after his initial return to school, on a day of his choice, he began to attend classes. He worked hard to catch up and seemed happy in school. However, the stress of report cards, oral reports, or return after vacation sometimes resulted in his staying home a day or two or returning to the principal's office for a day. On one occasion, when his parents were going away on Friday for a week end, his mother suggested that he stay home because he would probably be upset. He went to school, but came right home again. In spite of these occasional absences, he enjoyed the year and finished it and his subsequent eighth grade satisfactorily. About the time of Teddy's return to school, his parents arranged for his Bar Mitzvah instructions at home. He took great interest in this and learned readily. On the occasion of the Bar Mitzvah, his mother was sure he would break down, but he took his part with confidence and poise.

However, the sleeping pattern did not improve, and night fears grew more intense. Although Teddy would go anywhere happily during the day, at night he locked and bolted doors, locked windows, and refused to stay at home without a parent or grandparent. The parents accepted Teddy's sleeping with them, but they were angry at his inability to let them go out. His crying and trembling resulted in prolonged efforts to reason, reassure, and bribe. The parents would finally leave feeling shaken, angry, and guilty.

Continued clinic visits, about every two to three weeks during this period, led to better understanding of the pattern of extreme closeness in this family. The maternal grandparents had also lived in a four-room apartment, subletting one of the rooms. Teddy's mother and her sister had slept in their parents' bedroom until their adolescence. After Teddy's parents married, they moved into the second bedroom of the maternal grandparents because the mother really did not want to leave home. When she was pregnant with Teddy and the landlord insisted that two families could not occupy a four-room apartment, she cried at having to leave her mother and move into a separate apartment across the street. She continued to ask her mother's advice in most decisions and to talk with her several times a day.

It took many discussions to convince Teddy's parents of the inappropriateness of his sharing a bedroom with his teenage sister or a bed with his parents at the age of twelve, and the deleterious effect this was having on his development of independence and ability to separate. The pediatrician visited the home to help work out a better sleeping arrangement, but at first every suggestion was met with an objection. Realizing that they had to work it out their own way, the pediatrician continued to stress the need for this change. During the same period, Teddy's budding independence was encouraged, and his attainment of manhood at the Bar Mitzvah was emphasized. With the parents' permission, information about sex differences and adolescent changes was given. The grandparents moved into the apartment over Teddy's family and gave Teddy a room of his own in this apartment right over his parents' room. However, Teddy refused to sleep in the room alone. As a last resort the parents bought a convertible couch for themselves and gave Teddy their bedroom. Then the sleepwalking stopped, and since then Teddy has slept alone.

He is proud of his achievements in returning to school and sleeping all night in his own bed. He has voluntarily curtailed his food intake and lost a little weight, which with his slowly increasing height adds to a more mature appearance. Instead of spending all his time at home, he is beginning to show interest in making friends. His fear of being left alone at night continues. He is now visiting the clinic every six to eight weeks for help in his struggle with this aspect of his separation anxiety.

Because of these continued manifestations of anxiety, which have not been alleviated under pediatric management, it is now felt appropriate to recommend psychiatric evaluation and treatment. The parents would probably not have understood this referral earlier but now seem ready to accept it.

BIBLIOGRAPHY

Bowlby, J. (1960), Separation Anxiety. *Int. J. Psycho-Anal*, 41:89.
Broadwin, I. T. (1932), A Contribution to the Study of Truancy. *Amer. J. Orthopsychiat.*, 2:253.
Coolidge, J. C., Hahn, P. B., & Peck, A. L. (1957), School Phobia: 2. Neurotic Crisis or Way of Life. Workshop 1955. *Amer. J. Orthopsychiat.*, 27:296.
———— Willer, M. L., Tessman, E., & Waldfogel, S. (1960), School Phobia in Adolescence: A Manifestation of Severe Character Disturbance. *Amer. J. Orthopsychiat.*, 30:599.
Davidson, S. (1961), School Phobia as a Manifestation of Family Disturbance: Its Structure and Treatment. *J. Child Psychol. & Psychiat.*, 1:270.
Eisenberg, L. (1958a), School Phobia: Diagnosis, Genesis, Clinical Management. *Ped. Clin. No. Amer.*, 5:645.
———— (1958b), School Phobia: A Study in the Communication of Anxiety. *Amer. J. Psychiat.*, 114:712.
Estes, H. R., Haylett, C. H., & Johnson, A. M. (1956), Separation Anxiety. *Amer. J. Psychother.*, 10:682.

Johnson, A. M., Falstein, E. I., Szurek, S. A., & Svendsen, M. (1941), School Phobia. *Amer. J. Orthopsychiat.*, 11:702.

Partridge, J. M. (1939), Truancy. *J. Ment. Sci.*, 85:45.

Talbot, M. (1957), School Phobia: I. Panic in School Phobia. Workshop 1955. *Amer. J. Orthopsychiat.*, 27:286.

Van Houton, J. (1948), Mother-Child Relationships in Twelve Cases of School Phobia. *Smith Coll. Stud. Soc. Work*, 18:161.

Waldfogel, S., Coolidge, J. C., & Hahn, P. B. (1957). The Development, Meaning, and Management of School Phobia. Workshop, 1956. *Amer. J. Orthopsychiat.*, 27:754.

Warren, W. (1948), Acute Neurotic Breakdown in Children with Refusal to Go to School. *Arch. Dis. Child.*, 23:266.

The Physician's Attitudes Toward
Adolescents' Everyday Emotional Problems

• *J. ROSWELL GALLAGHER, M.D.*
Children's Hospital Medical Center, Boston

"You've got to help us, Doctor; we've tried everything. Nothing works. It must be our fault. We've tried to be good parents, but Bill's sixteen now and obviously we've failed. Sometimes he seems to hate us. Yet just the other day he was real worried when his father had to take a trip: it was right after that dreadful airplane accident. He won't talk to us any more; if he does, it's to tell us what his friends say about religion or Russia—maybe to shock us or upset us. We can't get him to dress decently. He doesn't want to be with us; it seems as if he couldn't wait to get out of the house. If he studies, he insists on having his radio on; I don't see how he can possibly get to college. Now his sister is acting up, too. What can we do."

What this general practitioner, pediatrician, or internist will do will depend upon such factors as his understanding of young people's emotional development, his own feelings toward adolescents, the relative degree of his interest in people and in disease, his feelings toward his own early years and their problems, and the nature of his own medical education—particularly the sort of teachers he has had in his medical school and hospital years. One physician will quickly say that this is a problem for a psychiatrist; another will tell the parents not to worry or say that "this is a phase" and that "this, too, will pass"; another will suggest that a no-nonsense approach and good old-fashioned discipline is what such boys—and most other young people today—need; but many others will recognize the boy's need for help, will defer any opinion or advice, and express a desire first to see the boy and to talk things over with him.

To whom is it more likely that these parents will turn at a time like this—or with a less serious problem—than the doctor whom they know and trust? They not only trust his judgment, but may have sought his help hoping that the boy's behavior will be found to have some physical basis and thus avoid the necessity for a psychiatrist's assistance which for one reason or another they find difficult to accept. In any event, a visit or two with the boy *alone,* providing an adequate opportunity for him to talk confidentially and also for a physical examination (anxiety about his growth and development or some other physical matter may be a contributing factor) is the obvious first step. Later it may be appropriate to refer one's patient or his family to a psychiatrist, child guidance clinic, or family agency.

Nevertheless, it is a fact that some doctors hesitate to become at all involved with such young people. Others quickly refer to specialists those patients whom it is reasonable to expect they themselves could help. The reason commonly given is that the psychological or developmental problems of the teen-age boy and girl require a great deal of one's time—time which is at a premium in a busy doctor's long day.

One reason that physicians regard these problems as too time-consuming and outside of their own province is that they believe they must follow a psychiatrist's methods and tempo in treating them. For instance, they erroneously assume that these patients must have hour-long appointments—and these at frequent intervals and over a long period of time. The fallacies here are three: first, in failing to differentiate adolescents who have developmental problems from those adolescents or adults having severe emotional disturbances; second, in confusing the simple sort of therapeutic techniques appropriate for most adolescents (and certainly for the physician to employ) with the more time-consuming, intensive, and intricate methods utilized by psychiatrists in treating more disturbed patients; and finally, failing to realize that the physician who has known a patient and his family for some time has already at his command information about and understanding of a patient's past, family, and environment. If one further remembers the responsiveness and the resiliency of youth, and that the adolescents we are discussing are those who are experiencing difficulty in what are, after all, *normal developmental changes* in their feelings, and that their conflicts often are readily accessible, the relatively short expenditure of time or specialized skill which many will require becomes even more evident. Seen promptly at the height of a problem, at a time of crisis— not weeks later as so often a specialist's crowded schedule may necessitate—often permits a resolution of the crisis and the conflicts evoked by the crisis in a more direct and practical fashion.

The adolescent who has a problem needs to feel that he has an adult's genuine interest, and he needs a chance to be heard without interruption and criticism. Neither of these requires countless hours nor psychiatric training. They do require privacy, undivided attention, and an occasional half hour of time. It is a myth that most adolescents who have significant but everyday emotional problems will require hour after hour of special and intense treatment techniques.

Years ago when discussing the pediatrician's psychotherapeutic role, Milton Senn (1948) expressed much of this very succinctly:

> Actually, in order to help the patient it is neither necessary nor desirable in every instance to offer anything more than opportunity for the establishment of a relationship. . . . Once the patient has had the experience of being accepted and understood, he begins to develop trust in the physician; the ever-present anxiety which he brings becomes less in time and the helping process has started before any specific remedial procedure has been offered . . . as a therapist (the physician) needs an awareness of the feelings, attitudes, and dynamics of behavior not only in the persons who come to him as patients, but also in himself as one who min-

isters to their needs . . . whence will come this insight? It is common knowledge that, to some individuals, understanding results from their own experiences as human beings. . . . Many of us who are teachers . . . have felt that around the relationship between pupil and teacher there may develop a process . . . which has all the characteristics of a psychotherapeutic kinship. . . . It seems logical to conclude that pediatric training, like all educational ventures, to be truly effective must provide ample opportunity for the establishment of intimate teacher and pupil relationship. With these at the core of training . . . they will be able to incorporate quite naturally psychologic insight with medical understanding.

Admittedly the physician will approach such a patient as Bill with more confidence and be more effective if through experience or training he has become comfortable with adolescents. After all, this visit basically is going to be a person helping a person, not a doctor treating a disease situation. Therefore, how this doctor feels toward adolescent boys and girls in general, the degree to which the problems of his own adolescence still influence him and consequently his treatment of others, and how his patient comes to feel toward him, will in large part determine his effectiveness. Impatience, quickness to advise, talking instead of listening, and quick referral are characteristics of those who are uncomfortable in the face of these young people's problems.

On the other hand, although a physician's ability to help these adolescents is not dependent upon his knowledge of such matters as identity formation, castration anxiety, or transference phenomena, he will be much more effective if he has currently, or has had, a psychiatrist as his mentor and collaborator. Such an associate is a source of suggestions and confidence, an interpreter of obscure symptoms, and a valuable safeguard against the physician's attempting more than his ability justifies. Furthermore, because a physician is so close to those patients of his whom he has known for some time, and because his training in emotional disorders is not likely to be great, the psychiatrist can be of help in pointing out to him the relevance of some significant factor which, because of its familiarity, the doctor may have overlooked.

This relationship is not a one-way street. Valuable as such a psychiatrist can be to a physician—it is difficult to imagine a more profitable use of part of his time and experience—yet it is fair to say that most psychiatrists will not only teach but also learn in such a relationship. This contact with the relatively normal workaday world, and particularly with the at times fantastic but unfortunately changeable aberrations of the adolescent, can also be very instructive and salubrious to the psychiatrist who may have too few opportunities to escape from the much more fixed abnormalities of his own patients' minds.

Specifically what are the facts and factors of adolescents' development which should be known and applied to the prevention and management of their personality difficulties and, in fact, to the evaluation and management of all their ailments?

There are many dangers in generalizing about adolescents and in oversimplifying explanations of the genesis of their difficulties. There are many individual differences between them, and now that they are more mobile than little children many more varying influences affect them. There are also significant differences between early and late adolescence. The few comments which follow should be interpreted with these cautions in mind.

The majority of adolescents' problems—their developmental crises—are not pathological ones and do not often lead to long-term, serious disturbances. Lability and experimentation are to a significant degree characteristic of adolescence. Those of us who treat adolescents need to remember to think of their futures—what they should be like as adults—as well as to consider the bearing of their pasts and their parents on their present state. We need to remember that youth is forever looking for leadership. They seek their own leaders and their own set of values when adults fail to furnish adequate ones. We also need to remember that these young people now move in an ever-widening circle and are therefore affected—and that their developmental crises are affected—by a multitude of people and events outside their families and beyond their physician's efforts.

Basic to an understanding of the personality, behavioral, and psychosomatic disorders which plague so many adolescents is a realization of the great influence of their pasts and their environments. Their families, their training, their early playmates, and their first teachers all exert a tremendous influence upon the degree of emotional stability (and therefore upon the prospects of whether they will have fair or foul weather sailing) with which the boy or girl will face the emotional processes of adolescence. Any adventure in living or learning is embarked upon and carried through more efficiently when the anxieties of the past are not too great. When these young people during those early years have grown in an atmosphere of being wanted, have lived in a predictable, solid home, have developed a faith in adults, and have not been pressured too much too soon, or too rapidly, into a mold of society's or of their parents' choosing, it is likely that their later reactions to their changing feelings will bring relatively little trouble. As they grow older, on the other hand, one also needs to think, when searching either for inimicable factors or for therapeutic allies, of the multitude of people and forces—companions, coaches, teachers, members of the clergy, employers, national figures, heroes, new ideologies, political events— which influence them and their adjustment. At times any of these may be of more influence than parent or physician.

Frequently it is asked: "What can we physicians do about adolescents?" Our most effective maneuvers have always been the preventive ones: the adolescent is no exception. Here as the family adviser regarding the early care and training of children is where the physician can play a most vital role. Efforts to solve the problems of the adolescent should be *concentrated* in the weeks and months and years of early life—from birth to twelve years of age—not during the adolescent years themselves. Admittedly genic factors and each individual's own unique biochemical pattern are of great significance; but environmental factors deserve even greater consideration and when we are assessing experiences and associations it is clearly those of the very early years which are most important. Once a child becomes an adolescent, the doctor's efforts will have to be curative as well as preventive. During adolescence, the processes and conflicts of the earlier years are again worked through and are near the surface, so, fortunately it will be less of a task to set them straight than in those later years of adult life when we so commonly find them deeply repressed and walled off by defensive attitudes.

This, then, is a major contribution the pediatrician or other physician can make to adolescents' emotional health. Nothing could be more fruitful than his efforts to assist parents and teachers to provide infants and children with those influences which will be most likely to foster their healthy emotional development. Without such guidance, despite youth's strength and resiliency, we can expect the normal emotional changes of adolescence to proceed less smoothly and to a less satisfactory end result.

As the infant and child and adolescent develops, his emotional processes, and therefore his major needs, will vary from time to time; but it is imperative to emphasize that although these processes follow an orderly sequence, they do not lend themselves to a rigid application of a timetable of expectancies. After all, though in many ways similar to others, each human being is unique and should not be expected to develop at just the same time, rate, or extent as does another. Furthermore, since many factors which strongly influence development at one time of life may be absent or negligible in later years, early predictions of future status, based on a comparison with age norms, will often be wide of the mark. Standard timetables, though convenient, are often misleading; it is more valid to think in terms of successive epochs of development—such as infancy, early childhood, preschool years, the early school years, etc.—than to talk or evaluate or prescribe in terms of age two or five or nine or fifteen.

No period of life is of more importance to one's future than the first weeks and months, the period of early infancy. These are the months of learning to relate to the mother in a warm, responsive way and of building the feeling of security that develops out of good mothering. When these opportunities are denied, it is not unreasonable to expect that in adolescence a boy or girl may be demanding, callous, suspicious or fearful. In the next two years of early childhood (from one to three) the processes of developing spontaneity, of learning to enjoy oneself and to develop one's own will, while at the same time beginning to learn that there are limits, all go on. There are several dangers at this time: so much control will be exercised that initiative and hope of success will be forever damp- ened, or so few limits are set and so little conscience encouraged that there will be little basis in adolescence for the graceful acceptance of a reasonable degree of authority or for independently solving the choices between right and wrong and shades of gray which will need to be made.

In the preschool years (from three to six) even though now other people than parents begin to make their influences more strongly felt, it is chiefly the interactions between the parents—their marital and sexual adjustment—which will color the child's beginning feel- ings about sex and marriage and families. Growing up in a home where parents set a good example of human relationships is a pre- requisite for a satisfactory adjustment to the increased sexual drives of adolescence.

Finally, the early school years (from six to twelve), the period of relative sexual latency, are far from latent as far as preparation for adolescence is concerned. These are the years when children's vast available energy may be poured into play and schooling and can yield those all-important successes and feelings of competency which the adolescent will later need if he is fearlessly to face the new processes of his emotional development. Lacking successes (and the confidence they could yield) during those earlier years, the adoles- cent may later retreat, or may try awkwardly to prove himself and to gain recognition in ways socially unacceptable.

Given a propitious start in life up through the primary school period, the processes of early and later adolescence may go quite smoothly. These are not inevitably years of storm and stress, nor are the traits and behavior some adolescents exhibit at this time of life always the dire pathological ones they seem to be. Just as their bodily growth is uneven and explosive, and therefore their control of their bodies awkward, so can those adolescents who are basically normal show little emotional control. Their opinions and behavior are the epitome of hyperbole; and their mood swings, fantasies, fears, and aggressive behavior would bode ill in an adult. Although such reactions are not to be taken lightly in an adolescent, more often than not they are only expressions of a normal personality finding difficulty in realigning its childhood relationships and attitudes. They may experience less difficulty if their world is not too competitive and aggressive, does not hurry them too much, does not further confuse them with a sudden multitude of choices, is not impatient with their occasional dreaming, and gives them time to think.

What are the emotional processes normally expected, though often annoying and disturbing, at this time of life? Their normalcy, their inevitability, their desirability—and they themselves—must be understood if we are to provide young people the sort of opportunities and the understanding support which many of them will require if they are to fashion for themselves an effective adult personality. The acquisition of comfortable feelings and acceptable attitudes toward sex; the gaining of the ability to be independent; the adjustment of feelings toward each parent; and the development of a mature conscience and their own identity appear to be the major processes. Each of these is normal and desirable, and yet under some circumstances may present anxieties, psychosomatic symptoms, or disturbing behavior.

New rapid changes in their bodies and their body chemistry confront the adolescent with new feelings and the need to adjust these to the mores of the society in which he lives. They are now more aware of their bodies, their size, their degree of sexual maturity, their attractiveness, and their acceptance by the opposite sex. Some find the prospect of becoming an adult male or an adult female frightening, and retreat from it; others, doubting their sexuality, attempt to reassure themselves in ways some societies find unacceptable. Still others become confused when they discover that the standards they have always been told were good are at variance with the standards so many adults whom they have respected appear to have adopted.

The transition over the years from complete dependence to independence is clearly desirable, and though young people seek it, and their parents and other adults feel their need for it, not infrequently the adolescent alternately seems to fight for it and then retreat from it, and adults at one time thrust it upon him and at another snatch it away. Those adolescents who have least confidence in their ability to stand alone are apt to be the most awkward, brash, and vacillating in their efforts to do so; and those parents or other adults who are most insecure are the most inconsistent, possessive, and confidence-depriving in their behavior.

When the relationships to each parent have been good prior to adolescence, it is usually not difficult later on for the girl to modify her close feelings toward her father and to want to become more like her mother, or for the boy to lessen his ties to the mother and to become closer to his father. As this goes on and as their early homosexuality changes into heterosexuality, these young people can be disturbed by these new feelings, and their parents by their new reticence, avoidance of caresses, and increased interest in members of the opposite sex.

And finally the adolescent now needs to acquire his own identity —a philosophy of life of his own, opinions and plans and hopes of his own. Compelled to work this out, wanting to be himself yet uncertain of himself, he may need temporarily to reject or deprecate his family's and his society's ways and ideals, fearing that the mold he will be cast in will not be his own. Those who in their early years develop feelings of competency, who have parents who are strong but not intrusive, who in their early years had as ideals people who did not evoke disillusionment, are least likely to find themselves vacillating and uncertain, or persistently to need to adopt ideas or activities contrary to their parents' or their society's standards. Their extremes of dress, behavior, and ideas are not a disease but expressions of their insecure search for their own values and way of life— better ones, they hope, than those they find about them, but in any event, their own. Given the support of adults, the example of adults' behavior which they can respect, the privilege of experimenting on their own, praise for what is good, and consistent criticism of their excesses (but not of *themselves*), most of them will satisfactorily free themselves from their childhood attachments and ideologies and achieve a mature conscience and ways of thinking and living of their own. Support and guidance without interference with their freedom to work these out will give them the confidence they must have if they are indeed to make a *free* choice.

These are the changes which go on—the new feelings, the vacillating, hesitant quest for freedom, the distrust of what was once trusted, the doubts about the future—and which, as in Bill, do not always proceed smoothly. One can see how these young people's past experiences *and* their present worries about school (the commonest worry of them all), about their popularity, their bodies, their family relationships, religion, death, sex, and a host of other matters can impede and be associated with them. Even when these changes are less upsetting than they were to Bill, they may proceed in a halting, irregular fashion. For an adolescent to behave in a very mature fashion one day, as if trying it out, and to be very childish the next, as though spent by the previous day's effort, is typical rather than unusual. After all, maturity is a goal toward which these people are striving, not a state they have achieved. Too often adults complain of adolescents' immaturity when in reality immaturity is normal at this time of life; it is a persistence of immaturity, a failure to become more mature, *and* adults' management of young people in ways which tend to perpetuate immaturity, which we should strive to change.

What can the physician offer these young people during this phase of their development? Primarily he can offer them an opportunity to form that sort of temporary relationship to him which just now they find difficult to have with their parents. He can offer his genuine interest, his respect, his understanding, an opportunity freely to express their feelings and ideas without interruption, criticism, or embarrassment. The adolescent's changing feelings block his ability to talk freely to his parents. Striving for independence but having little confidence in himself and his new ideas and feelings, he welcomes help from a trusted adult outside his family circle, providing that adult will listen, not be quick to offer advice or criticism, and makes clear his interest and respect.

Obviously if the pediatrician is to be the one to fill this role he must not be regarded as being exclusively a "baby doctor," and he must neither think, talk, nor act like one. This requires that he familiarize himself with the techniques appropriate for the care of the adolescent. The setting aside of one evening's or an afternoon's office hours exclusively for adolescents or a special or more appropriate place (free of little chairs and the infant's scale) are maneuvers which help to make clear that the physician has a genuine interest in adolescents and has taken the trouble to make special arrangements for them. More important, however, than a special time or a special place for their visits is his treating them in a different way than he would a little child. No one is of more importance to a young adolescent than himself, so if *he*, not his heart or tonsils or knee or rebellion, *and not* his parents, receives the major share of the doctor's attention, all is likely to go well. Seen alone, offered a chance to talk, given the advantages of privacy and of (perhaps for the first time) a confidential relationship, genuine interest in him or in her made clear, the setting of the visit then becomes of secondary importance. Without those the setting itself will be of little consequence.

Some of the other important differences between the conduct of an adolescent's and a child's or an adult's visit are worth mentioning. These stem from the fact that the adolescent is more verbal than the child, is seeking independence as he prepares to leave his home, typically is a hero-worshiper, and his worries are nearer the surface than an adult's.

The adolescent's quest for independence suggests both the desirability of fostering it by using methods which will increase this patient's responsibility for his own health, and also the likelihood that the patient himself can now give you a useful description of his problem. So the focus should shift from the parent to the patient. Though the parents at first will be seen alone and their story and requests given a thorough hearing, the adolescent will also be seen alone. He will be given an opportunity not only to tell his story but also to express his feelings, and will later himself be given directions and the responsibility for carrying them out. For the same reasons, especially in the case of older adolescents, when personality or behavioral problems exist, there is less effort to modify the parental management and more of an effort (without implying criticism of the parents) to increase the adolescent's understanding both of himself and also of his parents and their problems. This is not to say that the parents will not often need considerable help and attention (frequently if one is properly to help the adolescent, the parents' aid may need to come from another physician or agency), but rather to caution the pediatrician, who is so accustomed to dealing with the parents of little children, that this patient is now growing up and so requires a different approach than during childhood. As a matter of fact, this more grown-up patient-physician relationship should begin, albeit gradually, long before adolescence demands it.

Their hero worship and surface worries have much to do with the relatively small skill and small expenditure of time required to assist many of these young people with their everyday emotional problems. Given the sort of office-visit opportunity which has been described and a physician he respects, the adolescent, prone to hero worship and groping for the interest of an adult with whom he has not had a close emotional attachment, not infrequently will quickly (even at the first visit) develop feelings toward his doctor which can be a tremendous factor in his physician's ability to help him. The desire now to please and to imitate him may soon be reflected in neater appearance, a wish to report any new school or social success, or a change in attitude and interests.

Not only do many adolescents very rapidly form this useful sort of relationship, but also because time has not buried them deeply and strong defenses have not been built up around them, they readily bring their worries and conflicts out into the open. It does not take endless hours and anxiety-provoking situations to get these young people to talk, and, even more important, to talk with feeling. By showing genuine interest, by giving them undivided attention, by not seeming shocked, and by making them feel at ease, much of that which would seem to have been held back for years may pour forth. At times, in fact, the problem is not to get these young people to talk but rather to prevent their saying so much at their first visit that they may become embarrassed and therefore reluctant to return.

This relationship and this putting into words with feeling those things the adolescent may hitherto never have dared to express verbally are usually the most helpful strings to one's bow, but a few other factors are also important. Much can be gained at times by manipulating the environment: a change of a teacher, a new sport, or other new activity which will bring success and through it confidence, a job which can yield satisfaction and increase maturity, direct advice to a carping parent apparently dedicated to a policy of never praising. Discussions of what the future holds may help; and when advice is sought, it is *not* withheld and such supportive nonauthoritative comments made as "I'm not sure what you should do, but were the problem mine I'm sure I would. . . ." And finally, though naïve optimism is to be avoided, the value of hope as a therapeutic agent is not to be underestimated. When things are better, it helps to say so: when they aren't, it can help objectively but sympathetically to discuss the state of affairs. Optimism is frequently less justifiable when dealing with adults: adolescents have more resiliency and great capacity for change, and your prophesy that things are going to be better may be more likely of fulfillment if you will but mention it.

There are a few things that should be avoided. Most of them have already been at least implied. Do not prod; do not try to pry into areas which for the moment the boy or girl chooses to ignore; if they are important, in their own good time they will come out. Should they find it difficult to talk freely, talk about commonplace matters. Do not sit and stare hoping that then their mounting anxiety will open the flood gates: adolescents are already anxious and if made more so will usually persist in their silence or not return. Last but not least, though it is important not to be authoritarian or pretentious, do not be "palsy" and do not fail to behave with authority. These young people want a doctor, not a companion.

SUMMARY AND CONCLUSION

Practicing physicians have a large and vital role to play in the management of those everyday personality and behavioral difficulties and psychosomatic disorders which are expressions of adolescents' temporary inability to handle efficiently the adjustments and the new feelings which are normally a part of their emotional development. To do this is not as time-consuming as is generally believed, and the methods one needs to employ are neither mysterious nor difficult. The pediatrician, it is true, may be wise to alter his office setting, but his need to alter his manner and his thinking will be no greater than the general practitioner's or the internist's or other specialist's. Each will do most and best for adolescents if he will take their needs and characteristics and state of emotional development into account when talking to them and when evaluating and treating their disorders.

On the other hand, the physician who has regular or easy access to a psychiatrist who can act as his mentor will be able to be of much more help to his patients. He also will be less apt to consider himself a psychiatrist or to attempt to try to help those young people whose disorders are the province of a specialist. There are a number of young people whose character disorders, neuroses, homosexuality, schizophrenia, and less serious disturbances may demand not only a specialist's care but also, if satisfactory progress is to be made, an approach which can offer help to other members of the family.

The physician, however, can help many adolescents who have emotional problems, and be more effective with those whose problems are predominantly physical, if he will acquire more confidence in his understanding of their normal developmental processes. Their care can yield a physician many satisfying moments; fortunately, his inevitable errors and his observation of the frequency with which factors other than those under his control effect the desired result should maintain his humility.

BIBLIOGRAPHY

Balint, M. (1957), *The Doctor, His Patient, and the Illness*. New York: Int. Univ. Press.
Balser, B. H., ed. (1957), *Psychotherapy of the Adolescent*. New York: Int. Univ. Press.
Bibring, G. L. (1956), Psychiatry and Medical Practice in General Hospital. *New Eng. J. Med.*, 254:366.
Blaine, G. B., Jr. (1962), *Patience and Fortitude*. Boston: Little, Brown.
Blos, P. (1941), *The Adolescent Personality*. New York: Appleton-Century-Crofts.
Caplan, G. (1959), Practical Steps for the Family Physician in the Prevention of Emotional Disorders. *J. Amer. Med. Assn.*, 170:1497.

Erikson, E. H. (1950), *Childhood and Society*. New York: Norton.

Faegre, M. L. (1955), *The Adolescent in Your Family*. Washington, D.C.: U.S. Dept. Health, Education, and Welfare.

Frank, M. & Frank, L. K. (1956), *Your Adolescent at Home and in School*. New York: Viking.

Freud, A. (1958), Adolescence. *The Psychoanalytic Study of the Child*, 13:255. New York: Int. Univ. Press.

Gallagher, J. R. (1960), *Medical Care of the Adolescent*. New York: Appleton-Century-Crofts.

———— & Harris, H. I. (1958), *Emotional Problems of Adolescents*. New York: Oxford Univ. Press.

Josselyn, I. M. (1957), *The Adolescent and His World*. New York: Family Service Association of America.

Masterson, J. F. (1958), Psychotherapy of the Adolescent: A Comparison with Psychotherapy of the Adult. *J. Nerv. Ment. Dis.* 127:511.

Mead, M. (1928), *Coming of Age in Samoa*. New York: Wm. Morrow.

Menninger, K. A. (1959), Hope. *Amer. J. Psychiat.*, 116:481.

Nixon, R. E. (1962), *The Art of Growing*. New York: Random House.

Senn, M. J. E. (1948), Psychotherapeutic Role of the Pediatrician. *Pediatrics*, 2:147.

Williams, R. J. (1959), *Biochemical Individuality*. New York: Wiley.

Part V

Child Guidance Today

The child guidance clinic concept arose out of the realization that the complexities of child and family life would require the collaborative efforts of several disciplines before effective understanding and planning could be achieved. Milton Senn was one of those who added another dimension to this collaboration when he made clear from his own experiences and deliberations the mutual interests of pediatricians and the three disciplines—child psychiatry, social work, and clinical psychology—traditionally involved in child guidance clinics. When Senn organized the Yale Child Study Center in 1949 he instituted a child psychiatry unit as one of the essential components of this university department devoted to the study of children and their development.

In "Child Guidance Today" a social worker and clinical psychologist indicate some of the changing trends and the added knowledge available to the modern child guidance clinic. Laura V. Codling has described the increasing interdependence of clinicians and other workers in child development. She examines this development in the light of her observations that many more children than previously are now referred for psychiatric evaluation and treatment because of character difficulties. Conversely there appear to be relatively fewer children referred for symptom neuroses. Contributions from social work and child development enable one to understand the technical and theoretical questions raised by this epidemiological trend that has been observed in child guidance clinics. Reimer Jensen examines in some detail the highly charged and conflicted feelings many patients have when they apply to a child guidance clinic for help. He indicates that the clinician's anticipation that parents have such highly conflicted feelings enables him to work more effectively with the child and his family.

Psychiatric Clinics for Children: Contributions from Social Work and Child Development

• *LAURA V. CODLING, A.B.*

Yale University

Psychiatric clinics specializing in the diagnosis and treatment of children's problems have available today knowledge of human development and behavior, and experience with the treatment of children's problems of every kind. This is far different from the knowledge and experience available in the first clinics that were established in the early part of the century. Our present knowledge has been accumulated over a long period of years, and we now have the ability to use it in treatment. New methods have been introduced, and new formulations of diagnostic thinking and treatment have emerged as our knowledge has grown and as social and economic conditions and cultural values have shifted.

At each step the changes that have taken place in this field have been related to the current concept of children's problems and behavior and their treatment and the concern about these. However, development in any new field does not move forward constantly without some pauses to take stock of progress. New concepts have not always been readily accepted or easily integrated into current practice. This paper will review briefly the background and history of the development of children's psychiatric services. It will consider the contributions from other fields that have furthered our understanding of children's problems and their treatment, with special emphasis on the contributions to diagnosis and treatment that have stemmed recently from studies in child development. Further, it will consider one type of parent-child relationship problem coming to clinics today, the essential basis for the evaluation of the type of problem, and the plan of treatment.

The history of the past half century is one of increased understanding of the complexity of personality and behavior. The responsibilities of psychiatric clinics for children during the same period have progressed from having primarily a diagnostic and consultation function to treatment in all its various forms for problems of all degrees of severity. Increased knowledge of the important role that early child development may have in later functioning and increased understanding of the complexity of human behavior and personality have influenced the treatment role of the clinics. The changes in parent-child relationships in the normal growing-up process of the child from infancy to adulthood can be complicated by countless factors of lesser or greater significance. Psychoanalytic thinking about human behavior and the understanding of the interaction between child and parent that has come from studies of child development have been important guides in evaluating the child's state of health or illness. Thus, services that may be offered range from education and advice to mothers who are in need of guidance in problems of normative infant development to extensive psychotherapy of severe neurotic problems.

EARLY HISTORY OF CLINICS

Present-day psychiatric services for children had their beginnings in the child guidance movement that started a half century ago. The preventive role of the clinic was implicit in the work then as it is today. This was based on the assumption that, in the growing and changing years of childhood, intervention in the beginning of maladjusted behavior may prevent more severe manifestations in later years.

The early clinics were started because of concern with obvious problems that needed help, and they made use of the existing resources to find ways of modifying these problems. A few people became concerned with the rise in juvenile delinquency. They were aware that existing police and court methods were inadequate to deal with this problem, and they began to look to the emerging clinical fields of psychiatry and psychology to understand the interaction of new social conditions and stresses on the behavior of the individual. The collaborative work of the three disciplines, psychiatry, psychology, and social work, developed from the needs and demands of the problems and the contribution that each discipline had to offer. The first clinic in 1909, the Chicago Juvenile Psychopathic Institute, directed by Dr. William Healy, served the new Chicago Juvenile Court that had been established a few years earlier.[1] Behind this idea of the collaboration of psychiatric knowledge and the rehabilitation of the juvenile offender were theoretical concepts regarding children's behavior. These came from some of the newer thinking in psychology which had been shifting its attention from primarily abnormal behavior to normal, from psychiatry's observations about the causes of mental illnesses, and from the experience of social work in attempting to lessen the stresses and strains of economic and social conditions on family life.[2]

Dr. Healy began his work with a psychologist and a social worker as his colleagues. The clinic made use of the social workers in the established social agencies to obtain facts and information from which they compiled a comprehensive history of the delinquent child and his family and his social situation. The hope was that this would provide evidence of what had gone wrong in the child's brief number of years, and from this there would be clues to changes that could be made in his social environment that would effect changes in his

[1] "The organization [The Juvenile Psychopathic Institute] represented an effort in practical research which, as the result of several preliminary observations, had been for some time deemed highly promising" (Healy, 1915).

[2] The Juvenile Psychopathic Institute had representatives from the fields of education, psychology, law, social work, and the medical specialties on its Advisory Council and Executive Committee who worked closely with the Director, Dr. William Healy, and his assistant, Dr. Grace M. Fernald.

behavior. On the basis of social information gathered and clinical data available, the psychiatrist would make his diagnosis and offer recommendations. These were made to the probation officer of the court and to the social agencies which were directly responsible for the services or "treatment" of the child and family. Help that could be offered was limited and was related primarily to changes in the child's physical surroundings either by removing him from bad influences to new surroundings, or by attempting to change his present environment.

Implicit in this approach was the assumption that social maladjustment was caused by the external stresses of social and economic ills. These were only too evident in the lives of these miscreants. Social disruption and inequities were unavoidable with large populations from many different cultures transported to a new country; constant change and urbanization were superimposed on scarcely established new families and homes. The home life of the child was considered of great importance, and here also it was implicit that family relationships would be healthy and supportive if external factors could be modified or controlled. Advice, guidance, and material aid were provided for the parents. Indirectly the efforts that were made served to meet some of the psychological needs of the child, but the treatment was directed mainly toward changes in the physical environment.

DEVELOPMENT OF THE CLINIC TEAM

Social workers and psychologists became part of the staffs in the new clinics that were established in the years before and following World War I. The roles of each of the disciplines in the work became more defined. Clinical psychological testing was being developed and used as part of the diagnostic appraisal of the child's problems. The psychiatric social worker used her knowledge and the developing casework method to obtain a deeper understanding of the family and its strengths and problems. In George Stevenson's opinion (1939), "no intensity of need could have produced such an organization [of structure in the clinics] until psychiatry, psychology, and social work had arrived at a point in their respective developments where each had a substantial contribution to make to the task in hand, and at the same time was sufficiently appreciative of the contributions the other two could make to be able to work with them toward a common goal." The responsibility of these clinics was still much the same as in the beginning: diagnosis, prognosis, and recommendations. However, they were not attached to courts, and many problems besides delinquency were referred to them. The psychiatric social worker in the clinic was involved in both the diagnostic appraisal by the clinic and the recommendations for treatment. Her role in treatment was primarily coordinating the work of the clinic and that of other agencies, interpreting the recommendations of the clinic and the methods by which these could be carried out in the home, school, and community.

TREATMENT ROLE OF THE CLINICS

The clinics did not assume a direct role in treatment until the middle and late 1920s. The impetus for this came from changes in the requests that came to the clinic, from the knowledge gained from experience, and from new theoretical understanding of behavior. With the broadening of the clinic's responsibility to include problems other than delinquency and with the clinics no longer being a part of the court, parents began to seek the help of the clinics directly for many kinds of problems, so that there was no agency or court actively working with the child and the family to carry out recommendations. Experience gained in the early clinics had demonstrated that changes and improvements in physical environment and pressures did not provide the total answer to problems of maladjustment. The parents needed more than authoritative advice to help them with the problems, and the social workers in the clinics began to use casework as a method and process of helping.

The greatest impetus to the treatment role of the new clinics came from psychoanalytic psychology which contributed new knowledge about human behavior and personality development. This provided a greater understanding of the psychological environment of the child and the vital role of the relationship between parent and child in this environment. Psychoanalysis elucidated the difference between conscious and unconscious motivation, and gave insight into the influence of intrapsychic conflicts on the behavior of the individual (Fabian, 1953). It offered a theoretical framework for understanding the phenomena that had been observed repeatedly in clinical practice, and for understanding why the efforts toward change in one problem were successful whereas the same efforts in an apparently similar problem were unsuccessful. David Levy (1947) wrote of this period: "Those days were really exciting. There was the full feeling of adventure. We felt we were breaking new ground. However we may have questioned our theories, we thought surely we had at least the right approach to the new field, in fact to the larger field, of human behavior." New discoveries and observations of particular phenomena juxtaposed to new theoretical understanding offered hope of the ultimate answer.

As direct psychological treatment developed there was an increased effort to understand and alter attitudes and behavior of the individuals involved in the problems. The responsibility of the clinic was redefined and expanded, and included treatment which was based on a diagnostic understanding of the dynamic interrelationship of the physical and psychological environment of the child. The parent-child relationship was recognized as having primary importance in the understanding and treatment of the child's problems. Methods and techniques of treatment were adapted from the work and experience with similar problems in other settings such as schools, hospitals, and social agencies (Crothers, 1937). Treatment of the parents and those social and psychological problems that were interfering with their daily lives remained for the most part the responsibility of the psychiatric social worker in the clinic. Methods of direct psychological treatment of children were developed by the psychiatrist.

Casework and psychotherapy developed together in psychiatric clinics for children. The plan of joint treatment of children and parents by different staff members was a natural outgrowth from the collaborative diagnostic work of the earlier clinics. Within this structure new methods of treatment and modifications of techniques were explored and applied.

As often happens when a new idea is introduced, there was both use and misuse in the adaptation of psychoanalytic principles and thinking to the treatment work of the clinic. In the beginning, with the new emphasis on treatment of the individual and his intrapsychic conflicts, there was a tendency to deny the importance of the social environment and reality experiences that previously had been the main focus of concern, and thus to throw the baby out with the bath. Later, with the better integration of psychoanalytic concepts into diagnostic understanding and the growth of ego psychology in psychoanalytic thinking, treatment at various levels related to the total problem and the needs of the individual began to be developed. There were new theoretical formulations regarding methods of treatment, and case studies of the use of specific types of treatment with particular problems were assessed. As these case studies appeared in the social work and psychiatric literature, they contributed new understanding and knowledge.

THE CONTRIBUTION OF STUDIES IN CHILD DEVELOPMENT

Important contributions to the understanding of children's problems and child-parent relationships have come in recent years from studies in child development. Interest in normal child development and observational techniques of study have increased our information about deviant development and have shed more light on the etiology of problems of later years.

Psychoanalysis pointed out the crucial role of childhood experiences in later development and the importance of the mother's early relationship to the child. It also illuminated problems of the earliest years of childhood through an understanding of the psychosexual and psychoaggressive development of the child in his growth toward socialization and independence. Recent studies in child development have made clearer the complexity of early mother-child relationships and have modified some of the earlier assumptions about this.

To summarize the point of view that is utilized in this paper:

there is a mutual and reciprocal influence between mother and child, and both are affected by the impact of external realties. The child's development takes place in the ebb and flow of the interaction between the constitution of the child and the environmental forces. The latter include his physical care and handling, the emotional climate in which this takes place, and the impact of external realities such as illness and trauma. The ease or tension, comfort or discomfort, responsiveness or lack of response of both parent and child are determinants of the emotional tone of the relationship. The child's development at any point has resulted from interaction between the equipment and endowment he had, the reaction and handling of the adults who were his earliest world, and the experiences and events that have occurred.

In summary, we have a rich heritage from the past. Our armamentarium for understanding and helping children and their families include: the experience in the early diagnostic clinics; greater awareness of the effects of social and cultural factors; the contributions of psychoanalysis to an understanding of human behavior and personality development; and, more recently, an increased knowledge of early child development, especially as viewed in the dynamic interacting relationship of parent and child. Psychiatric and casework treatment methods have had different emphases as a particular aspect of knowledge or theory has commanded primary attention, or as a new insight into the child and his problems has taken precedence in current thinking. There have been experiments with and development of various methods and techniques of treatment; thus, there is a large volume of experience available for evaluation and use. We can agree with George Gardner (1958) that more systematic research in the field of child psychiatry is needed and that "the body of fact and knowledge of treatment techniques is woefully meager and much of what we do hold to be true perforce of our impressions and intuitions—has never been really tested out." At the same time we recognize the "rich heritage" to which Annette Garrett (1958) refers in the same volume. She reviews the early beginnings of casework and finds "modern casework practice cannot be defined in terms of new goals, aims, ideals, philosophy, or even of new methods or techniques. Rather, its modernness is evident in a more subtle depth of understanding and new meanings in familiar words and, at its best, in more precise and differential application of theory and skill." Gardner looks to research for the increase in "more precise and differential application of theory and skill." While we agree with this, we wish to emphasize that clinical practice, which makes use of already available knowledge and experience, can contribute to the same goal.

We now know that a diagnostic understanding of the behavior of the individual and the relation of this to his personality structure and his unique experiences are the bases for the choice of treatment for that individual who comes to the clinic for help (Hollis, 1951). As implied above, the plan for diagnostic evaluation and treatment is based on the total psychological environment of the child, past and present, including the physical surroundings and emotional climate in which he lives. His relationship to others and their relationship and reaction to him determine the impact of reality experiences on him. Most important in this is the relationship between child and parents.

ROLE OF CASEWORK

The role of casework, as a treatment process, with the parents who brought their children for psychiatric help has received critical attention in recent years. In the late 1940s there was much concern about differentiating between casework and psychotherapy. In recent years the examination and definition of the interaction that takes place in the treatment process have proved to be more fruitful than defining words or attaching labels. Helen Perlman (1957) in her examination of social work sees that "the casework process is essentially one of problem solving." She sees diagnosis as an ongoing process on which the problem solving is based. "Within each phase of problem-solving work there is the exercise of the client's adaptation capacities, whether to an idea, a relationship, or a situation, and whether about some small or some large part of the problem." The implication, with which I agree, is that casework treatment is a continuing diagnostic process which evaluates the ego strengths of the individual and his capacity for change at the same time that it enables him to find more healthy ways of coping with his problems.

There are differences in theory and in points of view about the responsibility for and goals of treatment of parents in children's psychiatric clinics. I believe that these differences are more apparent than real if treatment is seen as an ongoing process which attempts to help the parent deal with a succession of problems and conflicts, as the treatment process itself reveals his ability or inability to do so. As an example, the conflict between a parent and child over an increase in weekly allowance may have to be resolved and dealt with in the reality situation before one can evaluate the ability of the parent to deal in an insightful way with the basic conflict in himself which is evoked by the allowance problem as a symbol of the child's thrust toward independence. It is the difference between seeing the resolution of a specific problem as an end in itself or as part of an evaluative process, which provides the basis and groundwork for the solution of more fundamental problems. In the psychiatric clinic the treatment of all of the individuals involved in the child's problem and the goals of treatment for child and family must be based on dynamic considerations of the possibilities of change in human behavior.

CHILD DEVELOPMENT AND PARENT-CHILD PROBLEMS

Psychoanalysis focused attention on the neurotic child and the treatment of neurotic problems, and the new insights have been applied to the treatment of other types of problems. The greater number of children seen in psychiatric clinics today are brought for nonneurotic problems. Their difficulties are expressed in a lack of adjustment to the social demands of the outside world. They are variously referred to as behavior disorders, impulse disorders, and problems in personality adjustment. These problems vary widely in etiology and in manifestation. With these problems there is an unhappy and frequently very ambivalent relationship between child and parents, but this usually is not the problem for which psychiatric help is sought. It is the child's learning problem, or his immature behavior, or his lack of social adjustment, or his obstreperous or withdrawn behavior that motivate the parents to ask for the help of a psychiatric clinic. It is only in the course of the study and evaluation of the child and family that many aspects of the conflicts between child and parents become obvious. Although descriptively the problems of behavior and the interaction between child and parents may have many resemblances, the factors contributing to the disruption of adequate social adjustment may be of many different kinds and degrees. A careful diagnostic study of a child's problems should include an assessment of his medical, emotional, and intellectual status; his early medical and developmental history; and both early and present social and personality adjustments, especially the interaction between child and parents. One goal of treatment in most cases is to bring about a change in the interrelationship between child and parents, often a necessary condition for changing his psychological environment. An evaluation of the parents' ego strengths, the nature of their difficulties, and their ability to use help are essential determinants for the directions that treatment can take.

A review of present practices in psychiatric clinics and of current literature in the field (Coleman et al, 1953; Solnit and Stark, 1961) results in the following question, one that is often raised in any developing field: Are we making total use and the best use of the knowledge and experience that is available from both the past and the present, especially from the newer contributions from child development? These questions can be brought into sharper focus and discussed more readily in regard to a particular problem.

DEVELOPMENTAL DEVIATION AND MOTHER-CHILD DISTURBANCE

From the larger group of children with behavior disorders, I select for discussion children in whom problems of development were present in the earliest months of life, which resulted in a disturbance in mother-infant interaction. These children are of special interest because they are being seen in increasing numbers in the Child Psychiatry Unit at the Yale University Child Study Center as well as in other clinics. This group is one example of the need for "the precise and differential application of theory and skill" (Garrett, 1958).

In the light of our understanding of the reciprocal interaction between child and parents, we can assume that these very early problems have affected adversely the development of normal satisfying relationships and of the mutual adaptation of child and parents. The psychological implications of this for child and parents must be understood, but other factors should not be overlooked. Personality characteristics of the parents, the child's constitutional endowment, and the nature of the relationships of all significant individuals involved in the child's environment must be evaluated. It is necessary to understand and differentiate the reality aspects of the developmental problem from those tensions between child and parents which have arisen primarily from disturbances within the parents themselves, i.e., problems that have arisen because the parents' view of the child and their reactions to him are distorted by their own internal needs and conflicts.

The group I am discussing includes children whose normal process of development may have been delayed, or uneven, due to constitutional factors; or there may have been early severe or chronic illnesses that created special problems for the parents and aroused great anxiety, fears, and tensions. Such conditions as prematurity, temporary or long-lasting reactions and sequelae from a difficult birth, congenital defects of metabolism or body structure, and even persistent colic are examples.

How the parents have reacted to the child's particular characteristic or defect is related to their own adaptive capacities and their own neurotic needs and problems, and is not necessarily related to the degree of severity of the child's developmental problem. It is evident that even a normal developmental event, such as the emerging capacity for self-feeding or walking, may be experienced as a problem by a mother whose own conflicts interfere with her adaptation to the child's changing abilities and needs. In some instances the parents react to a deviation in the child's normal development with a distortion of their perception of him that is far out of proportion to the reality situation. Such a strong reaction reflects the parents' own problems. However, it must be realized that a severe illness or a deviation in the infant which has an uncertain outcome and is of long duration has a great impact upon even stable and mature parents. Normal anxiety and guilt are heightened and become intolerable as the parents' efforts to find a solution or to see evidence that they are helping the child meet with daily frustration. Sometimes the gradual recession of the child's problems over a period of years is almost unperceived by his parents because their attitudes have been set by their reaction to the earlier reality.

In our experience, by the time most of these children are brought for psychiatric treatment, frequently in the early latency years, the interrelationship of the reality problems that the child presented in the past and the parents' current distorted perception of the child have become inextricably interwoven. The parents' fears and anxieties, continued from the past, interfere with their ability to see him as he now is. They react to him as the damaged, deficient, or unmanageable child, as they saw him in the early years. They may react to him as though he were still fragile and vulnerable even though he now is robust and in good physical health. They may act toward him as though he were not able to function without help and as if he had very limited abilities, when this is not the case. This may be expressed by prodding and putting much pressure on him with the stated purpose of wanting to help him, or by taking the opposite extreme of expecting nothing of him at all and erecting psychological barriers to his moving from infantile behavior to behavior of greater maturity. The problem is complicated further by the child's acceptance of a self-image that is a reflection of the parents' perception of him. He sees himself as deficient and inadequate. He is discouraged and defeated before he tries. He reacts negatively to the parents' pressures on him; in accepting the parents' unrealistic devaluation of himself, he makes infantile demands and has temper outbursts when these are frustrated. The child senses the negative aspect of the parents' ambivalent feelings. This can be illustrated by Andy, five years old, who had been extremely uncomfortable in the first months of life with persistent colic, constant crying, and irritability. For many months his parents were unable to find any type of care and attention which would comfort him. The child reflected his parents' continuing attitude in his self-appraisal when he told a story to his therapist that began, "Once there was a little boy [great sigh], and his mother did not like him very much." Andy experienced his parents' attitude as a constant limitation of pleasurable activity "for his own good."

In such a situation, the everyday occurrences and interchanges between parents and child tend to repeat old patterns of interaction that were begun in the early months and years. Dependency on the part of the child and overprotection by the parents become methods of control that have unrealistic satisfactions for both child and parents at the same time as they arouse fear and anger. The interaction between child and parent becomes both circular and spiral. The behavior of the child provokes a reaction from the parent which in turn stimulates the child until the spiral reaches a peak of explosion.

One might say that this is a description that parents give of family interaction in many other problems brought to the psychiatric clinic. The essential difference in this particular group is the origin of the pathological child-parent interaction in the earliest months of life because of problems of mutual adaptation that persist and at the same time change as development proceeds. The interactional difficulties were related for the most part to past environmental realities which have not continued in the present. The dynamics of the conflict are primarily in the perpetuation of long-established interactions that are increasingly maladaptive as the child grows and develops. We know that the internal needs and disturbances of both child and parents also contribute to a mutually provocative interrelationship. In casework treatment, one must evaluate the ability of the parents to make use of new solutions as they examine old patterns of reaction to their child.

In some of these cases the child may still retain a residue of the early disability, for example, a minimal central nervous system dysfunction that interferes with his motor coordination or creates special learning problems. This adds to the complexity of the problem; but even when no visible problem remains in the child's physical and intellectual functioning, disabling scars are evident in the child-parent relationship and in the child's social functioning. The psychological reality is the current distorted perception of the child by the parents and the child's distorted image of himself.

In such instances extensive studies of the child, physical, psychological, and psychiatric, even with most positive affirmation of the child's adequacy often do not affect the central problem. The parents hear what is said to them and respond with appropriate verbal understanding, but later there is evidence that this is not assimilated as part of their perception of the child. It is not unusual for a mother, after having been assured that her child has normal intelligence, to mention casually several weeks later her concern that he may be placed in a retarded class by the school because there had been a discussion of his slow development in the preschool years. Parents may continue to be overprotective physically, cautioning about running or active play when they have been told and seem to understand that there is no physical indication for this. They remain quite unaware of the discrepancy between their current knowledge of the child's adequacy and their behavior toward him until this can be shown to them in their own casework treatment. The measurement of the success of treatment in these cases is the extent to which the parents' perception of the child can be modified. This is the desired outcome rather than the beginning of the treatment.

Treatment of these problems must be based on an understanding of the individuals who are participants and their interrelationships. One is accustomed to think first of mother and child and to focus attention mainly on them. The early difficulties in infant care and the resulting special relationship between mother and child may tend to overlook the total family interaction and minimize the role of the father in this. In some cases he may be more objective than the mother in his perception of the child and his development. More often he also has been traumatized by the anxiety of the early months and accepts the mother's evaluation of the child and her decisions in all things pertaining to the child. In what way the father is included in the total treatment plan depends on the assessment of the balance within the family. Frequently a coordinated plan of individual treatment with mother and child may seem to be the most essential element in the beginning phase, with the father's activity in the plan less defined until later. In other family constellations individual treatment of both parents or joint interviews with both might be indicated.

Frequently the mother has been made to feel responsible for the child's problems. She is angry and defensive. The interest of the caseworker needs to be directed toward the mother and the impact of the problems on the mother. The caseworker's immediate aim is to effect some change in the daily interaction between mother and child that provides the mother with evidence of her adequacy. It is important that this be within her concept of her role as parent. Many of these parents have great difficulty accepting the idea that something which might be easier for them, or add to their own pleasure, might also be a way of fulfilling their parental responsibilities in a way that is better for the child. The long history of protective care in strongly established ways is difficult to put aside.

The opening wedge in the modification of the problem may come simultaneously from the child's push toward maturity, reflecting support from his therapist who has offered him a different perception of himself, and from the mother's adapting in a new way to an old conflict situation. The change in the reality of the interaction creates a new interrelationship that provides a new precedent for the next transaction between child and mother. This is a process that may be called experiential relearning; it has in it a circular force of its own when this is consistently supported and reinforced by the treatment. That is, the therapists' alliance with the mother's and child's intact ego functions can result in mother and child reacting with more adaptive modes of behavior toward each other. This involves a learning process that usually does not include insight into unconscious attitudes. If the problems are primarily based on the early trauma of the child's developmental difficulties rather than on the neurotic needs of the parent, the experiential relearning may be sufficiently helpful to establish a more healthful and constructive parent-child climate for the growing-up process. The degree of pervasiveness of the neurotic reactions determines the efficacy of problem solving at this level.

The beginning of some relaxation in the tensions of the daily interaction helps the parents to be less defensive. They can allow themselves to look at the reality of the child, the situation in the family, and their own part in this, and to take conscious measures to change certain aspects of the family's environment and interactions. In some cases a modification of the problem area in the interaction between child and parent may be effective without any deeper insight into internal problems within the parent that have contributed to the development of the difficulty. One parent puts it, "Now that I have begun to do something about what I am doing to Danny, I have settled for myself that I do not need to try to find out why I have felt as I do about him." Another says, "Now I can bear to try to find out why I have felt as I do about him." In the latter cases the modification of the interaction is used as a basis for further treatment of the parents, which is now directed toward some resolution of other conflicts that have been expressed and played out through the difficult relationship with the child. In any case, understanding and insight that will effect some changes in an individual's habitual way of perceiving a child and reacting to him take time, even in families where the individuals and relationships are relatively healthy.

CASE ILLUSTRATION

An example of the complexity of such problems can be illustrated by Billy, a four-year-old boy whose impulsive, provocative behavior was completely uncontrollable in the home and neighborhood. He was referred after a careful pediatric study, by the fifth pediatric resource the parents had consulted. His early history was the usual one of feeding difficulties from birth, fretfulness, screaming, a sleep disturbance, and overactivity, all of which had persisted. In addition, he had an extremely short attention span and his very negative behavior was attested to by others who saw him. No doctor had been able to help the mother; rather each had made her feel inadequate with this, her first child. The father was as concerned as the mother, but became irritable and impatient with his wife when he returned to a chaotic home evening after evening. The mother's feeling of hopelessness and the disorganization of the household were all blamed on Billy. Assurance from the pediatric service that Billy had no organic basis for his behavior did not help the mother's problem, but she responded to the suggestion of referral for psychiatric evaluation and treatment *for Billy* as some assurance of interest in helping her.

During the next several months Billy and the mother were seen in separate interviews each week. The mother's caseworker also had monthly interviews with the father. The mother responded to the suggestion of two mornings a week in nursery school for Billy. Billy very soon made an adequate adjustment in the nursery school, and over the weeks responded to his therapist with a considerably increased attention span in his play and a modification in his impulsive behavior. It became evident that as Billy improved his mother's depression increased, and she began to question her own attitude and response to him. The period of treatment was thus a prolonged evaluation of the relationships within the family. The mother-child relationship was found to be the receptacle for the mother's conflicts about her marriage and her own parents. Billy's particular constitution and activity problems were reinforced by the mother's reaction to him and the circular, spiral interaction continued. Knowledge from child development had made us aware from the beginning that the child's colicky fretfulness and irritability in the early weeks and months of life could have the impact of a trauma on both parents. In the early weeks of treatment the specificity of this formulation became increasingly clear. It was only gradually with the push by the child, supported by his therapist, toward a different kind of relationship with his parents, that other facts in the past and present life experiences of the parents assumed their true proportions. The mother could make only limited use of treatment directed toward the problems in the child-parent interaction unless there was an understanding and acceptance of her reactions to her child as only one expression of her total problem.

SUMMARY

Psychiatric clinics have available today knowledge and experience that has increased and become more meaningful as we have gained new insight into human behavior and relationships. As contributions from other fields of study have been integrated into our thinking, we have gained in our understanding of the child and his development within the family. Psychoanalytic theory about human development and adaptation has contributed to our understanding of the dynamics of human behavior and the mutual adaptation of child and parent. More recent studies in child development, normal and deviant, have elucidated the interactional process that takes place in the early weeks and months and that may establish patterns for continuing problems. A consideration of pathological development resulting from such interactions must be integrated in the diagnosis and treatment of children whose later difficulties can be traced to early parent-child disturbances that have persisted in changing ways. Treatment at various levels, using appropriate methods, can be effective in these problems if it is based on a dynamic understanding of the conflicts of the individuals involved, developmental considerations, and early parent-child interactions.

BIBLIOGRAPHY

Coleman, R. W., Kris, E., & Provence, S. (1953), The Study of Variations of Early Parental Attitudes: A Preliminary Report. *The Psychoanalytic Study of the Child,* 8:20-47. New York: Int. Univ. Press.

Crothers, B. (1937), *A Pediatrician in Search of Mental Hygiene.* New York: Commonwealth Fund.

Erikson, E. H. (1950), *Childhood and Society.* New York: Norton.

Fabian, A. A. (1953), The Contributions of Psychoanalysis to the Child Guidance Unit. *Psychoanalysis and Social Work,* ed. M. Heiman. New York: Int. Univ. Press, pp. 124-152.

Feldman, Y. (1958), Understanding Parents of Disturbed Children. *Soc. Wk.,* 3:23-29.

Gardner, G. E. (1958), Clinical Research in a Child Psychiatry Setting. *Ego Psychology and Dynamic Casework.* New York: Family Service Association of America.

Garrett, A. (1958), Modern Casework: The Contributions of Ego Psychology. *Ego Psychology and Dynamic Casework.* New York: Family Service Association of America.

Healy, W. (1915), *The Individual Delinquent.* Boston: Little, Brown.

Hollis, F. (1951), The Relationship Between Psychosocial Diagnosis and Treatment. *Soc. Casewk.,* 32:67-74.

Levy, D. M. (1947), *New Fields of Psychiatry*. New York: Norton.
—— (1952), The State of Child Psychiatry. *Amer. J. Psychiat.*, 108:481-494.
Perlman, H. H. (1957), *Social Casework: A Problem-solving Process*. Chicago: Univ. Chicago Press.
Reiner, B. & Kaufman, I. (1959), *Character Disorders in Parents of Delinquents*. New York: Family Service Association of America.
Solnit, A. J. & Stark, M. H. (1961), Mourning and the Birth of a Defective Child. *The Psychoanalytic Study of the Child*. 16:523-537. New York: Int. Univ. Press.
Stevenson, G. S. (1939), *Child Guidance Clinics, A Quarter Century of Development*. New York: Commonwealth Fund.
Witmer, H. L. (1940), *Psychiatric Clinics for Children*. New York: Commonwealth Fund.

Why Do Parents Apply for Help at a Child Guidance Clinic?

• *REIMER JENSEN, Ph.D.*
Advanced Teachers' College of Denmark

When we first see a case at a child guidance clinic, it means not the beginning of a process but an intervention which was initiated when the parents perceived the difficulties for which the child was referred to the clinic. This process has already passed through several stages before the parents talk with the social worker at the intake interview; it also continues throughout the treatment of the child. It includes the awareness of a need for help in handling the child; the parents' reaction to the contact with the therapists at the different stages of the treatment; and finally their expectations of the treatment.

It might not be difficult for the parents to describe their complaints and the symptoms of the child, and the interviewer might easily classify the symptoms according to accepted nomenclature. Moreover, we are able to collect a great deal of data about the life history of the child and of the parents and, in fact, of the whole family with its cultural, economic, and social background. However, it often is more difficult to obtain the information clarifying the parents' motives for seeking treatment for their child.

481

Obviously we have to look at the information on this point from different angles. We must evaluate the material in relation to different layers in the personality of the parents. On a superficial level they want to free their child from disturbing symptoms or behavior disorders. They also want some kind of advice, or they may want some suggestions and arrangements to be made in relation to the placement of the child.

At other levels of the parents' personality quite different motives can be found, but usually they cannot be recognized until a closer relationship has been established with the parents during several interviews in connection with the treatment of the child.

The parents' motivation is closely related to the dynamics of the relationship between the parents and the child, and their ideas and fantasies of the goal of the treatment are incorporated in their motivation.

It is rare that a child is referred because of problems which appear suddenly. Usually the family has been dealing with the problems for some time, in some cases for many years in one way or other. How can we explain this delay? Even the most serious disturbances in the development of the personality can be overlooked. The reasons for this include the parents' lack of knowledge about normal and abnormal development. This lack of an adequate frame of reference promotes the parents' tendency to experience the disturbances as reactions falling within the normal varieties of behavior. They are looked upon as reactions which usually are seen in children of the same age and with the same social background. The disturbances will not be identified as symptoms of pathology but perceived as habits or character traits typical for the child and the group to which it belongs. A second reason for parents not to be aware of their child's disturbance stems from the patterns of accepted behavior and adaptation in a particular neighborhood or community. The child with his symptoms, behavior disorders, and nervousness may fit into a pattern in the community or the family, and nobody belonging to the same group would consider the child disturbed or in need of treatment. In control groups selected for research purposes many children show the same clinical pictures as found in the cases at the child guidance clinic, but they are not regarded as disturbed children who should be referred to a clinic. Sometimes problems become apparent only after a child is moved from one environment to another.

The parents' own pathology that excludes the perception of the child's disturbances would be a third reason for not seeking help. It may be that observers other than the parents will note that the child is in need of professional assistance; only the parents are unable to see that, and a discussion of the problem may not bring about any change in their perception of their child.

This observation can be explained as a characteristic of the relationship between the parents and their child. Their pathological reactions fit together and belong to a mutual pattern. During their own childhood the parents have encountered the problems which children normally have to deal with at the different stages of development. If their conflicts were not resolved to a sufficient degree but were internalized in their personality, they can now be reawakened by their child as he reaches the corresponding steps in his development. The parents' internalized conflicts can be the basis of a neurosis or remain latent in their minds without manifesting themselves in specific symptoms or character traits until their child reactivates the conflict situation. The child's problems become a signal to them. The parents' defense mechanisms aim at a control of their inner anxiety. They try to suppress all signs of danger, and they are tempted to administer restrictions and frustrations in their handling of the child in an irrational way. The child experiences a stress which makes it more difficult to overcome his conflicts. He is left alone at this point and has to deal with his own anxiety as well as that of his parents. The parents will not be able to perceive the conflict in the child just as they were not able to do so in themselves, and part of the child's difficulty now includes the parents' denial or negation of the disturbance they share with their child.

When the parents cannot identify a disturbance in their child, they cannot be expected to recognize the need for the child to have treatment. But even if they perceive the problems and are acquainted with the child guidance clinics or other similar facilities, many mechanisms will prevent them from seeking help. They might be fully aware of the disturbances and have some ideas of their development in the personality of the child. They hope, however, that the child will outgrow the problems by himself, i.e., that time will cure. They fear that a psychological examination or treatment will result in a concentration on the problems and make it more difficult for the child to outgrow them. The parents will fall back on many examples to confirm this view or to rationalize this wish.

Actually this attitude of optimism, of the belief that growth and time will help, can be favorable and in many cases be set up as a goal of treatment. With this attitude parents and educators give the child a chance to solve the problems. If the child is brought to treatment, the attitude of "you will get through it" will be the best support to a child, whereas the opposite attitude of "I don't think you will stand for it" or "I am afraid you cannot" might destroy the reassurance which the child needs.

The fear of treatment is often responsible for the postponement of asking for help. Or the family may be overwhelmed by problems and may not know where to start and therefore may be unable to do anything. Moreover, the changes that are characteristic of a growing child can give the false impression that the problems have been worked out all right, but in reality they are being internalized. For example, the aggressive child can give up his open hostility to the parents and the siblings and transform the overt behavior into an inner conflict characterized by inhibitions of the aggressive impulses. In these cases the parent's reluctance to seek help has not helped the child but has postponed adequate treatment.

It is one thing for a parent to perceive the problems in the child. It is quite another thing to say, "I have not been able myself to prevent these difficulties from appearing—somebody else must find out for me" or "I am not capable of dealing with my child's difficulties in the right way. I have to ask somebody else to do what I had expected to do myself."

Inevitably this step provokes intense feelings and a sense of failure. Uncertainty and anxiety are feelings derived from many situations in the parents' earlier life and can easily be aroused and re-experienced on the vital point of their child's need for psychiatric evaluation and treatment.

However, parents usually do not give in passively to these feelings of inferiority but may suppress them or rationalize or compensate in various ways which make the situation bearable for them.

Professional people working in this field are no exception. At times it appears that they, even more than other groups of people, will rationalize and postpone the decision to apply for help for their child. They seem to procrastinate in order to escape the feeling of shortcoming in relation to the expectations they as well as other people have. They feel that they should be able to convert their professional training and skill into parental care that prevents or cures all difficulties in their own children.

These feelings have by no means been overcome when parents start the contact with a clinic. They are often quite obvious and may create an irrational aggressive attitude toward the clinic or the therapist at a very early stage of the treatment. These reactions must be dealt with during the treatment of the child if the therapy is going to be a success.

The same thing is true about the parents' guilt feelings. In spite of all explanations and rationalizations they feel more or less responsible for the child's difficulties. They have a vague feeling, which will be very difficult to verbalize, of the dynamic relation between their own and the child's problems. They may feel they have not been intelligent and nice enough, and therefore the child developed the difficulties which they now cannot handle. This feeling may be further activated during the treatment if they feel that a therapeutic attitude containing these elements helps the child. They may become quite jealous of the child's therapist.

It is a pleasure for the parents to experience the positive feelings toward their child, but it is very difficult to bear the negative feelings of hostility and disappointment in relation to the child. These feelings will especially be provoked when the child shows some behavior disturbances and does not respond to the conscious expectations and the philosophy of the parents concerning the goal of their education. The negative or ambivalent feelings do not fit very well into a normal, and definitely not into an idealized picture of the parent-child relationship. An analysis of this relationship may reveal these negative feelings and create a strong reaction against the treatment that threatens to make the parents aware of these unaccepable feelings.

We are familiar with the primary and secondary gain in a neurosis. Parallel to that we find traces of similar mechanisms working in the parents' relation to their child, and therefore strong unconscious wishes may oppose any change in the child's behavior or personality structure. The parents have not given the child a chance to develop but pressed him into a certain role or identification process. The child not only reacts to the parents' overt and verbalized attitude, but he is influenced by the parents' whole personality including their unconscious wishes; and in some cases he will act according to these. Then the child behaves as the parents want him to be, even though the parents do not like to see the overt results of the attitude which they have induced in the child.

It may be that the parents use the child to express tendencies which they have difficulty repressing in themselves. They need the child as a tool in their own pathology. The child is a channel through which their unconscious wishes are fulfilled. They are not aware of the misuse of the child but may have some vague feelings of the mechanisms at work in the relationship. This in turn may evoke very strong and deep objections to any change which threatens to upset the balance of their neurosis.

Obviously many causes will be responsible for the time lag between the manifestation of the problem and the decision to arrange a referral to a clinic. It is understandable that the parents will swing back and forth in their considerations or change their attitude toward treatment several times and occasionally be prevented from doing anything at all. When they finally come to the clinic it does not mean that they have given up all their objections to treatment. It does not mean either that it has been possible for the parents to evaluate the whole situation and take the different constituent factors into consideration. They have had to make their decision on the basis of a very distorted picture including the complicated dynamic relations in which they personally are involved with their child.

Usually the parents ask for help in a relatively narrow area, while the orientation at the clinic is broader. The child's problems are seen by the clinic as family problems. The evaluation of the child and family as well as the treatment will concentrate on the relationships among the family members. This is a consequence of our knowledge of the dynamic forces at work in the formation of the personality structure and its deviations. Thus, it is understandable that the parents' expectations of treatment will cover only to a certain degree what the clinic offers them. There might even be a marked discrepancy between their wishes and the attainable goals.

During the treatment the parents may gain some insight into the dynamics of the relationships within the family and become aware of attitudes and conflicts which were disguised when they were referred to the clinic. It can be surprising and frightening, even shocking, for parents to experience the connections between their problems and the child's symptoms as they gain insight into their own unconscious feelings toward the child.

From a superficial point of view it often looks as if an accidental happening has caused the referral. Someone else has told the parents to go to the clinic. It may appear that the child's symptoms do not make an impact upon them until they experience or anticipate social reactions to the child's behavior or symptoms. For example, a boy had the habit of stealing his mother's clothes and dressing himself in them at home, from the time he was seven years old. The parents did not seek assistance for the boy until he was fifteen years old, at which time he planned to leave home and stay with some relatives for his apprenticeship. Then the parents asked for help because they did not want anyone else to know about his transvestite behavior, and they wanted to prevent the humiliation and shame for the boy and the family that would result from others knowing about his symptom. They did not seem to realize that the boy for his own sake might have needed help a long time before. However, when their son planned to take up training and work away from home the parents could sense that others would not adapt to his disturbed behavior as they had for eight years, and the threat of this seemed to be the main reason for their application to the clinic.

In some instances, the parents' motivation for the treatment of the child will reflect their unconscious wish to punish the child who has not reacted in a satisfactory way to their conscious wishes and requirements. These parents do not seem to know how to express their anger or hostility; it is not acceptable to express it directly or it is contradictory to their philosophy of education. They find an acceptable expression of their resentment in the referral to a clinic because they hope that the child's behavior will be exposed and that he will be compelled to correct it. The therapist is expected to tell the child how to behave and teach him to be good to the parents. In some cases the parents' primary wish is to separate from the child. Any conscious idea of that kind would probably awaken strong and threatening feelings in the parents because they cannot tolerate an awareness of what they really want, and it has to be worked out little by little.

Sometimes it is difficult to find out if the parents come for their own sake or for the child's sake. They want to be reassured themselves. They need to be relieved of their feelings of guilt or inferiority; they need someone else to tell them that they are not bad in spite of their difficulties with the child. They may feel isolated and want to establish some kind of contact which allows them to talk about themselves. They fear or cannot afford personal treatment and most often have no consciously formulated wish for treatment for themselves. It may be easier to bring the child than to involve themselves; in this way they contact a therapist and at the same time escape their personal problems which are hidden behind the interest in the child. Having to ask for help for the child can be humiliating but it may be still more difficult to admit, "I have some problems myself which require treatment."

In some instances their motivation is quite different from what is usually seen at a clinic and may be a surprise to everyone. One family went to the doctor with complaints of the child's nervous reactions. They stressed the complaints very much, and the doctor, agreeing that there was a need for treatment, referred the child to

the clinic where the usual procedure was instituted—an intake interview, testing, and examinations by psychiatrist and pediatrician. The
child definitely needed treatment and psychotherapy was initiated.
The mother was seen once a week. After some time it turned out
that the parents were very surprised at the whole procedure because
they felt that they had always been able to cope with the problems
and had never wanted anything to be done. They had stressed the
problems so much to the doctor because they had wanted him to
write a statement of their difficulties to the housing authorities. They
felt that the child's disturbance was caused by the crowding in their
apartment and that a statement to that effect from the doctor would
improve their opportunities for getting a new and larger apartment.

Before they come, the parents cannot anticipate what the contact
with the clinic will mean to them. They want some kind of help,
but their wishes are related to their own personality structure and
possible pathology, and may be mixed up with realistic and unrealistic ideas and fantasies. Their motivation may be a jungle which is
difficult to map out. It is important, however, to evaluate the motivation at the intake procedure. The fact that parents have a lot of
ambivalent or negative feelings does not mean that they should not
be accepted for treatment. They will show their resistance from the
very beginning when the first appointment is being arranged. But
even when the parents show a very positive attitude and expose a
warm interest and willingness to cooperate, they often have mixed
feelings toward the clinic and the therapists. From one point of view
it can be stated that the purpose of the contact with the parents
during the treatment of the child is to deal with their motivations
for treatment and to support them as new aspects of this motivation
appear according to the progress of the therapeutic process. They
need insight, support, and reassurance as the goals of treatment arise
and a new orientation becomes available to them. Although helpful
in some ways, this may at the same time create new problems and be
confusing.

At a child guidance clinic quite a few cases seem to be terminated
before the treatment has come to a point where, from a clinical point
of view and sometimes from a social point of view, it is advisable

to stop. The parents give up the interest in the treatment or resist it. They feel there is too great a gap between their expectations of the contact with the clinic and the results. This discrepancy can be worked out, but it sometimes becomes overwhelming and causes premature termination of the treatment. It may be that even in these cases the child and the parents have been helped during the contact with the clinic. It is always difficult to evaluate the result of a therapeutic contact, but it is felt unsatisfactory if it is not carried through. Incomplete treatment may be a waste of time for parents and child as well as for the clinic, which often is burdened with a heavy case load and a long waiting list.

SUMMARY AND CONCLUSION

An analysis of the parents' motivation for bringing their child to the clinic and a discussion of these findings with the parents usually make it easier for them to accept the whole procedure. What is going on in their child's treatment then makes more sense to them and increases the possibilities of closing the case as a successful one at the right stage of development.

Part VI

Medical Education Today

Although this section is almost exclusively concerned with pediatric education, its perspectives are important for all of clinical medicine. After viewing the pediatrician's opportunities to give suitable advice about the child's environment, W. Wallace Grant describes an educational program for medical students that enables them to develop an ecological understanding about pediatric patients and their families. Joe D. Wray uses his unusual background as a pediatric educator in Turkey and Colombia to examine the realities of child health abroad. From these observations he outlines what our pediatric exports should include. In the next article Mary H. Stark pertinently indicates that one of the social worker's essential contributions to pediatric education is in the area of interviewing. She discusses social work principles and techniques that enable the physician to incorporate these skills into a useful pediatric approach to interviewing. Morris A. Wessel considers the importance of "Training in Neonatal Pediatrics" by his discussion of its practical and theoretical importance, and by describing how this crucial aspect of pediatric education can be implemented. In the last contribution to this section, Seymour L. Lustman and Julius B. Richmond provide an essential perspective for all of medicine in their discussion of the necessity to define the limitations of the physician's work and responsibilities. They clearly explain why this attitude should be cultivated during the training period.

The Child's Environment in Relation to His Health: A Teaching Program in Pediatric Ecology

• *W. WALLACE GRANT, M.D.*

University of Manitoba

There is nothing new in the concept that patients' problems, whatever their nature, usually can be better understood and treated if one knows something about the setting in which they carry on their daily activities. The health problem may have been studied and treatment carried on at home from the beginning, or following discharge from hospital. In the days of learning by preceptorship students of medicine took this experience for granted. Their teacher, the family physician, could point out the things about the home that his pupil might not have seen, and discuss the family setting in relation to the disease when the home visit was over. As clinical teaching moved more and more into hospital wards and outpatient departments, there developed a tendency to treat the patient as he presented himself there without much consideration as to how much the problem

The author gratefully acknowledges the financial support of the Rockefeller Foundation which made possible the first three years of this program, the interest of W. Frank Horner Limited, which grants the annual award, the enthusiastic cooperation given by the City of Winnipeg Health Department Nursing Division, and work of the students (now graduate physicians) whose presentations are quoted or referred to extensively in this paper.

was related to the habitat in which he normally found himself. Osler is said to have sent his medical students into the homes of their patients as long ago as the beginning of this century. He was, however, until very recent years one of the very few who did this.

Lately, in many teaching hospitals new programs have been developed to relate the home, the school, and the neighborhood to the patient's health problem, whether he be child or adult.

My own interest in this type of learning was stimulated by Dr. Milton Senn in the years 1950 to 1952. As part of my training with him I spent time in the Outpatient Department of the Grace-New Haven Community Hospital and periodically visited the homes and schools of patients seen there. The experience with these children was subsequently discussed with him, usually to their benefit, invariably to mine.

For the past ten years in the Pediatric Department of the Medical Faculty of the University of Manitoba and at The Children's Hospital of Winnipeg, senior medical students have had such learning experience in their too-brief four-week period with us. In the beginning many of the patients selected were the chronically ill or those with frequently recurring illness, who seemed to be spending far too much time in hospital. At present, the program is centered in the Outpatient Department, although occasionally it involves children who have been, or are now, patients in the hospital. As often as possible the patient is one who has not been seen before in the clinic, so that the student is not helped, biased, or confused by the notes of many who have seen the child in the past. The decision about the potential value of a home visit is made by the supervising instructor who reviews the patient with the student. The arrangement is made directly with the parent and child as a means to help us understand the problem better and manage the treatment more efficiently. In presenting the idea of a home visit to the parent, a very definite effort is made to avoid any implication of parental blame for the condition of the child's health. The student is cautioned to avoid any appearance of criticism in his dealings with the child or parent wherever he sees them.

Because we feel that it is important for students in medicine to learn by practical experience the functions of public health personnel, we arrange that the student visit the home with a public health nurse from the City of Winnipeg Health Department. Each of these nurses is assigned to a specific district, visits the newborn children in that area, supervises the health of the children in one or two of its schools, and is an important member of the Child Health Center in the area. The student may visit also the child's school, perhaps observe him in the classroom or play yard, and talk to the teacher and principal about him. This may be on his own decision, or it may be recommended by the district nurse, or advised by his instructor.

Following this experience with the child in the clinic, at home, and in the school, he presents his conclusions in a conference held the same week. This is attended by five or six of his classmates on the service with him, representatives of the pediatric teaching staff, hospital Social Service Department, and the student's current "associate," the public health nurse. His sharpest critics are invariably his colleagues. They often find themselves de-emphasizing the techniques of physical diagnosis and laboratory investigations in the heat of argument over seeming parental inadequacy, presumed intolerance of schoolteachers, and questionable humanity of social agencies. Each student is required to submit a written report of his total experience. This review is not just filed away and forgotten but, after being graded as part of his final standing in pediatrics, is incorporated in the hospital record of the patient. For the past five years a money prize has been presented at convocation to the graduating student whose presentation has been considered the best of the year. This award is made possible by a Canadian pharmaceutical house, the interest of which is no less in spite of the fact that the emphasis in these case studies is less on treatment by medication than by bringing about changes in the environment.

The initial problem for which the child is brought to the clinic often turns out to be relatively unimportant as far as his total health is concerned. The "presenting complaint" is nonetheless always taken seriously and an opinion given about it, even when it appears to be used merely as a way of getting help with a problem which is far more complex. No effort is made to concentrate primarily on behavior disturbances. Many of the most effective presentations have concerned problems as widely different as communicable diseases (such as infectious hepatitis, typhoid fever, tuberculosis, bacillary dysentery); deficiency diseases (such as iron deficiency anemia and scurvy); growth failure; or obesity; and congenital malformations. More obvious complaints meriting this study have included poor school performance, recurrent headache or abdominal pain, behavior disturbance, and delinquency.

Unfortunately, because of the limitations of time, the whole study is often completed on three successive days: the clinic visit on the first day, home and school visit the next, and conference presentation on the third. As often as possible the child is seen by the student at least once more. Interest is maintained over many months, long after the student has moved on to another service. Some of these embryo physicians have gone to the extent of giving material help or arranging for it; others are inclined to greet one weeks or months later in the Medical School corridor or socially with, "You know that boy I did the visit on? How's he doing?" The things that impress themselves on student and teacher in a program such as this are very often situations or complications which never could have been predicted when the child was first seen. Examples of actual situations will now be presented. Due acknowledgment is made to the students concerned, each of whom is now in very effective medical practice, or well along in specialty training.

CASE 1: *Joseph's Typhoid Fever and the "Iron Curtain."*

Joseph had had severe abdominal pain and vomiting for three days. The illness began two weeks before with episodes of nausea, gradually getting more frequent and intense until he had to go to bed two days before admission. Appetite had also gradually diminished. For two days he had taken nothing by mouth and had no bowel movements. He was thought to be feverish for a day. The boy had come from Poland three months before with his parents and sisters of four and three.

He was a hot, tired, sick little boy of seven years with a flushed face, and some inflammation of the pharynx. There was guarding of the whole right side of the abdomen which was possibly more tender in the lower quadrant. The spleen could not be felt. The temperature was 103°F. Hemoglobin was 11.2 gms. Leukocytes were 4900, initially with 50 per cent polymorphnuclears. Sedimentation rate was 52 mm. per hour.

Because of the seriousness of his illness he was admitted for further study. Tuberculin test was negative. There was a slight growth of pneumococcus from the throat swab. Blood agglutinations were positive for typhoid O, to 1 in 320 and for typhoid H, to 1 in 40, but otherwise negative. Blood smear for malaria was negative. Initially the possibility of appendicitis or of an enteritis (bacterial or viral) was also raised, but the fever ranged intermittently from normal to 104°F. each day, rose spots appeared on his abdomen; stool culture established the diagnosis when Salmonella typhi were isolated. He was then transferred to the infectious disease hospital and was treated with chloramphenicol until five negative stool cultures were obtained. He was still in that hospital when the home visit was made by the student.

The purpose of this visit was stated as follows: (1) to determine if possible where the patient had contacted the disease, (2) to learn whether there was any danger to the community in general, and (3) to discover whether other members of the family or household were carriers, or ever acutely ill with typhoid. This visit was made in the company of a health inspector from the City Health Department. The house was three stories high in a low-rent district of the city and provided shelter for a total of sixteen people. The patient's family group of eight occupied the main floor. Eight tenants who lived on upper floors had a separate entrance and their own cooking and bathroom facilities. The patient's family group included the parents and the three children, an uncle, and two grandparents. All the adult members were gainfully employed except the patient's mother who cooked for the whole family.

Fortunately the student who made the visit was able to communicate with the mother in Ukrainian. She told him that the family had lived in a small town in Poland where the water was supplied from well-constructed, concrete-cribbed, deep wells. This matter was discussed at some length because the patient had mentioned that a well had been closed down in the area before the family left Poland. The mother explained that this had occurred more than a year prior to the family's emigration because the well was caving in. There was no record of any similar illness in the community or condemnation of the well by local health authorities. It was obvious that this topic had caused some degree of apprehension in the father and grandmother of the patient, and at the time of the visit an effort was made to reassure the mother that its purpose was not to gain evidence to send the family back to Europe. No like illness in the family was admitted, either in Winnipeg or before that in Poland. Allegedly no friends or relatives had at any time suffered from diarrhea. On coming to Canada the family had moved directly to Winnipeg, and they had not visited in other parts of the province. The patient had eaten all meals at home except for school lunches in September and October. The only other possibility was that the father, having spent some time in Siberia fifteen years before, had been exposed to many people ill with various maladies, some of them dysenteric. He himself was never ill but could have been in contact with typhoid. As to the possibility of any public health hazard it was noted that the grandparents were dyers in a dry cleaning establishment, the uncle a carpenter, and the father an upholsterer in a furniture manufacturing firm; the mother was at home looking after the house and cooking. It seemed obvious to the student that the house was well cared for, in spite of being somewhat old, and the two younger children were clean and appeared well nourished. The mother was informed of the regulations of the Health Department regarding collection of stool specimens from all members of the family. Specimen containers were provided and a list of names was made out in duplicate with a number for each member of the family. Specimen bottles were numbered, and one list of names with numbers was left with the family and the other taken to the City Health Department. Before leaving, a "sham run" was carried out to make sure that the mother knew exactly which bottle was for each person. Every effort was made to assure the mother that any measures which might be taken in the future were in the family's best interest, and a verbal promise of cooperation was obtained.

Following this experience with the Sanitary Inspector the student had good reason to believe that the home visit had achieved a worthwhile end. However, for the sake of completeness he gave an account of the course of events following the home visit, which led him to raise some questions as to the easy solution of such a problem. The only stool specimen from the family which grew the typhoid bacillus was that from the mother. She was then hospitalized at the infectious disease hospital, given chloramphenicol therapy, and after two negative stool cultures allowed to return home because of an acute shortage of hospital beds. However, the third stool specimen that was cultured again grew typhoid bacillus. When she was asked to return to the hospital she refused. She did agree to report to another hospital near her home, where a duodenal aspiration was done, and again typhoid was recovered. She was advised to have a cholecystectomy performed in order to get rid of the source of infection, but refused.

The student then proceeded to outline the courses of action open to the authorities: (1) insist on the cholecystectomy, (2) prescribe further chloramphenicol therapy at home or in the hospital, (3) deport the carrier, (4) continue surveillance of the mother as a known typhoid carrier, and (5) therapy with other antibiotics. It was decided to give another trial of chloramphenicol. This was to be given for two weeks to be followed by further stool and duodenal cultures. If both were negative, that therapy would be continued for another week. If cultures were positive, this medication would be considered inadequate, and the dangers of side effects with long-term therapy would have to be considered. It was noted that there was general agreement that if fourteen days of therapy with chloramphenicol failed to eradicate typhoid bacillus from the bowel, further therapy with this agent was probably worthless. It was suggested that "Deportation to Poland would be a tragic mistake; it seems a very unlikely course to be taken. Following the woman as a typhoid carrier is an undesirable method involving a considerable amount of bookwork by the medical authorities, and not foolproof in preventing spread. In addition to this all the close contacts should be immunized against the disease, a measure which had already been instituted in the family group. As for other antibiotics, two which would be considered are one of the tetracyclines (although sometimes effective in the active disease, not considered too much value in the treatment of the asymptomatic carrier), and the new antibiotic Synnematin Sodium (Salmotin Sodium—Abbott) which seems to be rather effective in preventing the development of the carrier state."

Comment: This student's experience demonstrated to him and his colleagues the methods used, the problems encountered in the diagnosis of typhoid fever, the difficulties in treatment, and the problem of dealing with a carrier who is unwilling to accept recommendations regarding surgery. Unfortunately time did not permit further study of this reaction, better understanding of which might have led to a changed attitude. The family's obvious concern about the possibility of being penalized for bringing a disease into the country added a further complication. The student was better able to understand the family's reactions since he could talk to this woman in a language which was more familiar to her than English.

CASE 2: *Mabel's Stomachache—The Mother's Cry for Help*

This child of eight years was seen a week after her mother phoned the hospital asking to have her daughter seen by a psychiatrist. It was explained that the child would be examined in the general medical clinic first, and then if psychiatric help was needed it would be arranged for her. The student who saw this mother and child recorded that Mabel was missing a lot of school because of "stomach trouble." This was vaguely described and not mentioned by the child herself. It occurred only on school days, causing her to miss one or two days a week and was not accompanied by vomiting. The mother had been reprimanded on more than one occasion by the school principal for keeping the child out of school so frequently. Four schools had been attended in the preceding three years, with five different teachers, although the child was only in grade three. She spent six months in the first school, one and a half years in the second, two months (with two teachers) in the third, and had been in the present school for only two weeks.

The mother appeared to be depressed, not too intelligent, inclined to a rather monotonous "whiney" speech. The child had been "slightly premature," birth weight being 5½ pounds, but there had been no difficulties with the labor and no postnatal problems with the child as an infant. The only questionably significant early illness was tonsillectomy at a year and a half.

Mabel herself was a quiet little girl, unwilling to talk much, especially about her sickness. She was in the 10 percentile for height and her weight in the 25 percentile. No organic cause for her complaint was discovered.

With the child out of the room the student talked further to Mrs. B. He discovered that she was a Jewish girl who had become pregnant at fifteen and married the father, Mr. A, a Gentile, of the same age. They were soon separated, Mrs. A going to live with her mother. At the same time she had a psychiatric disturbance for which she was treated for a week on the staff service of the local hospital by the psychiatric resident, who later saw her as an outpatient. There was a brief reconciliation with Mr. A four years ago, followed by the birth of the oldest boy (now three), allegedly the son of the present husband, Mr. B. About this time a common-law relationship was set up with Mr. B, and in 1958 after the divorce from Mr. A, they were married.

Mr. B adopted the two children she already had, Mabel and the brother of three. He fathered a boy, now two, and a girl, now five months. Mr. B was reported to get along well with Mabel but to be very strict with the younger children. When he became irritated with them he threatened to beat them, so that Mrs. B was often hit by him in her efforts to protect them. Just before his release from the

Army, two years before, he had been in the Veterans Hospital for two months with various somatic complaints, eventually being referred to the psychiatric department. One of the doctors at this hospital had told the wife that her husband should be in the provincial mental hospital. She was asked to sign commitment forms but refused, and the episode so frightened and disturbed Mr. B that he would not go back for any medical help. He was reported to drink a good deal, his wife commenting that "after six beers he is just as liable to kill the kids as look at them." Twice she called the police to the house at such times, but no charges were filed. A month before she had had brief contact with the family court regarding the possibility of a legal separation because the father's drinking was making them too poor to feed the children properly.

At the end of this interview and examination, supervisor and student felt that there was evidence of considerable instability, emotionally, financially, and geographically, but no evidence from physical examination of an organic lesion in the child. It seemed probable that Mabel had a "school phobia," which accounted for the complaints of stomachache. With a view to studying the situation further and by arrangement with the mother, visits were made the following day to home and school.

The family lived in the bottom half of an old four-family dwelling. Some of the furniture in their three rooms had recently been removed because of nonpayment, and a new refrigerator and stove replaced similar ones also recently repossessed. In general the dwelling seemed reasonably cheerful, clean, and tidy. Mr. B, who was mopping the kitchen floor when the student appeared, was reported to be a strikingly neat man, seeming younger than twenty-five. Although he had achieved only grade seven in school, he seemed quite intelligent, considerably more so than his wife. Most of his family still lived on the East Coast where they had been brought up by a stern father who exercised vigorous discipline and frequently used physical punishment. Mr. B. seemed ill at ease, rarely still, moving about the room rubbing his hands. He never looked directly at the student even when conversing with him. He suggested that he would be in better health if he were working and out of the house, since the children irritated him. He complained further that the psychiatric treatment, especially drugs and occupational therapy, two years before had not helped him. The succeeding year had been a happy one when he worked as a laborer in the railroad yards. Unfortunately he had been laid off for a year. His story about drinking, unlike that of his wife, was "Give me six beers and a television to watch, and I'm happy."

In the home Mrs. B appeared much as in the clinic, but she made no complaints about her husband. She focused rather on the school, which she said would not accept her statement regarding Mabel's illness as a reason for missing school. She already felt that Mabel had experienced prejudice at school, reminding her of her own childhood when she felt she had been discriminated against because of her race.

Financial support was welfare allowance and family allowance, with some help from a Jewish welfare agency, Mrs. B's mother, and the "Legion."

At the school the first contact of the medical student was with the principal. His information was that Mabel had been absent from the previous school on many occasions, and finally Mrs. B had requested that she be moved to this school. This was largely due to several letters from Child Guidance Clinic pressing them to see that the child attended regularly and threatening that there might be loss of family allowance if this did not occur. Phone calls about Mabel's absence were frequently answered by Mabel who reported that her mother was out. When contacted the mother always reported that the child was too ill to be at school. Even in the first two weeks in the new school there had been several absences and the principal, becoming hostile, was threatening to notify the Children's Aid Society that the child was being neglected. She was doing reasonably well in her grade but not as well as her tested intelligence suggested she should.

The student's summary was as follows: The problem is to determine what the cause or causes of the absenteeism from school may be. The gastrointestinal symptoms suggested three possibilities, namely, an organic lesion; a psychogenic disorder related to a school phobia; and "there may be nothing wrong with the child, but the so-called illness a device used by the mother to cover her neglect, her indifference, or ignorance of her responsibility for seeing that her child is at school." The evidence against organic lesion included the fact that the pains never occurred on nonschool days and had not been associated with vomiting; the physical examination and laboratory study revealed nothing abnormal. If the child were afraid of school, the possible reasons for this included physical or mental handicaps (neither of which appeared to be present); rebellion against the parent as a reaction to unusual dependency on the parent; and gratification associated with staying at home, and this could be related to fears of teacher or of other children. More thorough psychiatric examination might be required, but since the complaint appeared to be lessening this did not seem to be indicated at the time.

On the basis of his studies in clinic, home, and school, the student felt that although there was much in the child's environment to justify the development of psychogenic symptoms, he doubted that Mabel had actually been ill as often as reported by the mother. It seemed more likely that the mother was using this complaint "as a weapon in the battle which has developed between her and the school system." This possibility was supported by the fact that the child herself would not talk about her illness and evidence that Mabel was often at home alone with the younger children. The mother naïvely reported to the student that quite recently Mabel had missed school in the morning because the whole family slept until a quarter to nine; then rather than send her to school late and "having her scolded," she kept her at home. An additional reason, that it was storming, was unacceptable to the principal because they lived only two blocks from the school. The student raised the possibility that the mother's reference of her problem to the hospital clinic was really a "gesture for help for her total situation." His own feeling was that the most urgent need was for counseling. He went on to state: "Various agencies are all very well, but most often it is the agency, represented by different people, rather than one person, that is dealing with the family. This relationship almost inevitably becomes impersonal. If there could be one counselor assigned to this family, they then could relate to one person rather than a group of agencies. As a friendly, objective adviser such a person would be of great value to this family. Both parents seem to be quite inadequate in coping with a complex problem and no doubt would be only too glad to receive advice from someone on whom they could depend. The second important function of this counselor would be to co-ordinate efforts of various organizations which have been dealing with this particular family (Children's Hospital, Family Court, Police, Legion, School, and Child Guidance Clinic). In this way the family could be protected from continuous bombardment with bits and pieces· of completely unintegrated advice. This case is a good example of what happens when communications between groups fail, and each starts acting aggressively to achieve its own ends, such as the demand by the school that the child attend, with the threat to use legal authority without good evidence of regard for the total situation. If such a plan were established, the welfare of the child, the family, and the community could be considered and the most satisfactory solution for all found."

He suggested further that an early step in the investigation of the family would be psychiatric assessment of both parents. This might reveal "how much Mrs. B's acting out against the school system is due to her own lack of intelligence, how much is due to the de-moralizing situation she had been in for the past ten years, and how much is related to her husband's emotional disturbance." If this type of help could not be provided, there was serious danger of a break-up of the family. The student went on to suggest that such a scheme could be routinely set up whenever a social problem comes to the attention of the school or any agency. "Then something positive could be done before the situation becomes such that various groups have started to react with hostility toward the family involved. Once this happens a lot of false pride on both sides has to be overcome in order to establish a constructive and objective approach to the problem." Some discussion ensued as to whether the children might not be better off placed in a foster home, and the student noted "because I believe that the biologic home has many intrinsic advantages over a foster home, I believe that for children of this age an attempt should be made to re-establish this crumbling family unit."

Comment: Experience with this family and the various community agencies with which it had become involved was most enlightening to this student, and by report and discussion to his colleagues. He discovered that it is quite possible for parents to complain about a child's illness, which exists not even in the mind of the child but is manufactured to serve the ends of the parents. He was impressed by the relative ineffectiveness of the combined efforts of many agencies. Spontaneously he questioned the economic use of many expensive facilities and the high-priced professional workers carrying on independently without much association with each other, a problem recognized by many with much more training and experience in this field. They, too, have pointed out that workers from many community agencies beat a path to the doors of the recipients of their help, the one arriving to greet the other leaving, but having very little other contact. Who would care to argue against the idea of more cooperative effort among such agencies and their workers? Finally, in discussion with this group, it was admitted that much of the vague abdominal pain in childhood is extremely difficult to define as to cause. Adequate study is indicated in each instance, regardless of what environmental factors may be discovered which may make it appear to be psychogenic or a fantasy of a parent.

CASES 3 TO 7: *Whence Comes Scurvy?*

Like many other pediatric centers in North America ours had been concerned about an apparent increase in incidence of scurvy in small infants. In the past ten years we have seen each year an average of twelve established cases in clinic or hospital ward. A study of five of these infants led to student home visits, and subsequently to discussion of the preventive problem with the group as a whole. These infants ranged in age from five to ten months; three of them were seen in March and two in late February.

CASE 3

A five-month-old infant was the only child of a mother, nineteen, and a father, twenty-one, who were living with the paternal in-laws. The father was unemployed, but was not drawing unemployment insurance because of recent imprisonment for auto theft. Two weeks before our contact, the baby had had an umbilical hernia operated on in another hospital, with the hope thereby of "curing" its irritability. The only other illnesses had been frequent upper respiratory infections. The child had been breast fed for two weeks and then put on an evaporated milk formula because the mother phoned the doctor complaining of having to feed the baby so often. This was changed to a whole-milk feeding at three and a half months, when he developed an ulcer in his mouth. The current feeding was about forty ounces of whole milk daily, with a small portion of cereal. Vegetables and other solid foods were refused. Shortly after birth a vitamin concentrate containing ascorbic acid had been prescribed in adequate dosage. The initial preparation was used up at one month and replaced by a preparation supplied by a family friend, a much less concentrated syrup which the mother administered to the baby in the same dosage as the concentrate. Thus for the preceding four months the child had received only a fraction of the recommended daily dose of Vitamin C. This information regarding change in vitamin preparation was obtained only in discussion with the mother in her home. On this occasion the student learned something of the functions of the public health nurse who accompanied him. She left written advice regarding feeding, promised to return and help the mother with baby care, invited her to bring the baby to the next well-child clinic in the area, and promised to contact the Welfare Department about possible increase in financial assistance.

CASE 4

A six-month-old girl had been screaming for three days when the mother touched her legs but otherwise had seemed well. Physical and X-ray examinations confirmed the diagnosis of scurvy that was suggested by the history. The student visiting this home noted the relatively cramped quarters with kitchen, living room, and bedroom to accommodate the baby and three brothers, two, four, and eight years. The kitchen was largely taken up with the family wash. He discovered that the mother had been given a sample bottle of a vitamin concentrate when she left the hospital after the birth of the baby, presumably being advised to continue with this preparation. She discontinued it very shortly because the baby "did not take it well." At two weeks of age she offered orange juice, but stopped this when the baby developed a rash. She then acquired a vitamin concentrate which unfortunately had in it only vitamin A and D, and gave it in dosage recommended for the previous preparation, but with no other source of vitamin C except small helpings of tinned fruits and vegetables. The student in his report commented: "The responsibility for the development of scurvy in this child does not lie entirely with the mother who did not cause it knowingly. The fault lies rather with society—the economic, the social, and the educative sectors. It is not a simple problem but a complex one in which we are all involved, the doctors, the educators, the business men and the politicians."

CASE 5

A seven-month-old baby was brought to the clinic by its father because it cried when picked up. In the family there were also two brothers and a sister, two of them currently suffering from measles. None of these children had ever received vitamin supplements. The father was fearful of calling a physician lest he could not pay both his bill and the cost of the medication the doctor might prescribe. For some reason he had learned only recently that they could attend the clinic of the hospital. The student remarked that "there must be some way of reaching these people, as they are the ones who would benefit most from this type of service. It seems there is some defect in the medical service in a community when a case such as this occurs."

CASE 6

An eight-month-old baby was admitted to the hospital, the patient of a private physician, because of weakness of the left leg for a day. The consultant noted: "If this is polio, it is very mild, but at this stage I would be more inclined to call it a pseudo paralysis which could be traumatic, inflammatory or scurvy; I think X-rays are suggestive of scurvy." The family physician agreed to have us arrange a home visit. This was for the education of the medical student and also with a view of obtaining, for chemical analysis, some of the canned orange juice which the mother said she had given. The home was in a rather isolated area on the outskirts of the city, a two-story farm house with dilapidated outbuildings. Upstairs was one large room in which slept the seven siblings, ranging in age from two to nine years. The father, a corporal in the Army, seemed intelligent and concerned about the children. The mother was pleasant, rather worried-looking, and seemed not too bright. The total monthly income was barely adequate to supply food (including four quarts of milk a day) and shelter, and pay the family's debts. The father, the student reported, "revealed that his wife had been untruthful to the admitting intern, upset by the realization that she had not fed the baby the foods about which the family physician had questioned her beforehand." The mother added that at one time the infant was offered orange juice and cod-liver oil but refused both, and as a result the child had received no vitamin supplements of any sort, nor had it had citrus fruit juices or other sources of vitamin C.

CASE 7

A ten-month-old baby was seen because its legs had seemed extremely tender for a week. The child moved them hesitatingly. For several weeks she had been a poor feeder, taking only milk and some fruit juice. Although it was a full-term pregnancy, the child's birthweight was less than 5½ pounds. She was the youngest of seven, the oldest being a girl of seventeen. The child had never been nursed, and the mother was vague about the initial formula. She stated that the child used up six bottles of vitamins in the first two months, following which no more was given. Only small quantities of cereal were taken from four months, and other solid food was refused entirely. Intake at present was about forty ounces of whole milk daily. This was a small, extremely irritable infant weighing just over 16 pounds. The gums were purplish; there was suggestive swelling at costochondral junctions; and the abdomen appeared tender. Although the baby allowed the limbs to be moved passively, it tended to keep them flexed at hip and knee, and they seemed tender on palpation. The diagnosis of scurvy was supported by the discovery of classical signs on X-ray of the long bones of the legs, and also the X-ray film of the chest which showed the upper ends of both humeri.

The student found the mother in a three-room suite, one of twelve in a run-down two-story frame building. The rooms were dimly lit, and there was a musty dank odor. Refuse littered the floors; plyboard walls and ceilings were cluttered with water and furnace pipes, as well as being disfigured by scribbling. It was discovered that the mother and her husband had been separated for eleven years (eight of them legally), but there had been periodic reconciliations, so that three children had been fathered in the interim. The father was reputedly alcoholic with only intermittent employment, periodically delinquent, and currently in jail. The oldest child of seventeen had been in detention at fourteen because of truancy, alcoholism, and promiscuity. Two boys, now fourteen and fifteen, were in jail. The sixteen-year-old boy, no longer in school, worked sporadically but was currently at home. The whole source of income was welfare assistance; the only luxury a TV set.

The original vitamin supply used up in two months was not replenished for several reasons. The mother insisted that she did not know that it was necessary to maintain vitamin supplements. Unfortunately since the family moved shortly after the child's birth, without leaving a forwarding address, the public health nurse could not trace them. Finally the mother said she had raised six other children "without fancy diets," with no resulting ill effect. She stated that she knew about the need for fruit juices, but they were always rejected, and she blamed this on the child's repeated colds which interfered with her appetite. Because she vaguely knew that oranges were important she managed once in a while to force some carbonated orange drink into the child. In spite of all her difficulties this mother had great hopes for the future and spoke of the possibility of getting a small low-rent house in the suburbs, acquiring a few chickens and a cow, and gardening in the summertime, but definitely without her husband!

The student's summary referred to several questions that had been raised in discussion. One of these was why the older siblings had never shown symptoms like the patient's. This was felt to be partly due to the fact that all the others had been breast fed for several months, and in this way had received some vitamin C which they would not have obtained from pasteurized whole milk or evaporated milk. A further possibility was that the child's recurrent upper respiratory infections had increased vitamin C requirements considerably above what is considered basal. The student summed up his experience by referring to a brochure published by the Provincial Health Department in 1954: "There seem to be three contributing causes to scurvy: ignorance, inertia, and income. Undoubtedly this triad comprises the etiology in this case and untold others. Certainly it is our duty as doctors and fellow men to rectify this situation wherever we can."

Comment: These periodic reviews of the home situation of patients with scurvy have demonstrated a number of important public health facts to individual students and groups. The most obvious is the need for regular health supervision by a public health nurse or physician, especially in the first year of life. Almost inevitably they point up the necessity of being specific about the nature of vitamin preparations and why and how long it may be necessary to give them. In several instances it was shown that parents may very well falsify information given to the doctor, lest they establish their own responsibility for the child's illness or incur the wrath of the doctor, or both. One revealed that the financial reason for delaying a call to a doctor may be the fear that what he prescribes will cost far more than the fee for his visit. This further emphasized the need to educate the parents of small children as to the facilities in a community set up to give adequate medical care regardless of the parents' financial standing, with stress primarily on the prevention of the serious illnesses such as scurvy.

SUMMARY

This has been a description of a teaching program in environmental pediatrics, or pediatric ecology. The program is effective in so far as it involves the student in personal contact with patient and family in settings other than those found in the hospital. The socioeconomic status of most of the patients visited is probably quite different from that of his future patients, but much of what is learned in this way can be applied in practice with patients of any age regardless of their income level or intelligence.

What Kind of Pediatrics Are We Exporting?

• *JOE D. WRAY, M.D.*

Rockefeller Foundation

American[1] pediatrics is being exported to the rest of the world on a grand scale today, and the chief vehicle for this exportation is the foreign physician who comes to the United States for pediatric training. This is a phenomenon worthy of thoughtful consideration by responsible pediatric educators in the United States. It seems likely that such thoughtful consideration might improve the quality of the pediatrics thus exported, to the certain benefit of millions of children throughout the world.

This essay, in addition to being a part of a tribute to Dr. Milton J. E. Senn, was in fact largely inspired by a question raised by Dr. Senn in the summer of 1960, when he asked, "What should I try to teach the foreign physicians who come to Yale to study pediatrics?" The answers to be offered here derive from pondering this question in the light of a somewhat limited but thoroughly stimulating experience gained during nearly five years of work in a newly established

---

1 "American" here implies the United States and will be used in this admittedly narrow sense in this essay for the sake of simplicity; no offense is intended to other residents of the Western Hemisphere!

children's hospital-pediatric training center in Ankara, Turkey. Of greatest pertinence to this essay was the chance to observe at first hand some of the problems which confront the American-trained pediatrician when he returns to his own country.

One point, implicit in Dr. Senn's question, bears discussion at the outset. There is obviously implied a recognition of the fact that today literally thousands of foreign physicians choose to go to the United States for their postgraduate training and many elect to study pediatrics. Why is this so? It has been suggested that in a given community, the "common man" tends to take as his goal or his ideal the pattern of life he sees practiced by the wealthiest or most powerful men in his own community. If one considers the world medical community as a whole, and thinks of the contemporary role of United States medical practitioners in this community, a partial explanation of why the United States has replaced Europe as a medical Mecca is apparent. It certainly is a fact of the mid-twentieth century that youth the world over has a compelling desire to see or study in the United States.

There are, of course, more specific reasons and probably the most important of these is financial. Our system of postgraduate medical education enables the young physician to be essentially self-supporting, even if at a bare subsistence level at times,[2] while obtaining his specialty training and, until the recent advent of the Educational Council for Foreign Medical Graduates (ECFMG), almost any foreign physician who could pay his passage to the United States could find, somewhere, a post as an intern or resident. The requirement for certification by the ECFMG has not altered the financial situation; it has, in fact, strengthened the bargaining position of the foreign physician who is able to qualify. Postgraduate education in medicine remains, therefore, more easily attainable financially for the foreigner than education in any other field.

That a fair share of the foreign physicians who go to the United States seek training in pediatrics, and seem to do well in it, may

[2] Certainly this is not always the case. Foreign residents working in some American hospitals receive salaries substantially larger than those of full professors in their home countries.

be confirmed by a glance at the author index of any current American pediatric journal or, equally well, by noting the steadily increasing number of special certificates for foreigners being granted by the American Board of Pediatrics.

Financial considerations aside, what does the type of pediatric training generally available in the United States offer the foreign physician? What is there of value in these programs which entices him to leave his homeland for a year or two or more? Presumably, what he is seeking above all else is simply the opportunity to learn to practice competent pediatrics. But implicit in this is the assumption that he will gain in the United States something not to be had merely by reading the latest edition of Nelson's *Textbook of Pediatrics*. To suggest some of the values to be found by the foreigner in American pediatric training requires rather broad generalizations to which there will always be exceptions. However, several important features of specialty training in the United States which potentially enrich its value to the foreigner and are generally available should be pointed out as a way of defining our present position.

Perhaps foremost among these, and the key to the present status of American medical education, is the full-time faculty member. Not unique, perhaps, but certainly far more frequently found in the United States than in most countries of the world, the full-time system provides a quality of medical education at every level that simply is not available in the vast majority of the world's medical institutions; it requires no elaborate discussion here.

With regard to postgraduate medical training per se in the United States, what seems to be the outstanding feature can be summed up in the word responsibility. Along with the facilities usually available, the active help of a great variety of ancillary medical personnel, and the constant support and guidance of a competent and accessible teaching staff, the intern or resident is given the sure knowledge that though he is still learning he is the person really responsible for the care of a given patient. He becomes, of necessity, intimately involved in the total process of patient care and learns gradually and almost exclusively by example the importance of the twenty-four-hour-a-day devotion to the patient's welfare which is characteristic of the best medical practice. He learns to do automatically whatever needs to be done and rarely has time to wonder whether some essential chore is beneath his dignity. When this process is viewed in the light of the fact that in many foreign places today specialty training consists largely of following The Professor around on ward rounds for two or three hours a day, it takes on real meaning.

Another important feature is related simply to our prosperity. American physicians are likely to take for granted the really incredible wealth of physical facilities and equipment which undergirds any good training program; nor are they likely to be able to conceive of the shortages of hospital facilities, laboratory equipment, diagnostic and therapeutic instruments, drugs, and a multitude of other things usually considered essential, which prevail in many parts of the world today. A moment's reflection, however, is sufficient to recall how important such things are to the practice of first-rate modern medicine. And the fact that high-quality training depends on high-quality practice is as readily recognized by the foreigner as by ourselves.

The practical nature of American medical education in general has an importance which may also be easily overlooked. The American medical student learns a great deal by "doing" which his counterpart in many countries must hope to master solely by listening or by observing. The acquisition of technical and manipulative skills in medicine is a process which starts in the American medical school and continues all the way through specialty training. This is in contrast to the fact that even in Europe today there are students who graduate from medical school without ever having performed a physical examination on a live patient (Weir, 1960)!

In this day and age, the foreign medical graduate will have some notion of "the American way of life," and he is likely to associate this, perhaps vaguely, with "democracy"; that our democratic way of doing things influences the quality of the training he will receive probably does not occur to him. Yet it does: it is the free and easy spirit of our interpersonal relationships which, for example, makes possible a spirited and enlightening exchange between medical staff members of radically different rank, or which usually makes the "Chief" readily and comfortably accessible to the lowliest intern. The foreigner, likely to come from a society in which academic rank is taken so much more seriously that it may in fact be an obstacle to comfortable human relations and to the process of mutual learning, cannot fail to be impressed by this and to benefit by it.

Similarly, the foreigner will probably have heard that "teamwork" is widely practiced in the United States; he may not anticipate that this, too, will affect the quality of the training he receives. The practice observed in many European medical faculties of the physical separation of departments or "clinics," each operated as an autonomous empire, has been widely copied throughout the world and offers considerable contrast to the absence of interdepartmental barriers in a good teaching hospital in the United States. In fact, in observing his first "C.P.C.,"[3] the foreigner might well be shocked to hear the pathologist freely needle the surgeon, or the radiologist gleefully bait the internist. Genuinely collaborative efforts in learning, teaching, and patient care should provide him with a variety of new and stimulating experiences; and not until he has seen for himself is he likely to appreciate the tremendous advantages offered by an integrated, multidisciplined approach to many complex medical problems—perhaps best exemplified in pediatrics in a well-run pediatric cardiology-cardiovascular surgery unit or one of the better cerebral palsy clinics.

All of these features and many others will be available to a greater or lesser extent in any good pediatric training program in the United States. They are not unique to pediatric training, nor will they be found fully developed in every department. Primarily a product of American academic and medical traditions evolving within this century, they furnish, regardless of specific local deficiencies, a basis for considerable pride in the system in general, and

3 Clinical-Pathological Conference.

certainly thousands of pediatricians, both American and foreign, have passed on to their patients the benefits of this system.

What more can the foreigner ask? If we return for a moment to Dr. Senn's question, we may note that there is, in addition to the implication mentioned earlier, a more important one, an implication characteristic of Dr. Senn's approach to pediatric education. This is a desire to provide the foreign pediatric trainee with more than the usual or the routine, a desire to understand his particular problems and meet his particular needs. The question, then, might be rephrased: Does the foreigner have special requirements and, if so, how can they be met?

A strongly affirmative answer seems indicated if one is aware of the basic medical education likely to have been available to these physicians, has oneself undergone the experience of adjusting to life and learning to function effectively in a different cultural environment, or has some familiarity with the sort of problems encountered by American-trained pediatricians returning to their homelands as well as with the socioeconomic problems which demand solution in such countries today.

The following suggestions are offered primarily to point out some of the special requirements which a given individual might have, especially one from a so-called underdeveloped country. How to meet these requirements is another question and is discussed here only in general terms; good pediatric training, like good pediatric therapy, should be individualized. But an awareness of the existence of particular problems or needs, whether or not the trainee himself recognizes them, clearly must precede efforts to individualize a training program.

The English language, marvelously irregular, unphonetic, and idiomatic, is the first problem with which the foreign trainee must cope. Obviously a considerable degree of mastery is required for adequate understanding of modern medical concepts and for competent care and management. It is to be hoped that the ECFMG certification process will provide assurance that all those arriving for training will have that degree of mastery. Where this is lacking, however, it would be to the benefit of all concerned to face the problem candidly and deal with it. Perhaps this will not be a problem in the future, but certainly in recent years, when the problem was ignored either because of lack of facilities for dealing with it or through lack of concern, a considerable number of foreign physicians suffered a great deal of personal anguish on this score—to the detriment of their education and their care of patients.

Hard on the heels of language problems come cultural problems. A significant emotional adjustment is required of an individual removed from his native cultural environment and thrust suddenly into an alien one. This is recognized today and is aptly described by the term "culture-shock," which was coined by Kalervo Oberg, an American anthropologist who observed the phenomenon in his fellow countrymen working in Brazil.[4] Cleveland et al. (1960), again with particular reference to Americans working in a different culture, have emphasized its importance as a potential obstacle to effective performance. That it can also happen to the foreigner going to the United States is certain. How severe it may be is obviously a matter of individual variation. An awareness of this phenomenon, however, should temper attitudes toward the foreign doctor's problems of adjustment, and certain positive measures to counteract its effects would not be difficult to develop.

Aside from affecting the morale of the foreigner, cultural factors have an even more important and direct bearing on medical practice and training. The American pediatric teacher, regardless of academic rank, is working in a familiar and comfortable cultural environment which he shares with his patients and his students. He is thus able to take a great many things for granted, and he intuitively feels and responds to a multitude of subtle signs from his patient. More important, this kind of subvocal communication is utilized in his management of the patient: it affects the way questions are phrased in obtaining the history and the way the diagnosis is discussed, as well as directions for therapy. In short, it is intimately

4 Oberg's excellent description of "culture-shock," originally circulated as a memorandum for his colleagues, has since been widely utilized in orientation programs for overseas Americans by numerous organizations, both pubic and private.

involved in the "Art" of the practice of medicine. The foreigner, until he learns what is in effect yet another language, is likely to miss many of the signals and may, in fact, be quite bewildered by the whole process. If this process is called to his attention, if he is helped on ward rounds or perhaps in seminar discussions to become aware of some of these factors and to learn, gradually, to understand what is happening, his skill in the management of patients will be greatly benefitted.

Beyond the immediate usefulness of this ability, learning well how to communicate effectively with American, i.e., culturally different, patients may have a value to the foreigner not immediately apparent. The degree of sociocultural stratification which exists in some countries today is not appreciated by many Americans, and the social stratum from which the foreign trainee is likely to come is probably quite different from that which will produce most of his patients. Furthermore, the educational and cultural differences between these strata may be considerable. If, then, in his American pediatric training he can learn to communicate effectively and comfortably across a cultural gap, his effectiveness at home is likely to be increased, and in the end he may be better able to communicate understandingly with his patients, of whatever social stratum, than many of his local colleagues who have never been abroad.

Language and cultural problems may be important considerations, but the basic medical education of a given trainee is even more so. Internship and residency programs in pediatrics are based on the assumption that participants at a given level will have in common a certain basic fund of medical knowledge and experience. That this assumption should not be applied indiscriminately to the foreign medical graduate is amply and convincingly demonstrated in a description by Weir (1960) of the tremendous qualitative variations in medical schools outside North America. Various factors contribute to lowered standards in many schools, including huge classes, severe shortages of teaching personnel, limited laboratory and clinical facilities, and a myriad of other problems. That there are problems specifically in pediatric education was well brought out in the discussions at the IX International Congress of Pediatrics by the heads of pediatric departments from many parts of the world, as reported by Wegman (1961). Detailed statistical evidence of the variation in quantity and quality of pediatric education in Latin America, as an example, has also been reported by Wegman et al. (1958).

The essential fact to consider is that a given trainee may have had a grossly deficient medical education. This deficiency may have begun with secondary school education and extended throughout his medical education. To attempt to solve this problem by providing intensive refresher-retraining courses, mentioned as a possible solution by Weir, is certainly beyond the capacity of a single pediatric department. Until an effective solution is generally available, however, it seems that at a minimum the persons responsible for the training of any foreign individual have an obligation to learn as much as possible about his background and to make every effort to devise means of making up for any really serious deficiencies discovered. Among the variety of basic science deficiencies likely to be a problem in pediatrics, the biochemical and physiological principles governing the understanding and management of fluid and electrolyte problems will frequently require special emphasis. Directed reading or regular tutorial sessions could be of immense value to the foreigner in this and many other areas.

Fully as important as any efforts to help him *catch* up are those directed at helping him to learn to *keep* up. It should be borne in mind that many a foreign medical graduate has never had access to an adequate medical library and has no way of appreciating the importance of reading in the process of continuing medical education. That every opportunity to impress this on him should be utilized should not require emphasis; on his return home, journals may afford his only contact with the "outside world."

What about the actual content of American pediatric training as it relates to the needs of the foreigner? To a large extent, and rightly so, the content of a good training program is geared to the needs of the American trainee and is designed to prepare him to

cope with problems prevalent in American pediatric practice. Anyone familiar with pediatric problems in underdeveloped countries
will acknowledge readily that such a program will not equip the
foreigner to deal specifically with every problem he will encounter
at home. This deficiency of detail need be of no great consequence,
however, if in its stead he acquires a solid grasp of the fundamentals
of a good diagnostic work-up and masters the art of doctor-patient-
parent relations. The emphasis, then, should be on attitudes,
approaches, and general principles, and these should be spelled out
for him, not taken for granted as they might be with the American
house officer who was thoroughly grounded in these principles in
his clinical years of medical school. If, in addition, it is possible to
provide modifications or shifts in emphasis designed to meet particular problems which he can anticipate at home, so much the
better. In this regard it will be helpful to keep in mind that acute
infectious diseases and problems of malnutrition deserve emphasis
at every opportunity.

One particular aspect of the hospital practice of pediatrics in
America merits special consideration with regard to the foreign
trainee. The tendency of house officers to place too much reliance
on laboratory procedures, to order a great variety of tests indiscriminately and unthinkingly, is frequently deplored. If it is deplorable
for Americans in training, it is doubly so for the foreign trainee
who will almost certainly be forced to become much more self-reliant
on his return home than will his colleagues in the United States.
The better he learns how competent pediatrics is practiced in settings
lacking some of the ancillary services of a teaching hospital, the
more effective he will be at home. Visits to men in practice or, better
yet, periods of preceptorship training under such men, could be of
considerable help here.

This brings to mind another phenomenon sometimes observed
in American teaching services: the often poorly veiled derision of
the "LMD"[5] which, in turn, reflects a not uncommon tendency to
downgrade private practice in favor of "high-powered" research-ori-

[5] Local medical doctors.

ented hospital medicine. This can be poisonous for the foreign trainee—as well as for his American counterpart. In his eagerness to emulate his American teachers, he is likely to take on what he understands to be their medical values. If, as a result, he gets the impression that the day-to-day practice of pediatrics is distasteful, that coping with ordinary problems is somehow beneath him and not really worthy of the scientific pediatrician, he will really have been injured.

Another point should not be forgotten: most of the meaningful, workable knowledge of pediatrics, and of medicine in general, possessed by some of these men is, on their own willing admission, that which they acquire in the United States. If this is true, then in the realm of medicine, at least, one might anticipate a sort of reverse "culture-shock" on their return home, and there is no doubt that this occurs. Witness the large number of physicians who, having been well trained in the United States, return filled with ideals and enthusiasm to their homelands, where they are desperately needed, only to be frustrated in the extreme by their inability to practice exactly the kind of medicine they have been taught. Not a few of these men eventually give up and find a way to get back to North America, and, understandable though this may be, it must be acknowledged as tragic.

If anything will help these men it is the ability to approach a medical problem, especially the matter of therapy and patient management, with an open mind, free of any inhibiting notions that there is only *one* right way to do things. The overriding requirements of medical practice in many parts of the world today can be described in two words: improvise and compromise. The pediatrician who serves his patients best is the one who, well grounded in basic principles, is stimulated and inspired by the challenge of applying these principles under suboptimal conditions. The matter of nutrition illustrates this point more specifically. Malnutrition blights the lives of millions of infants and children in the world today and presents a problem whose magnitude is almost matched by its complexity. Yet infant nutrition as currently taught and practiced in the United States, with its reliance on artificial feeding and the wealth of readily available prepared formulae and infant foods, is utterly useless throughout most of the world. Only the knowledge of fundamental nutritional needs applied with imagination, understanding, and patience will enable the pediatrician to cope with the problems imposed by ancient, custom-dictated patterns of child rearing, primitive living conditions, and the agricultural and economic limitations which exist in many countries. The point which bears stressing is that this type of practice is no less worth while, need be no less scientific, and is quite possibly more important in lifesaving potential, than anything his former colleagues might be doing in the United States.

An open-minded approach to his own culture and its problems is essential. Furthermore, the foreign pediatrician needs to be aware that many traditional practices of child rearing, though their rationale has been obliterated by centuries of rote repetition, have a basis in scientific fact. Cow's milk, for example, is not fed to infants in some cultures because it is considered dangerous; bacterial studies of milk would almost certainly prove this assumption correct in most such societies. The practice of swaddling infants, seen in some contemporary cultures, comes as rather a shock to the American-trained pediatrician. Detached observation over a period of time suggests, however, that it is not discernibly harmful; not until capably conducted long-term studies have been carried out can one assert dogmatically that it is either good or bad. What is needed, obviously, is a willingness to consider all such customs objectively in order to distinguish those which are helpful and worthy of encouragement from those which are harmful and should be carefully discouraged or perhaps modified, as well as those which, though strange, are functionally neutral and not worth worrying with.[6]

---

[6] Jelliffe (1960) has pointed out that the modern pediatrician can completely negate his effectiveness with parents if he disdainfully refuses to acknowledge the local "gods" of his patients; the mother, able to interpret his refusal only as the act of a fool, will not follow the advice of such a man. Here, too, one is reminded of reports (Frey, 1952) that the medicine men among Navajo tribes in the Southwest have become admirably sophisticated. When tribesmen seek help for ailments with which the medi-

Closely related to this is the possibility that the more capable foreign trainee, interested in pursuing an academic career on his return home, will come to feel that the only really satisfactory research is the type he observes in the United States, extensively and expensively supported by complex laboratory studies, and likely to be concerned with problems which loom large in the United States mortality and morbidity tables but are relatively unimportant in his own country. American pediatrics, for example, can and does invest huge quantities of time, energy, and money in the study of problems the solution of which might lower the infant mortality rate by 0.2 per cent. That same investment, if such resources were available and channeled properly, would probably be sufficient to lower infant mortality ten times as much in many countries of the world today. The foreign trainee must somehow come to appreciate the fact that simple, thoughtfully planned, carefully executed studies of his own local problems can be exceedingly valuable and thoroughly respectable scientifically.

This brings to mind another point. There is in American medicine a tendency at times to take for granted the magnificent benefits gained by doctors and patients alike from the utilization of preventive medicine concepts and high standards of public health practice. A look at the world around us, however, suggests that somewhere between 75 and 90 per cent of the world's population lacks these benefits. The widespread application of such principles and practices, coupled with health education, is one of the outstanding needs of this great mass of people. No foreign trainee should leave our shores without appreciating this fact, nor should he escape without learning to appreciate the role of pediatricians in the United States in the development and application of these concepts. He should learn, too, that such things do not "just happen" but come about as

---

cine men can cope, traditional methods of treatment are used. If the medicine man suspects a serious problem, tuberculosis, for example, he solemnly assures his patient that he seems to have a "white man's disease" and sends him to a modern hospital. As medicine men have learned to recognize more and more illnesses as "white men's diseases" a very effective working relationship has been achieved.

the result of plain hard work on the part of devoted individuals, supported by their medical colleagues, and often are achieved in spite of apathy, ignorance, financial difficulties, and many other obstacles precisely like those he may expect to encounter in his own country. Any American-trained pediatrician should return to his homeland as an enthusiastic advocate and informed supporter of such programs, if not as an active participant in them.

Still another matter frequently and understandably taken for granted by American physicians is the efficient, if complex, operation of a good hospital. A busy intern is not likely to pause and wonder, for example, where his ever-abundant supply of sterile syringes and needles comes from. Nor is it necessary for him to worry about the problems of establishing and operating reliable laboratories, of developing an adequate nursing service, or of coping with the complexities of hospital accounting, supply, maintenance, and housekeeping, all of which, however, contribute materially to the quality of the medical care he provides. But although the American can safely assume that there will always be available competent, well-trained personnel to manage such matters, the foreigner is not so fortunate. It is generally acknowledged that hospitals in many parts of the world leave a great deal to be desired; it should also be realized that today the American-trained physician is playing an important part in raising the standards here and there and that he must, in the future, be even more effective. It is not to be expected, obviously, that in addition to becoming a competent pediatrician, he must become a well-rounded hospital administrator. It does seem feasible, however, and desirable, to provide him with opportunities to become aware of some of the principles of hospital administration and organization, and especially to learn how such problems are approached.

Similarly, if on a slightly different level, the foreign trainee who expects to pursue an academic career on his return home deserves special consideration. In his own country it is quite possible that, simply by virtue of having been trained in the United States, he will be given responsibilities far greater than those he might actually have had at his particular level in the United States.[7] Here, therefore, his training program will be enriched and his effectiveness at home increased if he can be provided opportunities to learn how a good pediatric teaching service is administered and organized, to appreciate the thought processes involved and the philosophic principles which guide such an operation. Even better, where possible he should be directly responsible for handling certain such tasks or participating in group decisions so that, as in clinical pediatrics, he can learn by doing. This also applies to the matter of research, where he deserves the chance to become familiar with both the philosophy and the administrative and technical mechanics of the whole process including defining the problem, planning the study, applying for the grant, ordering supplies, executing the work, and critically evaluating the end result.

One last point deserves emphasis. The American who bemoans the encroachment of the federal government on various spheres of individual or community responsibility today would be appalled at the degree of control exerted by the central government in a great many nations. Thoughtful consideration of the staggering problems facing these nations and objective appraisal of the resources available to their governments for solving them make it evident that this situation is not unreasonable and, furthermore, is unlikely to change in the near future. Committed as we are to our unique heritage of local initiative and responsibility, however, we can hope for these nations that as they mature politically and, more important, as the proportion of educated and responsible citizens in their total population increases, some of this control can be vested in the local community—where we feel it belongs. The foreign physician receiving training in the United States is potentially in the vanguard of that essential body of informed, responsible citizens of his homeland, and his function in this role could conceivably be as important in

[7] The reverse, though rare, may also occur: the foreign physician may give up a position of considerable prestige and authority in order to obtain resident- or even intern-level training in the United States. No less should be required of such trainees; understanding his position and providing due respect, however, will make his lot easier to take.

the long run as his performance as a pediatrician. He will almost certainly be more effective in that role if, during his stay in the United States, he becomes aware of the ways in which the private citizen or the private organization takes the initiative and the responsibility in meeting a variety of community needs. This need not be an elaborate educational process; it may be sufficient simply to point out for him the ways in which community resources are mobilized to deal with specific problems and also the types of resources available and how they came to be so.

Certainly many of these requirements have been and are being met in various ways in various departments of pediatrics in the United States. Certainly, too, this list is not complete. If all of these aspects of pediatric training, obviously considered in a broad sense, were dealt with adequately for every foreign physician receiving his training in the United States, there undoubtedly would remain significant deficiencies. This essay will have served its purpose, however, if it has succeeded in conveying the thought that every foreign physician should be considered as an individual, that he is likely to arrive in the United States with problems which deserve attention, and that he will almost certainly encounter problems on his return to his own country which thoughtful modification or supplementation of his basic pediatric training in the United States can equip him to deal with more effectively.

SUMMARY

Thoughtful consideration of the world today compels recognition of the fact that the lot in life of millions of children is appalling. In providing training for foreign pediatricians, the United States is helping to improve the lot of some of these children. Research activities in such fields as nutrition, the widespread circulation of American pediatric journals, the direct efforts of Americans fortunate enough to have an opportunity to teach or practice abroad, and the participation in a variety of international activities of many leaders in American pediatrics, are also helping. Considered in the light of the magnitude of the problem, however, these efforts seem little more than a beginning. And if the problem is considered, as perhaps it ought to be, as one segment of the total responsibility of the United States in the world today, it might reasonably be suggested that the welfare of all the world's children deserves a larger share of the concern of America's pediatricians.

BIBLIOGRAPHY

Cleveland, H., Mangone, G. J., & Adams, J. C. (1960), *The Overseas American*. New York: McGraw-Hill.
Frey, B. K. (1952), Personal communication.
Jelliffe, D. B. (1960), The Ecology of Protein-calorie Malnutrition in Early Childhood in Four Dissimilar East African Peoples. Paper presented at the Conference on Protein Needs, Washington, D.C., August 21-24, 1960.
Wegman, M. E. (1961), Pediatric Education Around the Word. *J. Med. Educ.*, 36:38-57.
——— Hughes, J. G., & Puffer, R. R. (1958), Pediatric Education in Latin America. *Pediatriçs*, 22 (Suppl., No. 1, Part II): 205-234.
Weir, J. M. (1960), Obstacles to Medical Education at the International Level. *J. Amer. Med. Assn.* 173:1451-1453.

A Social Worker's Contribution to Pediatric Education: Interviewing

• *MARY H. STARK, M.S.S.*

Yale University

According to a recent study, *Participation of Social Workers in Medical Education,* by the National Association of Social Workers (1961), 301 social workers in 55 medical schools had been assigned responsibility for instructing medical students during the academic year 1958-59. Nineteen pediatric departments in the 55 schools included social workers in this instruction. The content areas most frequently taught by the social workers in the departments of pediatrics were: (1) implications of illness to patient, family, and community; (2) socioeconomic factors; (3) implications of hospitalization; (4) common social problems; (5) family dynamics; (6) community resources; (7) interpersonal relations outside of family; (8) interviewing.

It is the purpose of this paper to illustrate how certain concepts and techniques of interviewing well known to the social work profession may be taught effectively to pediatric trainees by a caseworker in an outpatient clinic. In this setting the social worker has an

Supported by the Children's Bureau, U.S. Department of Health, Education, and Welfare, and the Connecticut Department of Health.

excellent opportunity to supplement the teaching of the medical preceptors through informal discussions with the pediatric trainees. For some medical educators this may mean a radical change in their image of the social worker, who too often has been considered an ancillary person helpful in the management of the psychosocial problems of patients rather than a teaching colleague.

The interview is one medium used by the caseworker for enhancing an individual's or family's potential for social functioning. Basic in all casework interviewing is the concept of a meaningful caseworker-client relationship. This includes the following elements: (1) respect for the client's uniqueness, and acknowledgment of his rights to self-realization and self-determination; (2) a warm, receptive, uncritical attitude, creating an atmosphere of trust for the client so that he feels he is being understood; (3) the realization that many of the client's reactions in the relationship with the caseworker represent feelings and attitudes belonging to past figures in his environment such as his mother, father, sisters, and brothers, and that an understanding of these displaced reactions is often therapeutic; (4) blocks to communication and understanding may occur when the client is anxious, panicky, or angry. These reactions need to be discussed and understood to make effective the collaboration of client and caseworker.

ESTABLISHING A POSITIVE DOCTOR-PATIENT RELATIONSHIP

The concept of a meaningful caseworker-client relationship can be adapted to the education of the pediatric trainee when he is learning the importance of a positive doctor-patient relationship in his own diagnostic and therapeutic work. The social worker helps the trainee learn how to establish a realistic, positive doctor-patient relationship as is demonstrated in the following considerations.

With new patients when the presenting complaint is known before the trainee's first interview, the caseworker helps him to speculate about the various implications the presenting symptom may have for both the child and the parent. This type of preparation fosters the trainee's attitude of acceptance of the patient and suggests clues as to the patient's fears and anxieties about the symptom and himself.

It is suggested by the caseworker that mother and child be interviewed together at first in order to observe their interactions and to demonstrate that the doctor is interested in both. Too frequently, young trainees tend to exclude the parent from the interview and devote most of their attention to the child. In such instances when a mother senses the doctor is interested in her child only, she interprets this as criticism and often withdraws the child from the clinic. It is important for the doctor to note how mother and child respond to the unfolding of events as the history is being taken and to observe the manifestations of their tensions, disappointments, and pleasures. This creates an atmosphere of trying to understand the patients, and the trainee does not barricade himself behind the medical facts.

When a child has made previous visits to the outpatient clinic or has been hospitalized, a discussion of the social and psychological aspects of the material in the chart may be helpful to the trainee before he conducts his interview. This provides an opportunity for discussion of preconceived ideas the trainee may have regarding unmarried motherhood, families receiving public assistance, minority groups, working mothers, etc. If prejudices exist, the trainee develops a beginning awareness of them and understands how such prejudices could interfere with the establishment of a positive doctor-patient relationship.

Many inferences can be drawn from reading a chart regarding the family's attitudes toward medical care. A series of emergency-room visits with broken follow-up appointments may reveal that the medical care has not been consistent, and speculation as to the reasons for this assists the trainee in helping the family receive more adequate medical care. Frequent changes in address, numerous accidents, division of medical care between two hospitals often indicate an unstable social environment. This awareness enables the physician to understand his patient's background and through such understanding the patient and his family will feel accepted and motivated to work closely with the doctor.

When a child comes to the outpatient clinic for a school examination or is sent by the Juvenile Court, the lack of self-motivation for coming may prevent his being receptive to the doctor. Understanding the nature of this reaction helps the trainee feel more comfortable in the interview and become more tolerant of the patient's evasive and resentful reactions.

At the end of the interview there should be ample time to discuss the need for further tests such as blood tests, EEG, psychometric tests, so that both child and parent understand the reasons for them. When medication is prescribed, preference for pills or liquid should be elicited so that choices may be adhered to if possible. This avoids such situations as the doctor learning later that the child will not swallow pills.

It is important to give clear explanations if further procedures are not necessary, especially if the parent thought his son needed further attention such as a tonsillectomy.

When it is necessary for the doctor to have a series of interviews as with the child, e.g., one who suffers from enuresis, both the child and parent should understand and react to this plan in order to prepare them realistically for what is involved in the pediatric management of the child's problem.

UNDERSTANDING THE PATIENT'S REACTION TO HIS ILLNESS

Anxiety and fear in varying degrees are significant components in any illness which brings the patient to the doctor. While some patients present their worries readily, others may need the doctor's help in expressing underlying concerns which seem too frightening to discuss. As a rule, patients do not wish to be thought of as "worry warts" or "foolish" by the doctor and, therefore, often harbor painful irrational concerns for long periods of time. The child's concern about his illness is very often a reflection of the parent's worry. Caseworkers have developed skills in interviewing which enable clients to express and clarify their underlying concerns. Such skills can be taught to pediatric trainees. As the doctor helps the patient discuss concerns which have been nagging him for a time, false impressions about the illness can become clarified and modified. The patient then is better able to accept and understand his illness, and to be more realistic in collaborating in a treatment plan.

The following example illustrates how a trainee in the pediatric outpatient clinic was taught to interview an adolescent girl of fifteen and a half years of age and her parents in order to understand their reactions to the diagnosis and treatment of her convulsive disorder.

Nancy had had a grand mal convulsion two years before coming to the pediatric clinic. This had occurred when she and her school friends were visiting historic points of interest in another city. She had responded well to the medication given and had not had any more seizures. What prompted the visit to the clinic was her withdrawal from her friends and her poor school grades due to lack of concentration. She had previously been an excellent student.

It is often difficult for trainees to consider that an illness, the onset of which was two years ago, and which appeared to be responding well to medication, could still affect the patient's psychological well-being. This hypothesis was pointed out by the caseworker as one for contemplation. The caseworker raised the following questions for the pediatric student to consider. What understanding or misunderstanding did the patient and parents have about the illness? What did they think had brought it about? How did it affect the patient's day-by-day experiences? How did the parents, peers, teachers, etc., react to the patient and her illness? What questions might the patient and her parents have about the prognosis and the patient's future development? Such an approach prepares the trainee to recognize and follow the clues given by the patient about her deeper concerns.

In the first two interviews, Nancy revealed her confusion regarding her illness—she had been told by the family doctor there was nothing to worry about, yet she had to take medication regularly. Her parents warned her against divulging to anyone that she was taking medication. Whenever they disapproved of her attending a social function, they reminded her that she might have another convulsion. This emphasis on her vulnerabilities added to her anxieties, with the result that she gradually withdrew from social activities and could not do her schoolwork. She was then criticized severely by her parents for having poor grades. Nancy wondered if she would have more convulsions. Would she die in one? Would she be an old maid? She questioned if anyone would marry her.

In discussion of these findings with the caseworker, the trainee was very much annoyed with the parents whom she characterized as blundering and cruel. The physician's identification was solely with the adolescent patient. It was pointed out by the social worker that in order to help Nancy, the reasons for the parents' blunders would have to be understood. Nancy probably would not mind if the doctor talked longer to the parents, especially if she felt this was being done to help her. It would be helpful for Nancy to know that the doctor respected her confidences and would not discuss them with her parents without her permission. In this illustration the trainee's attitude would have to be one of inquiry as to why it bothered the parents so much that their daughter was taking medication. Did they feel that this was dangerous or shameful? How did they feel about illness in general and this illness in particular?

Thus, with Nancy's consent, the parents were interviewed together for a half hour directly after the doctor had talked with Nancy on their second visit to the clinic. The mother said she had had tuberculosis before she was married and was in a sanitarium for a year. She appeared to be embarrassed about this, and attributed it to the way her own parents had dealt with her. All illness seemed shameful and she thought it should be kept within the family. She had carried over these attitudes to her daughter's illness. When she realized what problems this could create, she could modify her ways of dealing with Nancy. She came to see that using Nancy's fear of her illness and its treatment as a way of disciplining the child could hinder her daughter's adolescent development. The mother then could understand how her own need to conceal the illness conveyed to Nancy that she had an ominous disease. The parents realized that they had not always agreed on methods of disciplining Nancy, and began to comprehend how confusing this was to her.

In Nancy's three interviews with the doctor, she obtained a clearer explanation of her convulsive disorder and the need for medication. She was encouraged to resume social activities. She commented on the more pleasant relationship with her parents now.

The intervention by the doctor had brought about more satisfactory parent-child relationships. Nancy's school grades improved and she resumed her social activities as the tensions in the family were eased. The trainee had been able to see how the patient's and family's reaction to the illness had complicated the child's psychological development.

INTERPRETATION

The communication of diagnostic findings by the doctor to the parent is only effective when there is mutual understanding of key words and when the defensive reactions of the parent are understood by the doctor.

For example, young trainees find it difficult to interpret to parents certain findings with which they are not too familiar, and which cause them to feel helpless. This can be seen in the interpretation of psychometric testing of children who fall within the educable or trainable range of the mentally retarded. The young physician tends to present his findings quickly and abruptly, which in part is due to his feelings of inadequacy in dealing with such material. He often displays the same defensive reactions as the parent, such as avoiding the issue, denying the reality, and projecting blame on the school.

One method of helping the trainee become more competent in this task is to demonstrate how the social worker would conduct an interview dealing with the clarification and interpretation of a highly charged diagnosis or treatment plan with the parent. In this way the trainee has the opportunity to observe the casework process, while at the same time he remains involved as the child's physician who has introduced the caseworker as the person collaborating with him in discussing the implications of the findings.

For example, a trainee was amazed to hear a mother reply, when the caseworker asked her what she thought the word retardation meant, "He will never learn anything." This parent was annoyed at the school for labeling her child "retarded" and had refused to have him enter a special class. When the caseworker explained the various degrees of mental retardation and informed this mother that her son was at the top of the range and could learn to read and write and do many things for himself, the mother's whole demeanor brightened. She then was able to ask pertinent questions about special classes and agreed to permit her child to be enrolled in one. She had been so upset at hearing the word "retardation" that she had not heard anything else that the school principal had said to her. At the end of the interview, she confided that she really thought the school wished her to put her boy away in an institution for severely retarded children, and then added that recently a neighbor's child had been sent to such a place. This interview illustrated for the trainee the principle of making sure the patient and doctor have the same understanding of key words so that communication is effective. Technical terms, when given, should always be explained painstakingly and in a manner that makes sense to the patient and his family.

When the mother of a two-year-old kept repeating "I know my child is not retarded," and made flimsy excuses for his not standing, not playing pat-a-cake, etc., she cried when the caseworker asked her what she feared she would be told. She knew her child was lagging behind in his development, but facing this was too painful for her. After a good cry, she could ask the caseworker many questions as to why this had happened. The caseworker stressed the need for this mother to have several interviews with the doctor in order to be able to understand that she had a severely retarded child. From this observation, the trainee learned that although a parent may seek out a doctor to learn what is wrong with a child who fails to develop, there is also a strong wish to deny that anything is wrong. If this is not understood and dealt with, the parents do not hear what is being said to them, which in turn prevents the doctor from assisting them in a meaningful way.

A trainee was surprised to hear a mother assess quite accurately her child's intellectual level of performance when the caseworker asked her at the beginning of the interview how she thought her child had done on the test. She replied that she knew her youngster was slow, as he was not as alert as his brothers, and wished to have this confirmed so she could plan appropriately for his schooling.

This demonstrated to the trainee the principle of ascertaining first of all how knowledgeable the parents are in the assessment of the child's performance, or, according to casework vernacular, of "starting where the client is." When this is followed with a description of the test findings in lay terms, the interpretation becomes more meaningful to the parent.

ENABLING PATIENTS TO USE COMMUNITY RESOURCES

Enabling people to use community resources requires skill in interviewing. This concept is not understood by physicians who frequently assign this important task to their secretaries. What may seem to be an obvious solution to the doctor, such as referring an only child without playmates to a nursery school, may in the eyes of the mother be a forbidding suggestion. The doctor often is aware that a particular community resource, such as a child guidance clinic, would be of help to a child and his parents; yet when he suggests this the patient refuses to go. Because the doctor has overlooked the necessity of pertinent interviewing in the referral process, he may feel annoyed at the patient or personally defeated in his effort to help him.

The caseworker knows that before a referral to another agency is attempted, the client must understand his need for the new resource, and have some idea of the benefits to be derived. When he shows resistance to the referral, an attempt must be made by the caseworker to understand this and to help him overcome it. This may entail more than one interview in order to give the client the opportunity to think through at home what is involved for him and his family if he applies for help at a particular community agency.

The following case illustrates a trainee's development in interviewing with emphasis on the referral process.

A fourteen-and-a-half-year-old boy was referred by his family physician to the medical center because of headaches, nervousness, and a burning sensation of the eyes for which no physical basis could be found. Several aspirin a day had been prescribed by the family doctor to relieve the symptoms. When they persisted, the mother was told by the family doctor that her son was emotionally disturbed, and she was directed to the pediatric clinic rather than to the psychiatric clinic at the hospital.

Four pediatric interviews were necessary before the boy and his mother understood and accepted the meaning of "emotional disturbance" and then welcomed the referral to the psychiatric clinic.

In the first interview, Harold was examined carefully and told again that he was well physically. He was encouraged to talk about himself in this interview and in the next one. He was a bright boy.

He read Shakespeare's plays for fun and shunned athletic activities. Although he had acquaintances, he did not have any real friends. He had been placed in an accelerated class in school, and was finding some subjects very difficult. Although he received As in algebra and English, his marks in history and Spanish were Ds. He was unhappy in this accelerated class in the first year in high school. He also was disappointed that he could not take shop work, which he thoroughly enjoyed, especially since his father was a carpenter.

At the end of the second interview, he was agreeable to the doctor's suggestion of trying to go for a week without aspirin. When he returned for the third interview, he reported that his headaches were better but he still complained of his eyes burning. He insisted that at least one parent be home when he returned from school. When they went to bed early, he had to go to bed too as he was afraid to stay up without them. His parents complained that they could never go out at night. "It is like jail," the mother commented to the doctor. The boy's fears had increased when his twenty-one-year-old brother married the preceding year. They were intensified a short time later when his father worked in another state and was home only week ends. Just before coming to the clinic, the father had finally found employment in his home area, hoping that his son's symptoms would disappear, but they had persisted.

The doctor helped Harold understand that the anxious feelings he had when his parents left him were preventing him from reaching one of his goals, that of going to college. It was explained that his symptoms had to do with fears he had about growing up and could be understood better and allayed by future talks with a psychiatrist in the psychiatric clinic. In the last interview, the boy raised questions about psychiatrists. Were they for crazy people? Was he crazy? He was relieved to find only interviewing rooms when the doctor took him to see the physical setup of the psychiatric clinic. His ideas about psychiatrists had been associated with mental hospitals. He relaxed when told that there were psychiatrists who were helpful to troubled adolescents and that he was not considered crazy.

The interviews with the mother covered very much the same content as those with Harold. She talked to the caseworker while Harold saw the doctor, and then she, too, had a short talk with the doctor. She hoped Harold could go to college and realized that the fear of growing up might interfere with this plan. She knew his behavior was not appropriate for a boy of his age and regretted that she had not sought psychiatric assistance for him earlier. Psychiatric help had been suggested to her when Harold was five, because of the separation anxiety he displayed during the first year in school. This suggestion at that time had come from the school principal, but the mother said that the family doctor had prescribed Vitamin B-1 to help Harold with his nervousness. When Harold was six, a marital conflict upset the entire family. The mother said she felt guilty that she had shared her own problems so completely with her sons. She hoped this had not affected the patient. She was relieved that the aspirin had been discontinued as she thought Harold had depended on it too much. She, too, had questions about psychiatry, the way psychiatrists worked, etc. Both she and her husband now were very eager for Harold to get help. When finally she was given the name of the staff member in the psychiatric clinic to whom she could apply for psychiatric evaluation and treatment, her comment was, "Now why couldn't my family doctor have talked to us this way instead of saying only, 'Your son is emotionally disturbed; take him to a psychiatrist.' "

SUMMARY

The social caseworker has an important contribution to make in helping pediatric trainees develop skills in interviewing. In discussions of individual patients with the trainee and medical preceptor, she places emphasis on the importance of the following concepts: (1) establishing a positive doctor-patient relationship with both the child and his mother; the doctor's attitude should be one of inquiry, seeking to know the whys of his patient's behavior without being influenced by moralistic judgments; (2) eliciting underlying fears and concerns of the patient to gain better understanding of him and his illness; (3) interpretation of diagnostic findings and plans for treatment in a way that is understandable to the patient; and (4) before referring to an appropriate community resource, make sure that the patient understands the need for this and the benefits to be derived, working through of resistances before making the referral.

The teaching methods used by the caseworker to make effective the application of the above-mentioned concepts include the following: (1) discussion with the trainee of possible concerns of child and parent before the patient is seen; (2) assistance in the interpretation of the trainee's observations of the family interactions and social environment; (3) demonstration of the casework process in interviewing either in the presence of the trainee or interviewing the mother separately as the doctor interviews the child, and later sharing the content of the interview; (4) discussion of spacing of interviews, division of doctor's time with patients (mother and child), and presentation to them of plan for diagnosis and treatment.

The transferability of casework concepts and techniques to the pediatric trainee is dependent upon the competence of the caseworker, her knowledge of child development, and her willingness to familiarize herself with pediatric terminology so that she can assist the trainees in the formulation of their specific questions.

BIBLIOGRAPHY

Bartlett, H. M. (1961), *Social Work Practice in the Health Field.* New York: Nat. Assn. Soc. Workers.

Green, M. & Senn, M. J. E. (1958), Teaching of Comprehensive Pediatrics on an Inpatient Hospital Service. *Pediatrics,* 21:476-490.

National Association of Social Workers (1961), *Participation of Social Workers in Medical Education.* New York.

Perlman, H. H. (1957), *Social Casework a Problem-solving Process.* Chicago: Univ. Chicago Press.

Solnit, A. J. & Senn, M. J. E. (1954), Teaching Comprehensive Pediatrics in an Outpatient Clinic. *Pediatrics,* 14:547-556.

Stark, M. H. (1954), A Social Worker As Member of a Medical Teaching Staff. *Soc. Casewk.,* 35:245-252.

Training in Neonatal Pediatrics

• *MORRIS A. WESSEL, M.D.*

Yale University

"The perfect physician . . . knows how to strengthen the patient and take care of him so that he may overcome the hurdles of nature." Thus wrote the Hebrew physician Maimonides in the twelfth century. Pediatricians find this description applicable to their role as they provide professional assistance that helps men and women establish themselves as parents. This article considers ways to strengthen pediatricians' training so as to improve the effectiveness of their professional service to mothers, fathers, and infants during this period.

The experience as a house officer serves as an opportunity to integrate a student's basic knowledge into the performance of the duties of a physician providing medical care to patients. During this period, as Dana Atchley (1959) states, "the subtleties and responsibilities of the individual doctor-patient relationship must have high pedagogic priority."

Many students and house officers possess warm qualities of sympathy and compassion. However, the intense preoccupation about the correct diagnosis and treatment all too often leaves little time for the student or his supervisors to consider how a physician can most

542

effectively utilize his skill, knowledge, and personality in order to help patients and their families feel better and be prepared for future development. This is especially true in the case of the normal child and his parents.

The prenatal and lying-in periods are times when a physician provides professional service during one of life's normative crises. The majority of patients are healthy. There are fewer life and death situations than in other areas of hospital training. However, the psychological upheavals which many women experience during this time may be intense. Symptoms appear which in other circumstances suggest deep-seated emotional disturbance.

When a woman presents a serious obstetrical complication such as serological incompatibility, toxemia, diabetes, cephalopelvic disproportion, or other unusual findings, the pediatric and obstetric house officers are usually in a position to discuss the problem with senior colleagues. Unfortunately, in many clinics the house officer is expected to carry the sole responsibility for the intense psychological problems presented by many women during the prenatal period. Consultation in the psychological areas, where considerable skill and knowledge are needed to provide successful medical care, is too often unavailable. With careful supervision, a young physician can gain considerable understanding of how a patient's feelings about the pregnancy influence the way in which she accepts assistance from either her pediatrician or her obstetrician; and these feelings may also indicate how she will react to the new baby and his demands.

THE PRENATAL INTERVIEW

The pediatrician in training who has the opportunity to interview expectant mothers experiences an interaction with the patient that is different in many ways from that usually met on the ward or in the clinic, where the patient presents a specific complaint or illness.

Many women as they approach the care of their first child, relinquish many satisfactions, such as relative freedom to come and go, financial reward, and the social prestige often gained from certain occupations. The satisfactions of parenthood are often blocked or impaired by the difficulties encountered in adapting to a different way of life. Contemporary high-school and college education prepares young women for careers rather than for motherhood. The change from the somewhat well-demarcated responsibilities of a job to the continual and unpredictable demands of parenthood requires extensive reorganization of a woman's outlook (Benedek, 1959; Benedict, 1938; Bibring, 1959). Some women possess the capacity of moving quickly into parenthood, while others take longer to adapt to this responsibility. Men, too, need time to reorient their thinking so as to share the responsibility for a child. They need to develop ways of assisting wives in the maternal role.

The support during the transition from childlessness to parenthood which the extended family, neighbors, and church groups provided in former years is less available in this age of mobility. Couples frequently assume their initial parental responsibilities in a community distant from family and childhood friends. Ruth Benedict (1938), noting the decrease in support which society offers to individuals in this transitional phase of life, urged the development of social institutions to help young people as they assume new roles.

The concerns and questions of expectant couples often reflect the reorganization of their outlook as they consider the care of a baby. By listening to their plans, hopes, and concerns, and by making appropriate suggestions as to equipment, clothing, sleeping, and feeding arrangements for the infant, a pediatrician can help men and women prepare for parenthood. The relationship thus formed between the physician and couple can serve as a basis for understanding some of the attitudes which later find expression in the adaptation that the mother and father make to their child. This is often seen in how the parents handle the baby.

A pediatrician in training who is supervised in this prenatal pediatric role by a qualified psychiatrist or pediatrician interested in helping couples achieve mature parenthood becomes increasingly aware of the value of his services in this normative crisis of life. Such support of parents can to some extent replace the psychological support that may be lost in the trend toward specialization in modern medicine. When the trainee understands the diagnostic and therapeutic value of clarifying the expectant parents' fears and expectations, he will be less anxious and uncomfortable as he talks with the expectant parents. A woman may present no symptoms of physiological or pathological disturbance, but her questions and anxieties reflect intensely the psychological reorganization which often accompanies pregnancy (Bibring, 1959). Thus, her concerns about housing, finances, new responsibilities, and about how her husband will act when there is a new baby become legitimate areas for discussion in the prenatal interview.

The pediatrician's interest in the couple's life situation, including their concerns related to the delivery, to the health of the infant, and to plans for the care of the baby facilitates the establishment of a relationship between family and physician (Jackson, 1947; Olmstead et al., 1949; Senn, 1947; Wessel, 1961). In the interview, questions such as "How are you feeling? How long have you lived in this community?" can initiate the discussion and identify to some extent the socioeconomic and cultural background of the expectant couple. A question about how both husband and wife are feeling leads to comments such as "never felt better in my life" to "awful, I feel it will never end." The expectant mother, who is physically miserable during her pregnancy, has a very different background to initiate her parental experience than has the mother who has had very little discomfort. Many expectant fathers, too, report nausea, vomiting, cramps, weight fluctuations, and other gastrointestinal difficulties. They also benefit by a sympathetic interest in their physical and psychological state. As the couple tell of the family history, incidence of allergic, metabolic, neurological diseases, blood types, and other pertinent conditions, the physician can often sense specific areas of concerns related to their past experiences which may influence the later care of the child.

Following this introductory part of the interview, couples usually seek information regarding equipment for the baby. The pediatrician who listens attentively, making a suggestion here and there, helps them to develop their confidence as well as to make realistic preparations. His practical suggestions can be more appropriate than the persuasive arguments of well-meaning relatives and zealous salesmen.

Infant feeding is an important area of discussion during the pre-natal interview. Most women decide before delivery whether they wish to nurse or formula feed. The psychological factors determin-ing this decision represent deep-seated forces which are often incom-pletely understood by the woman herself. Although a pediatrician may feel that there are definite advantages to breast or bottle feed-ing, the most effective use of his professional role is to support a woman in her own decision as to choice of feeding. If he authorita-tively urges a woman who feels uncomfortable as she considers nurs-ing to breast feed, he may intensify already-existing conflicts and weaken, rather than strengthen, the mother-infant relationship. When a woman is uncomfortable in the nursing situation, the attempt at breast feeding is usually unsuccessful and she weans her infant shortly. A pediatrician who helps choose appropriate bottles, nipples, and sterilizing equipment conveys his desire to aid in the successful establishment of the best possible feeding relationship for this particular woman.

There are many women, on the other hand, desirous of nursing, whose confidence is shaken by cultural and familial pressures and, all too often, by nurses and physicians. The pediatrician's interest in the mother's desires and his promise to guide her during the early days of feeding help the woman to develop her capacity to nurse successfully. Discussion of the details of the first feedings reassures the woman as she approaches the experience. She should be urged to seek help from nurses with the initial feeding, which often can occur with great satisfaction shortly after delivery.

Expectant couples have many questions regarding the care of their infant in the hospital. They feel more at ease when they know the exact details as to when they will first see the baby, when the first feeding occurs, and what the geographic relationships will be between mother and infant. Physicians at the Grace-New Haven Community Hospital, where the lying-in routine provides a period shortly after delivery for the father, mother, and infant to be together, report that this procedure is enjoyed greatly by patients and staff. When such a plan is practical under existing administrative and architectural circumstances (and one might ask why it isn't more often considered possible), the expectant couples look forward to this first family visit.

The pediatrician should also discuss with the parents the manner in which the infant will be cared for during the lying-in period. In some hospitals rooming-in facilities are available. When they are administered by professional personnel firmly convinced that it offers unusual opportunities to help mothers achieve physical and psychological comfort, they present advantages to many women (Jackson, 1947, 1949; Jackson et al., 1948). The rooming-in nurse, unlike the nursery nurse who constantly is taking the baby away from the mother, is free to offer assistance by helping mothers care for their infants. The success of this plan depends to a great extent upon the interest the nurses and doctors have in utilizing the bedside arrangements to improve the psychological and physical comfort of the mothers (Jackson, 1949). The opportunity gradually to assume the responsibility for the care of an infant appeals to many women. Husbands, too, often anticipate with excitement and pleasure the prospect of donning a gown and holding their babies. Some women, however, find that the presence of the infant makes them feel that they must take more responsibility than they are physically and psychologically ready to assume. These mothers are more comfortable utilizing the nursery for the care of their infant during the lying-in period.

As rapport develops between couple and pediatrician, there arise questions concerning the health of the unborn infant. The husband or wife may ask: "When will you first see the baby?" which infers: "When will you be able to assure us that the infant is healthy and normal?" Expectant couples always have this concern for they know there can be no guarantee that an unborn baby will be in perfect condition. As they tell of previous experiences and the misfortunes of friends or relatives, they benefit by sharing these thoughts with their pediatrician. A few reassuring comments, such as "I expect that your baby will be in good condition," "The chances are, you know, definitely in your favor," or "I will examine the baby as soon as I can, and tell you how he looks to me" are helpful. When there is a specific reason for unusual anxiety (such as a previous stillbirth, or infant with a congenital anomaly, or a close association with other families with serious difficulties), the pediatrician may decide to examine the infant in the delivery room immediately after birth. When a physician is aware of concerns and offers to do everything within his capacity to alleviate fears, he strengthens the couple's own capacity to cope with anxiety.

Another area which can be discussed with advantage concerns household help during the first few weeks at home. Some women do best with a housekeeper or relative who functions primarily to help with cleaning and cooking, thus allowing the mother more freedom to care for the infant. Other women prefer someone to care for the baby, while they manage the house and gradually assume the responsibility for the infant. Many couples find that if a husband can arrange vacation time appropriately, they can often function effectively "on their own."

Mothers experiencing a second pregnancy can benefit by the opportunity to discuss the care of an older child during the lying-in period and afterwards. The first-born child, who is frequently of toddler age, often behaves during the pregnancy in a way which is difficult for the parents to understand, and to handle effectively. He may be increasingly restless, more and more demanding of his mother's attention, and openly aggressive. The mother, weary and physically uncomfortable, may be uneasy at this change in behavior. She is often bewildered as she attempts to solve the difficulties before the arrival of the new baby. She often hopes "to complete toilet training," "get him off the bottle," "get him out of the crib" before the birth of the baby. The child often reacts to these pressures by becoming increasingly difficult.

Parents may become distraught and wonder how they will ever manage with one more. The sharing of this feeling with the pediatrician serves as a supportive measure in itself. The suggestion to provide a frequent baby sitter, preferably a consistent one, is helpful. Interpretation of the child's psychological reactions often increases the parents' ability to cope with the behavior. Many three- and four-year-old children are concerned about the physical process of birth. A simple discussion of the delivery process is often followed by improvement in behavior.

The pediatrician also can help parents make plans which strengthen a child's capacity to adjust to a mother's absence, and to her return with the baby. The importance of keeping the child informed about the mother's leaving and how long she will be away should be stressed. Telephone and mail contacts are valuable means of helping the child in his struggle to cope with the mother's absence. Arrangements should be made for the child or children to meet the substitute mother prior to the eventful day.

Couples awaiting a family through adoptive placement present specialized needs when they seek out a pediatrician (Wessel, 1960). Although looking forward to the arrival of the baby, they are usually overwhelmed by the fact that within a few days they will be parents. They miss the physical and psychological experiences of conception, pregnancy, and delivery that normally precede parenthood. Their experience is unique. They have *suddenly* arrived at having a baby. They are often immobilized with anxiety as they attempt to become parents quickly. They feel "on trial" lest they fail to achieve acceptable standards of parenthood.

The discussion between the prospective adoptive couple and the pediatrician usually focuses on the necessary equipment, sleeping arrangements, and preparation of feeding mixtures. Whether or not adoptive parents benefit from the help of a baby nurse depends upon their capacity to assume the care of the infant. Some couples need to have a person care for the infant while they become adjusted to the new responsibility, whereas others feel displaced by a nurse's "superskill" and do well carrying the responsibility themselves with the help of a public health nurse and the pediatrician.

THE NEONATAL PERIOD

After the birth of the infant, the pediatric house officer has many responsibilities to fulfill. First of all, he must examine the infant and ascertain the state of health. The difference between normal physiological variations and findings indicating serious pathology is often difficult to define. Considerable clinical skill is necessary to recognize when there is, or is not, cause for concern.

The examination of the infant, with the mother looking on (Wessel, 1961), allows the pediatrician to convey the full weight of medical skill and knowledge. When he declares that the infant is healthy, the mother can release many of her fears that there might be something wrong with the baby.

Mothers participate in an examination by asking questions about the variations which, though within the limits of normality, do arouse concern. The intense desire of each mother that her infant be perfect results in anxiety which often appears excessive. The pediatrician, as he examines the infant, can point out many findings, such as scleral hemorrhages, the hemangiomata of the eyelids and forehead, and peripheral cyanosis that will disappear in time. Other findings, such as molding of the head, overriding of sutures, breast engorgements, malpositions of feet, mucoid vaginal discharge, hiccoughs, physiological icterus, are also of concern to many parents.

Various aspects of infant behavior such as the stepping, placing, rooting, Moro reflexes, blinking response to auditory stimuli, visual acuity (which can frequently be demonstrated by slowly moving a red object, such as a flower, back and forth eight inches from the infant's eyes) are interesting to parents. A pediatrician can share with the mother his impression of the baby's physiological temperament by such comments as "he's a good-natured, placid baby," or "he's cuddly and relaxed," or "he certainly waves his arms and legs when he gets mad." These descriptive phrases help a mother to identify some of the specific qualities of her own particular infant.

Congenital defects, even of a relatively minor nature, such as vestigial digits, skin pedicles anterior to the ear, or major ones such as cleft palate and hare lip, naturally evoke intense reactions from parents. Each couple has the strong desire that their infant should be a perfect extension of themselves. The presence of even a minor abnormality is very upsetting. Since the realistic defect may be small, yet the response intense, it often appears that the reaction to a small defect is greater than to a larger one. The larger defect seems to overwhelm the parents, and their reactions may be evident only over a period of time. The pediatrician realizes that the parental reaction to a defect is an expression of their own disappointment that the infant they have produced is imperfect.

Some infants who are easily perturbed by the examination tend to be the same infants who are difficult to comfort at home. This is particularly true in families where exhaustion and anxiety are accompanied by an increase in kinesthetic tension. The experienced pediatrician frequently can identify the infant who will develop the "normal" but exhausting "paroxysmal fussiness of infancy" (Wessel et al., 1954).

The new mother may be quite uncomfortable in her first experiences of handling a tiny infant. The immature responses of the infant may be disappointing or frightening to her. However, the repeated experience of holding and feeding an infant gradually helps many mothers to feel more comfortable and competent in the parental role. At this time women often demonstrate swings in mood, varying from a highly elated state to episodic weepiness known as the "baby blues."

The pediatrician in his daily visits can help a mother as she assumes this new role in life. His frequent encouragement and his willingness to answer questions assist the mother to develop her own skills. Suggestions which improve the comfort of the mother increase her confidence in the performance of her new responsibilities. Practical hints, such as suggesting a pillow under the mother's arm to help support the infant during feeding, or a more effective position for burping, improve the mother's physical comfort and help her realize that the pediatrician is interested in *her* well-being. These are little items, simple, and extremely helpful; yet they are often lost in the rush of ascertaining the satisfactory state of a woman's condition as measured by temperature, pulse, blood pressure, fluid intake and output. Careful consideration of every aspect of the mother's physiological and psychological comfort is of importance since it increases her capacity to assume, and enjoy, the care of the baby. She needs help to recognize her worth during these first days of maternal responsibility. A mother of a tiny infant does not realize as she relieves the hunger and discomfort of her baby that she is providing care which will be increasingly rewarding as the infant matures and can show by mood and facial expression his appreciation for her care.

The feeding relationship between mother and infant provides one of the best opportunities for a pediatrician to observe a mother in the maternal role. The way in which a mother adapts to the needs of a baby provides clues as to how she feels about her maternal role. Some women experience great enjoyment as they feed their infant, while others, in spite of considerable help from nurses and physicians, are overwhelmed with responsibility. The physician may find it difficult to be present at more than an occasional feeding, but his interest in the details of the experience will be supportive to the mother, and stimulates the nurses to be cognizant of the importance of helping a mother over some of the initial hurdles (Barnes et al., 1953). Each pediatrician should see that the physiological and psychological needs of the mother and infant take precedence over hospital routines, which "like arteries become rigid with age" (Waller, 1947-48).

Personnel familiar with discussions of physiological and psychological aspects of breast feeding by Barnes et al. (1953), Middlemore (1941), Naish (1948), and Waller (1938) make a valuable contribution to a lying-in service by putting this knowledge to active use in the care of mothers and infants.

There are many difficulties which may arise during these early days. The mother's milk may be late in appearing, or the onset may be before the infant is ready to suck vigorously. These normal vicissitudes often appear overwhelming to new mothers, causing much discouragement and weeping. The efforts of the physicians and nurses can frequently insure success of the breast feeding, and help the mother gain satisfaction as she succeeds in one of the first major challenges of motherhood.

Some women find the nursing difficulties insurmountable and, although they try desperately, are unable to succeed. The pediatrician learns to recognize the woman whose expressed wish to breast feed is complicated by intense psychological conflicts. The initial attempts, even if for only a few days, may give the mother a feeling of having tried, but since it did not work out satisfactorily, she responds easily to suggestions to bottle feed.

Mothers who find that bottle feeding offers the most satisfactory way of achieving a successful relationship with their infant also need professional help during the early days. They need to be helped to find a suitable position so that a satisfactory flow of milk is achieved, and the baby feels comfortable in the mother's arms and can suck at the bottle with a minimum ingestion of air.

Methods of formula preparation should be discussed in detail. Printed forms are helpful, but serve only as a supplement to the pediatrician's discussions with the mothers. Most women benefit by knowing that flexibility of quantity and feeding intervals can occur with bottle feeding as with breast feeding. It is helpful to discuss the details of feeding a day or so before the mother is to be discharged, and to review the directions again on the final day of hospitalization.

Women differ in the way they accept professional help during this transitional period. The house officer needs to be aware that the mother's mood at the moment affects her enjoyment of her infant, and also that it can interfere with her capacity to utilize a physician's suggestions. Physicians and nurses are often confused by the intensity of these reactions and the sudden changes in a woman's affect. Their reassurances often appear to be inadequate. The experienced physician can help the house officer recognize the value of his consistent, helpful, supportive relationship to a mother as she strives to be psychologically more at ease with her infant. He can also help to distinguish the temporary mood changes so common in the lying-in period from the more serious, profound, emotional disturbances which occasionally occur.

There is much to be learned from the observation of newborn infants that will allow the physician to give better child-care advice. Babies vary in their response to wet diapers, hunger, auditory, tactile, visual, and kinesthetic stimuli. There is wide variation in the amount and tempo of motor activity. Some infants *are* difficult to feed; they fall asleep early at a feeding, only to awaken a short while later to suck for a few more minutes. Other infants are impatient, and become agitated if their hunger needs are unmet for more than a few minutes (Barnes et al., 1953). Too few medical students and house officers actually feed or handle a baby, other than during a physical examination. Utilizing this opportunity to be intimately involved with an infant during feeding or diaper change provides a specific awareness of an individual infant's characteristics.

THE FRAGILE, SICK OR ABNORMAL INFANT

There are, unfortunately, many occasions when an infant, weak from illness or prematurity, needs the facilities of an intensive-care unit. The separation of the infant from the mother and the concern about the infant's condition combine to make mothers anxious and somewhat depressed. Hospital architectural planning and regulations should make it possible for the mother to see her baby if only through a glass partition, as soon as she is able to move by wheel chair. Gradual improvement is reassuring. If, on the other hand, the infant is critically ill, the mother and father need the opportunity, if they so desire, of seeing their infant even if a fatal outcome is feared. Women who have never seen their infant alive are left with a great sense of emptiness and find it difficult to believe that they have produced a baby. Seeing the infant allows them to adjust to a realistic experience. The grief which follows the death of an infant may be intense, but this often represents a healthy reaction to a tragic loss.

On the other hand, many women prefer not to see their critically ill babies, particularly if there is a grotesque appearance. Parents should not be forced to observe the baby unless they desire to do so.

When a newborn infant is sick and cared for in a special unit, the pediatrician must continually inform the mother of the course of events. The critical condition of an infant for days on end is taxing to all involved. What may seem to be excellent progress to a pediatrician (i.e., a 5 gram weight gain or a 2 milligram drop in blood bilirubin) may be meaningless to parents who really want to know when the baby will come home. A mother's anxious questions may be interpreted as being unnecessarily demanding. The house officer needs help in understanding these reactions. They represent understandable feelings of a woman who, having conceived, carried, and delivered an infant is frightened about the baby's survival and does not know whether to consider herself a parent or not. The effective handling of the parents' feeling when an infant is critically ill, deformed, or stillborn, demands considerable knowledge of general and specific psychological reactions as well as a skillful use of one's own compassion. This professional responsibility is all too often relegated to a junior house staff member who, deeply involved with his own feelings about the tragedy, handles the situation as best he can. Never having had the opportunity of observing an experienced physician in such a role, he struggles with his own inner strength and weakness as he talks with the distraught parents. The pediatrician may feel relieved when the infant's downhill course is ended. Effective professional service to parents during times of such crisis demands great skill and maturity, and most house officers need help in understanding how to combine effectively their medical knowledge and compassionate feelings so as to provide suitable professional care in these difficult situations.

When a mother and infant are discharged from the hospital, the pediatrician's role becomes increasingly important. Whenever possible, a home visit is valuable (Jackson, 1945; Wessel, 1946). As the pediatrician examines the infant at home, he can help the parents to understand the baby's state of health or illness. This gives them an opportunity to ask questions and to express their concerns; this can help the mother to relax and function more effectively. At the same time, the pediatrician gains an impression of the home setting which provides him with a clearer picture of the family under his care. He sees at first hand the realistic and practical problems of caring for a tiny infant. He learns of specific areas of concern to new mothers. He can learn much about effectively using pediatric knowledge to provide comprehensive professional service to new parents and their infant (Jackson, 1945). Unfortunately, the needs of the sick infants in a newborn nursery usually demand so much time and energy of the house officer and attending pediatrician, that there is often little attention paid toward developing skills in the basic areas necessary to provide day-to-day home care of sick and healthy infants.

SUMMARY

Newborn care is one of the specific areas which distinguishes pediatrics as a specialty. The challenge is to integrate our present physiological, psychological, and pathological knowledge to provide effective scientific care (Senn, 1946; Solnit and Senn, 1954). Concentration on the pathological, enzymatic, and biochemical aspects of newborn care to the exclusion of training in the other areas leaves too wide a gap in many training programs.

There are many ways for a pediatrician providing care in the newborn period to offer psychologically effective help to couples as they assume the responsibilities of parenthood. The pediatrician in training who is assigned to the newborn service should have the opportunity to be supervised by a mature and competent physician interested in the members of a family as individuals involved in one of life's normative crises. In this training experience he can learn a great deal which increases the value of his professional services and his satisfaction in his future work. The newborn service as an area for pediatric teaching offers great resources for the development of better understanding of parent-infant relationships. Further development of teaching and supervision of house officers assigned to this area should be encouraged.

BIBLIOGRAPHY

Atchley, D. W. (1959), The Science, the Art and the Heart of Medicine. *J. Med. Educ.*, 34:17-22.
Barnes, G. R., Jr., Lethin, A. N., Jr., Jackson, E. B., & Shea, N. (1953), Management of Breast Feeding. *J. Amer. Med. Assn.*, 151:192-199.
Benedek, T. (1959), Parenthood as a Development Phase. *J. Amer. Psychoanal. Assn.*, 7:389-417.
Benedict, R. (1938), Continuities and Discontinuities. *Psychiatry*, 1:161-167.
Bibring, G. L. (1959), Some Considerations of the Psychological Process in Pregnancy. *The Psychoanalytic Study of the Child*, 14:115-121. New York: Int. Univ. Press.
Jackson, E. B. (1945), Prophylactic Considerations for Neonatal Period. *Amer. J. Orthopsychiat.*, 15:89-95.

——— (1947), Theoretic Considerations and Parental Observations Relating to Unified Hospital Care of Mother and Infant. *Proc. Third. Amer. Congr. on Obstetrics and Gynecology*, pp 8-17.

——— (1949), Pediatric and Psychiatric Aspects of the Yale Rooming-In Project. *Conn. State Med. J.*, 14:612-621.

——— Olmsted, R. W., Foord, A., Thomas H., & Hyder, K. (1948), Hospital Rooming-in Unit for Four Newborn Infants and Their Mothers. *Pediatrics*, 1:28-42.

Middlemore, M. P. (1941), *The Nursing Couple*. London: Hamish Hamilton Med. Books.

Maimon, Moses Ben (Maimonides), *The Preservation of Youth; Essays on Health*. New York: Philosophical Library, 1958, p. 39.

Naish, C. (1948), *Breast Feeding*. London: Oxford Univ. Press.

Olmstead, R. W., Svibergson, R. I., & Kleeman, J. A. (1949), The Value of Rooming-In Experience in Pediatric Training. *Pediatrics*, 3:617-621.

Senn, M. J. E. (1946), Relationship to Pediatrics and Psychiatry. *Amer. J. Dis. Child.*, 71:537-549.

——— (1947), Anticipatory Guidance of the Pregnant Woman and Her Husband for Their Roles as Parents. *Problems of Early Infancy* (Trans. of First Conference, March 3-4). New York: Josiah Macy, Jr. Foundation, pp. 11-16.

Solnit, A. J. & Senn, M. J. E. (1954), Teaching Comprehensive Pediatrics in an Out-Patient Clinic. *Pediatrics*, 14:547-556.

Waller, H. (1938), *Clinical Studies in Lactation*. London: William Heinemann.

——— (1947-48), Incidence, Causes and Prevention of Failure of Breast Feeding. *Brit. Med. Bull.*, 5:181-188.

Wessel, M. A. (1946), The Pediatric Interne. *J. Ped.*, 29:651-662.

——— (1960), The Pediatrician and Adoption. *New Eng. J. Med.*, 262:446-450.

——— (1961), Parent-Pediatrician Relationships in the Newborn Period. *Ped. Clins. No. Amer.*, 8:441-453.

——— Cobb, J. C., Jackson, E. B., Harris, G. S., & Detwiler, A. (1954), Paroxysmal Fussing in Infancy, Sometimes Called Colic. *Pediatrics*, 14:421-435.

On the Acceptance of Realistic Goals in Medicine

• *SEYMOUR L. LUSTMAN, M.D., Ph.D.*

Yale University

• *JULIUS B. RICHMOND, M.D.*

State University of New York, Syracuse

In the process of providing health services, although many para-medical professions are involved, the individual physician is traditionally viewed as the most significant agent or instrument directing the implementation of these services. It is quite important, therefore, that appropriate attention be given to the effective employment and the conservation of the energies of the physician in order that he may provide services of a high quality with comfort and satisfaction over a lifetime of practice.

It will be the purpose of this paper to call attention to the potential hazards of current medical training which does not incorporate within it certain concerns with the productivity and gratifications to be derived from the subsequent lifelong career as a physician. It is fitting that this matter be considered in a volume honoring Dr. Milton Senn, who has devoted so much of his professional career to the interests of young people in professional training for work with children and their families.

The problems we will raise here face all men in medical practice, and are lifelong issues. However, for the purposes of this discussion we will limit ourselves primarily to the experience gained in the training of pediatricians and psychiatrists; we will focus on two periods of particular, and universally shared, enforced adaptation because the internal stress experienced throws these issues into bold relief. The two periods are those of the transition from medical student to responsible physician as experienced in the internship, and the transition from postgraduate training to practice. These are periods when new modes of functioning must be developed in order to cope with new patterns of responsibility set within new environmental circumstances. It is quite clear that this will occur through the alteration of established patterns of behavior and attitudes, and that the probability of a successful reality adaptation (both in terms of internal comfort and external function) will depend in part on precisely what the established patterns and attitudes are, how rigidly or flexibly they are defined, and how well they fit the emergence of new needs.

We will be particularly concerned with the matter of limitations with which every physician must ultimately come to grips, the conflicts they produce (internally and with the environment), and the resolution of which has profound basic import for his subsequent happiness and function. Our feeling is that there is very little in current medical education—from medical school through residency training—which is designed to aid the young physician in his appreciation of these realistic limitations, or in his making his "personal peace" with them. In actuality, because of the structure of the educational process, in some ways the problem may be made more difficult.

As constituted today, it is usually the internship period during which the young physician comes to grips with the frustrations of the realistic limitations of what can be done as contrasted to what one *should be able* to do. In the transition from training to practice, the problem may be stated as coming to grips with what can be done as contrasted to what ideally *could or should* be done.

INTERNSHIP

As stated above, while such a concept of limitations is applicable to any stage of professional activity, internship as a period of accelerated professional growth and development not only makes the needs more blatantly obvious; it is, in addition, a period when crucially needed help could have lifelong beneficial repercussions. It is usually here that the young physician is forcibly faced by his own limitations, the limitations of his science, and the limitations of community resources. It is our feeling that the young physician is left to grapple and grope toward his own solution of these issues with frequently too little support, understanding, preparation, and frequently under the most adverse conditions. In current training practice there is no planned way in which these issues can be even raised, let alone settled. Our not recognizing these issues as part of our professional training responsibility makes for a haphazard approach within the training program. Barring the unforeseen good fortune of the presence of someone who is concerned with such issues, the intern runs a very great risk of resolving them in an unnecessarily painful manner, and one which is not necessarily constructive. For example, one common manifestation during the internship period takes the form of periods of greater or lesser disillusionment accompanied by varying degrees of therapeutic nihilism. One very unhealthy way of resolving this is vehement partisanship. We too frequently offer the intern the opportunity of "interservice rivalry" with its accompanying derogation of the methods or therapeutic results of one specialty as opposed to another. In actuality, this in many ways makes the selection of subsequent specialty a rather haphazard one for the intern and may blur his true interests. It is to be understood that there are great individual differences in terms of the duration, the severity, and the residuals of such experiences.

We must for a brief moment look to the academic preparation for this particularly stressful period. For the purposes of this paper we will restrict ourselves to the medical curriculum and not discuss the premedical training, although it has obvious implications. While much has been said, and much more could be said, about the medical curriculum, we will for the moment concentrate on the fact that the student's first two years are rooted in the "basic sciences." During this time he comes to accept the scientific method as basic to his field. However, much more often than not he comes to accept the scientific method in terms of an exaggerated certainty of exact answers to exact questions. This atmosphere or "climate" of the relatively more exact basic sciences continues with little or no change in the less exact clinical sciences.

While we accept that this scientific atmosphere is vital—even crucial—to the study of medicine, its presentation which stresses more of the certainty than the hope of science, more of the content than of the spirit of science, is what we feel becomes misleading to the medical student who hears it without the professional maturity and experience of his teachers. Those of us who try to teach or encourage research are often surprised by how superficial is the understanding of science itself. Students, for the most part, are not only uninspired by the progress of science but also uninformed—not only of the stirring but the agonizing aspects of this progress. This is so readily apparent in both the history and the philosophy of science that we can feel surprised at how little of this is absorbed by the medical student, even though so much of his preparatory work calls for immersion in science. This may be due to the fact that, unfortunately, he often has not had any direct involvement in scientific work. The increase in summer research fellowships and other direct research experience is in some measure overcoming this deficiency.

It is not at all uncommon for the medical student to come to believe in all sincerity that for every disease entity there is a diagnosis, an etiology, and a treatment. Perhaps the most pernicious aspect of this is that all therapeutic emphasis is in terms of cure, and even the malignancies are spoken of in terms of "cure rates," albeit five- or ten-year rates. Most medical students are led, understandably, to believe that the best men in the field can "cure" almost everything —and these expectations and demands become his own. Perhaps we can make clearer the difficulties this presents to even the mature practitioner by the following example. A very well-known and very competent surgeon found that as he grew older in his profession he was having to do more and more cancer surgery. On one particular morning, after operating on three "inoperable" patients, this man retired to the doctor's dressing room where he fell to his knees and vomited. He turned somewhat helplessly to his colleagues, and in his distress said, "I haven't done this in a very long time."

In part, it is this reality of the sometimes awesome responsibility of the physician which we feel the medical student is not prepared to integrate into his daily psychological life. On the other hand, it may well be that the somewhat exaggerated self-confidence that he picks up from his teachers and reading serves a useful purpose. Without this exaggerated trust in his field and in himself, he might fear ever to tread into the "wilds" of clinical medicine. However, these great expectations of his own skills and those of his profession do him and his future patients a great disservice in the sense that they ill prepare him for the somewhat brutal facts of pain, chronic disease, and death. Furthermore, the training program is such that he has been essentially protected from the patient throughout his medical school curriculum in spite of clerkship and bedside teaching. This is inevitable, for in this period the ultimate responsibility for the patient is not his, and the primary objective of the student clerk is learning, not healing, although these cannot be completely divorced.

He is further protected by being exposed in only very well-circumscribed contacts with patients, in which for the most part the teaching wards serve as a kind of laboratory for the educative process. Indeed, he may very well be more concerned with his instructor than with the patient. He is further protected from the patient by the fact that he is learning basic skills of such a nature that it is quite easy to separate a murmur from the fact that this may ultimately mean death to a man and anguish to his family. A necessary, though sometimes overemphasized involvement with the learning of laboratory procedures puts additional distance between pain, death, and the embryonic physician, who must of necessity concern himself with the biochemical, physiological, and pathological processes.

All of this serves to make the transition from medical student to intern a precipitous one. Of course, the degree of change will vary to some extent with the types of internships ranging from the private pavillion to the large public hospital. If the internship is such that the intern remains almost in a continuation of the clerkship role, it merely puts off and prolongs his ultimate dealing with the problems we here raise. On the other hand, precipitous inundation with clinical responsibility may not be the most advantageous atmosphere in which to face such issues. At any rate, as educators we must concern ourselves with the impact of such experiences on a lifelong career, and what can be done to make this the most constructive experience possible.

It is in many ways unfortunate that the intern's first professional responsibility for patients is in the hospital, where the very seriously ill and the most perplexing diagnostic problems are to be found. It is a paradox that it is the intern, the man in the hospital who is least prepared in terms of skill, age, experience, emotional maturity, and confidence, who spends the most time carrying out the most intimate procedures to the painfully ill and dying. It is a little reminiscent of the "sink or swim" philosophy of education. It is no wonder that under these circumstances therapeutic "nihilism" can become an important implicit or explicit concern to the young physician. There is a quality of therapeutic zeal which characterizes most medical students early in their careers. This cannot survive unchanged through the long, arduous training and generally undergoes considerable distortion by the time of residency, most frequently replaced by a seemingly sophisticated attitude which is actually characterized by varying degrees of cynicism.

To us this would mean that somewhere during the internship experience the physician has developed an increasing awareness of the fact that every disease does not have the clear-cut diagnosis, etiology, and therapy that he was formerly led to believe by his instructors, his own needs, and the atmosphere of the medical school curriculum. Illustrative of this, in one large hospital in which patient care is for the most part directed by a rotating intern, it is well known to all the interns that the death rate of all services correlates with the rotation of the interns. There is a rise when new men take over the service which then falls off as they get some experience.

To face this disillusionment at a time when he is surrounded by the desperate needs of the patients around him, when life itself seems to hinge on his immediate act, is most inopportune timing and will possibly leave deeper scars on the maturing physician than are necessary. The issue is not whether naïve therapeutic zeal is or is not an asset in the intern; the issue is what happens to it and what takes its place. As it exists today, there is every reason to believe that the internship represents a period of great swings, but with a necessary structuralization and consolidation of lifelong defenses to shield the physician from what he may come to regard as failures.

The process of "internship" can profitably be viewed from the vantage point of how interns defend themselves against self-recriminations, and a depressed feeling of hopelessness and helplessness. Obviously deep personality characteristics within the intern himself will in a very major way direct how he will deal with these problems. This may range from an exaggerated denial of the seriousness of his work in which he gives the impression that it is all a stimulating, intellectual "game"; to a near paralysis of his function accompanied by depression which may in some cases necessitate his leaving hospital work. One must not forget that this is accompanied by a rather chronic state of physical fatigue; and it is not uncommon that under the combined stress men break down with physical illnesses such as ulcers or tuberculosis during this period. The more pathological the defenses are, the greater is the probability that the men will be singled out by both their peers and teachers. However, this in itself is never consistently dealt with throughout the country, or even within the same hospital. Reaction may range from considering it a health problem to considering it a disciplinary problem.

However, we may now turn from the individual defenses of individual interns to some of the more general factors which come into play. For example, it is not insignificant that for some men in medicine the two brief periods of greatest laughter and sometimes macabre humor are those during their first contact with cadaver in anatomy laboratory, and their first contact with dying patients for whom they are responsible in the internship. Another very common phenomenon is the fact that both internship and residency are notoriously periods of "griping." While there is much reality in many of the gripes, very frequently they owe their intensity to a factor of displacement from precisely the concerns herein stated.

Helplessness brings with it a concomitant anger which finds expression most usually in a general dissatisfaction with everything ranging from food and schedules to individual staff members and *patients*.

An extremely important factor in what occurs is the amount of support available from older colleagues, and perhaps the most important aspect of this is the techniques of defense used by such colleagues as they continue in their own lives to face the same problems.

As indicated above, our feeling would be that the essence of this defensive process is the avoidance of the painful awareness of ignorance and therapeutic impotence. While this would probably always be true with humane strivings of any and all physicians, it cannot help but be made a more difficult problem if the student has approached his work cloaked by, and believing in, the omnipotence of his profession. Wearing such armor can only bring him to either a dissatisfaction with himself as not "measuring up," or an equally disastrous dissatisfaction with his profession, or a variety of other defensive maneuvers such as boredom, loss of interest, inability to understand or relate to patients, etc.

While speaking of such defenses, it is germane to point to the conclusions reached by Stanton (1954) in his studies of psychiatric hospitals, even though they relate, for the most part, to residents in training and staff members. We particularly agree with the fact that some of this later resident training is tinged by the earlier experiences as an intern. Stanton points out that the house officer now approaches his work having had the experience of episodes of sheer mutual helplessness with patients. It quite clearly follows that ". . . ignorance always contains the threat of such general helplessness."

The following are some of the techniques used most commonly by all of us to avoid the awareness of ignorance, and thereby evade the threat of helplessness. First, the physician may fill in the gaps in his knowledge and skills by the use of "professional opinion." There is here the "temptation to use highly empiric, vague appraisals." The risk is great that the professional armamentarium of the physician becomes opinionated, dogmatic, rigid, and sometimes far too intuitive in the treatment of disease. The converse of this may also occur in that the intern may become "superscientific" to the exclusion of any of the so-called art of medicine. As someone once put it, such rigor may well become rigor mortis for clinical thinking.

Another defensive pattern is one in which the physician may "avoid the emotional impact of failure by depersonalizing the patient and taking refuge in an emotional detachment so great that he sacrifices his grasp of the meaning of the disorder to the patient." We are all too much aware of the reference to patients as "cases" rather than by name, and of the deep intellectual involvement with tissues rather than with people.

The physician may avoid awareness of ignorance by "attributing greater certainty to the hypotheses than he can possibly demonstrate." Thus, in spite of the previously mentioned deep immersion in science, the physician may become more a defender of "causes" than a scientist. The disservice resulting from any and all of these defenses to the maturing physician and to his present and future patients is blatantly manifold.

To return for a moment more specifically to the intern, the first technique of defense mentioned above is, for the most part, denied him. He has had too little experience to indulge in much "professional opinion." No matter what degree his erudition and knowledge of the literature takes, he cannot help but at this stage retain great awareness of his own rather limited experience. However, he may still use this defense by accepting too readily the professional opinions of those around him. There is even a greater temptation to do this because of the hierarchical structure of all hospitals, and the further internal relief of the burden of responsibility. Much too often one hears, "So and so has done this many times with great success, although he can't explain why it works." Often manifest in this attitude is a readiness to give up the hard-learned, scientific methodology so rigorously taught in the medical school. Perhaps again, this is because in the practicality of the usual internship-doctor-patient relationship, it does not serve him as readily as he has been led, and had the need, to believe. It is a great injury to his future career that he may at this point put aside those painfully learned lessons and that in the future he may adopt an attitude of "Those who can't, teach—and those who can, do." It is, however, abundantly clear that some measure of influence on this will be possible through the scientific attitude of his seniors, and the use made of the literature and scientific methods within the hospital.

It is the second technique of depersonalization of the patient which is unfortunately the most frequently used technique during the internship period. He does this in numerous ways; first, as indicated above, he can become readily preoccupied by a diseased organ to the exclusion of the patient. One can see this in the irritated attitude of the intern to the patient whose fracture is healing well but who cannot sleep at night, or has headaches, or complains of any myriad of ancillary symptoms. With such an attitude the intern can only react with irritation and an inability to understand such complaints.

The most prevalent technique is the more dangerous one of using the intern's wastepaper-basket diagnosis of "crock." One is aghast when one realizes that the "crock" is, or has become, any older patient who may or may not complain, with a chronic refractory disease. This is of singular import, since it is precisely this type of patient that the growing area of geriatric medicine indicates will fill more and more hospital beds. In reality, the disturbing factor about the "crock" is his chronic illness which either cannot be modified at all or only slightly so. This dangerously threatens the intern's economy by further emphasizing his already existing feelings of helplessness and awareness of ignorance. By relegating a human being to the "crock" basket, the intern takes himself out of perhaps the most uncomfortable situation in medicine, i.e., his inability to derive deep personal gratification out of the minimal effect that he can have on the suffering and the course of such an illness.

The converse of depersonalization is also seen in the young intern, and can be an excruciatingly painful experience. Frequently one sees an intern so overwhelmed by his inability to cure or modify a disease process that he loses all sense of objectivity and plunges into an intensely personal relationship with the patient or his family. This has the quality of trying to "make up" for his medical helplessness by sharing the suffering. This is quite frequently seen in pediatric services, and is most blatant in contact with children with malignant diseases. To learn the difference between sympathy and empathy is a hard lesson.

Perhaps an illustration will make this clear. A young house officer, who was caring for a young child with leukemia during his prolonged hospital stay, broke down and cried with the family when he had to inform them of the death of the child. He was, for the moment, not able to cope with what was aroused in himself and was unable to recognize that this degree of involvement was of no help to the family and that in fact he was on one level apologizing, and on another level asking the family to help him. Actually, this example bears on the issue of the extent of the physician's responsibility. With medical practice developing as it has over the years with such concepts as total health and community health, one cannot divorce himself from his function of support to the family during such a bereavement. Considering one's full responsibility as discharged with such a death, or crying with the family, are both extremes in which the defensiveness of the physician impairs his adaptation and function.

The search for security by attributing greater certainty to a hypothesis than it deserves is a most familiar mechanism. Sometimes it takes the form of either misquoting the literature or, in the more sophisticated, the lulling of one's critical attitude about the work reported in order to permit one to accept what at the moment rescues him from helplessness. This is undoubtedly one of the factors which accounts for the persistence in medicine of much "folklore," and is abetted by the hierarchical structure of medicine.

Nowhere in the medical curriculum is the student very realistically made aware of the limitations of his profession, medicine. Actually, there is available to him great comfort in the realization of the rapid strides made in medicine and the potential of scientific methodology. If the student can be given a grasp of this broad fact, additional maturation and support within his profession will help him face the rather grim fact that there are not many diseases which his profession can CURE, but that there are many which can be modified, and there is always something that can be done to increase the comfort of the patient and his family.

It is unfortunately true that in some instances all the physician can accomplish is the alleviation of pain. This is indeed meager service to render if one is convinced that the role of the physician is a curative one such as is fostered by current medical curriculum. It is not only an unrewarding and dissatisfying service, but in the intern runs a greater risk of being misinterpreted as his own inadequacy. What we speak of is the rather persistent feeling of, "Have I done everything? An older, more experienced man could have cured this."

On the other hand, we must concern ourselves with the immediate sense of gratification the young intern derives from his work. If, in fact, the alleviation of pain is the only service the physician can render to a dying patient, that is hardly a meager service. But to accept this with appropriate satisfaction and gratification requires great maturity.

It would seem to follow that the immediate needs of the intern must involve an awareness of the problems with which he is faced, support and understanding from his older colleagues, and some greater degree of success in treatment. This is in some ways rendered difficult in hospital practice because of the nature of the patient population. However, it is quite possible to offset this by more outpatient service, particularly in the infectious disease clinics, and by a greater attendance on the part of older colleagues to the needs of the young physician.

The greatest satisfactions in medicine depend on a concept of the acceptance of realistic, although limited, goals in terms of oneself and one's own profession. This is never to be misunderstood to mean not trying all within one's ability and within the scope of one's profession to aid the patient. It merely means that while doing this, one remains aware of the likelihood and degree of possible success, so that even while making a Herculean effort, it is rooted in reality and one need not be shattered by failure. If one truly accepts that for the present, with our current knowledge and techniques, a patient with a terminal malignant disease is beyond one's "curative" power, the physician can then comfortably function and be gratified by the fact that, as indicated above, he has aided his patient through the alleviation of pain. He will in a sense be much freer to derive ancillary gratifications from the opportunity to study and understand the processes which are entrusted to his care. In addition, it will permit him the gratification of an extension of his function by his ability to be of service to the family of such patients. This is in sharp contrast to what can be currently noted in far too many medical, pediatric, and surgical services, where on daily ward rounds the refractory, dying patients are left to the end of the working ward rounds and frequently, because of "lack of time" or some other rationalization, do not get seen.

TRANSITION TO PRACTICE

We would like to turn now to some of the problems faced by the transition from training to practice. Again, although many of the issues are applicable to all aspects of medical practice, we would like to focus on those faced by pediatricians. They will take with them into the process of adapting themselves to the demands of practice all of the above-mentioned conflicts which usually come to the fore in the internship period. However, if we look more closely at this period of the physician's life, another dimension of the problem is seen to be clearly added. This has to do with the transition from the kind of community represented by the training hospital to the kind of community in which the practice is established. In many ways this can be perhaps best categorized as the issues surrounding the "demands" of the community.

In recent years there has been considerable concern that pediatricians have, after a few years of practice, found themselves overtaxed, weary, and somewhat demoralized and disillusioned concerning the unending demands on their time and energies. In such a discussion we would presume good training, which invariably carries within it concepts of adequate services for children in the community which go far beyond that of hospital practice. The problem again highlights the omission from training programs of some concept of self-protection for the physician which permits reasonable functioning and personal gratification. Depending on the original conceptual framework of the medical training, the concept of adequate services for children in the community can be overwhelming. Obviously this is not universally true, for many pediatricians manage to deal with heavy community pressures for service and yet derive considerable gratification. However, for most, some concept of self-protection is desperately needed. We do not mean self-protection in an unwholesome and self-centered way, but rather with the objective of maximizing his usefulness to the community in the long range.

In our experience, this has been frequently exemplified in the problem of the pediatrician who, feeling thoroughly harassed, seeks either to move from the community or to change his specialty in the belief that he will thereby solve his problems. The question we raise is whether such a solution is consonant with his having made his fullest contribution to the community or to himself.

In the period of attempting to establish oneself within a community, it would appear to be quite reasonable to respond to all the demands which the community makes. However, when this continues to the extent where the physician feels overextended because of community pressure for service, one must then question the real source of such overextension. The simplest and the most common response is to project the sense of pressure and to experience it as coming from the faults of the particular community. Indeed many physicians tend to make this assumption and thereby feel that a situational change will resolve the problem. Actually, a change may only compound the problem, particularly if it is based on just such a projection. Man cannot flee his internal state, and such "solutions" are as ineffective for the physician as they are when given as advice to patients. In many ways, the issue boils down to how difficult it is to distinguish between "being unable to say no" and "being unable to let go." We accept that the physician, like all men, is driven into overextension of himself by a variety of causes such as competition, ambition, and with some, greed. However, in addition to these, one must never ignore the matter of a professional and human conscience.

Interestingly enough, this problem is often particularly acute among those physicians (the same holds true for others in the "helping" professions) who are motivated by a conscience which leads to social action. Indeed, this is particularly true of those who wish to work with children. There must be many reasons for this, but we are most impressed with those stemming from the fact that work with children presents not only the opportunities but the obligations for both preventive and social medicine. While any physician can find himself so moved, it is noteworthy that those who work with children manifest this strong desire to provide services for others, both at the personal level (practice) and at the broader community level (public or private agency programs).

We especially wish to point out that we are not critical of such motivation for social action; rather, this can be the basis for effective work if the professional worker does not destroy himself in the process of responding to it. It is our feeling, therefore, that during the training process students and house officers can be helped to develop some insights into their social motivations in order that they may channel their energies most constructively.

Certainly one of the most critical factors in the reality adaptation which the physician makes to the demands of work from the outside has to do with the effective use of his time. Therefore, some interpretation to the student concerning time as a factor in the helping process seems indicated. To us this suggests making maximum use of time units customarily employed in the practice setting, rather than trying to provide longer periods of time "in order to do the most thorough job." In terms of pediatric care, it means that he must come to appreciate *continuity* as a factor in his care of patients over a period of time as contrasted to lengthy individual sessions. It means that he must recognize that he can provide advisory or consultative services only to so many agencies in the community and still remain effective. It also means that he must learn to deal clinically with many families for whom the ancillary community services (which may have been available in the teaching center) are not available.

Under these circumstances, it becomes necessary for the physician to *learn to live* with what are destined to be limited services. He must make decisions concerning the investment of his energies on an appraisal of both external and internal pressures. This must be conceived of in the reality atmosphere of not being all things to all men, but rather functioning within one's own capacity. For example, in terms of the current increase in concern with emotional problems, and the increasingly noted shortage of trained personnel, the pediatrician can no more permit himself to become involved in trying to provide psychiatric services beyond his capacity than he would elect to undertake major surgical procedures.

In a training program he can be helped to understand that these limitations are neither the full responsibility of the community nor the full responsibility of the physician alone. The combination of factors must be individually evaluated, and it may prove true that in some instances his greatest contribution may be as a responsible citizen who is able to interpret the need for more children's services to responsible people in the community. This becomes an individual determination in relation to each issue as it arises.

It is further to be hoped that in his training program, when there is more time for self-contemplation and more people to aid in this, the student can achieve a degree of self-awareness which will permit him to recognize those instances where he is being driven by internal pressures. It is not too infrequent that under such circumstances one finds the physician utilizing his involvement in work as a defense itself. For example, one may find this flight into work functioning as a defense against intimacy in his own family relationships.

Such occasional problems can very frequently be spotted in a training program where it is quite clearly recognized that they are not issues of more training, or of a different kind of training, but must be resolved through psychotherapeutic help. In this regard, of all the training programs available, perhaps those in psychiatry and social work have most effectively incorporated the greatest concern for the internal comfort of the trainee. In psychiatry, the trainee is helped to gain insight into his professional role, in terms not only of the needs of the patient and the community but also of his own needs as part of his technical skill, and as an omnipresent variable always to be considered. In other fields we have left this largely to the intuition of the trainee with the resultant risks to himself, his patients, and his community responsibilities.

SUMMARY

It is our feeling that medicine as a career, because of the intimacy and the responsibility which are so much a part of its daily transactions, continually confronts the physician with extraordinarily severe tensions. These can be seen most clearly in the transitional periods as exemplified in the internship and the entry into practice. We feel that by taking cognizance of these problems, the medical student, intern, and resident can be far better equipped to resolve these struggles constructively than he is at present.

BIBLIOGRAPHY

Aring, C. D. (1958), Sympathy and Empathy. *J. Amer. Med. Assn.*, 167:448-452.
Christie, R. & Merton, R. (1957), *Procedures for the Sociological Study of the Values Climate in Medical Schools*. Fifth Teaching Institute, Amer. Assn. Med. Colleges, Atlantic City, N.J.
Richmond, J. B. & Lipton, E. L. (1961), Studies on Mental Health of Children with Specific Implications for Pediatricians. In: *Prevention of Mental Disorders in Children*, ed. G. Caplan. New York: Basic Books, pp. 95-121.
——— & Lustman, S. L. (1954), Total Health. *J. Med. Educ.*, 29:23-30.
——— & Waisman, H. (1955), Psychologic Aspects of Management of Children with Malignant Disease. *Amer. J. Dis. Child.*, 89:42-47.
Senn, M. J. E. (1948), The Psychotherapeutic Role of the Pediatrician. *Pediatrics*, 2:147-153.
——— (1951), The Contribution of Psychiatry to Child Health Services. *Amer. J. Orthopsychiat.*, 21:138-145.
——— (1957), The Changing Role of the Children's Hospital. *Canad. Med. Assn. J.*, 77:647-655.
Stanton, A. H. (1954), Psychiatric Theory and Institutional Context. *Psychiatry*, 17:19-27.
——— & Schwartz, M. S. (1954), *The Mental Hospital*. New York: Basic Books.
Solnit, A. J. & Green, M. D. (1959), Psychologic Considerations in the Management of Deaths on Pediatric Hospital Services. *Pediatrics*, 24:106-112.

Part VII

Education for Children, Parents, and Teachers

This last section deals with nonmedical education. Many of the areas of endeavor that are discussed in this section have occupied Milton Senn's attention and interest for many years. In "The Child's Estate," Eveline B. Omwake delineates the importance of teaching young children to play as an aid to cognitive development as well as for its contributions to physical and social development. G. M. H. Veeneklaas utilizes comparative observations to examine the scientific value of a day-care nursery program for children from a background in which there have been deficits of nurture, psychological and physical, in postwar Netherlands. Anna W. M. Wolf presents reflections about parent education stemming from her rich experience in this work. Her individual contributions to this field and her collaboration with Milton Senn in parent education enables Mrs. Wolf to provide a perspective for the future derived from past experiences and current trends. In "Child-Rearing Practices and Their Consequences," Julius B. Richmond and Bettye M. Caldwell critically assess child-rearing patterns and their influence on child development. They are judiciously skeptical of those deductions that are based on a narrow view of this crucial sector of child development. Seymour B. Sarason concludes this section with an appraisal of the public school teachers' opportunities to collaborate with members of the mental health professions in the daily work of educating children.

The Child's Estate

• *EVELINE B. OMWAKE, M.A.*

Yale University

The child's estate[1] refers to the "right to play," which I view as a natural phenomenon of childhood complete with the privileges and responsibilities, freedom and restrictions, pain and pleasures attached to all conditions of life. While this estate with all its rights and rites is shared by the adult world, it comes into the individual's possession in his infancy and is maintained largely through his own efforts.

PLAY AND LEARNING

Parents, teachers, pediatricians, child psychiatrists, and psychoanalysts learn to know the personality of a given child through a familiarity with his unique patterns of play as well as through other behavior revealing his adaptive and developmental capacities. The social scientist has gathered much of his knowledge of human growth and behavior and the inner workings of the child's mind through the intensive observation and study of children's activity in a play setting.

---

[1] This phrase is borrowed from the writings of St. Augustine.

Play has many aspects which have invited investigation: its contribution to psychosocial and physical development and mental health has been extensively explored; its effectiveness as a socializing experience, as an avenue for discharge, and as a catalyst of available energies has been well considered; and its possibilities for the development of motor skills and as a source of pleasure have been fully recognized (Biber, 1959; Peller, 1954; Greenacre, 1959; Erikson, 1950).

In this regard, it is also useful to consider the work of Piaget (1945) and his colleagues who have provided major theoretical formulations concerning the nature and order of cognitive thinking and the role of experience in learning. Their investigations into the nature of thought were pursued through intensive observations of children's play and conversation. They considered children's play to provide a suitable medium for the study of cognition because in play the learning activities were observable.

This paper will be concerned primarily with an assessment of the child's play behavior, his "estate," with particular attention to that aspect of play which pertains to mental activity. One can say that there is a potential for mental exercise inherent in the type of play which the young child creates for himself, and which is often referred to as free, spontaneous, self-initiated, or natural play.

For the purpose of this discussion I conceive of play as a perceptual-motor experience in a broad sense. Its affective and cognitive elements appear in crude form in the play of the very young child but gradually are refined to become the problem-solving activities and concepts later associated with more formal learning experiences. This refinement is achieved as the animate and inanimate objects in the environment assume a relatively constant meaning for the child and as he becomes able to use the symbolic communications and abstract ideas that are used to influence him and the conduct of those around him.

As such processes and capacities develop form and substance the child tests his knowledge of them in play situations. For instance, the toddler might spit and scratch in imitation of the cat who demonstrated feline defense measures in response to the child's inept approach. A similar example would be the slightly older child who, having been told that the cat scratched because it was feeling playful, offered as an explanation when she herself was reprimanded for scratching that she was "feeling playful." Another incident of a child expressing and attempting to understand a perplexing experience through play is that of a three-year-old boy who had been examined in the emergency room of a hospital and had overheard that he might be sent "up to X-ray." This procedure was neither explained nor carried out, and a few days later he played raising and lowering a doll by rope and pulley, taking it "up to X-ray." In this instance the word "up" had meaning for him, which "X-ray" obviously had not. This play also served to aid the child in his efforts to master the anxiety he experienced as a result of his accident and visit to the emergency room.

The four-year-old housekeeper turns on the bathroom faucet to effect the sound of running water in another part of the house as she works in the doll corner kitchen announcing, "I'm making coffee while my bath is running." Later she cautions her playmates, "If you wake the baby you'll get a spanking." Through such acts of play children reveal the extent and limits of their knowledge, communicate their capacity for testing it on home ground, and gain a measure of relief from the anxious feelings aroused by the original experience. The relief is achieved through mental activity in play that can lead to an intellectual mastery as well as to the discharge of feelings necessary for the mastery of intense and threatening feelings.

For emphasis, at the expense of repetition, play of this nature provides a proving ground for the development and gradual refinement of the full range of emerging ego functions. These include language, motor skills, memory, concept formation, reality testing, control of impulse, and secondary-process thinking. In terms of the mental exercise involved in play, its important components include the child's curiosity, his use of language, perception and use of his own body, self-initiated activity, and imitation of peers and adults. These are observable in play as early as the second year of life and can be viewed as forerunners of ego functions that become operable in the later years of childhood.

The achievement of body mastery is particularly useful as an illustration of this concept. In the self-initiated play of the two- to four-year-old child, problems in body control and adaptation are constantly being presented. In the process of exploring his surroundings the child is faced with many difficult tasks. He must maintain his balance on a variety of surfaces: smooth floors, rough gravel, soft snow, wet grass, ice, etc. Throughout his day he is faced with problems of adapting his movements to obstructions and movable objects in the home and yard such as doors, stairs, furniture, climbing apparatus, swings, and tricycles. These activities require the practice and application of essential motor skills such as reaching, pulling, throwing, lifting, and carrying articles of varying weight, size, shape, volume, texture, and consistency. Thus, body mastery is linked to the comprehension of space, size, form, and texture. Additionally, in play the child will manipulate fasteners, containers, implements, and mechanical devices in his toys. Through trial and error and imitation of his peers and elders he gains the control over his body necessary to continue with his explorations into the environment, and at the same time these physical activities facilitate the development of mental representations of space, form, texture, and depth perception. These mental exercises are among the earliest experiences necessary for the development of the later intellectual capacities involved in forming and utilizing the symbolic representations essential for reading, arithmetic, and geography. When Piaget (1936) speaks of a sensorimotor intelligence, he implies a similar explanation of these mental phenomena.

Eventually the child's explorations extend beyond the home. Several years later, in elementary and junior high school, the problems imposed by the curriculum will require the child to use his experience and knowledge of space, shape, size, weight, etc., in acquiring concepts that relate to physical laws in the study of biology, mathematics, geology, etc. Thus one can say that the child's early experiences in self-mastery through play are largely perceptual and motor. Through the mental exercises involved in these sensorimotor activities the child develops the later intellectual capacities involved in forming and utilizing the symbolic representations necessary for reading, writing, arithmetic, and geography. These symbolic representations are later elaborated, differentiated, and synthesized into conceptual thinking and communication. Conceptual thinking represents a more efficient way of exploring the environment and of using the trial-action functions of thought which earlier were present in rudimentary form in the young child's play.

With the above considerations of play in mind, the discussion will continue with the assessment of the "estate."

PLAY IN EARLY YEARS OF CHILDHOOD

By the time a child enters the primary school a major portion of his time has been devoted to a variety of play activities. His experiences may have been limited to informal contacts at home and in the neighborhood or extended to include nursery school.

Spontaneous play by younger children is universal wherever children happen to be. It can develop in an empty basement, city dump, elaborately furnished living room, expensively landscaped lawn, or a nursery school especially arranged and equipped to invite and promote play. A unique feature of such spontaneous play is the subtle, frequently nonverbal, communication among the players as to the theme, the assignment of roles, and the rules. While an adult may be needed as a stagehand, prompter, audience, or to make certain the cues are understood, the inspiration and ideas come from the children's own interests and experiences. Another characteristic of such play is the children's ability to endow whatever is at hand with the features and functions of the thing they want it to represent. For instance, the dirt and water may be combined to make "coffee," "cakes," "atom bombs," or "castles"; the stick may become a gun, the chair a train, the rope a lariat, the hillside a fort, or the woods a jungle.

Although the organized setting of the nursery school provides opportunities for spontaneous play, its curriculum also features structured play suited to the educational needs of young children. These structured play activities are especially planned and presented with regard to the developmental capacities, interests, and experiences of a group of children. At the same time such planning depends upon attention to the differing developmental rates of the individual children.

The two forms of play can be differentiated by the degree and nature of adult participation. In the structured form teachers decide the time and place and provide the materials to be used, establishing appropriate limits for their use. Activities of this nature include music and art experiences, stories, woodworking, science projects, block building, puzzles, games, and any activity which depends upon particular materials or equipment and takes its leadership from the adult. It should be added that while music and art invite spontaneity and are considered to be creative activities, they are usually adult structured to a greater degree than spontaneous play either in the nursery school or at home.

The nursery school can be a more effective setting than the home or neighborhood for the development of play skill as part of the child's education. In the context of this paper it is important to point out that the essential features of a healthful, challenging play environment as present in the sound nursery school include space, equipment, continuity in play relationships, and supervision which considers the children's learning as well as their safety and pleasure. Supervision which is designed to help the child establish effective modes of appropriate learning over a period of time complements the curriculum specific to the nursery school. The nursery school's curriculum, setting, and supervision cannot be duplicated in the informal setting of the home or neighborhood.

It is important to stress in this connection that nursery school teachers are the professional individuals in the lives of children who are most concerned with play as a learning experience. "Educational" supervision is an art which requires that the adult know when and how to make suggestions; when to take decisive action, and when to let the children's own experience become the teacher. It involves knowing what is going on, clarifying misconceptions, adding relevant information when indicated, and assisting children to resolve the frequent natural conflicts of social play. The nursery school teacher encourages children to listen and talk, supporting their appropriate offensive or defensive action, and helps them to understand one another's behavior and intentions. Knowledge of children and play and pedagogical techniques are as important in the teaching of play skills as in the teaching of reading skills.

The teacher's judgment is based upon knowledge drawn from various sources. One must be well versed in basic concepts of growth and development. An awareness of the child's readiness and motivation to advance in independence and competence is essential. In addition, familiarity with the child's home experience is necessary in order to know when his behavior reflects affectively charged events at home. A knowledge of the properties and functions of a wide variety of play materials is necessary in order to provide an appropriate balance of the materials which invite the child's own fantasy (e.g., mud, old box, piece of rope, etc.) and those materials which direct the play action as well as to suggest the play theme (e.g., commercial toy) to the child.

Many of the commercial products frequently advertised as "educational" are well designed to add challenge and content to play and serve as an important means of nourishing children's natural interest in learning and mastery. The imagination as well as the vested interests of toy manufacturers have burgeoned under the pressure to provide children with toys that teach. This pressure derives from concern about whether children are being exposed to an appropriate degree of intellectual challenge. Such concern also has led zealous adults to exert pressure on teachers to increase the formal learning experiences in the school day at the expense of scheduled play periods. Even the nursery schools are vulnerable to the influence of such pressures. This is evidenced by the fact that some nursery schools are being asked to include the teaching of reading, numbers, and languages in a curriculum already rich with play, science, art, music, and other activities appropriate to the developmental capacities of the age group.

It is interesting to observe that in many schools play is looked upon as a pastime activity offering relief from learning rather than as a stimulus to it and as a natural field for its advancement. It is important to realize that the play periods in the primary school, now scheduled under the guise of recess or recreation, could be usefully exploited for their learning possibilities if they were given the amount of careful study, planning and supervision available for the teaching of academic subjects.

The concept that play in itself is educational can be best demonstrated by further reference to the nursery school. In the early days of the nursery school movement such phrases as good play environment, appropriate play experiences, free play, dramatic play, group play, parallel and solitary play, social play, quiet play, play materials, etc., comprised much of the nursery school teacher's professional vocabulary. An examination of these terms in action makes it apparent that teachers in referring to these functions of play were including those that served the child's intellectual development as well as his social and emotional development.

Play created and initiated by the children often forms a natural background for the other more organized educational activities introduced by the teacher. In the sound nursery school, children are free to leave the ongoing play to engage in painting, clay, dancing, puzzles, looking at books, etc. Sometimes the movement is in response to their own inclination to do so, sometimes in response to the teacher's signal. It is not unusual then for a child to return later to take up his former position in the group play, adapting to the changes which have occurred in the period of absence. This sequence of play-learning is determined by each child's characteristic ways of learning as well as by the developing importance of the group's impact on the individual child. Such flexibility is crucial for an optimal educational experience in three- and four-year-old children, since their physical, intellectual, and emotional functioning is not sufficiently mature to yield profitably to the demands of a less flexible, more formal educational plan. True, many children will comply with a more formal or structured curriculum, but it may be at the expense of inhibiting their curiosity and initiative. Stirred by their curiosity and initiative, they reach out for knowledge with an investment that permits learning to be associated with pleasure and increased self-confidence. It is my conviction that a well-balanced nursery school curriculum does not permit the "scheduling" of a child's curiosity and initiative.

NURSERY SCHOOL PLAY OBSERVATIONS AND DISCUSSION

To the trained observer, play initiated and conducted by children often has a logical structure and a sensible theme that is used by each child in accordance with his readiness to learn new knowledge and skills. An example of play demonstrating the changing use of the same material was observed in a group of four-year-old children who began one September to build a tunnel-like structure from hollow blocks. As the months progressed the same group of children continued daily to erect buildings of this nature in order to play "housekeeping," "hiding out," "evacuating people in case of fallout," "tunneling under the river or superhighways to permit traffic flow" or secretly preparing for "blast offs." The block structure always looked more or less the same, but different children could enter, contribute their bit, and stay or leave.

The next example of ability to learn important concepts through play is as significant for its simplicity as the above is for its complexity. A three-year-old girl said to two teachers as she rolled her ball to them, "We're playing sharing." Another three-year-old in the process of dealing with the same concept aptly stated one view of the sharing process when she peremptorily told her friends, "We have to share, give it to me." These and many other nursery school play sequences that are emotionally significant are also experiences that involve rudimentary reasoning, i.e., a type of mental exercise involving the opportunity for recognizing and adapting simultaneously to the child's impulses and the social reality. This also involves the development of motor and language skills and the use of various modalities of communication that children employ to express their ideas and fantasies.

The striking importance of imitation in the child's learning, especially from peers, is demonstrated in the readiness with which children of this age borrow and elaborate one another's ideas for play, copy techniques for adapting equipment to suit their purposes, and learn from one another how to solve puzzles, do acrobatics, and play games. The first imitative behavior can be perceived when infants learn to play "clap hands," "peek-a-boo" or to wave "bye-bye." This same mode of learning is elaborated by the older child when he picks up clues from his classmates as to how to perfect his technique on the playing and athletic field and in his intellectual exercises in the classroom. Interestingly enough, a unique and refreshing quality of the "teacher-pupil" relationship which exists among children in the nursery school is the generosity with which they share their skills and discoveries.

Ideas, knowledge, and new skills are common property, whereas many problems arise over the sharing of toys and adult attention. Although the child's pleasure in having produced an original idea or mastered a new skill is experienced as increased competence, he is also gratified when others use the idea and imitate him in acquiring a new skill. In the child's world no one demands a copyright for authorship, a patent for invention, and plagiarism carries no penalty. It becomes clear that the child experiences considerable conflict over sharing or giving up things which come to him from outside himself—the toys and loving attention—but generously offers to others the intangible "gifts" which come from inside himself. Thus it appears that there is a minimum of conflict in learning knowledge and skills from peers in a nursery school setting, and for this reason cognitive development can be easily facilitated in the play curriculum of a nursery school. The satisfying expression and communication of ideas, fantasies, and information to classmates through self-initiated play indicate that such experiences can be viewed also as forerunners of later sublimated activities.

PLAY AS A DIAGNOSTIC AID

Since play reflects mental activity, it can serve also as an important aid to either an educational or psychological diagnosis of the child's difficulty. This report emphasizes consideration of play activity observations as an aid to the understanding of early learning difficulties.

In nursery school and kindergarten there are some children who spend a major part of the day in individual activities such as puzzles, painting, etc., and are rarely seen to be involved with other children. Whether this is viewed as preference for structured activity or avoidance of the unstructured spontaneous group play depends upon many factors. When such play activity is explored it frequently appears that the child found the simple individual task easier than the hard work of learning and playing with the group. While there need be no question as to the intellectual challenge of puzzles, problem-solving games, and other such acceptable solo activities, it is false to assume that the child who regularly prefers them is primarily seeking challenge for his intellectual powers. In fact, children often involve themselves in such activity as a protection against their fear of interaction with children. Our experience indicates that it is easier to teach a socially active child to engage in individual tasks than it is to teach an isolated child to participate in group activity.

There are other children who are socially active but whose participation in group activity is consistently destructive to themselves and the situation because of their hyperaggressive, hostile, or literally disorganizing behavior. Although many factors in the nursery school environment can facilitate or minimize such behavior, the problem usually arises because such children are, among other things, indicating that they have a learning problem, i.e., an obstacle to their cognitive development that may be initiated by a psychological disturbance or a neurological deficit. Such children lack the controls, tolerance, discrimination, language, knowledge, and ideas necessary to maintain a place in group play.

It is a general observation of our teachers that play which is meager and bizarre is usually a clue to a problem in intellectual functioning. Sometimes there are signs of good endowment despite a limited performance as illustrated by the child who can complete complicated puzzles and match all the pictures in a card-matching game (structured problem-solving activities), but who cannot establish relationships with other children. Such a child usually avoids spontaneous group play, does not paint, block build, or participate in dramatic play.

The following examples illustrate problems of a more serious character as revealed in the observations of a child's play activity. A four-year-old girl in a visit to the school preliminary to enrollment spent the entire half hour in fumbling attempts to remove from a doll a dress with simple snap fasteners. The teacher first undressed and redressed the doll for the child, then showed her how to pull the snaps apart. No other activity interested the little girl, and after repeated demonstrations she was still trying unsuccessfully to undress the doll. She could learn neither by imitation nor by trial and error, and was lacking the problem-solving capacity for such a task that one expects to see in a child her age. The failure to respond to the other attractive toys, the inability to master the single act of undressing the doll, the absence of any verbal communication from this four-year-old girl suggested a learning deficiency. When the family's physician was consulted, he replied, "She's very shy and slow when I see her, and I have never had a chance to observe her play. I recommended nursery school because her mother says the child depends on her for everything, including use of toys." Her mother commented that the child had always been very dependent, and she thought that her poor speech and play were due to lack of contact with children. This child was obviously functioning at a retarded level. She was enrolled in nursery school in order to gain a more accurate picture of her functioning and with provisions for special help from the teachers to enable her to learn how to play and how to master certain simple tasks. The pediatrician kept in close touch with the teacher around the girl's progress and later referred her for psychological study and evaluation when nursery school observations clarified the nature of her difficulties.

In attempting an educational evaluation, the teacher will also observe in the child's play other aspects of ego development, especially when there is a major deviation. A two-and-a-half-year-old boy's mother described him as very active, "into everything," and aggressive toward other children. In his preliminary visit to the nursery school he ignored the teacher, raced around the room brushing the shelves clear of cars, animals, and blocks, tossing all loose toys in the air, and finally settled down to spin the saucers from a tea set oblivious to his mother's urging to "see the nice train, ball, blocks, etc." His mother added, "He plays that way all the time; sometimes I wonder if he's normal." The teacher, noting the absence of language, the poor quality of his relationship, and the disorganized play, encouraged the family to seek developmental and psychiatric consultation because of their son's atypical development. As one result of the clinical evaluation, it was recommended that the nursery school teacher work with the boy individually in an effort to teach him how to play and speak, and also to contribute observations to the study of this atypical child's developmental needs.

PLAY SUPERVISION IN THE PREVENTION OF LEARNING PROBLEMS

In view of the fact that major deficits and normal problems in development regularly come to light in the way a child plays, the nursery school presents a source of potential strength in the battle against learning problems. Not only is there the opportunity for early recognition but also the availability of special attention to the problem before it becomes elaborated. A useful type of assistance for very young children with deficits in communication, in forming personal relationships, and in problem-solving activities appropriate to their age is "play tutoring" or "remedial play teaching." In this educational experience the teacher offers individual help to children whose play reveals a learning problem. It is fruitful to make direct connections between play problems and school learning problems, because it appears that many of the roots of the later learning problem can be discerned and remedied early in the play-learning situation. Qualified teachers who are aware of the child's poor cognitive functioning in early play behavior are in a strategic position to show him more appropriate techniques and help him develop skills that may enable him to resume a progressive development in learning via play.

One example of remedial tutoring could be seen in the four-year-old child whose neuromuscular development was within the normal range but who was conspicuous in a group of physically skillful children because of his general clumsiness. Peter's clumsiness was due to a distorted or underdeveloped body image.[2] He knocked over the chair as he tried to sit in it, regularly dropped the load he carried, fumbled with blocks, and was poor at climbing, bicycle riding, jumping, etc. Ordinarily the response to clumsiness is one of sympathy or anger depending on whether it inconveniences the child himself or other people, and he feels accepted or rejected accordingly. Peter benefited significantly from consistent, specific teaching as to how to manage his hands and feet and how to use his eyes to help himself. In this sense the educator's understanding of the child's perceptual-motor difficulties, including his inexperience in relating his body to the environment, enabled her to teach him ways of mastering these difficulties.

The teacher's encouragement to work out a problem rather than to leave a play situation because it is difficult is another type of help available to the child in the nursery school. The presence of so many inviting activities in the nursery school requires the teacher to keep in mind the children who always appear busy without completing anything because they can move from one thing to another at will. The observant adult notices at what point a child moves away from a dilemma in search of a fresh project. Many times she can help him to examine his problem and modify his behavior or approach so that he can bring what he started to a successful finish. This happens in helping a child find the clue to complete a difficult puzzle rather than to push it aside to begin a fresh one. In the case of a crowd of little girls all wanting to be the mommy, one could suggest to the outmember that she could be an aunt, visitor, or cleaning lady if she would like to play with her friends rather than to sulk on the sidelines. In brief, this is a matter of helping children finish what they start and gain experience in understanding the nature of, as well as finding a solution for, the problems they meet in play. Although such learning is essential for the development of later work capacities, the child regularly indicates in his own way

---

[2] The causes of such clumsiness are many and multiple. It is beyond the scope of this paper to consider the comprehensive diagnostic evaluation and therapeutic planning that such children require.

the importance of such education by a look of relief and pleasure on achieving mastery of a task which he had almost failed.

One bright four-and-a-half-year-old boy regularly appeared to "borrow" his pleasure by briefly joining a group, provoking noise and excitement by jumping and shrieking, and then moving on to another crowd to arouse a similar response. He never stayed beyond the point where a child would react angrily to the interruption. Then he would shout, "Good-bye, you guys." Occasionally he would kick down a building or charge into some other child with his tricycle, but he never contributed ideas or labor to the other boys' play projects. One day he complained that the other children made him unhappy. His teacher, who had decided that the child's relationship to her was "solid," questioned this explanation of his behavior. She informed her student that she would help him with some play of his own, pointing out that he had some good ideas but never did anything in play with others except to jump and shout. She insisted that he complete a block building which he did much to his own delight. For several days she insisted that he choose some activity and stay with it until he had accomplished something. Her "insistence" involved standing next to him to invest the activity and to prevent his slipping away or intercepting his invitation to other children to come finish his work for him. He became a better worker at school and began to elaborate the social aspects of his learning experience.

In another instance a four-year-old girl had been observed repeatedly to speed up the final steps of every project as soon as the end was in sight. She always completed what she began but kept an eye on others to make certain she would finish first. In her hurry she became careless, spoiling her own pictures with spilled paint, colliding with equipment as she rode, falling off her bicycle because she watched the other children instead of her surroundings, or spilling water as she served "coffee" too hurriedly. Speculating about future problems in written examinations in which this intelligent little girl might suffer disappointment when she discovered that unnecessary errors contributed to a lowered grade, her teacher began to keep an eye on her progress. As the student worked puzzles, kept house, and painted pictures the teacher moved near her toward the end of a particular task to encourage her to value her product more than her impulse to "beat the other children," which usually ended with a self-defeat. In such a case the structured nature of games and puzzles which must be done in a certain way to be "finished" proved a useful means of slowing her down. The child responded well to such efforts with an improvement in self-esteem and a more realistic sense of her own competence. These advances in her education were accompanied by a lessening of the pressure to compete both with siblings at home and playmates at school.

In both of the above illustrations the teacher's work with the parents helped them to understand in what ways they could modify the home environment and their own expectations in order to facilitate the child's mastery of the problems I have focused upon.

PLAY AND PLEASURE

The serious side of play has been the aspect most fully developed in this presentation because of the trend in educational thought to attach less rather than more significance to its importance and usefulness in learning and intellectual development. In the light of my emphasis on the educational value of play it is important to point out that I also attach high value to the experiences more readily recognized as educational—reading, writing, and number-readiness activities. It is a confirmation of these values of later learning to share the excitement and delight of a child when he has printed his first word, read his first primer, learned to tell time by the clock, or discovered the world of industry and travel in the social studies program. However, the child's pride and pleasure in that kind of mastery are ordinarily expressed to adults and older siblings rather than to his agemates. This suggests that an important element in his feeling of satisfaction lies in having earned adult approval on the adult's terms. To the close observer the expression of pleasure which accompanies the mastery of a difficult task appears as frequently and genuinely in the hard work of play as in the hard work of formal learning. The "Look what I did!" shout of the young block builder when his high-towered structure stands on its own and the satisfied look on the face of a boy or girl actively playing astronaut express a quality of self-appreciation comparable to that experienced when he or she announces, "See how I write my name," proudly waves a perfect spelling paper, or participates in a school assembly program. In the children's vernacular it is entirely logical to announce with pride and exuberance, "We're working," to adults who consider them to be at play.

It is well to keep in mind that the play of childhood, while essentially serious, is also gay, exuberant, amusing, and delightfully entertaining both to the child cast and the adult audience.

Healthy children voluntarily attack play with the same full measure of seriousness, effort, and pleasure that they are expected to apply to other types of learning experiences which have been invested for them by their parents and teachers. One could say they play and work this way for the fun of it.[3] It is this implicit feature of the play experience—the pleasure in the *work* of play with its constant demands on the child's equipment for learning—that suggests that it be looked upon as an "estate" rich in resources for his future gain.

SUMMARY

Play experiences are important in the intellectual development of young children. In this paper two forms of play are discussed: the self-initiated or unstructured form which can develop wherever children happen to be; and the structured or adult-prescribed activity which occurs in situations where teachers participate in the initiation and direction of the play, game, or activity. The nursery school provides an appropriate balance of the two forms of play and includes professional educational supervision for both types of play ordinarily not available to children in the home or neighborhood. The natural play of childhood is seen as a suitable medium for the promotion of ego development, especially of those functions essential for cognitive growth. Observations of children at play are of value to educators

3 In the preparation of this paper I have become freshly aware of the many uses, meanings, and forms of the word *play*. At various points it has been tempting to "play" on the word facetiously. However, I have resisted such "playfulness" to protect the children's rights to make fun of play in their own way.

as well as other professional specialists as an aid to the assessment of learning difficulties. Such observations also are useful as a basis for providing play-tutoring designed to help the young child with early learning problems. Illustrative vignettes are presented.

Children's attitudes toward self-initiated, unstructured play are seen to differ from those of adults, in that children view it as a major effort or work and derive their pleasure from the mastery as well as the creativity it represents. Adults may erroneously consider play of this sort as requiring less mental activity than the imposed intellectual task.

BIBLIOGRAPHY

Biber, B. (1959), Play As a Growth Process. *69 Bank Street Publications No. 4.* New York: Bank Street College of Education.
Erikson, E. H. (1950), *Childhood and Society.* New York: Norton.
Greenacre, P. (1959), Play in Relation to Creative Imagination. *The Psychoanalytic Study of the Child,* 14:61-80. New York: Int. Univ. Press.
Peller, L. E. (1954), Libidinal Phases, Ego Development, and Play. *The Psychoanalytic Study of the Child,* 9:178-198. New York: Int. Univ. Press.
Piaget, J. (1936), *The Origin of Intelligence in Children.* New York: Int. Univ. Press, 1952.
———— (1945), *Play, Dream and Imitation in Childhood.* New York: Norton, 1951.
St. Augustine, *The Confessions of St. Augustine,* Book 1. Translation John K. Ryan. New York: Image Books (Doubleday), 1960, p. 62.

Aspects of Group Rearing in a Day Nursery 1945-1960

• *HENK VEENEKLAAS, M.D.*

University of Leiden

HISTORICAL DEVELOPMENT

Geography and Demography of the City of Leiden

The Netherlands occupy a delta in northwest Europe formed by three rivers, the Rhine, the Maas, and the Scheldt. The surface of this delta measures approximately 12,500 square miles, and on it live 12 million people, an over-all density of almost 1,000 per square mile. The population density in the western part of the country, which lies for the most part below sea level, is 5,000 per square mile. Here the three cities of Amsterdam, Rotterdam, and The Hague are situated about 30 to 50 miles apart, with populations of between 750,000 and a million. Between these cities lies Leiden with 100,000 inhabitants.

The lowness of the country and the cheapness of water transportation led, centuries ago, to the construction of waterways corresponding to the routes of the overland roads. In the cities, too, canals were cut along the streets. Slow growth and an urge to preserve the past have left the western part of The Netherlands with many canals and very old houses. The largest of these canals are still used for shipping. The mansions along the canals of Amsterdam have become offices; the small houses in Leiden offer living conditions which have long been outmoded.

A large proportion of the population of Leiden has been employed in the textile industry since its establishment in the twelfth century. This industry has had periods of decline during which the population suffered great poverty. Those with the least energy remained in Leiden, and now form a residue of not very vital, somewhat acquiescent individuals, who are not particularly interested in the possibilities that life has to offer. Although the economic situation has improved in recent years, this has not yet shown much appreciable effect on the mentality of the population. This is one side of Leiden.

The other side is completely different. During the war which won independence from Spain (1568-1648) Leiden resisted a prolonged siege, in recognition of which William of Orange, the forerunner of the ruling royal family, offered the city in reward the choice between a university and freedom from taxes. The city chose the university, which made the University of Leiden the oldest in The Netherlands. It has played a significant role in many aspects of science through the centuries and has a commensurate reputation. Over the centuries the townspeople and the University have lived in a rather distant symbiosis in which the students, who rent rooms from the townspeople and attended lectures at the University, form the *trait d'union*.

The Day Nursery

These two aspects of Leiden are to be found reflected in the history of the development of the children's day nursery. The children are the products of the city; the University Pediatric Department takes an important part in establishing policy.

Before the Second World War there were two day nurseries elsewhere in The Netherlands. They collected fifty to sixty preschool children in the morning, fed and bathed them, and kept them busy indoors and out on five of the seven days of the week. In the evening the children returned to their own homes. The children were recruited primarily from the group of children whose physical condition was inadequate: weight too low, hemoglobin too low, prolonged convalescence.

At the end of the War, day nurseries were established in other cities to cope with the very real physical deficiencies among the preschool population. Some of these are still in existence.

This was also the way in which the day nursery in Leiden came into being. It was called Margriet, after the third daughter of the royal family. At the time at which it was started, however, there was no one here who knew much about such an institution. In addition, the country had just been liberated from a five-year occupation which had spared neither country nor people, so that exhaustion and deprivation were general, and everyone had their hands full caring for themselves. This was also true of the authorities responsible for supplying the necessary funds who, through unfamiliarity with day nurseries, naturally could not see immediately what the purpose of a day nursery could be. A committee of townspeople was formed, and the Provincial Association for the Promotion of Child Hygiene requested the Provincial pediatrician, Dr. Boekhold, to provide the medical direction of the nursery.

This day nursery has now been running for more than fifteen years. Its function has been adapted over the years to the demands of the changing society in which it finds itself. I will describe the various facets of this function, and then follow the course of the principal phases in its development.

FACETS OF THE FUNCTION OF THE DAY NURSERY

These are embodied in persons and authorities and can be divided into an external and an internal climate. It must be stressed here that for the sake of clarity persons and authorities are placed in the foreground because they exert such an influence from their key positions. Naturally, their functions and interrelations which are described briefly are even more important to what goes on in Margriet. Even though it is the internal climate which interests us most, it must not be forgotten that the internal climate is totally dependent upon a well-functioning external climate. To the external climate belong: (1) supervisory authority (national government); (2) subsidizing authority (national government, province, municipality); (3) suppliers of goods and services; (4) referring physicians. To the internal climate I assign: (1) board; (2) key figures; (3) staff and personnel—working conditions; (4) parents—living conditions; (5) children.

External Climate

Supervisory Authority. The supervisory authority is the Chief Medical Inspector of Public Health, who delegates his task to the Inspector of the Province of South Holland in which Leiden is situated. He is aware of the daily procedure of the nursery and of any important changes made. In the event of the occurrence of certain infectious diseases he must be notified. The inspector visits the house once a year.

Subsidizing Authorities. For the subsidizing authorities, Margriet is a small institution, and for them economical management was in former years the primary requisite. The relation with the state and the province is administrative. That with the municipality has a more active character because Margriet is a living part of the Leiden community. In addition, the municipality is interested further because Margriet provides its children and parents with curative and protective care. Subsidizing authorities become used to and learn to take into account the future economic significance of preventive work which costs money currently. A disturbed preschool child costs the community less than a disturbed adult. The threat which disturbed preschool behavior represents to the development of normal adult life can be made clear to the municipal authorities by the Board. This provides grounds for what is a reasonable subsidy by municipal standards and at the same time demonstrates the importance of the Board.

Suppliers of Goods and Services. Firms which occasionally supply goods or services and firms which do so regularly cooperate by charging cost prices and by giving other reductions. This is prompted by a sense of guilt which is compensated by taking a share in the care of weak and unhappy children and also by an awareness that good will is not to be underestimated.

Referring Physicians. The general practitioners of Leiden request placement of a child in Margriet when they are fed up with that child. The indication is nearly always a chronic complaint which has developed under the existing conditions and which will not disappear quickly. The physician cannot change the living conditions and the parents' attitude rapidly. His advice and their capacities often do not reach far enough. Together they attempt to escape the tension which has developed by placement of the child outside the home during the day under trained supervision. This change has many advantages. The tie with the home is maintained at night, the period out of the twenty-four hours which puts the least demands on the parents. Parents and physician relax as a result of the absence of the child; the daily circumstances which led to the disturbance have been removed. The stay in Margriet does not have the character of a measure which must give rapid results, and can be extended to one or even two years.

Internal Climate

Board. On the Board are represented the most important socioeconomic and religious groups among the townspeople. A working committee of board members carries the responsibility for over-all planning, organization, and execution.

Key Figures. The most important of the key figures is the pediatrician, Dr. Boekhold, who works several hours daily in Margriet and observes the whole organization, the children, the staff, and the mothers, and who also gauges the interpersonal relations. Most of the initiative originates with him.

In our case, the medical director can devote only part of his time to Margriet, which makes two other key figures essential to the organization. For smooth functioning within the house, a matron with insight and understanding of the problems is indispensable. Outside the house, the assistance of an authority in the field of psychosocial pediatrics, in this case the professor of pediatrics, is of substantial value. Collaboration with the University began in 1952.

Staff. The pediatrician is the part-time medical director. There is a full-time matron and household personnel of whom one is in charge. There are twelve children's nurses, about twenty years of age, eight with an education consisting of one to two years of home economics school, and four nurses with one to two years of formal training in child rearing. They are under the expert guidance of one highly trained person of broad background and experience. There is one man who spends half time on the business administration and one other man, also half time, for maintenance, both retired men who serve as grandfathers for the children.

The director, the matron, and the supervising expert observe and guide the nurses; they form the staff. The nurses observe and supervise the children. Their task is executive. One of the main characteristics of their work is that they have learned to have a non-directive attitude toward the children. They must be able to notice when a child needs support and to give that support appropriately.

Regarding the working situation in Margriet, the building is a very large old house with many rooms, halls, and staircases, and with a large garden. In- and out-of-doors there is ample space for fifty to sixty children and the twenty adults who care for them. This space can be used in different ways as will be described presently.

Parents. The majority of the parents who send their children to Margriet belong for the most part to the second-weakest socioeconomic layer of the population. From the weakest layer no children are admitted to Margriet; such children and their parents cannot benefit from the work done by Margriet, and require another kind of support.

The mothers leave their children in Margriet from nine to five o'clock, five days a week, for a year on the average. The mothers develop ambivalent feelings toward Margriet, of which they are usually unconscious and which they therefore cannot control or correct. Besides gratitude for the relaxation which the absence of the child brings about at home and for the improvement in health and behavior in their child during its stay in Margriet, there is resentment and jealousy on the part of the mothers because their children are cared for by other people who can and actually do make a better job of it than they themselves did. In this confusion of feelings the modest payment which is required from them creates a certain counterbalance. It provides a feeling of: I pay and thus I, too, have some weight and value.

In all cases it is indispensable to have to a large extent the co-operation of the parents in the admission, so that their positive feelings outweigh their negative ones. A child cannot relax sufficiently to profit from a new milieu if that milieu does not have the parents' substantial approval. The medical director and matron evaluate the parents' attitude carefully before admission.

The parents themselves have almost all had a difficult youth. They grew up under conditions of poverty; there was seldom harmony between their parents—a father often unemployed, a mother careworn; there was little or no cultural development; schooling was brief; and they began to work very young. Almost without exception, the parents married early and could find only a small house which was often hardly livable, difficult to heat, and with too little space for living, moving about, and sleeping. Their earnings are low; they are not accustomed to harmony and do not know how to create it. The father is sometimes unemployed; they have children young and know nothing or very little about them. They do not know what kind of food a child needs, or what kind of affection, what forms its development will take, and what sort of directive training it has need of. In the course of a few years there develops in both parents a more or less apathetic attitude toward the way life is going. By a combination of their own inadequacies or inadequate insight and their inescapable living conditions, especially as the number of their children increases, they become extremely vulnerable. When a disturbance then occurs in one of the children, they reach an impasse and give signs, through the repeated requests for advice from their family doctor, of their readiness to be helped.

Housing conditions in the old, central part of Leiden can be improved only slowly. There are two important reasons for this: the city has limited means, and it requires lengthy deliberation before a decision is taken to eliminate irrevocably those remnants of earlier centuries for which a certain attachment has grown. As a result, there are quite a few streets and canals lined with small, decaying old houses which are in themselves a source of continuous irritation. But, in addition, the width of the street between the house and the exposed water of the canal is often less than seven feet, so that outdoors, too, there is no adequately large and safe place for the children to play. This intensifies the irritating situation.

Children. During the first years after World War II the material deprivation experienced by the children found expression in underweight, low hemoglobin, and protracted convalescence. Such cases have become rare. Indications for admission gradually changed; at present we admit mostly children who are unable to adjust to the demands of the adult world, and who therefore show one or more deviations in such behavior patterns as sleeping, moving, playing, talking, eating, bowel movement, and micturition. These children also have been subject, often in addition to a lack of physical care, to a lack of affection and proper rearing, as well as a lack of physical possibilities for playing during the day and resting up at night.

Such children and their parents go through a period of adjustment lasting from the first weeks to the first months that the children spend in Margriet. This finds expression in the characteristics and interrelationships of the behavioral functions listed above. It can, for example, be repeatedly seen that a child during the first months rocks for long periods each day, or that it will take several months before he will succeed in moving his bowels daily in Margriet.

PHASES OF DEVELOPMENT, 1945-1960

Attention must now be given to the developmental phases through which Margriet has passed in fifteen years. Taken broadly, three phases can be distinguished, each of approximately five years' duration.

First Phase, 1945-1950

In the first phase, 1945-1950, the children came with long-standing physical symptoms caused by deprivation. Treatment consisted of making up for these deficiencies. Good, varied food, adequate rest, and regular living formed the regimen. In response, body weight, hemoglobin, and vitality increased, and the results could be measured easily. This made the work satisfying to the personnel. The staff was satisfied; the Board found their work good. The general practitioners of Leiden saw some point in placing a child in Margriet.

In this period, the children were cared for in groups of eighteen with three nurses in one room. For bathing and sleeping they were taken care of by two other nurses, so that in the course of a day the children came into contact with five adults. The pattern of daytime activity and the presence of the adults are shown on the left in Figures 1 and 2.

LIVING AND WORKING SITUATION IN MARGRIET

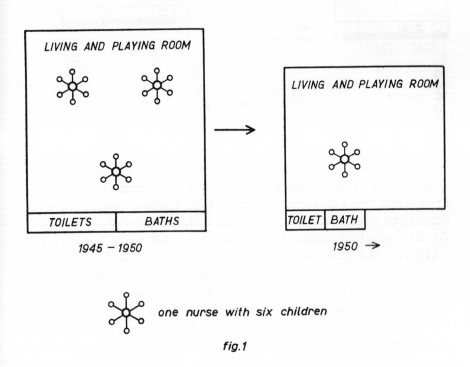

fig.1

SCHEME OF CHILDREN' AND NURSES' DAY-ACTIVITIES IN MARGRIET

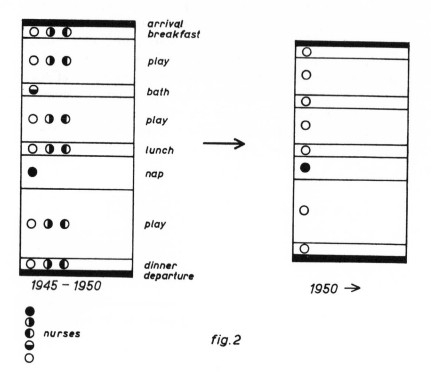

fig.2

Second Phase, 1950-1955

After several years, general economic improvement considerably diminished the number of children with physical symptoms, and admissions were primarily of children with problems of adjustment. At this point the system of care showed itself to be inadequate. Analysis of the situation showed that the most unsatisfactory aspects were a lack of quiet in the house, the unnaturally intense and confusing contact with five adults daily, and the difficulty of assessing functional behavior. At the same time it became apparent that the course of events in the institution was determined predominantly by the work schedule of the adults. It seemed desirable to modify this fundamentally, to make the needs of the children the central factor, and to adjust the activities of the adults to them. It was also clear that one nurse could not give adequate attention to more than five or six children. The following then took place; the house was rebuilt internally so that one group of five or six children with one nurse could consider one room as their home. This meant that in this room it was possible to play, to eat, to wash, and to use their own adjacent toilet. By having the day start half an hour later in the morning and finish half an hour earlier in the evening, it was also possible to arrange the daily schedule of the nurses in such a way that they could satisfy our requirements without coming into conflict with labor laws. Only for the afternoon nap did all the children come together under the supervision of one nurse.

The daily pattern of the children's activities then took on the aspect shown on the right in Figures 1 and 2. The results were immediately perceptible. The house ran smoothly and quietly. This gave satisfaction to the staff and permitted the personnel to concentrate their attention entirely on the children. The children also became more quiet and more relaxed. The new arrangement gave the staff a chance to reflect and to act on their need for self-evaluation. Moreover, daily charts were instituted for the recording of some of the qualitative and quantitative aspects of the behavioral functions of eating, sleeping, bowel movement, and micturition. These charts are handled in the same way that temperature and pulse rate charts are kept in a hospital.

The outer world could not possibly be aware of any of these changes. This led to a sometimes confused relation between internal and external climate. External members knew that different children were admitted to Margriet than formerly, but could not so easily grasp the significance of behavioral problems in the preschool years. This made it even more difficult to explain to them that it was necessary to analyze the situation in order to understand the background factors and to achieve insight into the changed problems that the children presented. Insight into the behavior problems required a rechanneling of the children's behavior. This was the more difficult during this process because things were not always clear even to us.

In this period a great deal of effort was expended to obtain sufficient subsidy to keep the house running. The authorities often had the feeling that we used Margriet for scientific experimentation, which was considered to be an activity which ought not to take place at the expense of the municipal budget.

Third Phase, 1955-1960

Around 1955, we noticed in working with the chart records that impressions of behavioral activity which had previously been impossible to measure now could be measured to an important extent. It was possible then for the first time to satisfy our wish to find out what actually took place in Margriet: we no longer had to depend entirely on intuitive judgments.

First, the question of what happens is of obvious interest, especially to those who expend appreciable amounts of their time and energy on such a project. But secondly, it is also understandable to want to know this in a broader context. Society as a whole invests large amounts of money and energy in institutions concerned with attempts to educate children in order to enable them to become members of adult society without serious disadvantage to the society or themselves. The work in such institutions is done largely according to intuitive standards, and the authorities extend the financial means on the basis of intuitive motives. In actual fact, we know very little about the value of such institutions. In some of them there are, of course conditions which are out of date by present standards; but even more important, we have no idea what processes actually take place in them, what kind of effect they have on the children, and how long it lasts. Indeed, we often do not even know whether a period in such a home has a favorable effect on the child or whether another approach would not offer more possibilities. This can be traced back directly to the early history of these institutions. Their genesis lies in the fact that society wished to be rid of the burden of these children and was rid of it if they were packed away together. This character is still unmistakably recognizable in children's homes in less industrialized countries. As prosperity and knowledge increase, more attention is and can be given to the children themselves.

Evaluative Study. We received a subsidy from T.N.O. (National Health Research Council) to make a study which would answer the question, "What takes place in Margriet." Together with co-workers from the Netherlands Institute of Preventive Medicine and the University's Pediatric Department, a team was made up consisting of a psychiatrist, a psychologist, a psychiatric social worker, a pediatrician, and the matron. Then a program was designed for this investigation. This took nine months; a pilot study took six months; and the definitive study took two years. It was concluded in 1959. The processing of the data is now nearly completed, and the outlines of the results can be discerned.

In this study, three groups, each comprising fourteen children, were compared. They were comparable as far as age and socioeconomic background were concerned. The children of one group caused no problems and therefore were considered to be normal (i.e., problemless) children. They were collected from welfare clinics. The children of the two other groups were comparable also in respect of their complaints, which were all of the behavioral kind described above, and had all applied for admission to Margriet. In order of application, the comparable children were alternately either admitted to Margriet or left at home. These three groups were examined on various items by the team members, according to their respective disciplines, three times at six-month intervals. The period of admission to Margriet lasted six months. Admitted children were examined before admission, before discharge, and six months after discharge.

Results. The following observations and interpretations were evident:

1. The children admitted to Margriet showed, six months after admission, better physical and behavioral functioning than those who had remained at home.

2. Six months after discharge, these differences were barely measurable or distinguishable. This does not imply, however, that no effect was present.

3. An admission period of six months is perhaps too short to accomplish longer-lasting, measurable modification of behavior.

4. One of Margriet's social functions is to lessen the over-all daily burden of life's complexities for the mother during the most heavily loaded hours of the day. As such this function is a mechanism by which society relaxes the tensions and pressures created by social demands for adaptation. Margriet therefore can be looked upon as one of the many self-defending mechanisms of society.

5. The determination of what actually takes place during admission to Margriet is not an easy procedure as our evaluation has shown. It also costs a great deal of time and energy. We are by no means sure that we have really grasped the major points of importance.

6. There are many children with behavior problems. Modern society is faced with the need to apply a fair amount of energy to the readjustment of these children. This happens in many ways, of which a day nursery like Margriet is only one example. It is not yet sufficiently known what takes place in this type of institution and what admission means to the children and their mothers. In this investigation there has been an attempt to get an approximate answer to this question. If anything this study has proved to be a stimulus for further investigation.

DISCUSSION

It might be asked whether psychosocial help to the parents, and particularly the mother, during admission and after the return of the child to the family, would lead to a more permanent improvement in the child. It can also be asked whether such an expenditure of energy would not be doomed to be rather ineffective as long as other conditions such as housing, milieu, and the mental and emotional attitudes of the parents themselves cannot be modified. This, too, would require investigation before an answer could be given. It is clear that changes in the milieu background are, in their turn, dependent on the slow-acting developmental forces in human society which lead to more material prosperity and more consciously motivated educational systems. Our energy is now expended in counteracting problems caused by the external forces of the milieu. Future improvement in the milieu, however, will expose a new range of problems, but these will be caused more purely by forces inherent in the individual.

It might also be asked, and justifiably, why no psychiatrist, psychologist, and social worker were on the staff of Margriet. The answer to this must be that Leiden is not yet ready to make this possible financially. It was only temporarily made possible by the University's participation in the study carried out during Phase 3.

SUMMARY AND CONCLUSIONS

In the fifteen years of its existence, Margriet, a day nursery in Leiden, Holland, has undergone quite a change. Originally it was a home to take care of physically deprived children. As their material deficiencies were corrected, the children became better, and the adults involved were satisfied. They knew what they were doing, and they were successful. We felt less successful and less satisfied when children with behavior problems came. We had to make radical changes in the house and its management in order to reach an adequate approach to their problems. This, too, led to a certain satisfaction. It was then the extent to which we still remained unsatisfied that led to the organizing of an evaluative investigation. We know now that we need more studies in the future for a real understanding of what takes place in Margriet. This is because we wish to know what we are actually doing, and, secondly, whether society, according to our criteria, applies its energy (and money) in this way in the most satisfactory way for both society and its children.

If one asks which background forces have in only fifteen years led to these changes in Margriet, it then would appear as though it is society itself which has provided the principal pressures for these changes. The changing society was responsible for children with other problems being referred to Margriet. These children with behavior problems demanded other insights on the part of those responsible for their care, and other treatment. The course of events can be reproduced in a schematic review (see Figure 3), in which for each successive step in the development it would hold that a need must first increase until it is felt, becomes a burden, and is no longer bearable. Only then do analysis, insight, and change come into being.

It seems useful to reflect on the background factors acting on such a small part of the entire machinery of our society as a day nursery. The community automatically assumes that the effort involved in establishing and maintaining a day nursery is desirable and the successful results therefore certain. There is a growing tendency to abandon this intuitive evaluation.

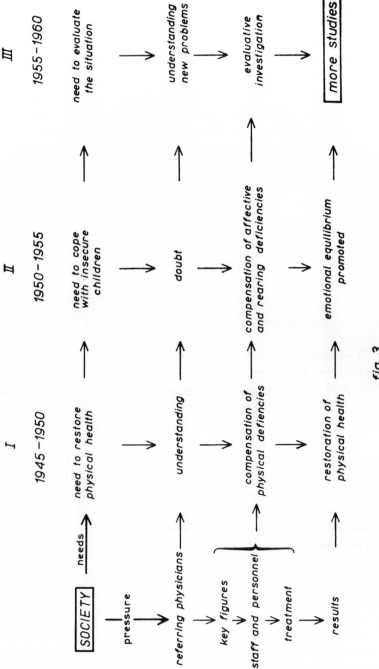

SCHEME OF FORCES EMERGING FROM SOCIETY, ACTING VIA CHANNELS
AND RESULTING IN THE NEED FOR MORE STUDIES.

fig. 3

Parent Education: Reminiscence and Comment

• *ANNA W. M. WOLF*

New York, New York

It has often been said that ours is a society which assigns to amateurs the most important task there is, the moral and emotional education of the young. We are not inclined to look on parenthood as an art to be formally studied or as a subject for undergraduate learning. A few schools and colleges offer brief "personal problem" courses. But these have been sporadic, confined largely to encouraging young people to explore their quandaries on matters like dating, social life, feelings about their parents, the choice of a mate, and sex relations. Some schools also offer opportunities for private counseling along these lines. But though these represent some attempts in the direction of premarital education, they rarely include consideration of the needs of children and experiences of parenthood.

There are some exceptions. A few women's colleges today do offer courses in child development and sometimes provide opportunities for working with young children in nursery schools attached to the colleges. "Wiping noses and changing panties is a sobering experience," some students have declared. There is one girls' private high school which operates, under a trained nurse's direction, a day-care setup for a few infants where the seniors may have at least a brief introduction to what a baby looks like, feels like, and requires. Very recently, too, one women's college with high intellectual standards offered a lecture series on such subjects as the pros and cons of natural childbirth, the psychology of motherhood.

But these efforts are scattered, optional, and likely to be regarded as "frills." Students themselves are often uninterested. This is a time of life when young people are so involved in emotional storms around sex, around self-doubt of all kinds, and (in the case of girls) in simply "getting their man" that parenthood and children seem very far away. The urgency of present anxieties crowds out any realization of the all-important part children will play in their lives in but a few years' time.

So, for the most part, we continue to assume—and we may be right—that young couples will pick up what they need to know as they go along, drawing on memories of how their own parents performed, learning from their friends, their doctors, their reading—and from their mistakes. We assume that these mistakes will not be so fatal that the first child, like the first pancake of the batch, had best be thrown out and that somehow he will struggle through; yet we are also quick to heap blame on parents when something does go wrong.

ON-THE-JOB PARENT EDUCATION

The major part of parent education goes on outside of academic institutions and is directed to parents "on the job." It is based on the belief that those who are charged with so heavy a responsibility are entitled to help and that increased understanding can mean more satisfying and effective parenthood. The rearing of children is a delicate and difficult task made infinitely harder by the crowding and complexities of modern life in a new and heterogeneous society in which families are constantly on the move and lack deep roots in their communities. Besides, parenthood has never been a "job" in the usual sense or even a profession. It is a human relationship of great depth and complexity in which intellectual learning, though it plays a part, is secondary and in which the whole emotional climate of the home is what counts most. Yet it is not enough merely to proclaim this. It must be communicated by contagion, spelled out in many contexts before it is truly learned.

The young parent with her first child is eager and conscientious. She wants to do everything "the right way" from the very beginning. So she may at first be disappointed when it begins to dawn on her that there are no simple directives to be offered and no tidy answers to every troublesome problem with children. She finds that the "expert," whether writer, counselor, or group leader, cannot tell her "the cause" of lying, of shyness, of quarrelsomeness, or prescribe exactly what disciplinary measures to employ when a child defies authority. Instead, she is asked to look at the whole picture in a new way which may at first seem meaningless. Nevertheless her simple questions and the search for answers have not been in vain. They have led to radically new approaches and over the years have yielded something of immense value, infinitely worth passing on. They are among the springs which have fed the great stream of man's new awareness of psychological forces at work deep within him and have offered the hope that the human condition may one day be improved by a scientific approach to these forces. This new era in our culture, to which Freud gave so great an impetus, is apparent everywhere— in medicine, religion, social welfare, education. It permeates literature and the theater; the vernacular of psychology appears even in advertising copy.

Milton Senn and I had our own small share in this as we worked together through the columns of a mass magazine for women. We wanted to tell mothers, largely of the high-school graduate level, some well-established medical facts and give them practical suggestions in behalf of their children's greater well-being. Even more important, we tried to lead them also to greater understanding of new ways of looking at child rearing. Milton Senn was painstaking and he was courageous. He never believed that science is sacrosanct. He held that if a scientist knows something that everyone should know, he should say it to people directly. Subject matter ranged

widely, treating not only such specifics as childhood illnesses and
their prevention and management but also parental and family attitudes toward such illnesses and the part these played in any complete
picture. Articles explored also fresh approaches to common emotional disturbances and possible ways of preventing them. Besides
these, Milton Senn wrote also of his own personal philosophy of
religious education. Once, he openly questioned the findings of another scientist whose name was a household word. There were those
who criticized him for doing so, claiming that the only proper forum
for this was a professional journal. Milton Senn disagreed. He felt
that when someone has directly misinformed parents they should be
told so directly, and he welcomed a chance to do this for 5,000,000
women. He reported also on a trip he made to Russia to survey the
Soviet approach to the study of children, partly, I suspect, because
he wanted to show what common ground there might be with our
cold-war enemy and to let Americans know that, whatever our differences, child-care agencies in the Soviet Union are not manned by
heartless robots. Almost every article brought letters from readers
and physicians in all parts of the United States. He found time to
answer most of these personally with courtesy, warmth, and medical
knowledge.

Though respect for the word of the expert is conceded to be a
typically American phenomenon, it has surprised some to find that
we consult specialists even about the best ways of bringing up children. Doubtless this dependence on the expert is typical of a new
country, one in which there has been a sharp break with the past.
In Russia, for example, the word of the expert seems even more
venerated than here. Soviet health officers pay regular follow-up
visits to new mothers in their homes to make sure that "the regime"
prescribed for every baby by the central authority is being con-
scientiously followed. This is in sharp contrast to older countries
where long-established and persistent traditions powerfully influence
child-care practices.

Several years ago, I was queried by a thoroughly up-and-coming
young French woman, an editor of a Paris women's magazine. She
expressed amazement at American ways. "You teach your children

details about sex which we think belong only in medical schools," she commented. It was hard for her to understand "running to an outsider," as she put it, for help with a private family problem. I asked her what French parents would do if, for example, a child was a persistent and unhappy enuretic or masturbator. Somewhat taken aback, she replied that one might then consult "a neurologist." Nevertheless, she realized that a neurologist's training did not necessarily include knowledge of the meaning of such symptoms. "In that case," she said, "I'd ask my grandmother." It is significant that in France the grandmother is seen as someone wise, experienced, and authoritative. American parents are more likely to see her merely as out of date. Attitudes in France may already have changed since that conversation and, as our own society matures, divergences among us are apt to be lessened.

Here in New York where I have worked, it has been striking that those parents who are most consciously in quest of learning all that will give their children the best possible chance in life come from homes where European—often Eastern-European—ideas about family life still have a strong hold. For the younger generation of parents, part of the process of becoming wholly American, consists of asserting independence of these traditions and embracing the new. In large measure this proceeds from a healthy eagerness to discover what modern psychology has to offer, to gain fresh concepts of how children develop and all that family life involves. But present also is to be found a considerable element of fantasy. How much happier their own childhoods might have been, they tell themselves, if only their parents had not made such egregious blunders which they now are determined to avoid with their own children.

A parent educator, whether group leader or counselor, must recognize such fantasies when they arise and be ready to help a parent sort out what is a legitimate desire to do what is best from what is merely the need to demonstrate her superiority and prove how much better she can do than her mother did. With added insight, she can then reappraise her own practices. Because her own mother told her untruths about sex and made her "feel guilty" about all sorts of normal impulses is no reason for plying a child with sex information he does not seek and cannot use. Her own parents may have punished her thoughtlessly and unjustly for childish errors; nevertheless discipline still has a place, and there are other alternatives to the extremes of permissiveness. It is no easy task to make this point concrete and usable to those who have not known in their own childhoods the kind of control which is based on affection, resourcefulness, and humor.

This conflict between the generations is by no means limited to families who are close to old-world practices. To a greater or lesser extent, many young mothers are caught up in a need to demonstrate their superiority. Yet, when encouraged to delve into their memories for what in retrospect seems to them valid and constructive, they can often do so and put such memories to good use.

Less far reaching than the written word, the parent study group has enjoyed considerable popularity in this country. In addition to disseminating knowledge and stimulating thought, it also brings parents together in a process of cross-fertilization under the leadership of someone who can keep discussion above the level of park-bench chit-chat or chance conversational encounters at the supermarket. One of the abiding values of these group meetings is the support that parents get from one another. The discovery that others share their problems comes as an enormous relief. They are no longer alone in guilty isolation. Relieved of this anxiety, they can see their children in perspective and act with increased self-confidence.

The single lecture or series of lectures, even when followed by questions from the floor, cannot provide parents with the kind of sustaining help that depends on free interchange in more informally organized meetings. Nevertheless, a lecture often whets the appetite for going further and deeper. Another popular approach has been through films or playlets focused on some detail of family life. Concrete and dramatic, they afford a welcome change of pace. For full value, they should be followed by free discussion in which parents have time to call each other's attention to points which are not apparent at first and in which valuable differences of opinion as to the "message" may be brought out. A clear-headed, quick-thinking leader, ever ready to puncture gently the oversimplified formula approach from a member of the audience, is almost a necessity. But he must also lead the way to something positive and useful. Sometimes even an inferior play or film can be made to serve a useful purpose for a group that, in the course of discussion, discovers its lack of clarity or shallowness.

Temperamental differences among parents are apt to show up rather quickly. Some are impatient of the slow pace of the parent group or are unwilling to submit personal family matters to a forum. Some just want to sink quietly into the back seat of a lecture hall and listen, or brouse among books and articles. Others want no part of the whole thing, believing that common sense will enable them to muddle through about as well as their psychologizing neighbors. Among this group, many are not as self-confident as they seem and, when baffled, may go quietly to a counselor for advice.

WHO SHOULD DO PARENT EDUCATION?

Counseling services for parents have been developing widely on many fronts and with varying goals and degrees of competence. Often they operate on diverse theories or with no theories at all. In addition to the psychiatric clinic and the school guidance counselor who is often a psychologist, a good deal of informal counseling goes on in the pediatrician's office, in nursery schools, in day-care centers and —if parents are encouraged to discuss matters that are troublesome at home—with the doctor or teacher. Family agencies also provide help for families through a casework approach. A few of these have set up services specifically planned to help parents with childhood problems *before* they become serious and while they are still fluid enough to respond to improved parental management. The aim is to prevent later trouble calling for psychotherapy.

More recently, ministers, rabbis, and priests have recognized that their roles as spiritual advisers can take them into deep waters calling for specialized knowledge. Accordingly, associations for pastoral counseling have sprung up, and the more forward-moving of the clergy of the three faiths are giving serious study to psychoanalysis and all that modern psychology may contribute. Divinity schools are beginning to include courses in pastoral counseling as a necessary part of the future minister's understanding. There has also been a rash of books on psychiatry and religion proclaiming that, far from being natural antagonists, these two fields of endeavor are natural allies and should proceed hand in hand. Some in both camps dispute this view.

There are, of course, differences of opinion and undercurrent hostilities, trade unionism and dogmatism among the adherents of various approaches to parent education, often depending on which "school" of psychology or casework they are linked with. As for the various disciplines, psychologists, psychiatrists, and social workers long ago discovered each other's special contributions and are now inclined to work together collaboratively. There is still debate on who should be permitted to do therapy and indeed on the very meaning of "therapy" as differentiated from "education." Many find it useful to keep the terms closely linked with the concepts of sickness and health respectively and to view "education" as an effort directed toward strengthening and utilizing whatever is healthy in an individual. Parent "educators" in this context, while fully recognizing the areas of "sickness" in the individual they are confronted with, will deliberately manage to skirt around such areas.

There have been varied responses also to the whole idea of popularizing depth psychology through the mass media—a trend which was at first regarded askance as tending to cheapen and degrade a serious science. Now, however, there are more and more like Milton Senn, who recognize the value of enlarging public understanding whenever this can be done truthfully and usefully.

From one point of view, parent education suffers from the fact that it is not a closely defined field or specialized discipline limited to those who have undergone standardized training. Therefore it has had a semiamateur rating. Parent educators, unlike teachers or social workers, have not for the most part been to school to win degrees specifically in this field. Though some graduate schools do offer training and degrees in "family life education," parent educators, as we have seen, may be writers, teachers, nurses, social workers.

They also may be religious leaders whose duties bring them into close contact with parents and family problems. They may even be just plain parents who know or believe they know more than most, who may have taken "a course," or perhaps merely maneuvered themselves into the position of leader of a parent group in connection with a school, church, or club. Yet for the present, at least, there would seem to be value in some variety. Standardization would tend to freeze an effort which, loaded with intangibles as it is, had best remain fluid.

This raises the question of who are equipped to be parent-group leaders. How should they be selected? What training do they need? My own experience leads me to believe that parent groups are at their best under the leadership of someone whose knowledge and grasp are pretty thorough, who knows when to speak and when to keep silent, at what points a mother is ready to be helped forward by a word or so, and when she is, for the moment, stuck where she is. Leaders should know how to limit their own role to dealing only with motives that are near to consciousness. Efforts to bring deeply buried conflicts to the surface mean trespassing into the domain of therapy. They must be able to gauge the needs and potentials of each group member and be ready to shift their course when necessary. The leader must also be on the watch for the occasional mother who is disturbed so deeply that she is unable to gain through the usual group experience and must know how to enable such a mother to accept more appropriate help. Actually, in the hands of a skillful leader, a member who really wants to remain in a group rarely fails to get value from the experience. Other members of the group come to perceive her difficulties and almost invariably respond with friendliness and tactful support. These are delicate and difficult matters calling for finesse and experience in the leader.

I am wary, therefore, of the complete amateur, who though he or she may have "taken a course," attended some lectures, or read some books, is still more confused than he knows and leaves those who turn to him for help not only confused but frequently soured on the whole idea. In parent education my preference is for drawing on those who have had professional training in a field where considerable knowledge of psychoanalytic thought, including its extensions to medicine, education, and sociology are required. In addition, a leader must know how to make this knowledge come alive for parents and serve their needs.

This raises the much-debated question of whether it is possible to develop these capacities through training courses? Can we teach teachers to teach? Is knowledge of content so basic for teachers in any field that we can afford to leave the methods of conveying it to take care of themselves? Obviously both content and the ability to convey it are important. When it comes to parent-group leadership, highly knowledgeable professional people, for example, may be quite baffled when faced by mothers asking naïve but urgent questions. They may find that they lack the talent or inclination, or both, to distill complex matters into a form that will take relatively unsophisticated minds one step further along the road to understanding.

Creative leadership with parent groups, I suspect, goes beyond the gift for lucid explanation or sound advice-giving. Some of the best leaders rarely explain, theorize, or even offer very many suggestions. They act largely as guides in a free discussion focused directly on parents' personal experiences with their families. Such leaders know how to underscore whatever comes up that may enlarge and deepen insight and that throws light on the problem at hand. They know how to query the glib and the stereotyped without threatening the dignity of the person in question, and how to evoke instead something personal and fresh. They may, at times, summarize what has gone on—adding small doses of their own insight, but sparingly and only as they sense that a group can grasp and apply it, and only when it stimulates rather than shuts off further discussion by the parents.

Nevertheless, in spite of the skill and experience usually required, it would be rash to rule out entirely the occasional leader whose background knowledge may be quite limited, yet who mysteriously possesses the gift of fermenting thought and influencing parents in such a way that they go home and do better. I have seen very few of these "naturals," but doubtless they do exist.

We should be especially leary, I have found, of leader candidates who believe they understand children and family life and lack only the "techniques" to work well with parents. Almost invariably, this demand for techniques cloaks the thinness of their knowledge or the shallowness of their understanding which are the real causes of their fumbling. I am skeptical also of training leaders through a brief course of lectures even when conducted by high-grade professionals. I doubt that this can take candidates who start from almost complete ignorance to a state where they have an adequate knowledge of human dynamics. To be properly assimilated and made usable, such knowledge has to be lived with over the years. But the novice leader, already equipped with such knowledge, has much to gain through watching experienced leaders at work and through a period of being observed and "controlled" in her maiden efforts. Supervision, however, should not be too long. There is danger in cramping the naturalness of the new leader. Like parents, she must build confidence in her own personal ways of doing things even at the price of some mistakes. What she always can profit by, however, are frequent opportunities for pooling experiences with colleagues in a mutual learning endeavor. Of this, there is far too little today.

Besides the richness of background knowledge, what are the basic qualities of personality which one who works with parents must have and which justify a belief that here is someone able to liberate and quicken whatever is good and constructive between parents and their children?

I would mention first the ability to identify oneself with parents. Not only must he genuinely like and respect parents, he must know in his bones how possible it is to get into an impasse with a child and how prodigiously demanding family life is. Yet he must not overidentify. This parent with whom he is face to face is not himself. A parent is indeed someone wholly different who must find her own way. He must therefore be prepared to do much listening, never seduced into revealing his own understanding prematurely, holding back until the moment comes when what he says can be truly understood or when, as is often the case, it serves to clinch what the mother herself was on the verge of discovering.

TRENDS AND CHANGES

What trends are discernible today both in parent education as it is practiced and in the American family itself? There are wide local differences as well as variations in educational groupings. In spite of the difficulties of assessing trends, the publications business which takes the pragmatic view may suggest some answers.

Editors of the mass magazines are convinced that when it comes to children, the public has reached a kind of saturation point. Such matters as sibling rivalry, what to tell your child about sex, toilet training, and the "need for emotional security" are now sure-fire duds until such time as new knowledge emerges. Except in those publications which specialize wholly in child-rearing problems, the public wants no more of these topics in the magazines. Perhaps this is because government and other widely circulating manuals fill the need. But parents are willing to read what is entertaining, fresh, sharply focused, and brief. As for books, those published today are less for parents than for those who work with parents or children in a professional capacity—for social workers, public health nurses, teachers, ministers. What books there are for parents are less concerned with broad problems of family life than with specific matters such as helping children do well in school, getting into college, religious training, problems of the handicapped child.

Interest in study groups has undergone a parallel change. Parents are apt to look dubiously on committing themselves for more than four or five meetings, though, as these draw to a close, they may decide to continue. This is a change from the time when we used to run double sessions of fifteen scheduled meetings. The expectant mother, however, is an exception. Before the birth of her first child, the mother-to-be is eager to get a preview of what she may expect of herself, her husband, and her child now that this great new experience is really upon her. Meeting with others with the same queries, she gains ease and reassurance. This type of group seems to be growing in number and acceptance.

In general, interest in group attendance is greatest when the discussion centers on a specific subject or narrow age range. Children change fast and parents grow impatient of talk about problems which for them may be long past. There has been increasing response, too, from parents of handicapped children who welcome the chance to meet others who share their problems. Nowhere else, perhaps, is support from those "who understand" more needed and valued. Together they pool their experiences of what has been most useful in bringing out such a child's full potential, establishing him as a member in good standing of a family group and leading the way so that other "normal" children will accept him comfortably.

The generalized diffuse parent discussion group seems to be on the wane. Time is at a premium and today's young mother of even one child finds it hard to get replacement for herself when away from home or to buck transportation and parking problems at distant meetings. When mothers can leave home and want something educational, they are quite likely to prefer the arts or a dance group or other culture courses. Doubtless they are glad to forget their children for a while.

Among the relatively well-informed, there is an increased appreciation of the occasional single lecture provided it is of top-level quality and given by someone qualified to sift research findings for what is reliable, interesting, and relatively durable. It has been a common complaint that "authorities" keep reversing themselves and that since it is impossible to keep up with the pendulum swings in child rearing, one might as well give up. Parents are aware that recent studies are questioning old dogmas. Is early toilet training *really* harmful if the mother proceeds tentatively and the child seems to cooperate? Do children of divorced parents *really* turn out worse than children of the undivorced or of stay-at-home mothers? Parents point out, too, that the pendulum which swung all the way from discipline to permissiveness has now come back to discipline again. Yet the more discerning know that the pendulum never swings back to exactly the same point from which it started. Always there are important modifications. We move forward in a spiral.

We may count among signs of progress that there is a greater degree of parental self-confidence. This would seem to belie what some have so vehemently asserted—that parent education is increasing parent anxiety without increasing competence. Mothers who yesterday were dependent on the word of almost anyone who would tell them what to do are now aware that there are many "right" ways and that each mother must work out for herself what seems best for her family. Yet they are willing to listen, especially when there is something new to be said. Many have accepted the idea that when something goes wrong with a child, it is wise for parents to look within themselves for the part they may unwittingly be playing. But they are less overwhelmed with a sense of personal failure than they used to be when shortcomings appear in a child. We know that genetic as well as environmental factors play a role in the emergence of personality. It used to be part of avant-garde ideology to deny any part to heredity.

So there is more relaxation on the part of parents about such matters as .toilet training, eating the balanced diet, discipline, and "instilling good habits." Some may complain that today's parents are *too* relaxed about these things. Perhaps a balance is still to be achieved between old ways and new. But certainly we can count it a real gain that children can now be heard as well as seen, that they are encouraged to speak out—and often do! It is no longer considered wrong for a child to be sexually curious, to live with fantasies formerly inadmissible, or to harbor hostile impulses toward those he is supposed to love. Yet if the child's "fifth freedom," which is his right to feel and think as he must without condemnation, has been largely won for him, we have learned that it is no easy matter to get him to put his feelings into words. Though in many ways, there is greater communication between the generations at all ages, we are forever running into the child's deep need for concealment, his rooted belief that grownups, no matter how gentle, belong to a different order of beings with standards which they seem always to be trying to impose on him. Grownups are not wholly to be trusted.

In the end and in spite of the gains, we must face the fact that even with all we have learned about human development and all we have done to spread the word, we have failed to stem the tide of widespread mental illness, crippling neurosis, juvenile delinquency, or to cope with the ever-increasing threat from destructive power drives in the human race. Doubtless society itself is proliferating new problems faster than we have been able to solve old ones. Doubtless, too, psychological knowledge is woefully incomplete; the very essentials perhaps are still lacking. Yet we may all still share the hope that in becoming more widely aware of the magnitude of the problems we have taken at least one small step on the way toward finding the means to surmount them.

Child-Rearing Practices and Their Consequences

- *JULIUS B. RICHMOND, M.D.*
- *BETTYE M. CALDWELL, Ph.D.*

State University of New York, Syracuse

The implications of child-rearing practices for later development have been the continuing concern of workers in the child-care professions. Dr. Senn has been in the forefront of the movement to foster a deeper understanding of methods of child care in order that practical assistance to parents may be made available. It is fitting, therefore, that a portion of this Festschrift be devoted to child-rearing practices and their consequences.

In the United States the task of providing guidance in child rearing is hampered by certain ambiguities related to the lack of a stable tradition of child-rearing goals and practices. A first source of ambiguity can be found in the lack of homogeneity in our population. Although as a nation we are nearing the end of the second century of experience, American parents still represent highly diversified backgrounds. The continued immigration over the years has brought together cultural groups with varied backgrounds and dissimilar or even conflicting traditions of child rearing. Associated with this process of amalgamation are intergenerational problems among the descendants of each cultural group as they become parents.

A second factor associated with the lack of stable traditional models is the geographic mobility of our population. It is estimated that 20 per cent of families move each year, thus often removing the possibility of stabilization due to immediate contact with relatives and their accumulated traditions and values. Our incapacity to arrive at a national consensus accounts in part, no doubt, for the popularity of child-rearing texts, for magazine and newspaper articles dealing with various facets of child behavior, and for the programming of parent-directed material on television and radio. The professional literature also reflects interest and concern in this field. Indeed, some observers from abroad cannot understand our preoccupation with these issues, which to them seem trivial and not proper subjects of concern for professional workers.

In spite of these difficulties in defining consistent patterns of child rearing in the United States, considerable pressure has arisen— especially in the years since World War II—for identification of child-rearing practices which would assure sound psychological development. Not many years have elapsed since emphasis on a return to breast feeding, rooming-in programs, natural childbirth, and self-regulatory feeding patterns began to appear in the professional and lay literature. The implication was clear that these procedures were advocated because of their influence on subsequent "mental health" of the child. The considerable concern of the American people with mental health and their search for preventive psychiatric efforts may stem from the following:

1. *Improvement in the physical health of children.* The continuing decline in infant and childhood mortality has made available time and energy for fuller consideration of the psychological and social development of the child by parents and professional workers. There has developed an expectation that professional workers have competence in guiding psychological and social development which is comparable to their skill in guiding physical growth and development. And here it should be mentioned that professional workers have done little to destroy that expectation. Though generally paying lip service to such factors as sample size, need for

replication, nature of population to which results may be generalized, etc., they may at the same time be inclined to speculate on
the broad implications of their work. An almost caricatured historical example of this tendency can be found in the work of John B.
Watson (1928), who, on the basis of a few ingenious and provocative
experiments with infants and young children, formulated and popularized an approach to child-rearing practices which influenced professionals and parents for more than a decade. Certainly Watson is
not the only scientist who has tended to overgeneralize; in fact,
premature application of research findings in this field is something
of an occupational hazard.

The conceptualization of mental health as analogous to physical
health has also led to some confusion. The inference is made that
since specific preventive practices such as immunizations and vitamin
supplements are effective in preventing certain physical diseases,
equally reliable factors which would assure mental health can be
identified. Another breakdown in this analogy can be found in the
definition of mental health as the absence of disease. Not entirely
satisfactory as a way of characterizing physical health, this concept
becomes meaningless when offered as a definition of mental health.
In a relatively static culture content with the *status quo,* the con-
flictless, homeostatic individual may represent the prototype of
mental health; however, in a continuously evolving and competitive
culture, the energetic and achieving (though perhaps conflicted)
individual may be a desirable model. This realization complicates
the picture of mental health based on the model of physical health.
Even if we had evidence that specific practices could "immunize"
against certain types of later behavior, we would have to consider
whether the behavior precluded by the immunization might be adaptive under some circumstances within the framework of certain
values.

2. *Relatively high prevalence of neuropsychiatric disorders in the
young adult population.* Interesting data on this problem emerged
from the mobilization statistics of World War II. There has been
considerable debate concerning whether this apparent increase indicates that larger numbers of young adults were psychologically

ineffective than previously or whether it simply signifies better recognition; nevertheless, the fact remains that we were made aware of the significance of the problem to the nation. One result of this awareness was increased interest in those child-rearing practices which would help to prevent psychiatric problems in adult life.

3. *The increasing literacy of our population.* With increasing literacy has come a *conscious* desire on the part of parents to do a more effective job of rearing children. This has resulted in a plethora of literature and communications in other mass media on child care. These communications obviously are too numerous to have any consistency. Furthermore, they may serve to undermine any sense of consistency or adequacy which the parent might have by implicitly advocating a conscious and volitional rather than an intuitive basis for the selection of child-rearing practices. Certainly it has not been possible to obtain an objective assessment of the value of these mass communications.

4. *The professionalization of services for children.* The previously mentioned mobility of the population, which often precludes help with child rearing by immediate family members, has fostered this trend. The modern social acceptability of recognizing and admitting mother-child conflict has led in many instances to an abrogation of maternal models—the last thing many young mothers want to be is like their mothers. As one consequence parents have increasingly sought the help of "experts"—particularly pediatricians—for problems which would have been within the province of family members in previous years and which still are family concerns in most parts of the world. As another consequence, professional persons have come to take for granted their right to fill the gap and to provide models for the solution of many child-rearing problems, generally offering the awesome "Research has shown . . ." as their authority referent. Thus, in some respects, professional child-care workers are becoming the cultural carriers of modern literate social groups. If they are to fill this role effectively, it is imperative that they develop objectivity and, in so far as possible, free themselves of their cultural biases and "decontaminate" their own views of child-rearing patterns.

The desire to base professional recommendations upon sound

research evidence is healthy, if occasionally frustrating. In the field of techniques of child care, research which started out to "provide answers" and "establish principles" has produced a plethora of inconclusiveness, contradictions, and alternative explanations. In spite of this, recommendations have appeared, lived out their time, and been supplanted by more promising ones. Vincent (1951) has pointed out that most of the popularized materials seem to shift in unison. This suggests that all such materials must be nourished from a common source—the contemporary research literature as interpreted in terms of prevalent social values. A sampling of some of the relevent investigations dealing with one or another aspect of the consequences of child-care practices would thus be in order.

IMPLICATIONS OF THE RESEARCH LITERATURE

Much of the research relating antecedent parental variables to consequent child personality variables has been oriented around certain polarized conditions, one end of which is presumed to be conducive to optimal development and the other to social and emotional disturbances. Thus we speak of breast versus bottle feeding, scheduled versus demand feeding, early versus late toilet training, single versus multiple mothering, restrictive versus permissive parental philosophies, and so on. It is not our intent here to offer a comprehensive review of the research literature relating to any of these polarities. Rather we wish to discuss briefly representative studies which will illustrate the kinds of data available for making judgments and some of the difficulties involved in arriving at any stable conclusions.

Infant Feeding

Breast, Bottle, and How Long? Probably there is no other subject which has received more emotional treatment in both the professional and lay literature than that of infant feeding. The advantages of breast feeding to both mother and infant have been extolled in innumerable publications, as have been the virtues of longer periods of unrestricted sucking and of flexibility in the scheduling of feedings. As the emphasis of these materials has been quite one-sided, with breast feeding favored over any substitute, Vincent (1951) has speculated about why they continue to appear. In a survey of some 644 articles appearing between 1890 and 1949, he notes that hosts of new defenders have been incited to literary action whenever any threat to the custom of breast feeding appeared. During this period there was a general trend away from emphasis upon health and mortality statistics as reasons for advocating breast rather than artificial feeding and an increasing concern with emotional security of the infant as the chief reason. Wolfenstein (1953) has analyzed the recommendations made to mothers in the successive volumes of *Infant Care* from 1914 to 1951. She found that from the first volume through 1945, breast feeding was emphatically recommended. However, from 1921 on the discussion of this point was somewhat defensive, as though the authors of the booklets suspected that mothers did not really want to breast feed their infants. Not until 1951 were mothers granted an honorable exemption from the practice if they wanted one, at which time they were told that if they weren't happy nursing their baby and did so only out of a sense of duty, then it might be better for both mother and baby if bottle feeding were used.

In spite of this ocean of persuasive literature, there seems little doubt that breast feeding has declined sharply during the present century. In a survey of almost 2,000 hospital obstetrical services in this country, Meyer (1958) found a decline from 38 per cent in 1946 to 21 per cent in 1956 of mothers who breast fed their infants in the hospitals. He also reported that a substantial number of mothers who breast fed in the hospital changed to bottle feeding after leaving the hospital. In a study by Sears, Maccoby, and Levin (1957) of 379 mothers of kindergarten children, 39 per cent of the mothers reported some breast feeding, but only 15 per cent breast fed for three months or longer. It might be significant to note here that in a current longitudinal study of mother-infant interaction with which the authors are associated, not one mother out of some sixty cases has chosen to breast feed her infant.

Empirical evidence of the superiority of breast feeding has been difficult to marshal. From the standpoint of physical development, the situation has altered dramatically during the last three decades, during which time the health hazards associated with bottle feeding have been eliminated. In his oft-quoted review dealing with infant care and personality, Orlansky (1949) concluded that there was no evidence to support the conviction that breast feeding is necessarily superior to bottle feeding. Hardly any generalization can survive a scanning of the research literature. For example, Pearson (1931) and Hoefer and Hardy (1929) found that a moderate period of breast feeding was superior to either a brief or prolonged period, ratings of physical and mental development being the criterion in one study and signs of emotional maladjustment in school children in the other. On the other hand, Maslow and Szilagyi-Kessler (1946) found that college students earning the highest scores on a security inventory were those who had been breast fed little or not at all or more than a year.

In the above-mentioned study by Sears and associates (1957), no general effects on the children of breast feeding or lack of same could be determined. No significant differences could be detected among children breast fed not at all, less than three months, or more than three months on the following variables: aggression in the home, level of conscience, amount of dependency behavior, feeding problems, bed wetting, or strong emotional reaction to toilet training. The authors attempted to determine if the group of mothers who cited physical inability as their reason for not breast feeding differed from breast-feeding mothers in certain ways that might express negative feelings. They found highly similar proportions of mothers in the two subgroups pleased at becoming pregnant, who showed warmth to their infants, and who felt reasonably confident of their mothering ability. However, there was a suggestion that they differed in their general feelings of permissiveness about sex, from which the authors inferred that a strong sense of modesty or anxiety about sexual matters may lead a mother to avoid breast feeding.

An interesting study which utilized differences in feeding history to shed light on the motivational aspects of nutritive sucking has been reported by Sears and Wise (1950). Interviews were conducted with mothers of eighty children, all of whom were judged by their pediatrician to be normally healthy children from stable and intact families. In this group there were ten who had been fed by cup from birth or before two weeks of age and another eighteen weaned to the cup before three months. On the basis of rated maternal interviews, for which satisfactory rater reliability was obtained, certain hypotheses relating to the strength of the oral drive and the severity of oral frustration were explored. The authors found that negative reaction to weaning increases as a function of length of time that sucking is permitted. That is, their relatively late-weaned group showed a greater degree of weaning frustration than the twenty-eight cases weaned before three months. Weaning disturbance was absent in the ten children weaned before two weeks of age. Likewise, there was a suggstion that thumb sucking was more likely to occur in those children who had more rather than less opportunity to suck. There was a relationship between abruptness of weaning and severity of reaction to weaning, but no clear association between abruptness and tendency toward thumb sucking. There were no feeding problems in the ten early weaned children. The authors interpreted their data as suggesting that the oral drive is strengthened, not reduced, by continued sucking. Their data do not contradict the assumption of a primary sucking drive but suggest that such a drive is increased by continued practice at breast or bottle feeding. And, lest their findings be misinterpreted as advocating an abandonment of sucking as a means of ingesting milk during the infancy period, the authors are careful to state, "If there are other reasons for favoring breast or bottle feeding, the present data suggest no reason of sufficient importance to contraindicate them" (p. 137). The results of the Sears and Wise study have been presented in slightly more detail because they illustrate an approach to the study of the feeding situation which involves more than a superficial analysis of between-group differences and which attempts to increase understanding of some of the possible meanings of the behavior under study.

Feeding Schedules. Another dimension which has had considerable attention is that of the flexibility of feeding schedule permitted by the mother. Although to the best of our knowledge no reliable data have ever been assembled to show just how prevalent rigid feeding practices actually were, there is no doubt that during the heyday of the behaviorist era they were strongly recommended. As part of the program designed to assure proper development by establishing desirable habits of behavior early in life, carefully timed feeding sessions were recommended. In 1938, just before the swing of the pendulum, *Infant Care* taught that through regularity of feeding, sleeping, and elimination "the tiny baby will receive his first lessons in character building. He should learn that hunger will be satisfied only so often, that when he is put into his bed he must go to sleep, that crying will not result in his being picked up or played with whenever he likes. He will begin to learn that he is part of a world bigger than that of his own desires" (p. 3). That recommendation was one which had outlived its time, however, for in the very next revision (1942) we find reflected a completely different point of view. After a description of the salutary effects of prompt satisfaction of the baby's hunger needs and of the way in which this need satisfaction leads to an acceptance and enjoyment of the people in his world, the following consequences are postulated to occur if schedule is put before baby:

> Instead of having his needs for food and affection satisfied soon, this baby is allowed to cry on and on, and finally a bottle is put into his mouth. . . . He may have so exhausted himself that he is too tired to obtain much pleasure from the food. . . . Eventually . . . the baby may develop an attitude of dislike toward the world and instead of responding in a friendly way he remains withdrawn, fearful and a little suspicious—an attitude that will make his ultimate adjustment to life difficult [p. 30].

It should be noted parenthetically here that roughly in the period between these two editions of the valuable *Infant Care* pamphlet, the transition from an *adultocentric* to an *infantocentric* orientation to child rearing occurred. The first passage conveys the importance of adjustment by the baby to the adult world; the second attempts to describe the feeding situation from the vantage point of the hungry infant.

In spite of the theoretical importance ascribed to this aspect of child care, little objective information can be mustered to demonstrate any specific salutary effects on the child. In a number of "preliminary" studies, differences in opposite directions are reported and happily explained away—that is, self-regulated infants, if advanced, may be so because of greater confidence in their ability to control the environment; if babies are accelerated, this might be attributed to their greater frustration in infancy which forces earlier response to environmental influences. In a doll-play study of seventeen children, Holway (1949) reported a relationship between early self-regulation and the amount of realism exhibited in doll play. Her assumption that realistic play (carrying out imitative household tasks, etc.) offers a measure of adjustment and that fantasy play reflects anxiety and a need to retreat is open to challenge. Sewell and Mussen (1952) found no relationship between feeding gratification (demand as compared to schedule, gradual as compared to abrupt weaning, and breast versus bottle) and subsequent good or poor psychosocial adjustment of kindergarten age children. In the Sears et al. study (1957), data for which were collected during 1951-52, it was found that 29 per cent of mothers reported use of a demand schedule and 22 per cent a fairly rigid schedule. A slight but significant relationship between choice of a rigid schedule and lack of warmth in the mother was found. The authors suspected that this variable was perhaps more related to the pediatric advice received by the mothers than to a maternal personality variable per se and reasoned that scheduled feeding was still being advocated during the infancy of the children in this study. They found some inferential verification of this hunch in a significant correlation between use of scheduled feeding and general anxiety about child rearing.

Bowel and Bladder Training

Of considerable importance in psychoanalytic theory, the development of sphincter control has received considerable attention as a source of influence on child personality. Recommendations about how to handle this developmental task are generally implicit in discussions of regularity of feeding. That is, regulation of bowel and bladder release may be viewed as part of the total process of control and regularity already referred to under the discussion of scheduled versus demand feedings. Likewise, research investigations of parent practices in this area are generally embedded in studies dealing with other infant care practices. Consequently some results have already been presented or seem more appropirate for other discussions. Accordingly, at this point only certain relevant data from the Sears et al. study (1957) will be mentioned. They found considerable variability in the age at which training was begun and the length of time involved in the process. The prevailing tone of the training process was not very severe, as most of the mothers used no punishment other than scolding for accidents. As the authors commented, "In spite of the tremendous material emphasis on bathrooms attributed to American culture, there was not a desperate severity in the training of children to use them. Many other cultures, some that even lack outhouses, begin their training earlier and are more severe in their punishments of deviations" (p. 120).

Several relationships were found between maternal training practices and certain child personality variables. Using duration of training and amount of upset shown by the child, the authors advance the interpretation that there are possibly two periods which may be chosen for the initiation of toilet training. These are during the second six months of the child's life and some time after twenty months. They offer as a tentative explanation of the greater resistance encountered during the intervening period newly acquired motility patterns which make sitting still quite difficult and the number of reinforcements for incorrect (from the standpoint of the mother) habits. If begun at the earlier period, the process takes longer but does not seem to cause any significant upset. The authors rather apologetically admit that later personality differences may possibly appear as a result of the choice between these two age periods, but data currently at hand cannot establish any.

In contrast to the timing of the training process, severity of training stood out sharply as a maternal practice with discernible consequences in child behavior. Pressure, impatience, irritability, and punishment were seen to arouse resentment, resistance, or emotional upset in the child. Furthermore, such techniques did not seem to speed the process in the least. Maternal warmth seems to be the crucial determinant of whether severe training will produce negative consequences, as severe training from a warm mother had little effect while in a cold mother it did. This latter finding points to an interaction effect between maternal practice and maternal attitude, a point which in a later section will be discussed at greater length.

Maternal Deprivation

Of all the child-rearing variables given attention during the past decade, the nature of the total mothering experience has undoubtedly led the field. Psychoanalytic writers such as Ribble (1943), Spitz (1945), Bowlby (1952), to mention but a few, have emphasized the importance of the mother-child relationship for the normal physiological and psychological development of the infant. Clinical reports (Lowrey, 1940) as well as research studies such as those of Goldfarb (1943, 1949, 1955), Spitz (1945, 1946), Fischer (1952) and Provence and Lipton (1962) described the dramatic consequences of maternal separation and deprivation in groups of children reared in institutional settings where relationships with their own mothers might be nonexistent, reasonably good, or inconsistent. The implication was that maternal separation had an almost inevitably detrimental effect on the developing child.

In spite of the fact that the design of such studies might have been less than exemplary, to euphemize the militant charges made by Pinneau (1951, 1955), they served the important function of stimulating interest in the quantitative as well as qualitative aspects of mothering. Subsequent studies (Beres and Obers, 1950; Bowlby et al., 1956) began to question the inevitability of detriment, and the current point of view seems to have moderated considerably.

In a current review dealing with this problem, Yarrow (1961) attempts to clarify some of the types of maternal deviations which need to be considered in order to facilitate the formulation of more precise hypotheses relating to the effects of specific maternal experiences and subsequent development. In the past, institutionalization, brief or prolonged separation from a mother or mother substitute, multiple mothering, and distortions of mothering (e.g., rejection, overprotection) have seldom been studied as pure conditions or with adequate attention to interaction effects among them. Likewise, important variables such as the quality and amount of sensory stimulation available to the infant, characteristics of the emotional environment, the social stimulation of the environment, and the learning characteristics inherent in the various atypical child-care situations need to be more completely explored before definitive statements can be made about the effects of variations of the maternal functions per se. A recent analysis by Stolz (1960) of the available research studies pertaining to maternal employment—one type of maternal variation—offers leads as to some of the controls which must be secured before definitive statements about this aspect of child care can be made. It should also be noted here that various approaches to experimental variations of mothering patterns among different species of animals (Hersher et al., 1958; Harlow, 1958) offer many leads as to the classes of behavior which can profitably be studied at the human level.

Permissiveness-Strictness

The dimension of permissiveness-strictness refers to a parental philosophy or an orientation to discipline rather than to a specific parental practice. As generally defined, it subsumes such behaviors as scheduled versus demand feeding or early versus late toilet training. Being difficult to define, this variable has been difficult to measure; or rather different approaches to its measurement have not always dealt with precisely the same behaviors. In a sort of omnibus study dealing with many of the infant-training practices which traditionally define the syndrome, Sewell (1952) found no more than a chance relationship between parental practices and child personality. His technique for securing information about the parent behavior was a structured interview with mothers of 162 rural five- and six-year-old children. Data on the adjustment of the children came from that same interview plus a number of personality tests. Out of some 460 chi-square tests, only 18 were statistically significant and could thus be attributed to chance when so many tests were made. Furthermore, only 7 of these were in what might be considered the expected direction; that is, more leniency and permissiveness in these child-training acts were associated with better child adjustment. The author concluded that "practices as breast feeding, gradual weaning, demand schedule, and easy and late induction to bowel and bladder training . . . were almost barren in terms of relation to personality adjustment as measured in this study." It should be noted that in this study the parent behaviors under scrutiny dealt only with the infancy period, whereas behavior related to the permissiveness-strictness continuum can be specified for all developmental periods.

The validity of the assumption of a pervasive trait of permissiveness or strictness has been questioned by Sewell et al. (1955). They found little relationship between maternal permissiveness in different types of socialization activities; that is, a mother who adhered to a rigid feeding schedule might start toilet training rather late and be quite lenient about accidents. However, Sears et al. (1957), who were concerned with a broader spectrum of maternal behavior, report a definite underlying dimension of permissiveness-strictness in their study of almost 400 mothers of normal kindergarten children. They state (p. 308):

> Our conclusion is that these mothers behaved fairly consistently in respect to the dimension of strictness-permissiveness. If a mother was quite tolerant of her child's aggressive behavior, she was likely to be tolerant of his sexual behavior, too. And if she was permissive in those respects, the chances are she was not very strict about table manners, or noise, or neatness around the house. Likewise, she probably did not insist on rigid obedience to her every command.

In relating the antecedent maternal practices to child behavioral consequences, they found that permissiveness for dependent behavior had no discernible effects, but that permissiveness for aggressive behavior was definitely associated with continuing aggressive behavior in the children.

Data from the Yale Rooming-In Project which bear on this point have been reported by Klatskin et al. (1956). They selected records on fifty primiparous mothers and their infants and rated independently certain aspects of parental care and of child behavior. For the mother, ratings were made of her degree of flexibility in feeding, sleeping, toileting, and socialization activities, with the scales ranging from extreme rigidity at one end to extreme permissiveness at the other. For the children, ratings were made of behavior in feeding, sleeping, toileting, and socialization, and a judgment was made of degree of emotional maladjustment. The authors report no association between deviant maternal practices in feeding or socialization in the first year and problem behavior in the children. In years two and three there was an association between maternal deviation in all four areas and problem behavior in the children. No one direction of deviation was consistently associated with disturbance; rigidity of maternal behavior in feeding and socialization activities, and over-permissiveness with respect to sleep schedules were associated with problem behavior in the children.

Several studies (Baldwin, 1948, 1949) from the Fels Institute have been concerned with the impact of parental philosophy on the behavior of the child. On the basis of scales designed for rating parent behavior in the home, they have by factor analysis arrived at certain descriptive syndromes of parent behavior. The syndrome which they have labeled "democracy" is related to but not identical with what is generally regarded as permissiveness. "Democratic" parent behavior is said to be characterized by a high level of contact between parent and child, lack of arbitrariness in decision making, and a general permissiveness of expression. In several studies dealing with the influence of this parental philosophy on the behavior of nursery school children, they have found children from "democratic" homes to be high in curiosity and creativity, to show qualities of leadership, to be lacking in conformity, and to be higher than average in aggressiveness and competitiveness. It is as though this parental orientation accepts a broader range of socialized behaviors and encourages individuality. One consequence of this is that aggressiveness as well as some of the more highly valued social traits will also be implicitly encouraged.

A comprehensive study by G. Watson (1957) is very relevant here. He studied seventy-eight normal children from kindergarten to sixth grade who represented the extremes of a much larger sample drawn from a public school in an upper-middle-class community. Information about parental permissiveness came from mothers' responses to a questionnaire and individual interviews with a social worker. The children were compared by means of a variety of criterion measures (teachers' ratings, objective and projective tests, and drawing and performance tests). The results in general showed that children from more permissive homes were more independent, better socialized, friendlier and more cooperative with other children, more creative, and more realistic than children from stricter homes. The author concludes that there is no clear personality advantage associated with strict discipline in a good home. What differences were found were in favor of the children from the more permissive homes. An interesting sidelight of this study was the relative paucity of homes that would be characterized as extremely permissive, even though the sample was drawn from an area in which this attitude might be expected to be prevalent.

Although it is difficult to compare directly the different studies bearing upon this issue, this brief survey would suggest that there is greater uniformity of results here than in most of the areas of child rearing which have been discussed. It seems difficult to establish a relationship between modes of handling during the infancy period and subsequent personality in the child, but general permissiveness or strictness during later infancy and the preschool period seems to show a relationship with psychological adjustment. One emerging uniformity which is not highlighted by between-group comparisons is the tendency to eschew extremes. In the G. Watson (1957) study extremes of permissiveness were difficult to locate; in the Sears et al. (1957) study extreme deviates at either end of the scale were rare. Preference for a moderate course seems strong, and one wonders if much of the missionary zeal devoted over the years to challenging unwarranted recommendations (e.g., rigid scheduling) might not have been out of proportion to the number of persons who applied such recommendations in their everyday parent behavior.

ANALYZING THE VARIANCE

This scanning of the research literature involves what we consider a representative though small sample of the studies available. It would seem that conclusions drawn from different research approaches to the various problems explored are either as polarized as the topics investigated or else are inconclusive. However, practical recommendations related to these problems tend to be highly specific once they find their way into the parent-education literature, and trends get started. Sometimes it is difficult to decide whether the research data influence the trends or the trends influence the data. Senn (1957) has offered to the investigator who would like his research work translated into immediate family action a formula for starting a trend:

> For example, the "success formula" for starting a trend, or at least a fashion, in child care would be to choose a subject like adolescent behavior which is puzzling many parents and educators; then to interest a person well known for his work with children to the extent of having him state his opinions about adolescence, even if these are based only on a small sample of observations and clinical impressions. The opinions if presented in writing to an enterprising literary agent will find a ready publisher, and with skillful and abundant pre- and post-publication advertising may not only become the contents of a best seller but find even greater distribution by radio and TV. For the time being, the answer to the riddle of adolescence will seem to have been found; but only until disillusioned parents have learned that the problems of life are not so easily dealt with and until another prophet appears to lead them out of the wilderness [p. 44].

This tongue-in-cheek formula is perhaps too often applied, with the result that the educated parent, the one who is trying to be "upwardly mobile" from intuition to science, is left with the responsibility of reconciling the differences. Explicit recognition of several factors which conduce to the observed variation in research findings should assist in the degree of reconciliation possible at this juncture.

Approach to the Problem

Differences associated with the choice of retrospective versus prospective designs have been emphasized by various authors (Ainsworth and Bowlby, 1954; Graham et al., 1957) and are now generally recognized. Likewise there seems an implicit recognition of differences likely to be associated with depth versus superficial methods, or clinical versus experimental. For example, in the area of possible consequences of maternal deprivation, it is the intensive clinical evaluations which have tended to support the hypothesis of the detrimental effects of a lack of intensive mothering. More controlled studies, often by the same investigator, which use as criteria of impairment such measures as ratings by impartial and uncommitted individuals, psychological test data, or community statistics, may lead to somewhat different conclusions. Bowlby, whose early observations on the deleterious consequences of maternal separation directed worldwide attention to this matter, was led, as a result of subsequent controlled research carried out under his direction, to the following amendation of his earlier position:

> Meanwhile it is clear that some of the former group of workers, including the present senior author, in their desire to call attention to dangers which can often be avoided have on occasion overstated their case. In particular, statements implying that children who are brought up in institutions or who suffer other forms of serious privation and deprivation in early life *commonly* develop psychopathic or affectionless characters . . . are seen to be mistaken. . . . Outcome is immensely varied, and of those who are damaged only a small minority develop those very serious disabilities of personality which first drew attention to the pathogenic nature of the experience [Bowlby et al., 1956, p. 240].

No criticism is implied in making this point, for this course of events—enthusiasm followed by confirmation or modification—seems to parallel the general course of the history of ideas. Clinical data have traditionally served the function of originating, not conclusively testing, hypotheses; without this source of material our attempts to understand human development might be pedestrian indeed. For purposes of this discussion the point is raised not to look haughtily down at clinical data, but simply to remind ourselves that data originating from these different sources do not always yield comparable results. Yet conclusions from data of any type are generally translated back into the language of everyday discourse, and in this transfer the dependency of fact on source of data is often forgotten or overlooked.

Length of the Evaluation Interval

The question of the optimal interval for evaluating the effects of a child-rearing experience is an important one. Concern may be with the effects of contemporary child-rearing variables (as in current permissiveness or strictness) or with the residual effects of earlier practices (as in the effects of breast versus bottle feeding). When effects of an earlier experience are sought, some attention must be paid to the course of events transpiring between the presumably causative influence and the criterion behavior. In some of the studies mentioned here, the intervening time period was long, and no attempt was made to control for the multitudinous variables which could have influenced the findings. An example of this can be found in the study concerned with security in young adults as a function of duration of breast feeding (Maslow and Szilagyi-Kessler, 1946). Here the independent-dependent variable interval was roughly twenty years—a long time for any significant life experience to maintain its effects. Perhaps such intervals have been chosen partly because of the greater accessibility of young adult subjects. However, many of the tested relationships have their origins in psychoanalytic theory, where consequences for adult personality are predicted (e.g., the oral character) and thus require testing after a lengthy time interval.

Until more of the possibly relevant but confounding variables have been isolated and can thus be controlled, it would seem overly ambitious to try to show a cause-and-effect relationship from early infancy to adulthood. Personality formation is cumulative, and the state of the organism at any one time will affect it at the next developmental stage. And whether, at this point, a clear-cut sequential swath from early child rearing to adult personality can be fashioned, either theoretically or empirically, is questionable.

An example of the attenuation of relationship occurring with time may be found in the research of Rheingold (1956) and Rheingold and Bayley (1959). Working in an institution with high standards of sanitation and physical care but with the usual problem of insufficient personnel to supply as much mothering to the infants as might be desirable, Rheingold tried experimentally to modify the social responsiveness of a small group of the infants. Her subjects were eight infants about six months old at the start of the experiment to whom she supplied constant "mothering" for eight hours a day, five days a week, for a total of eight weeks. Eight carefully matched control infants received the routine institutional care, which was described as benevolent, with deviations from what is considered optimal mothering being due to lack of personnel rather than lack of affect or information. Both groups were given a battery of tests at the beginning of the study and at weekly intervals throughout the experimental period. These were tests of general development (posture, grasp, etc.) and social responsiveness (quickness and duration of visual regard, positive facial expressions, negative expressions, pattern of physical activity, and number of vocalizations) to the experimenter, to the person who administered the developmental tests, and to a stranger. Results showed that the experimental babies became more responsive to the experimenter than did the control subjects; also they became more responsive to the experimenter than to the examiner who administered the developmental tests. There was a suggestion that the experimental subjects became more rather than less responsive to the examiner, although it had been anticipated that the infants who had a chance to develop a more intense relationship with one person might show more negative responses to other people (i.e., separation anxiety). Findings on this point were not definitive, but it seemed that rather than showing a stronger negative response to persons other than the major caretaker, they generalized positive feelings to other adults with whom they had contact. Experimental subjects made slightly but not significantly higher scores on the Cattell and on the postural and cube tests. In sum, the results of this study evaluated a child-care variable after a relatively brief interval of time and demonstrated that social behavior of institutional babies can be modified by certain environmental events. In spite of limitations of sample size (one need only reflect on the amount of the experimenter's time involved in collecting data on only one subject to understand this) and inability to control pre-institution conditions, this study, well designed and painstakingly executed, offers rather impressive corroborative evidence relating to the social consequences of lack of mothering.

A follow-up study was carried out by Rheingold and Bayley (1959) on fourteen of these sixteen infants a year later, at which time the children were approximately twenty months old. In this study they sought to determine whether any residual effects of the behavior changes induced in the experimental group during their institution residence could be detected. By this time all but one of the infants had been placed in adoptive or boarding homes or returned to their own homes. Again tests of social responsiveness and of developmental level were administered to the infants. The increased social responsiveness formerly shown by the experimental babies was no longer observed. The children seemed not to remember the experimenter or to relate to her in a way demonstrably different from the control children. Nor was there any significant difference in level of intellectual functioning. The only significant difference which could be noted was that more of the experimental than control infants vocalized during the social tests. The authors concluded therefore "that the experience provided by the more attentive mothering, while great enough to produce a difference at the time of study, was not great enough to maintain this difference over time, except in one class of behavior" (p. 371).

In further analyses of their data no differences were found between infants placed in their own homes and in adoptive homes (generally of higher socioeconomic status); nor was the total group of children dramatically different in any measured way from infants reared in their own homes. Admittedly no depth analysis of the quality of mothering received by the different infants or of other possibly relevant aspects of family structure was made. But one cannot escape the tentative conclusion that, after a longer time interval, results of the crucial child-rearing practice in this case had somehow been neutralized. Whether this could be attributed to the greater cumulative effect of the social and interpersonal environment in which the infants had spent a greater proportion of their lives, or to the relative impermanence of learning occurring during infancy cannot be determined from these data. Nevertheless, these two studies illustrate the point that varying length of criterion periods under the typical field-study conditions where no controls can be exerted probably account for some of the variance observed in the research literature.

Choice of Samples

Basically our child development data and our theoretical ideas have come from two main sources: clinical studies of individuals with egregious psychological or social characteristics; and normative and experimental studies dealing, for the most part, with samples which have ideological identification with or geographic proximity to universities. Whether such twain samples shall ever meet is questionable. The increasing use of the public schools and of various public health facilities offers some hope that these core samples will be broadened. At the present time, most of the samples which are available for such research are probably too homogeneous to permit the establishment of population parameters. Even in our better designed and executed studies, care is seldom taken to specify the population to which results can be generalized. Hypotheses are most often tested in terms of group differences between extreme samples, e.g., institution versus home-reared children. Such differences are seldom hard to establish. But implicit is the assumption that quantifiable variations of some essential attribute (e.g., mothering, amount of stimulation, etc.) that are smaller in magnitude will also affect the developing child. Such assumptions about the vast middle range of an unstudied population are then often acted upon, and it is these *verbalized assumptions,* not the actual data on which they are based, which frequently find their way into the parent-education literature. To be specific, absence of mothering is detrimental; *ergo,* smaller degrees of reduction of mothering (as in maternal employment) will also produce proportional detriment. With respect to this one variable, current research evidence (Stolz, 1960) would suggest that this full-range assumption may be entirely unjustified. Being careful to stress the nature of the population to which results may be generalized, and the magnitude of the units of the independent variable about which we have information, should help to minimize some of the conflicting generalizations found in our scientific and lay literature.

Problems of Assessment

Another major source of factual variance relates to choice of instrument for measuring the dependent variable—the perennial problem of assessment. Although in the past several decades many improvements have been made in the measurement of personality, it is still far from an exact process. Operational definitions, while scientifically essential, do not necessarily conduce to uniform data. For example, one may legitimately define anxiety in terms of scores obtained on a paper-and-pencil test or in terms of a measure of autonomic instability under stress. Both definitions are equally defensible and operationally anchored, but there is no guarantee that they refer to similar "anxieties." Similarly, aggression might be measured in terms of maternal report of incidence of aggressive behavior, by direct observation in a nursery school, or in terms of the frequency of aggressive acts in one or more doll-play sessions. Now if interested in the effects of a rigid, "cry-it-out" (presumably frustrating) schedule on aggressiveness in the child, one must choose among these, or possibly other, alternative ways of operationally defining the concept. It is known that the correlation between overt and fantasy aggression is positive but very low, with reported correlations generally somewhere between .10 and .20 (Korner, 1951; Sears, 1950). Furthermore, it has been demonstrated that maternal practices differentially affect these different measures of aggression in children. That is, children from highly frustrating homes where punishment for aggression is high tend to show less aggressive behavior in the home (where it could be observed and thus accessible to maternal report) and in their preschool behavior, but to show more aggressive behavior in doll play (where it would be recorded in an experimental or clinical situation but not be available for maternal report). Thus it can be seen that the choice of which type of operation is to be used for defining the personality variable one is studying is more than academic.

Perhaps one of the healthier consequences of this problem is what might be called a retreat into methodology. In many research centers one finds intense concern with the development of new methods by which relevant child development problems can be explored. The recent publication of a new *Handbook* (Mussen, 1960) focusing on research *methods*, not *findings*, in the field of child development illustrates this current emphasis. Hypotheses may fail to find support either because they are incorrect or because the methods by which they were tested are inadequate. In this assiduous search for newer and better methods, from which more definitive experiments yielding new explanatory concepts can hopefully emerge, Conant's paradigm for any type of scientific advance is approached (1957, p. 37): "science emerges from the other progressive activities of man to the extent that new concepts arise from experiments and observations, and the new concepts in turn lead to further experiments and observations."

Parent Attitude or Parent Behavior

One remaining source of variance which can be factored out of this discussion is a complex one indeed—the relationship between child-care practices and the underlying attitudes on which they rest. Some of the conflicting results referred to earlier are often interpreted as offering proof that it is the underlying attitude and not the specific practice which is of importance. A mother may spank because she has a great deal of hostility toward her child, because she is determined to win out in a power struggle, or because the experts recommend placing limits on a child. Yet if only the overt behavior is studied, all three underlying feeling states would perhaps fall into the same category. Some data bearing on this point can be found in a study by Newton and Newton (1950). On the basis of ninety-one interviews conducted while mothers were still in the hospital, two judges classified the women into three groups with respect to their expressed attitudes toward breast feeding. Of the ninety-one women interviewed, fifty-one were judged to have positive, seventeen doubtful, and twenty-three negative attitudes. Of the mothers classified as having positive attitudes toward breast feeding, 74 per cent were able to breast feed successfully. For the mothers classified as having doubtful or negative attitudes, only 35 and 26 per cent respectively were successful breast feeders. Now had any follow-up of these women and their offspring been concerned with the relationship between breast feeding and child personality, the breast-fed group would have included three fourths of the women with favorable attitudes to breast feeding, but also about one third of those who had doubtful or negative attitudes toward the practice. In this instance, attitude might be said to influence, but not control, behavior.

THE IMPORTANCE OF BASIC RESEARCH

It is apparent that we very much need basic research on the implications of child-rearing practices which attempts to control some of these sources of variance. For without more basic data concerning the transactions between parents and child, it becomes impossible to develop an orientation toward child rearing which is based on more than tradition, or a wheel of chance selection from among the many expert opinions. Such studies must be permitted to range from genetics and basic biology to psychological, social, and cultural factors and the interaction among them. The emphasis on basic investigation is significant, lest investigators experience undue pressures for practical results. Particularly in large-scale programs such as public assistance for dependent children, foster care, and institutional care, it is tempting to seek research reports which will provide direct suggestions for planning individual child care in the best interests of the child, his family, and the community. Unfortunately research generally does not provide a direct formula for practice any more than the physiology laboratory worker interested in gastric secretion provides an immediate answer for the clinician in the treatment of peptic ulcer.

This emphasis on basic research should not be construed as suggesting a moratorium on all community child-care programs until more definitive information is available. Programs in child health and welfare, foster care, aid to dependent children, adoptions, and care of handicapped children must be dealt with now, not at some hypothetical future date when relevant questions will hopefully have been answered. Likewise, parents must rear and train their offspring now and not be paralyzed by the possibility that today's dogma may be tomorrow's mythology.

A review of what has been done should not lead to professional nihilism, for with more meaningful data available, more effective judgments concerning the care of children should be possible. Out of research in child development we should ultimately be in a more favorable position to plan effectively for all types of child-care programs. Out of such research we may ultimately come to know more about the implications of infant and early child-care practices for the development of perceptual capacities, creativity, curiosity, learning patterns, and personality, which will enable the organism to cope effectively with the vicissitudes of growing up in a rapidly changing and increasingly complex world. Such is the challenge for parents, the child-care professions, and research workers in child development.

BIBLIOGRAPHY

Ainsworth, M. D. & Bowlby, J. (1954), Research Strategy in the Study of Mother-Child Separation. *Courrier*, 4:105-131.

Baldwin, A. L. (1948), Socialization and the Parent-Child Relationship. *Child Develpm.*, 19:127-136.

——— (1949), The Effect of Home Environment on Nursery School Behavior. *Child Develpm.*, 20:49-61.

Beres, D. & Obers, S. J. (1950), The Effects of Extreme Deprivation in Infancy on Psychic Structure in Adolescence: A Study in Ego Development. *The Psychoanalytic Study of the Child*, 5:212-235. New York: Int. Univ. Press.

Bowlby, J. (1952), *Maternal Care and Mental Health*. Geneva: World Health Organization Monograph No. 2.

——— Ainsworth, M., & Rosenbluth, D. (1956), The Effects of Mother-Child Separation: A Follow-up Study. *Brit. J. Med. Psychol.*, 29:211-247.

Conant, J. B. (1957), *On Understanding Science*. New Haven: Yale Univ. Press.

Fischer, L. K. (1952), Hospitalism in Six-month-old Infants. *Amer. J. Orthopsychiat.*, 22:522-533.

Goldfarb, W. (1943), Infant Rearing and Problem Behavior. *Amer. J. Orthopsychiat.*, 13:249-265.

——— (1949), Rorschach Test Differences Between Family-reared, Institution-reared, and Schizophrenic Children. *Amer. J. Orthopsychiat.*, 19:624-633.

——— (1955), Emotional and Intellectual Consequences of Psychologic Deprivation in Infancy: A Revaluation. *Psychopathology of Childhood*. New York: Grune & Stratton, pp. 105-109.

Graham, F. K., et al. (1957), Anoxia as a Significant Perinatal Experience: A Critique. *J. Ped.*, 50:556-569.

Harlow, H. (1958), The Nature of Love. *Amer. Psychologist*, 13:673-685.

Hersher, L., Moore, A. U., & Richmond, J. B. (1958), Effect of Post-partum Separation of Mother and Kid on Maternal Care in the Domestic Goat. *Science*, 128:1342-1343.

Hoefer, C. & Hardy, M. (1929), Later Development of Breast-fed and Artificially Fed Infants. *J. Amer. Med. Assn.*, 92:615-619.

Holway, A. (1949), Early Self-regulation of Infants and Later Behavior in Play Interviews. *Amer. J. Orthopsychiat.*, 19:612-623.

Klatskin, E. H., Jackson, E. B., & Wilkin, L. C. (1956), The Influence of Degree of Flexibility in Maternal Child Care Practices on Early Child Behavior. *Amer. J. Orthopsychiat.*, 26:79-93.

Korner, A. F. (1951), Relationship Between Overt and Covert Hostility. *Personality*, 1:20-31.

Lowrey, L. G. (1940), Personality Distortion and Early Institutional Care. *Amer. J. Orthopsychiat.*, 10:576-585.

Maslow, A. H. & Szilagyi-Kessler, I. (1946), Security and Breast-feeding. *J. Abnorm. Soc. Psychol.*, 41:83-85.

Meyer, H. F. (1958), Breast Feeding in the United States: Extent and Possible Trend. *Pediatrics*, 22:116-121.

Mussen, P. H. (1960), *Handbook of Research Methods in Child Development*. New York: John Wiley.

Newton, N. R. & Newton, M. (1950), Relationship of Ability to Breast Feed and Maternal Attitudes Toward Breast Feeding. *Pediatrics*, 5:869-875.

Orlansky, H. (1949), Infant Care and Personality. *Psychol. Bull.*, 46:1-48.

Pearson, G. (1931), Some Early Factors in the Formation of Personality. *Amer. J. Orthopsychiat.*, 1:284-291.

Pinneau, S. R. (1951), A Critique on the Articles of Margaret Ribble. *Child Develpm.*, 21:203-228.

—— (1955), The Infantile Disorders of Hospitalism and Anaclitic Depression. *Psychol. Bull.*, 52:429-452.

Provence, S., & Lipton, R. (1962), *Infants in Institutions*. New York: Int. Univ. Press.

Rheingold, H. (1956), The Modification of Social Responsiveness in Institutional Babies. *Monogr. Soc. Res. Child Develpm.*, 21:48.

—— & Bayley, N. (1959), The Later Effects of an Experimental Modification of Mothering. *Child Develpm.*, 30:363-372.

Ribble, M. (1943), *The Rights of Infants: Early Psychological Needs and their Satisfaction*. New York: Columbia Univ. Press.

Sears, R. R. (1950), Relation of Fantasy Aggression to Interpersonal Aggression. *Child Develpm.*, 21:5-6.

—— Maccoby, E., & Levin, H. (1957), *Patterns of Child Rearing*. Evanston: Row, Peterson.

—— & Wise, G. W. (1950), Relations of Cup-feeding in Infancy to Thumb-sucking and the Oral Drive. *Amer. J. Orthopsychiat.*, 20:123-138.

Senn, M. J. E. (1957), Fads and Facts as the Bases of Child-care Practices. *Children*, 4:43-47.

Sewell, W. H. (1952), Infant Training and the Personality of the Child. *Amer. J. Sociol.*, 58:150-159.

—— & Mussen, P. H. (1952), The Effect of Feeding, Weaning and Scheduling Procedures on Childhood Adjustment and the Formation of Oral Symptoms. *Child Develpm.*, 23:185-191.

———— ———— & Harris, C. W. (1955), Relationship Among Child Training Practices. *Amer. Sociol. Rev.*, 20:137-148.

Spitz, R. A. (1954), Hospitalism. *The Psychoanalytic Study of the Child*, 1:54-74. New York: Int. Univ. Press.

———— (1946), Hospitalism: A Follow-up Report. *The Psychoanalytic Study of the Child*, 2:113-117. New York: Int. Univ. Press.

Stolz, L. M. (1960), Effects of Maternal Employment on Children: Evidence from Research. *Child Develpm.*, 31:749-782.

U.S. Children's Bureau (1938), *Infant Care*. Washington, D.C.: U.S. Government Printing Office.

———— (1942), *Infant Care*. Washington, D.C.: U.S. Government Printing Office.

Vincent, C. E. (1951), Trends in Infant Care Ideas. *Child Develpm.*, 22:199-209.

Watson, G. (1957), Some Personality Differences in Children Related to Strict or Permissive Parental Discipline. *J. Psychol.*, 43:227-249.

Watson, J. B. (1928), *Psychological Care of Infant and Child*. London: Allen & Unwin.

Wolfenstein, M. (1953), Trends in Infant Care. *Amer. J. Orthopsychiat.*, 23:120-130.

Yarrow, L. J. (1961), Maternal Deprivation: Toward an Empirical and Conceptual Re-evaluation. *Psychol. Bull.*, 58:459-490.

Teacher Training and the Mental Health Professions

• *SEYMOUR B. SARASON, Ph.D.*

Yale University

We are living in times when the goals and adequacy of our educational system are constantly being debated. Sides have been taken on three major issues: curriculum content, the nature of teacher training, and the development of programs for children who for one or another reason require special consideration.

I have yet to meet a member of the mental health professions who did not feel that this debate was of professional significance for him, although in most instances it was not at all clear what that significance was. It may be that one of the reasons for this lack of clarity is that the leaders of the mental health professions have not participated in this debate. Novelists, engineers, and historians, together with the educator, of course, have been in the national aspects of the controversy, but the mental health worker has indeed been conspicuous by his absence—conspicuous, that is, to the mental health professions and not to the combatants (and I use that word advisedly) in the debate. The way in which the debate has been conducted does not indicate that there is any strongly felt need for the participation of those in the mental health professions. We have, then, the situation in which the mental health worker is (and feels he should be) interested in our educational system, is not sure of what his contribution can be to current issues, is not participating in any important way in the discussion and decision, and is not viewed by others as having anything central to contribute to the current debate.

The crucial question, of course, is whether the actual or potential contribution of the mental health professions is peripheral or central to the educational process. But before taking up this question it should be noted that the present situation in regard to the relationship of the mental health professions to educational issues should not be a cause of surprise. There is little or nothing in the training of the mental health worker (social worker, psychiatrist, clinical psychologist) which makes him either an informed individual in these matters or prepares him to operate professionally in the educational setting. In fact, when one studies the professional training of these workers in terms of course contents, technical skills, and work settings, one might justifiably conclude that these professions do not perceive themselves as having other than a very peripheral role to play in the educational setting. Such a perception would not necessarily be noteworthy were it not that the offspring of ignorance is usually prejudice and misconception, by which I mean that mental health workers share certain attitudes with the general public which do credit to neither.

We would probably all agree that a teacher has certain goals which she wishes her children to reach by the time her contact with them ends. Hopefully the teacher does not set the same goals for the children in her class but varies them according to the needs and personal and intellectual capabilities of each child. The most serious misconception which the mental health worker (and the general public) has about the "goals" of the teacher stems from two implicit assumptions: (1) that the goals are exclusively educational in the narrow sense (e.g., at the end of the first grade children should be reading at the beginning second-grade level); and (2) that reaching these goals is an engineering or technical problem involving books, drill, audiovisual aids, etc. In other words, teaching is a kind of gimmicky affair. Such a statement usually draws the reply that obviously there is more to teaching than *that*. If one asks the mental health worker what more there is to teaching, one usually receives in reply such statements as "You have to know how to arouse and maintain motivation to learn"; "You have to know how to handle the problem of discipline so that it helps rather than inhibits learning"; "You have to be able to get children to work with each other as well as by themselves"; "You have to be as aware of the shy as of the aggressive, acting-out child." With these addenda the "goals" of the teacher take on a psychological complexity of somewhat overwhelming proportions, particularly when one takes seriously the implications of teaching a *group* of children.

It would not take more than a few hours of observation in a classroom for the mental health worker to arrive at two conclusions. First, and most important, would be the realization that whether she likes it or not, the teacher is constantly being confronted with decisions involving psychological issues and having psychological consequences—in principle no different than what is involved in a parent-child or therapist-patient relationship. It makes no difference whether the teacher does or does not respond to a problem in an overt way; in either case there are psychological consequences for the child. The question is not whether the teacher influences the child but rather how he influences the child. A second conclusion to which the mental health worker would come from his classroom observations would not be strange to him, although his appreciation of its significance for the teacher would acquire new depths. I refer here to the artificiality of the distinction between educational and psychological goals and issues. To maintain such a distinction is as meaningful (or squares as little with the facts) as the view that toilet training is an educational rather than a psychological process or problem.

Perhaps I can bring this discussion into focus by expressing the following opinion: *for the teacher to do his or her job effectively requires as much psychological knowledge and sophistication as is required of any mental health worker.* It is worthy of note that this opinion generally arouses a reaction of utter disbelief from the mental health worker, as if it is incomprehensible that there are other professionals whose work does or should demand an equal amount of psychological knowledge and skill. What is significant in this extreme reaction concerns not the truth or falsity of the above opinion but the implicit rejection of the possibility that the teacher is asked to recognize and handle problems requiring a training background more like rather than unlike that of the mental health worker. When I have pursued this problem with colleagues, I have never received a clear statement describing the criteria or data on the basis of which one concludes that the teacher requires less psychological knowledge and skill to do his job effectively than does the mental health worker. Even if future studies should indicate that such a conclusion is correct—and I have no reason to believe that such studies are being contemplated presumably because it is not interesting to prove the obvious—we should at the present time be aware that it is unbecoming anyone who purports to operate by the rules of evidence to conclude that something is so because one says it is so. It was such an attitude that allowed and still allows people to conclude that infantile sexuality is obviously a preposterous idea.

But in order to avoid the impasse to which extreme positions lead, let us assume that the teacher is in need of a fair degree of psychological knowledge and sophistication. Where, from whom, and under what conditions of learning does the teacher get such knowledge and sophistication? More specifically, to what extent do psychiatrists, psychiatric social workers, and clinical psychologists actively participate in training of teachers? The answer, unfortunately, is that these professions are rarely found in teacher training institutions. Psychology is learned by reading and listening to lectures, practice teaching periods are viewed as opportunities for gaining technical proficiency (developing lesson plans, etc.), and the opportunities are practically nonexistent for acquiring under supervision observational skills and diagnostic acumen—and it cannot be overemphasized that the teacher does observe, diagnose, and manage children.

Let me give but one example of the inadequacy of the preparation of teachers for handling psychological problems. There is one function which all teachers are expected to perform, do perform, and yet feel grossly inadequate to perform. *I refer to how one talks and communicates with parents.* I know of no teacher-training institution which even attempts such a preparation, as if the methods and ways of communicating with parents were inborn gifts. When one considers how much time and effort are expended in teaching the mental health worker how to listen to and communicate with others, it is not surprising that the cold war which goes on so frequently between teacher and parents often erupts into a hot one.

In a recent publication some colleagues and myself (1960) report the results of a number of studies of anxiety in elementary school children.[1] As a result of conducting these studies and of my experience in various teacher-training institutions, it is heartening to report that, as a group, teachers are the ones who are most aware of the inadequacy of their preparation for the handling of the psychological issues which confront them in their daily work. This is not to say that teachers are quick to express such felt inadequacies. In these days when everyone feels competent to pass judgment on teachers, teaching, and our schools, it should not be expected that teachers would provide ammunition for their critics. It would be a mistake for the mental health worker to conclude that the teacher eagerly awaits his entrance to the school. For one thing, teachers have too frequently been given advice which clearly reflects profound ignorance of what goes on in a classroom and of the social psychology of a school—and there are precious few mental health workers who have the appropriate experience which has taught them how to approach and communicate with teachers. Just as the teacher is not prepared for how to talk *with* (instead of to) parents, so the bulk of mental health workers is not prepared for how to talk with teachers.

The mental health professions do have, in my opinion, a very important role to play in the educational setting. At the present time their contribution, such as it is, centers on that small proportion of children whose behavior interferes with classroom activities or who

[1] Of particular relevance to the present discussion is the chapter on implications for education.

have obvious learning difficulties. However, many other types of psycho-educational problems and issues confront a teacher for which her preparation has been inadequate.

It would be a mistake, in my opinion, for the mental health professions to view their role solely in terms of the school setting. It would be much more fruitful if we searchingly studied the contribution which can be made in our teacher-training institutions.

BIBLIOGRAPHY

Sarason, S. B., Davidson, K. S., Lighthall, F. F., Waite, R. R., & Ruebush, B. K. (1960), *Anxiety in Elementary School Children. A Report of Research.* New York: John Wiley.

Publications of Milton J. E. Senn, M.D.

1927

(& Leake, Chauncey; Grab, J. A.). Studies in Exhaustion Due to Lack of Sleep. II. Symptomatology in Rabbits. *Amer. J. Physiol.,* 82:127-130.

1932

(& Hartmann, Alexis F.). Studies in the Metabolism of Sodium r-Lactate. I. Response of Normal Human Subjects to the Intravenous Injections of Sodium r-Lactate. *J. Clin. Invest.,* 11:327-335.

(& Hartmann, Alexis F.). Studies in the Metabolism of Sodium r-Lactate. II. Response of Human Subjects with Acidosis to the Intravenous Injection of Sodium r-Lactate. *J. Clin. Invest.,* 11:337-344.

(& Hartmann, Alexis F.). Studies in the Metabolism of Sodium r-Lactate. III. Response of Human Subjects with Liver Damage, Disturbed Water and Mineral Balance, and Renal Insufficiency to the Intravenous Injection of Sodium r-Lactate. *J. Clin. Invest.,* 11:345-355.

1933

(& Hartmann, Alexis F.; Nelson, Martha V.; Perley, Anne M.). The Use of Acacia in the Treatment of Edema, *J. Amer. Med. Assn.,* 100:251-254.

(& Marriott, W. McKim; Hartmann, Alexis F.). Observations on the Nature and Treatment of Diarrhea and the Associated Systemic Disturbances. *J. Pediat.*, 3:181-192.

1935
The Effects of a Gelatin Hydrating Solution on the Newborn. *J. Pediat.*, 7:352-357.

1937
(& McNamara, Helen). The Lipids of the Blood Plasma in the Neonatal Period. *Amer. J. Dis. Child.*, 53:445-453.

1940
(& McNamara, Helen). Glutathione and Red Cells in the Blood in Infancy and in Childhood. *Amer. J. Dis. Child.*, 59:97-106.

1945
Influence of Psychological Factors on the Nutrition of Children. *Amer. J. Pub. Health,* 35:211-215.

The Voluntary Hospital Looks Ahead (Report of Proceedings, Third Wartime Symposium). New York: United Hospital Fund, pp. 14-18.

Emotional Aspects of Convalescence. *The Child,* 10:24-28.

(& Newill, Phyllis K.). *All About Feeding Children.* Garden City, N.Y.: Doubleday, Doran.

1946
Relationship of Pediatrics and Psychiatry. *Amer. J. Dis. Child.*, 71:537-549.

Role of Psychiatry in a Children's Hospital Service. *Amer. J. Dis. Child.*, 72:95-110.

1947
Anticipatory Guidance of the Pregnant Woman and Her Husband for Their Roles as Parents. In: *Problems of Early Infancy* (Transactions of the First Conference). New York: Josiah Macy, Jr. Foundation, pp. 11-16.

What Have We Learned about Emotional Growth and Development Through Clinical Observation and Common Pediatric Practice? In: *Pediatrics and the Emotional Needs of the Child,* ed. H. L. Witmer. New York: Commonwealth Fund, pp. 1-9.

(Editor) *Problems of Early Infancy* (Transactions of the First Conference). New York: Josiah Macy, Jr. Foundation.

1948

Emotions and Symptoms in Pediatric Practice. *Advances in Pediatrics,* 3:69-89. New York: Interscience Publishers.

Constructive Forces in the Home. *Ment. Hyg.,* 32:382-391.

Trends in Infant Feeding. *Wisc. Med. J.,* 47:195-198.

The Psychotherapeutic Role of the Pediatrician. *Pediatrics,* 2:147-153.

Focal Points in Child Development. *Wisc. Med. J.,* 47:861-864.

Pediatrics in Orthopsychiatry. *Orthopsychiatry 1923-1948: Retrospect and Prospect.* New York: American Orthopsychiatric Association, pp. 300-309.

(Editor) *Problems of Early Infancy* (Transactions of the Second Conference). New York: Josiah Macy, Jr. Foundation.

1949

(Editor) *Problems of Infancy and Childhood* (Transactions of the Third Conference). New York: Josiah Macy, Jr. Foundation.

1950

After the Midcentury White House Conference—What? *The Child,* 15:81-86. Washington, D.C.: Children's Bureau.

(Editor) *Problems of Infancy and Childhood* (Transactions of the Fourth Conference). New York: Josiah Macy, Jr. Foundation.

(Editor) *Symposium on the Healthy Personality.* Supplement II. *Problems of Infancy and Childhood* (Transactions of Special Meetings of Conference on Infancy and Childhood). New York: Josiah Macy, Jr. Foundation.

(& DelSolar, C.). *Readings on the Psychological Development of Infants and Children.* Washington, D.C.: Children's Bureau.

Psychological Aspects of Adolescence. In: *Textbook of Pediatrics,* ed. W. E. Nelson. Philadelphia: Saunders, 5th ed., pp. 1600-1604.

(& Plant, J. S.) Chapters on: Mental and Emotional Development; Psychologic Disorders. In: *Textbook of Pediatrics,* ed. W. E. Nelson. Philadelphia: Saunders, 5th ed., pp. 74-87; 1252-1282.

1951

The Contribution of Psychiatry to Child Health Services. *Amer. J. Orthopsychiat.,* 21:138-147.

1952

History of the Art and Science of Growing Up in America. In: *Perspectives in Medicine*. The New York Academy of Medicine Lectures to the Laity. New York: Columbia Univ. Press.

(Editor) *Problems of Infancy and Childhood* (Transactions of the Sixth Conference). New York: Josiah Macy, Jr. Foundation.

1953

(Editor) *Problems of Infancy and Childhood* (Transactions of the Seventh Conference). New York: Josiah Macy, Jr. Foundation.

1954

Research on Personality Development of the Child. In: *Genetics and the Inheritance of Integrated Neurological and Psychiatric Patterns* (Proceedings of Association for Research in Nervous and Mental Diseases, Dec. 11-12, 1953), 33:232-238. Baltimore: Williams & Wilkins.

(& Solnit, A. J.) Teaching Comprehensive Pediatrics in an Out-Patient Clinic. *Pediatrics,* 14:547-556.

Chapters on: Mental and Emotional Development; Psychologic Disorders; Psychologic Aspects of Adolescence. In: *Textbook of Pediatrics,* ed. W. E. Nelson. Philadelphia: Saunders, 6th ed., pp. 67-78; 1108-1130; 1497-1501.

1955

A Proposal for a New Department of Child Health. Printed Privately.

What Do We Know about Religious Education? Boston: Division of Education, Council of Liberal Churches (Universalist-Unitarian).

Common Problems of Sickness and Growth. *Child Study,* 32:14-20.

Changing Concepts of Child Care: A Historical Review. In: *Society and Medicine* (The New York Academy of Medicine Lectures to the Laity; The March of Medicine No. XVII), ed. Iago Galdston. New York: Int. Univ. Press, pp. 83-103.

(& Escalona, S. K.; Ross, H.; Horton, M. M.; Ginsburgh, S. W.; Stein, M.; Wolfson, T.) Common Problems of Sickness and Growth. In: *Living and Growing with Our Children: Impact on Parents of Children's Growth Phases* (Annual Conference Report). New York: Child Study Association of America.

1956

On Finger-Sucking (Editorial). *Pediatrics,* 17:313.

An Orientation for Instruction in Pediatrics. *J. Med. Educ.,* 31:613-619.

When Your Child Goes to Hospital. In: *How to Enjoy Good Health,* ed. C. Solomon and B. Roberts. Toronto: Random House.

Psychologic Aspects in the Care of Infants and Children (Report of Twenty-first Ross Pediatric Research Conference). Columbus: Ross Laboratories.

1957

Fads and Facts as the Bases of Child-Care Practices. *Children,* 4:43-47.

The Changing Role of the Children's Hospital. *Canad. Med. Assn. J.,* 77:647-655.

Psychological Implications of the Current Pediatric Practice (Report of the Twenty-fourth Ross Pediatric Research Conference). Columbus: Ross Laboratories.

1958

Common Psychological Problems in the Management of Patients with Congenital Heart Disease. *Conference on Cardiovascular Surgery.* New York: New York Heart Association, pp. 82-93.

(& Green, M.) Teaching of Comprehensive Pediatrics on an Inpatient Hospital Service. *Pediatrics,* 21:476-490.

Russian Children and Their World. *Child Study,* 36:7-13.

1959

Observations on a Trip to Russia. *Pediatrics,* 23:1168-1174.

Chapters on: Mental and Emotional Development; Psychologic Disorders; Psychologic Aspects of Adolescence; Psychoses. In: *Textbook of Pediatrics,* ed. W. E. Nelson. Philadelphia: Saunders, 7th ed., pp. 62-72; 73-91; 156-160; 1148-1149.

1960

Some Learning Problems in Adolescence. *Ped. Clin. No. Amer.,* 1:115-130.

Equipping Our Children to Meet Community Responsibilities. *Nova Scotia Med. Bull.,* 34:3-8.

Common Emotional Problems of Children. *Northwest Med.,* 59:1264-1274.

Personality Development in Children. In: *Roles of the Medical Disciplines in the Study of Personality Development,* ed. I. Iscoe & H. Stevenson. Austin: Univ. Texas Press, pp. 73-91.

1961

The Pediatrician's Role in the Prevention and Treatment of Emotional Disturbance. *Conn. Med.*, 25:276-278.

Role of the Senses in Early Parent-Child Relationships: A Review. *Quart. Rev. Pediat.*, 16:71-85.

1962

School Phobias: The Role of the Pediatrician in Their Prevention and Management. *Proceedings of the Royal College of Physicians* (London), 55:27-30.

A Relook at the Effects of Maternal Deprivation. Essay Review on W.H.O. Public Health Paper No. 14, "Maternal Deprivation." *Children*, 9:237-239.

Education—East and West. *Sarah Lawrence Alumnae Mag., Men's Issue,* Fall, pp. 1-4, 19.

Preface to *Infants in Institutions,* by Sally Provence & R. C. Lipton. New York: Int. Univ. Press, pp. ix-xi.

1963

Some Observations on Child Psychiatrists and Their Training (Editorial). *J. Amer. Acad. Child Psychiat.*, 2:561-563.